1984
YEARBOOK
OF
SCIENCE
AND THE
FUTURE

1984
YEARBOOK
OF
SCIENCE
AND THE
FUTURE

Encyclopædia Britannica, Inc.
Chicago

Auckland   Geneva   London   Manila   Paris   Rome   Seoul   Sydney   Tokyo   Toronto

1984
YEARBOOK OF SCIENCE AND THE FUTURE

CONTENTS

Feature Articles

PROBING THE ORIGIN OF LIFE

by Robert Shapiro

After a decade of scientific discoveries our ideas of the way life on Earth began are less clear than ever, but a number of exciting possibilities have opened up.

We do not know how life began on Earth. The question poses a greater mystery today than it did in the early 1970s. In the interim much has been learned in related fields: other planets have been surveyed by spacecraft; older fossils of microscopic life have turned up; radio astronomers have compiled a catalog of organic molecules in interstellar dust clouds; a complicated mixture of organic compounds has been discovered in meteorites; and models and calculations have provided a new picture of Earth's early atmosphere. Above all, a wealth of information has emerged concerning the genetic organization of living creatures. These new discoveries, however, have not clarified scientists' thinking concerning life's origins. Rather, they have undermined the central unifying hypothesis in the field: the Oparin-Haldane theory.

In response to the void thus created, a number of startling proposals have been put forward—in some cases by very noted scientists. It has been said that life originated on the bottom of the ocean, that it arrived on Earth in spaceships or comets, and that it evolved from clay rather than from mixtures of simple organic chemicals. To better portray the disagreements that have led to such diversity, the article breaks the central question into smaller ones, which focus on prominent features of life on Earth.

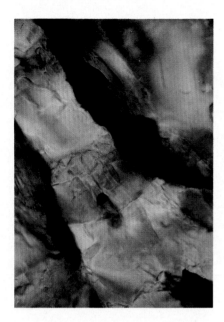

Hydrogen-rich environments conducive to the formation of reduced carbon compounds are not rare in the universe. Such compounds have been detected in dark, widely distributed interstellar dust clouds similar to the Horsehead Nebula (above right) and in certain meteorites called carbonaceous chondrites, which scientists believe are preserved relics of the very early solar system. The Murchison meteorite has been particularly well studied in this regard. In a magnified thin section of the Murchison meteorite photographed in polarized light (above), carbon-bearing substance appears as dark streaks in the mineral matrix.

ROBERT SHAPIRO is Professor in the Department of Chemistry at New York University, New York City.

Illustrations by John Youssi

Some key questions concerning Earth life

(1) How were reduced carbon compounds, needed for the construction of life, first assembled?

All life on this planet depends heavily on the chemistry of carbon. In particular it uses compounds containing carbon-to-carbon and carbon-to-hydrogen bonds. Compounds of this type are said to contain reduced carbon. They form readily in environments rich in hydrogen (reducing environments). Such environments are not rare in the universe, as hydrogen is by far the most plentiful element. Reduced carbon compounds occur in the atmospheres of Jupiter and of Titan, a moon of Saturn. They have also been detected in interstellar dust clouds, widely dispersed collections of small particles and molecules that make up much of the mass of our Galaxy.

The commonly accepted theory of the origin of the solar system holds that it formed from the collapse of an interstellar dust cloud 4.6 billion years ago. Meteorites are valuable sources of information because many of them are preserved remnants of that time. Certain of them, called carbonaceous chondrites, contain a few percent of their mass in the form of carbon compounds. The Murchison meteorite, which fell in Australia in 1969, has been shown to contain a large number of reduced carbon compounds.

As bonds from carbon to hydrogen and carbon to carbon are replaced by bonds from carbon to oxygen in a compound, that substance is converted from reduced to oxidized form. Carbon dioxide, a gas, and the carbonate group, a component of certain rocks, are fully oxidized forms of carbon. They are simple substances and form readily in oxidizing (oxygen-rich) environments. They must be reduced in order to form the more complicated structures characteristic of Earth life.

Carbon dioxide is an important component of the atmospheres of Mars and Venus and is present to a lesser extent in the atmosphere of Earth. Earth's atmosphere today, with its high content of oxygen, is oxidizing. This oxygen was released by photosynthesis. It is a result of the presence of life on this planet. As is discussed below, the nature of Earth's atmosphere prior to the origin of life has been the subject of a debate whose outcome is vital to theories concerning life's origin.

(2) How did life get organized?

The intricacy involved in the construction of living things is obvious at many levels. Even a small bacterial cell displays many complex substructures. Each of them in turn is put together from numerous parts. For example, the ribosome, the protein-synthesis factory of the cell, contains more than 50 subunits fit together as a three-dimensional jigsaw puzzle. Further, each of these subunits has been put together from specified components. The resemblance between the cell and a machine has led some observers to conclude that both must be the product of an intelligent creator. Of course, this assumption simply postpones the problem, for one must deal with the origin of the creator, either scientifically or theologically.

If one does not wish to invoke a creator, then it is necessary to presume that life arose from simple chemicals by some process of self-organization. This presumption need not violate the laws of nature. The second law of thermodynamics states that isolated systems tend invariably to lose their order; more precisely the entropy of the system increases. But things can go in the reverse direction—to negative entropy—if the system is not completely isolated and can absorb usable energy from its surroundings.

Earth life has increased its order during the course of evolution, using Darwinian natural selection as a mechanism. Organisms maintain their basic patterns through accurate reproduction, but occasional random variations occur. Those offspring better suited to their environment survive and are perpetuated, while others perish. Simple organic chemical systems, however, do not have a mechanism for accurate replication. A challenge for origin-of-life theories is how the first steps of self-organization took place.

(3) What principles were involved in the selection of the particular compounds used in life on Earth?

Large quantities of oxygen were released into Earth's atmosphere about two to three billion years ago by primitive microorganisms using much the same kind of photosynthetic processes seen today in green algae (below, left and right) and cyanobacteria, or blue-green algae. The nature of the atmosphere prior to that time has been the subject of much debate whose resolution is crucial to theories about the way life began.

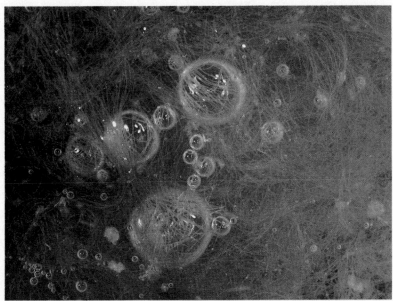

Photos, Bruce Coleman Inc.: (left) E. R. Degginger, (right) William H. Amos

Many more than a million organic compounds (of moderate size) have been described by chemists. A much larger number are possible but have not yet been prepared or discovered. Of this multitude a select few play important roles in the presence of Earth life. In particular a few smaller molecules are employed as subunits for the construction of the vital larger ones (macromolecules) that dominate life processes. Two macromolecules have special importance: proteins and nucleic acids.

The proteins are the laborers of life. They transport materials about, serve as building materials themselves in some cases, assemble and disassemble structures, repair or replace damaged units, and regulate the speed at which everything takes place. Proteins are constructed from smaller molecules called α-amino acids (or, simply, amino acids). Only 20 amino acids are used in proteins, though a much larger number exist. It is not known why these particular ones are used. Further, all but one of the 20 can exist in two mirror-image forms, called D and L. These forms bear the same relationship to one another as do right- and left-handed gloves. However, only the L forms of the amino acids are used in proteins.

There is probably some advantage gained in the construction of proteins if only one of the forms of each amino acid is used, but it is not obvious why the L form rather than the D form is used. Possibly the selection was made at random during the course of evolution of the first living thing, and this choice became locked in place for all subsequent organisms to the present day. Arguments have been made, however, that the choice reflects some fundamental asymmetry in nature such as the polarization of electrons produced by radioactive decay of elements or the effect of circularly polarized solar radiation.

In 1982 chemists Michael H. Engel of the Carnegie Institution of Washington (D.C.) and Bartholomew Nagy of the University of Arizona reported that an excess of the L form over the D form of certain amino acids was present in the Murchison meteorite. This result suggested that some cosmic factor favored the production of L-amino acids. But it also contradicted the findings of earlier analyses of the same meteorite. Unfortunately such extraterrestrial bodies pass through the biosphere of Earth en route to the chemist's bench. The chance for contamination of the sample by terrestrial biology is great. If it did occur in this case, it would be a far less exciting explanation for the excess of L-amino acids in the sample.

The other class of macromolecule considered important in the origin of life is the nucleic acids. Nucleic acids dominate the hereditary processes of life. They store the information that determines the kinds of protein a cell can make—and hence the form and function of an organism. Like proteins, nucleic acids are assembled from subunits. The components in this case are called nucleotides. Nucleic acids occur in two forms: DNA and RNA. The ultimate storehouse of genetic information is DNA. When a cell divides, a copy is made of its DNA, and one set is bequeathed to each descendant. During the normal operation of a cell, portions of the information stored in DNA are copied into RNA molecules. This information is then used in the construction of proteins. A rule called the "central dogma" of molecular biology states in its simplest form, "DNA makes RNA makes protein." The interrelations between these molecules are much more complicated, however, than the simple statement would imply.

DNA cannot replicate, nor can it transfer information to RNA, without the aid of proteins. Proteins are assembled in the ribosomes, most of the mass of which is RNA. In general, proteins and nucleic acids are mutually dependent in their function; each needs the other. Yet, during the origin of life one presumably arrived first and managed for a time on its own. There is sharp disagreement over which, nucleic acids or proteins, preceded the other.

(4) Why is there a remarkable biochemical unity among living creatures?

Bees, trees, and chimpanzees may look and behave very differently, yet all are made pretty much of the same chemicals. They use proteins made of the same amino acids and DNA built of the same nucleotides. The genetic code, which relates the information in nucleic acids to that in proteins, is basically the same in various forms of Earth life. The obvious chemical differences between species, as expressed in the smell of the rose and the color of the peacock, are submerged in a sea of molecular similarities.

The situation cannot be due to coincidence, nor is it reasonable to expect that only the precise molecular mix present in an organism can sustain life. Another answer easily comes to mind. All living things on Earth are descended from a common ancestor, which had the central features that all life shares today. Presumably it was a simple, one-celled creature. Although no physical evidence supports the existence of this creature, the logic has had sufficient force to limit scientific debate on the subject. Theories of the origin of life usually end with the arrival of this ancestor.

There has been dispute, however, about the reason for the absence of any visible competition today. It has been assumed that the evolutionary advance that led to the common ancestor gave it sufficient advantage to ensure elimination of its rivals. An alternative view is that the ancestor arrived, without competitors, from elsewhere than Earth.

About 20 different kinds of amino acids serve as the building blocks of proteins. Shown are the left- and right-handed (L and D) forms of a generalized amino acid, which are mirror images of each other. The letters C, N, O, and H stand for carbon, nitrogen, oxygen, and hydrogen. R represents any of several different chemical structures ranging from a single hydrogen atom to large molecular units. For some reason not yet known only the L forms are used to make proteins.

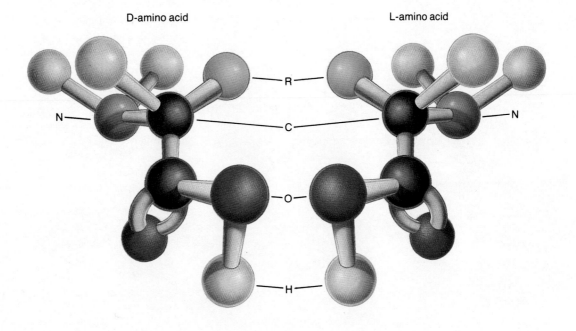

D-amino acid   L-amino acid

R

N — C — N

O

H

amino acids

a

b

c

d

protein

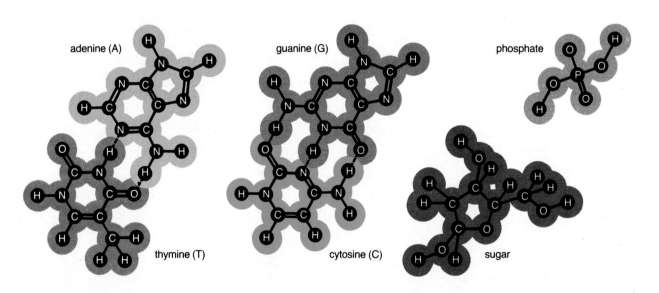

adenine (A)

thymine (T)

guanine (G)

cytosine (C)

phosphate

sugar

The Oparin-Haldane theory and its erosion

In the 1920s Alexander I. Oparin in the Soviet Union and J. B. S. Haldane in England put forward a related set of concepts. These were combined and embellished by others to form a theory that has dominated thinking on the origin of life. Its principal points can be stated briefly: (1) The Earth in its early history had an atmosphere rich in hydrogen, methane (the simplest reduced form of carbon), and ammonia (the simplest reduced form of nitrogen). This atmosphere was formed when the Earth and solar system condensed from interstellar material with its abundant hydrogen. The nature of this atmosphere changed only after the development of life. (2) This early atmosphere was exposed to a number of energy sources: solar radiation, lightning, volcanoes, and encounters with meteors. (3) As a result a large supply of reduced carbon compounds, suitable raw material for the construction of life, was formed. These compounds dissolved in the oceans to form a vast solution, called among other names the "prebiotic soup." (4) Further chemical transformations in this soup ultimately produced life.

The third point was supported strongly in a dramatic experiment designed by U.S. chemists Stanley Miller and Harold Urey in the 1950s. A mixture of hydrogen, methane, ammonia, and water was subjected to an electric spark for a number of days. When the resulting mixture was analyzed, a number of organic compounds including several amino acids were found to have formed. This demonstration indicated to many observers that the correct processes had been discovered. Furthermore, some bias present in the processes of chemistry favored the formation during the experiment of the very chemicals vital in the biology of life. Adherents of the Oparin-Haldane hypothesis could disagree on the events involved in the last step, but their unity on the initial ones gave coherence to the field.

This theory has grown weaker as scientists' understanding of planetary development has increased. Most geologists and geochemists now believe that the Earth's initial atmosphere was neutral in character rather than reducing. It was not formed of the raw materials that coalesced to give birth to the solar system (the present atmospheric content of noble gases is too low to fit that hypothesis) but rather by the release of gases trapped within the Earth's interior. The composition of those gases probably resembled the emissions of certain volcanoes today. The early atmosphere was then composed largely of carbon dioxide, nitrogen, and water.

Methane and ammonia would have been absent. If formed, they would quickly have been destroyed. Observation by satellite of young Sun-like stars suggest that the Sun in its youth emitted much more radiation than at present. The resulting photochemical processes in the Earth's atmosphere would have destroyed reduced gases and even have produced a trace of oxygen. Small amounts of hydrogen released by volcanoes may have been present. The atmosphere would have been neutral or, at best, slightly reducing.

Under these conditions no rich, vast prebiotic soup would have been formed. Experiments of the Miller-Urey type afford poor yields when the gaseous mixture used is nearly neutral. Studies of the earliest rocks (those of the Isua series in Greenland are more than 3.8 billion years old) show carbon in oxidized carbonate form. No extremely nitrogen-rich carbonaceous deposits, the expected relics of a prebiotic soup, have been discovered.

Thus there exists a monumental paradox. Earth is the only place where it is certain that life exists. Yet the surface of the Earth, where life presumably arose, appears to be a nonreducing oasis in a reducing universe. Either scientists have not understood the conditions needed to generate life, or the necessary reducing environment was formed in some other way.

New approaches to the origin of life on Earth

It need not be necessary, of course, to have a planetwide reducing environment for the origin of life. A local area of the right kind might have been sufficient. One striking suggestion of this type involves hydrothermal vents at the bottom of the sea. Such vents exist today. One series, east of the Galápagos Islands in the Pacific, has been investigated by scientists using a deep-diving submersible. These subterranean openings emit hot water as well as a

Proteins and nucleic acids are two kinds of macromolecules that play especially important roles in life processes. Proteins consist of amino-acid subunits linked together chemically in a chainlike fashion (opposite page, left). By contrast nucleic acids, also built of subunits (opposite, bottom), are much more complicated, organized structures. Each strand of double-stranded nuclear DNA, for example, is made of a long backbone of alternating sugar and phosphate molecules (this page, bottom). Attached to each sugar is one of four large organic molecules called nucleotide bases: adenine, cytosine, thymine, or guanine. The two strands are linked together in parallel by means of hydrogen bonds (in this case, weak bonds between hydrogen and oxygen or nitrogen) across pairs of nucleotide bases on opposite strands: adenine always pairs with thymine, and cytosine with guanine. Proteins and nucleic acids depend on each other for their continued replication, and scientists sharply disagree over which preceded the other; i.e., which could have replicated independently for a time when life was first forming.

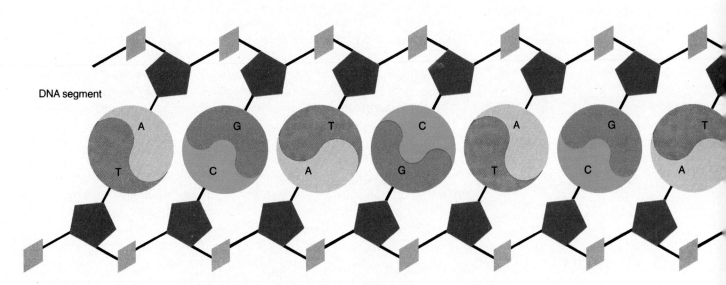

DNA segment

"The Primeval Landscape" (above) was painted in the early 1950s when the Oparin-Haldane theory dominated thinking about the origin of life. Evident are the volcanic activity and lightning that were thought to have helped transform a reducing atmosphere of hydrogen, methane, and ammonia into reduced carbon compounds. These substances then dissolved in the Earth's ample oceans to produce a vast "prebiotic soup" from which life emerged. Although the Oparin-Haldane theory has weakened in the past 30 years, the painting itself remains timely. What has been altered by new scientific thinking are the invisible elements of the picture: the reducing atmosphere has given way to a neutral one formed from the outgasing of volcanoes, while the site of life's origin has shifted from the ocean surface to several "offstage" possibilities. (Opposite page) A local reducing environment on the early Earth may have been provided by deep-sea hydrothermal vents similar to those that exist today on the Pacific Ocean floor (top left). There giant tube worms (top right), clams and crabs (center right), and other higher organisms ultimately depend on bacteria (bottom right) that derive their energy from reduced carbon compounds emitted from the vents.

mixture of reduced chemicals including hydrogen sulfide, methane, and ammonia. Microorganisms live on the chemical energy in the hydrogen sulfide, while higher organisms such as clams, mussels, and worms ultimately depend on the microorganisms for food. Thus an entire ecology, independent of sunlight, exists on the ocean floor.

It is likely that similar vents existed on the early Earth. In many ways their conditions appear attractive for the synthesis of organic compounds, but such synthesis has not yet been demonstrated in suitable experiments. Prospects for the origin of life in this environment are limited by the finite lifetime of individual vents and by the fact that their combined volume offers a much more constrained realm for natural experimentation than the oceans.

For such reasons efforts have been made to resurrect the concept of a primeval sea of organic compounds of global extent by using the cosmos as a source of reduced materials. In alternative scenarios reduced carbon compounds are ferried in by repeated encounters of the Earth with meteors or comets or by the passage of the Earth through an interstellar dust cloud. To substantiate such ideas it would be necessary to demonstrate that sufficient amounts of organic substances to populate the ocean were delivered and that the material was not incinerated during delivery. Unfortunately the necessary hard data do not exist. The current rate of infall of cosmic material is inadequate for the purpose. Extrapolations to earlier times can vary with the optimism or pessimism of the observer.

The origins of life beyond Earth

The ideas that envision cosmic material coming to Earth to start life can be reversed. The origin of life can be moved off the Earth altogether, to other locations in the cosmos where more suitable material may exist. One incentive for such thinking is the realization that the time available for the origin of life on Earth, like the supply of suitable space, is shrinking with new geological discoveries.

Knowledge of the antiquity of life comes from the discovery of very old

16

(Left) Robert D. Ballard—Woods Hole Oceanographic Institution; (top right and center right) Scripps Institution of
Oceanography, University of California, San Diego; (bottom right) Carl D. Wirsen—Woods Hole Oceanographic Institution

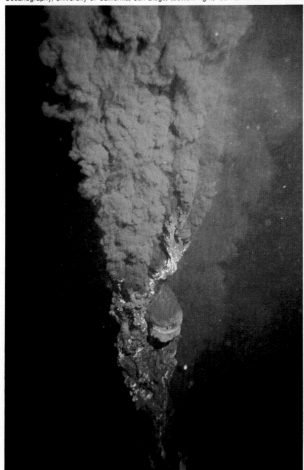

fossils. Most of the fossils that exist today were formed within the last 600
million years, after the creatures of Earth had attained larger sizes and
developed durable parts such as shells and bones. At one time it was believed
that life had originated less than one billion years ago.

This picture has changed as geologists have developed techniques for
detecting microfossils, the impressions of the walls of individual cells or of
arrays of cells that indicate the existence of microbial life. Remnants of stromatolites, which are layered mineral structures deposited by microorganisms, also testify to the existence of ancient life. Recently 3.5-billion-year-old
fossils of filaments of cells and preserved stromatolites were discovered at a
remote site in northwestern Australia. Other microfossils of almost the same
age, showing cells apparently in the process of division, have been reported
in rocks from South Africa. Current estimates of the time when the Earth
"settled down," with the formation of a stable crust, run to perhaps four billion years ago. Life thus had at most a few hundred million years on Earth in
which to develop to the cellular stage. (The time would have been even
shorter had fossils reported in the 3.8-billion-year-old Isua rocks proved au-
thentic, but at last report they appeared to be mineral artifacts.)

As the available time and space shrink for the origin of life on Earth, it is

17

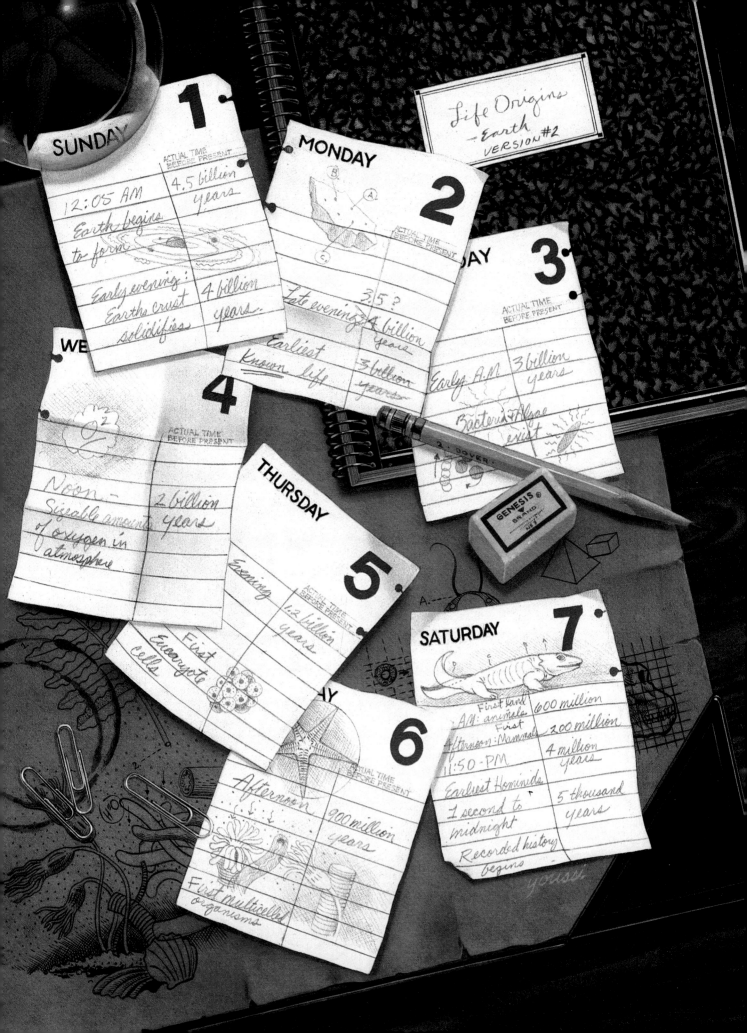

possible to conclude that life did not start on Earth at all. While possible, this conclusion is by no means necessary. With scientists' limited understanding of the process, a million years (or perhaps even seven days!) and a small but suitable area may have sufficed. Two distinguished scientists, however, have accepted the temptation and have developed detailed possibilities for an extraterrestrial origin of life.

One is Nobel laureate Francis Crick, one of the outstanding theoreticians of modern molecular biology. In his book *Life Itself*, published in 1981, Crick has summarized the case for an idea that has appeared now and again in scientific thought: life was sent here deliberately.

To start, it is known that the universe is more than twice the age of the Earth. If the time taken for a technological civilization to appear on Earth is typical, then there was time enough for this process to occur at least twice since the universe was formed.

Suppose then that an advanced civilization had evolved elsewhere, before the Earth was created. Assume that for technical reasons the beings could not colonize other star systems on their own. They felt themselves to be doomed eventually, and since life might not exist elsewhere, they considered it their duty to spread life throughout the Galaxy. Bacteria would be the creatures of choice for this purpose, since they are hardy and adaptable and could be sent for lengthy voyages with a minimum support system.

Thus, four billion years ago a spaceship bearing colonizing bacteria could have visited Earth. Even if Earth were unsuitable for the formation of life, for reasons discussed above, it might be suited for its propagation. The organisms that landed would be the earliest common ancestors of Earth life.

Crick does not insist that these events must have occurred, but simply points out that this is an alternative solution to the question concerning the appearance of life on Earth. He recognizes that it does not solve the problem of the origin of life elsewhere. Furthermore, he calls it premature, as no evidence in support of his theory has accumulated. His position is sober and restrained in comparison with that of Fred Hoyle.

Hoyle is a well-known and much honored astronomer who with his colleague Chandra Wickramasinghe has published three books advocating their own theories concerning the extraterrestrial origin of life. In brief, they

Important events in the 4½-billion-year history of the Earth, reduced in time scale to one week, are summarized on the opposite page. Discoveries of increasingly old fossils have reduced the time available for the origin of life on Earth to a few hundred million years.

Stromatolites, which still form today along coasts in various parts of the world (below left), are laminated structures produced from an interaction of mat-forming microorganisms and sedimentary deposits. Knowledge of the antiquity of life has improved with the recent discovery in northwestern Australia of fossilized stromatolites about 3.5 billion years old. Cross section of one such fossil (below) reveals alternating light and dark layers of sediment and fossilized mat.

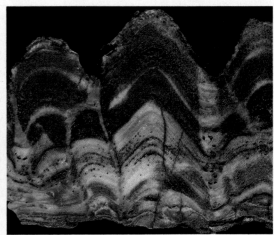

(Left) Ronald Templeton—Oxford Scientific Films; (right) Donald R. Lowe, Department of Geology, Louisiana State University

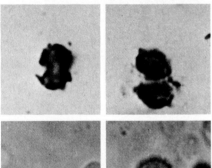

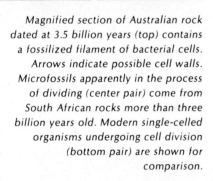

Magnified section of Australian rock dated at 3.5 billion years (top) contains a fossilized filament of bacterial cells. Arrows indicate possible cell walls. Microfossils apparently in the process of dividing (center pair) come from South African rocks more than three billion years old. Modern single-celled organisms undergoing cell division (bottom pair) are shown for comparison.

propose that the interstellar dust particles are largely composed of frozen bacteria, which are protected from radiation by a coating of graphite. The bacteria first entered the solar system at the time of its formation. They amplified their numbers by reproducing within the interiors of comets (in an earlier book the authors claimed that the bacteria were first formed inside comets). Life on Earth originated when a cometful of bacteria first landed. Subsequent landings have introduced fresh microorganisms and started some of the infectious plagues of recorded history.

How then did life originate? According to Hoyle and Wickramasinghe it was created by a higher intelligence—one of an ascending series of intelligences that ultimately converges to the authors' conception of God. The argument by this time has also ascended out of science and into theology. The evidence, which would need to be massive to establish these points, is rather insufficient to support the simplest of the speculations. The authors appear to have constructed a cathedral upon a base of toothpicks.

In their presentation Hoyle and Wickramasinghe are more successful in criticizing the defects in other theories than in supporting their own. They recognize the gap in organization, or order, between living and nonliving systems. A major problem for origin-of-life theories has been to explain the principle that produced order from disorder.

The order gap

Even if it were assumed that some suitable environment (on Earth or elsewhere) afforded a convenient supply of reduced organic molecules, scientists would still not understand the origin of life. The question remains: what steps led from this mixture to a simple cell?

Some theories emphasize the importance of the formation of the first self-replicating molecule. Life began, it is said, when the first such "naked gene" appeared, together with a supply of the subunits needed for its replication and a suitable energy source to permit the process to take place. At this point natural selection could take over.

Experiments have indicated that evolution indeed could proceed from this humble starting place. In the 1960s Sol Spiegelman and his co-workers at the University of Illinois at Urbana initiated an elegant series of studies using RNA derived from a virus called Qβ. If the RNA were mixed with appropriate subunits and a necessary protein catalyst (called replicase), the RNA could proliferate indefinitely. As it underwent chance mutations, which changed the order of nucleotides within it, it could respond to environmental challenges. Thus, when a drug was added that reduced the rate of RNA replication (a threat to continued "survival"), compensating changes in nucleotide sequence took place to limit the effect.

Manfred Eigen and his colleagues have built a complex theory of the origin of life that incorporates these experiments. They postulate that a naked gene was formed (for technical reasons they specify RNA rather than DNA) that could reproduce and mutate without the aid of a protein. After a certain amount of evolutionary development, proteins would be enlisted to aid in controlling the environment. Complex interactions between the two types of molecule, called hypercycles, would result in a parceling up of the medium

20

In one concept of an extra-terrestrial origin of life a robot-controlled spaceship from another solar system deliberately seeds the Earth with bacteria. Released into the atmosphere or on the ground, these organisms would be the earliest common ancestors of all life on the planet.

youssi

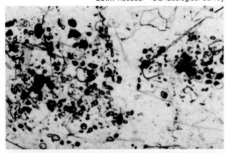

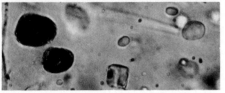

Discovered in 3.8-billion-year-old rocks from Greenland, microscopic dark objects similar to those shown above were first thought to be yeastlike microfossils. Subsequent examination indicated that they were probably mineral artifacts of nonbiological origin.

into competing cells. Classical natural selection could then begin.

Naked-gene theories unfortunately do not provide a satisfactory account of how a system containing the first self-replicating molecule, together with supplies of subunits and energy, came to be formed. It is generally specified that the first self-replicator was a nucleic acid, as these are the only replicators known. But nucleic acids are complicated, organized molecules. Unlike much simpler amino acids, the formation of nucleotides in experiments of the Miller-Urey type has not been reported. Nor would this be expected to occur. A prebiotic mixture in which nucleotides had formed at random would also contain hundreds of thousands, or millions, of other chemical species of similar complexity. The chance that the occasional nucleotide units in that immense mixture would seek each other out and combine specifically to form a nucleic acid capable of replication is insignificant.

Alternatives to nucleic acids

If one accepts the argument that life began with the formation of a self-replicating system but that this system was unlikely to be as complicated as a nucleic acid, then one must find a simpler alternative.

One obvious candidate would be a system based on proteins. Amino acids are formed readily in the Miller-Urey type of experiments. There are fewer complications involved in the assembly of amino acids into proteins than in the construction of nucleic acids from nucleotides. It would be considerably easier to get a short protein by prebiotic processes than a short nucleic acid.

In the case of proteins the product would also be more likely to be of some use. Even a chain of amino acids too short to properly be called a protein could have some useful catalytic ability; it could affect its environment. This is unlikely to be true in the case of nucleotides, should they be stuck together. In fact, natural nucleic acids have not even been shown capable of replication without protein. In Spiegelman's experimental system the replicase protein was indispensable. Surprisingly the RNA was not. In the absence of added RNA the protein, after a pause, assembled an RNA on its own, using the subunits. Thereafter the RNA replicated nicely.

The above scene may mimic the actual events of evolution. Proteins may have been made first and then assisted in the creation of the first nucleic acids. But one more item is needed to complete this step: a way in which the proteins could replicate themselves. Suggestions have been made for ways in which proteins might accomplish this, but no experimental demonstration has been carried out thus far.

Of the molecules visible in biology today, proteins are the most obvious alternative to nucleic acids as the first replicator. But another haunting possibility remains. What if the first replicators were replaced entirely and are no longer represented in life on Earth. A. G. Cairns-Smith, a chemist at the University of Glasgow in Scotland, has made a startling suggestion: the first primitive living things on Earth were made of clay minerals.

Clay minerals have a complex chemistry. They can catalyze chemical reactions, speeding up the rate at which they take place. Irregularities present in crystalline sheets in the minerals have the potential for information storage. In some cases these irregularities can be duplicated in crystal

22

growth (an analog of replication). Thus the minerals have some of the features of living systems. If they had the capacity to evolve and gain in complexity, they might be considered alive.

Suppose that such a living mineral system did exist on the early Earth. Assume that at some point it gained the ability to reduce carbon dioxide in the atmosphere by photosynthesis, as plants do today. The organic molecules thus formed would first be used as an aid to the metabolism of the minerals. Gradually they would take over the metabolism, eventually replacing the clays entirely. This then would be the start of the present form of life.

There are many attractive features in this scheme. It needs no prebiotic soup or reducing atmosphere. There is no obvious gap in order to be closed. However, in order to adopt this tidy solution to the origin-of-life problem, scientists would need to accept an idea of even greater consequence: that a system made of minerals can serve as a basis for life. Scientists and authors of fiction alike have written of the possibility of alternative life forms elsewhere in the universe. It would be ironic if the first such example to be recognized should turn up on the surface of the Earth itself.

Fortunately this proposition can be tested. Clay minerals can be studied in the laboratory to see whether in the proper circumstances they can evolve to greater complexity and perform other functions associated with life. In addition, the minerals present in the environment today can be examined to learn whether such evolved forms do exist in nature.

Further possibilities

The above discussion presumes that replication accompanied by natural selection is the only scheme by which systems can gain order and evolve. This need not be the case. Possibly other principles exist that permit simple mixtures of chemicals to become organized if given a suitable flow of energy. Nobel laureate Ilya Prigogine, Harold Morowitz at Yale University, and others have tried to describe such processes mathematically. It might be simpler to demonstrate them experimentally, but this has not really been attempted. Ideally one would need to run experiments of the Miller-Urey type, but with the energy source kept on, and then see what emerges.

Not long ago a number of scientists felt that the solution to the problem of the origin of life required only the filling in of additional details in existing theories. Now everyone is less sure even about the framework of the answer. A number of exotic possibilities have been described above. The solution may yet be different. Whatever the answer, it will most likely surprise us.

FOR ADDITIONAL READING
A. G. Cairns-Smith, *Genetic Takeover and the Mineral Origins of Life* (Cambridge University Press, 1982).
Francis Crick, *Life Itself* (Simon and Schuster, 1981).
Gerald Feinberg and Robert Shapiro, *Life Beyond Earth* (Morrow, 1980).
Sir Fred Hoyle and Chandra Wickramasinghe, *Evolution From Space* (Simon and Schuster, 1981).
L. E. Orgel, *The Origins of Life: Molecules and Natural Selection* (John Wiley and Sons, 1973).

Scanning electron micrographs show two magnified views of kaolinite, a clay mineral. A complex chemistry and the potential for information storage and replication give the clay minerals some of the features of present-day living systems, and it has been suggested that the first living things on Earth indeed were made of such minerals.

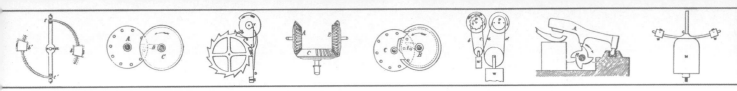

THOSE WONDERFUL OLD
MECHANICAL
TOYS

by Athelstan Spilhaus

Mechanisms that later were used widely in the "real world" often were first incorporated in toys.

Large or miniature, lifelike in form or caricatures, static as in dolls' houses and furniture, or dynamic as in mechanical action contrivances—toys are almost limitless in their variety. Defined as things that provide pleasure and are not essential to physical well-being, toys also can be useful and are not only for children. From model airplanes to dolls, diamonds to video games, toys enable people to tarry pleasantly during the fast whip of ordinary life.

It is difficult to distinguish between engineering innovators and toymakers—both leaven their practical ingenuity with a measure of fantasy. The line between an innovative toy and the workaday world is sometimes hard to draw. For example, the Greeks used their knowledge of rising hot air and water columns and of compressed air to give statues movement, cause doors to open, and give artificial birds voice and flight. Though some of these mechanisms may not have been toys in the conventional sense, they lifted the spirit. Also, in those devices the Greeks' knowledge of engineering principles was first put to use. In this same way the marvelous clocks of the Middle Ages were in part toys; the precessions of figures and concerts of music that occurred at intervals were just as important as the counting of the hours. Both the Greek devices and the clock mechanisms were the forerunners of many applications in practical machines.

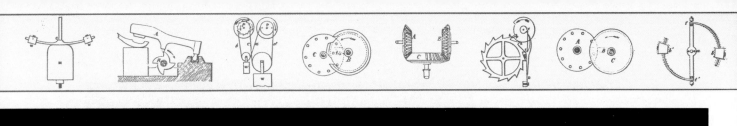

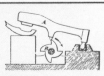

ATHELSTAN SPILHAUS, an oceanographer, meteorologist, and former administrator of scientific institutions, has written several books and many articles for magazines and scientific journals.

Photographs by Nelson C. McClary; drawings by John Draves

(Overleaf) Photograph by Bill Arsenault

When air is blown into the mouthpiece of The American Songster (right), it bubbles through water in the egg-shaped reservoir at the bottom of the bird's perch, and the bird bursts into song. The tune of this 1913 toy is modulated by air bubbles as air is forced through the water. In the tin German singing bird of about 1900 (bottom right) a bellows-driven piston moves in and out to change the whistle note, and the irregularly shaped cam produces the tune (below).

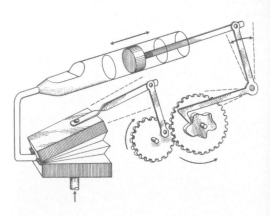

An extension of the Greeks' use of pneumatics and hydraulics is seen in The American Songster. When air that is blown into the mouthpiece bubbles through water in the egg-shaped reservoir at the bottom of this bird's perch, he bursts into song. A piston in the air cylinder above the reservoir oscillates a wire that extends up the hollow perch and moves the bird's tail and bill. Both motion and tune are modulated by the bubbles as air is forced through the water. "Highly appreciated by ladies," said toymaker Ives and Co. in 1913, "who use it to teach birds to sing. . . . When used near a bird will induce it to start up its best notes immediately." A tin German singing bird is only the size of a small thrush, yet internal clockwork drives a remarkable array of mechanisms. A piston bellows blows a tiny flute similar to a Swannee whistle (a 19th-century bird whistle). A cam moves the stop to vary the notes of the song. Other levers make the bird flap its wings and tail, turn its head, and open and close its beak.

A child's hand was the primary source of power for pre-20th-century toys—for lifting sand or water, raising a weight, winding a spring, pressing an air-filled bulb, or spinning a flywheel. Thus, one of the charms of these toys is that they are hand-sized—handy, one might say. The hand in the mechanical toy world is like the Sun in the real world: its energy is stored in springs, flywheels, and weights, just as the Sun's energy is stored in wood, coal, oil, wind, and water.

Action toys and automata

Before the use of plastics action toys were made of tin, iron, wood, cloth, paper, and papier-mâché. Many of them embodied imaginative applications of the principles and devices that are the very stuff of modern machines and structures. Indeed, they often represented the first use of principles and mechanisms that were later widely applied in engineering practices.

Player pianos and music boxes with their punched-roll or spiked-barrel memories were the ancestors of computers. An 18th-century serinette, when cranked by hand, plays a program of high-pitched bird whistles through tiny organ tubes. Such bird organs were designed to teach canaries how to sing—an early response to the realization, later confirmed by biologists, that birds do not sing if they do not hear singing. Modern breeders use tape recorders for the same purpose.

Toy boats called putt-putts because of the noise made when they alternately sucked in water and expelled steam from a heated chamber, preceded practical jet propulsion by almost a century. The first Chinese firecrackers, used for amusement and display, led to the use of gunpowder in weapons and to toy rockets, signal rockets, and, finally, to rocket propulsion.

Automata of the 18th and 19th centuries were programmed by intricate cams to execute series of motions. The length and complexity of the series distinguishes the automaton from the simpler toy. Complex automata included lifelike, life-size dolls that drew pictures, played pianos, and performed magic tricks. Among the latter was a gypsy doll that played the shell game to musical accompaniment. In this French automaton of the 1850s clockwork-driven cams lift the gypsy's arms to expose different combinations of colors, and objects changed, as if by magic, on the table. The legerde-

27

main on the spindly-legged table is accomplished by rotating ratchet wheels in the tabletop, activated by a fine wire passing up through one of the legs. The General Grant Smoker, patented in 1877, featured a cam-operated piston that pulls smoke in from a small cigar while a lever lowers the general's hand and the piston expels the smoke through his mouth.

Automata were precursors of programmed tools and industrial robots. A German clown, made in 1895 by Phillip Vielmetter, sketches a picture, the X-Y position of his pencil being controlled by a double cam that could be changed to draw different designs. "Living pictures" made by a Philadelphia toymaker adorned Victorian walls. In one entitled A Good Joke two clerics sharing a toddy move their arms and jaws while rocking with laughter. Inside the picture is an array of clockwork, string, belts, cardboard cams, and wire levers with counterbalancing weights. The scene is animated by a belt-driven cam from a slow-moving shaft in the clockwork, while the highest-speed axle carries a fast-moving fan that acts as a governor.

Still more complex is the Democratic Decision Maker, a two-foot-tall cast-iron, satin-robed donkey seated atop a four-foot pedestal. It has seven cams rotated by a rack and pinion to chatter its mouth, nod and turn its head, waggle its ears, raise its monocle, lift its arm, and rotate its elbow so that it spins the decision-making wheel of chance. When a penny is pushed into this machine, the rack extends two helical tension springs, which, governed by a fly fan, provide the power. Equal time must be given to a Republican elephant, which flips the pages of a book until its trunk picks one to make an equally random decision.

Randomness—sought to introduce the element of chance and variety to toys—is difficult to achieve mechanically. In one successful effort toy horses leap forward when they are hit by steel balls that have been randomly struck by a rapidly spinning square arbor rotated by the inertia of a flywheel spun by pulling a string. The balls roll down an incline to be shot up again. A European hand-painted tin jouster of about 1880 tilts at a ring as his horse trots around the course. An eccentric crank on the wheel causes him to post,

A child's hand was the main source of power for most toys made before the 20th century. A clown on a unicycle (opposite page, left) balances on a string and pedals backward and forward as one end of the high wire is raised and lowered. In the pull toy (opposite page, bottom) the small train travels around and around as the toy is moved. Another example of a balance toy is a monkey that rocks on its perch (left).

and his lance misses the ring more often than not. These devices bridge the gap between mechanical toys and games of chance.

There were attempts to synthesize speech long before Thomas Edison recorded and reproduced the human voice. As far back as 1770 toymaker Friedrich von Knauss showed the Austrian emperor an automaton that reproduced speech, and in 1779 the Russian Imperial Academy of Science at St. Petersburg awarded its annual prize for a device that pronounced all the vowels by projecting air from a bellows into tubes of different shapes. Edison himself produced and marketed a "talking doll." These were the predecessors of today's electronic voice synthesizers. Toys showing animation (called zoetropes, pantascopes, praxiniscopes, phenakistoscopes, and thaumatropes) with motion provided mechanically so that the eye could glimpse successive positions of an image were the forerunners of modern cinematography.

The gyroscope, so important in modern inertial guidance systems, found its first use in one of the most ancient of toys, the spinning top. A toy mono-

29

Player pianos and music boxes with their punched-roll or spiked-barrel memories were ancestors of computers. The Secor Pianist of about 1885 (above) moves her head and hands to the tune of the music box. Cranking the serinette of about 1740 (above right) causes the music box to play a program of high-pitched bird whistles through tiny organ tubes. When the handle at the rear of The Pumper of 1880 (opposite page) is turned, the man pumps and water pours from the spout.

rail train traveled upright on a single track using a gyroscope long before gyroscopes were employed in aircraft instruments and to stabilize ocean liners. The principle of the Bourdon tube, a flattened, flexible tube that straightens out under pressure, was used in pneumatic toys such as the rubber monkey that plays a drum when a rubber bulb is squeezed by hand. The Bourdon tube is used today in many steam and other pressure gauges. Compressed air, which works the monkey, also powers the noisy jackhammers that dig up streets.

Foretellers of the future

As with good science fiction toys show the shape of things to come, as in various flying devices made in the 19th century. The fantasy of man-powered flight is suggested by a hand-painted tin toy in which four balloons circle and descend a mast. Under each balloon a man with oars sits in a row-boat. The twirling motion is accomplished by gravity pulling the balloons down the helical screw, which is the mast. This toy is reversible since it can be turned over to repeat the process. Another reversible toy is the 1910 Gibbs mechanical seesaw. On a vertical strip of corrugated metal, gravity seesaws the girl and boy, while pallets at the fulcrum of the seesaw alternately engage the corrugations.

That engineering in toys should precede engineering in practice is not at all surprising, for toys inhabit an environment in which they are free not only from the constraints of "good engineering practice" but even of social responsibility. Toys can do all sorts of things that real-life machines cannot because they do not have to be efficient. In relation to their size a huge amount of energy can be used to work them: a toy has at its command one whole "child-power." Toys also do not have to run smoothly. In the real world flywheels are balanced to eliminate vibrations, but in toys the forces of

30

vibration are either too small to be destructive or are emphasized to achieve comic effects. Less rigorous engineering requirements surely stimulated toymakers to experiment with systems and devices not yet successfully adopted elsewhere.

Many toys use sudden reversals of motion to achieve comic effects. This can be compared with moving forward in one's car and then jamming it into reverse. Using the resulting inertial shocks is the basic principle of such toys as those in which two cocks fight, a steamroller moves back and forth, and a donkey-pulled cart jerks so as to cause the donkey to kick and buck.

Among the reversing mechanisms is a crank with a toothed rack that is moved back and forth to rotate a pinion, causing wheels to turn one way and then the other. In the cock fight the reversing is accomplished by a half crown wheel that alternately engages a pinion on one wheel and then, after half a revolution, turns the other wheel in the opposite direction. A flat spring connecting the combatants absorbs the inertial shock by bending and straightening, giving the lithographed tin birds a fierce, lifelike dodging and pecking action. This can be found in many different applications involving two figures, such as birds fighting for a worm, goats butting, and a toreador striking at a plunging bull.

An out-of-balance flywheel that rotates freely can cause toy animals and

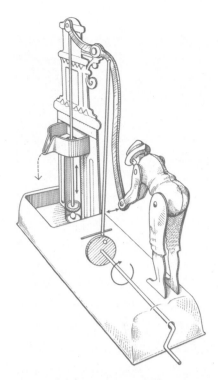

A spring mechanism inside the 19th-century peacock (above) struts the bird along as it alternately raises and lowers the real peacock plumes of its tail. In a French automaton of the 1850s (right) clockwork-driven cams lift the arms of a gypsy playing the shell game. The objects on the table are mounted on rotating ratchet wheels that are activated by a fine wire that passes up through one of the table legs.

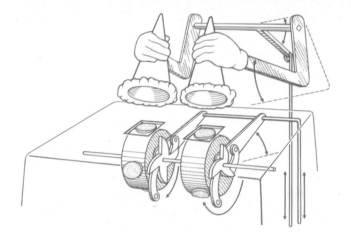

A 19th-century clown made in France (top) balances on a rolling ball by moving the hoop, its arms, and one leg. Also from France the monkey artist (bottom), covered with real hair, moves the brush from palette to canvas, paints, turns its head, and shuts its mouth. Such cam-driven automata foreshadowed programmed tools and industrial robots.

In a "living picture" from 19th-century France a magician alternately covers his face and a box on the table and then opens each in turn to show his head in the box and no head on his shoulders. Each is covered again, and when opened the head has returned from the box to the magician's shoulders. Such toys were animated by an array of clockwork, string, belts, cardboard cams, and wire levers with counterbalancing weights.

humans to jiggle around and birds to peck. The mounted cowboy's twirling lariat jerks his rearing horse in circles. In 1938 a U.S. toymaker marketed a marvelously ingenious simple mechanism in the brightly lithographed Ferdinand the Bull. In this version of the bull who would rather smell the flowers than fight the toreadors, Ferdinand's tail is an out-of-balance flywheel. As the tail swings downward on each rotation, the back feet are lifted slightly and the hindquarters are free to move in reaction to the tail's rotation. Thus Ferdinand, while unsuccessfully trying to dislodge the bumblebee on his rear end, stomps around the tabletop in circles with a brightly colored flower clamped firmly in his teeth.

In the days when real machines were built to last, be repaired, and last again, many toys were manufactured in quantity without thought of repair. Hand-painted toys were soldered, and, later, lithographed tin toys were held together with bent tabs. Neither was designed to be repaired; resoldering destroyed the delicate hand-painted colors, and the tabs broke off by fatigue if the toys were taken apart—certainly a foreshadowing of today's throwaway culture.

Designers of toys found that they could play on people's fantasies. Toy ornithopters became the embodiment of Leonardo da Vinci's imagination. They actually flew, though their full-scale counterparts never did. The brothers Montgolfier discovered in their paper factory that if they trapped heated air in a lightweight paper bag it would float upward. After they sent up their hot-air balloon in 1783, balloons immediately claimed the public's fancy and toymakers responded with whimsical creations.

Motion transformation and energy storage

The toymakers' ingenuity shows itself most clearly in the devices used to transform motion from one form or function to another, such as rotation to oscillation or to linear movement. Various climbing toys—monkeys on strings, sailors on ropes, and ascending balloons, for example—depend on simple differential pulleys in which the string that is pulled from below is wrapped around a smaller pulley rotating a larger one on the same axle. When the string is pulled down, the toy goes up, and when the string is released, the toy comes down by gravity. The lithographed tin balloon marketed under the names Luna, Mars, and Jupiter, produced about 1900, utilized a mechanism that is akin to the ancient Chinese windlass, in which two pulleys of different sizes gave a mechanical advantage for lifting weights. With the upside-down engineering of the toymaker, the pull of the hand replaces the weight and raises the windlass, in this case the balloon.

Once energy is stored in a toy, there must be a mechanism to govern its release. The governors in the early Greek temple doors and singing birds were controlled openings through which air or water passed. In toys small openings let sand, water, or marbles fall at a regulated rate, as in an hourglass. These are the early counterparts of modern hydroelectric power plants. A cast-iron sand toy consisting of a hopper over a wheel that is turned by falling sand and a crank that activates a workman has essentially the same simple mechanism as is inside a forge.

The pendulum was a common device in toys. A whole class of toys called

Horse race made in England (top) succeeded in introducing randomness to mechanical toys. When the flywheel is spun by pulling a string, it causes a square arbor to rotate rapidly and randomly strike steel balls that have rolled down an incline. The balls in turn hit the horses, causing them to leap forward. In the French Le Zanzinet (bottom), as dice are thrown, the corresponding key on the toy is pressed to bring up the tail, an ear, and other parts of the pig until the picture is completed.

nodders, because the head rocks or an arm beckons, was based on a moving part delicately balanced with a counterweight to form a compound pendulum. Escapements, devices invented for clocks in the Middle Ages in which a tooth escapes from a pallet at regular intervals, prevent springs from springing; this action gave rise to the term clockwork toys. In some clockwork toys the toy itself simulates the oscillation of a pendulum bob. A delicate mechanical horse, rocked by the motion of an inverted conical pendulum, is as elegant in the simplicity of its mechanism as in the grace of its design. The clockwork in the body of the horse rotates a bent shaft that protrudes from

35

the horse's back into the rider. As the horsewoman's weight shifts from pommel to cantle, her mount rocks in harmonic resonance.

Other types of governors employ air resistance, a rapidly rotating fly fan, or the rotation of the toy itself to control the rate of energy release. A carousel, made in 1870 by Althof Bergmann, a famous U.S. toymaker, is rotated smoothly by clockwork that is governed by the air resistance of the hand-painted tin gondolas and horses themselves. The overworked girl who appears to be turning the carousel by hand is cranked by the clockwork that is hidden in the base. In toy boats the propeller has a dual function: it moves the boat and acts as a fly-fan governor, just as propellers do in rubber-band model airplanes. In toy vehicles and figures that move on

36

wheels the friction of the toy itself traveling over the surface is an adequate governor.

Many old and new toys store energy by spinning a flywheel so that the toy proceeds on its own with friction as the governor. Flywheel storage is now contemplated for slowing down and accelerating subway trains that stop and start frequently. Spring-driven cams, commonly used for transforming rotational energy into other motions, are used in great variety. Eccentric wheels cause toy ships to pitch and roll and horses to gallop. In one British toy of the 1890s an equestrienne is powered by the momentum of a rapidly spun flywheel. The conical end of the flywheel axle rides as a bevel pinion around the outside of a circular baseplate to rotate the assembly of flywheel, horse, and rider. A horizontal cam in the base causes the rider to leap over a bar and regain her seat on her steed. The horse, in turn, is given a galloping motion by an eccentric wheel between its hind legs.

In toys a trigger provides a surprise ending. Perhaps the oldest and best known is the jack-in-the-box. Madeline, a Dutch serving maid walking with difficulty with a huge stack of dishes, suddenly spills them all. A ski jumper schusses down a ramp and throws himself over a high jump. A torpedo fired at a ship unexpectedly blows it to bits.

The British-made Gyrocycle, an elaboration of the ancient spinning top, features a heavy gyroscope wheel mounted inside the front wheel. When the gyro wheel is rotated rapidly by pulling a string, the bicycle moves forward. The gyro wheel prevents the cycle from falling.

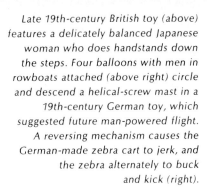

*Late 19th-century British toy (above)
features a delicately balanced Japanese
woman who does handstands down
the steps. Four balloons with men in
rowboats attached (above right) circle
and descend a helical-screw mast in a
19th-century German toy, which
suggested future man-powered flight.
A reversing mechanism causes the
German-made zebra cart to jerk, and
the zebra alternately to buck
and kick (right).*

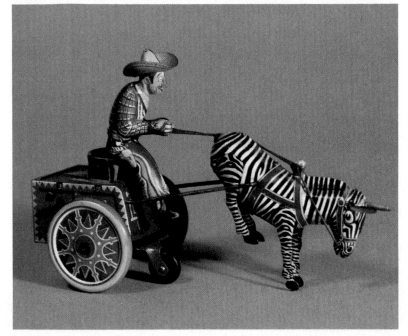

Rubber-band-powered, bird-shaped ornithopter flaps its wings and flies (left). Climbing toy (below left) is actuated when a string pulled from below is wrapped around a small pulley that is rotating a larger one on the same axle. An out-of-balance flywheel that rotates freely jerks the cowboy's rearing horse around in circles (below).

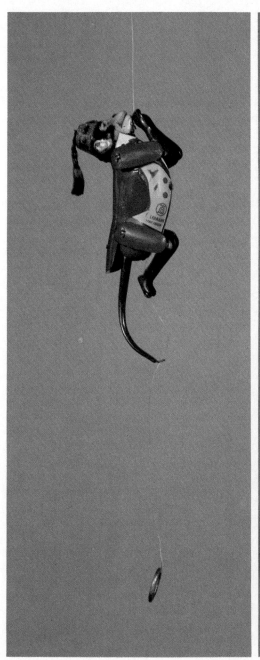

A carousel made by U.S. toymaker Althof Bergmann in 1870 (above) is rotated smoothly by a clockwork mechanism that is governed by the air resistance of the tin gondolas and horses. The girl who appears to be turning the carousel by hand (above right) is cranked by clockwork hidden in the base.

Magnets have been used in toys for centuries. In a magical book the professor's hand is placed on a question. When the book is closed, magnetism operates so that when it is opened again the figure opposite the professor is pointing to the answer. A much more modern bear quickly flips the metal pages of a book with a tiny magnet in his hand—he is, indeed, a "speed reader." The Nürnberg figures from the famous toymaking center of Germany also use magnetism. The vertical axis of a spinning flywheel that protrudes from the center of the dance floor is a permanent magnet. Different iron shapes on the feet of the figures are attracted to the magnet, the rotation of which causes them to perform appropriate motions—a triangular base for the three-step waltzers, a kidney shape for the turning and gliding skater, and a hollow circle for the clown to chase the pig.

Even the archimedes' screw of antiquity is frequently used to cause clockwork rotation to lift balls to the top of inclines. Archimedes (287–212 BC) devised this screw for removing water from the hold of a large ship. In one Japanese toy a celluloid ball coasts down an intricate ramp and then is lifted again to its starting point by an archimedes' screw powered by clockwork in the base. A simple escapement at the top of the tower adds movement while serving as a governor. These are antecedents of the screw feeds that lift grain into silos.

The first use of the wheel may have been in a toy. A pre-Columbian tribe in Mexico made clay animals on wheels, the only example of the use of the wheel by those people. The ball, originally a round stone and later fashioned by hand from wood or clay, was the precursor of modern ball bearings. In fact the material expression of newly discovered physical principles often was a plaything. Many times toys depicting engines of war preceded the real ones. The ray gun of comic-book hero Buck Rogers antedates modern laser

Camel (above) nods as a result of a mechanism in which a moving part is balanced with a counterweight to form a compound pendulum. The wheel of the cast-iron sand toy (below) is turned by sand falling in a controlled flow.

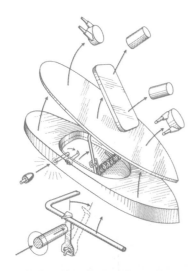

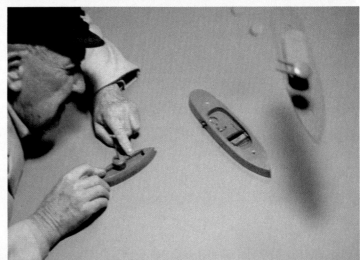
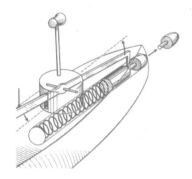

Propeller in the rubber-band model airplane and in the German-made warship (opposite page, top right and bottom right) moves the vehicles and also governs the energy release. A spring mechanism blows a battleship apart when it is hit by a torpedo from a submarine (opposite page, center). The reading bear (top left) turns the pages of a book by means of a tiny magnet in its hand. When the dirigible (top right) ascends to the top of its string, the parachuting man is released and carried gently to the ground. "One-way shoes" of the walking figure (left) contain ratchets inside the heels that allow the back roller of each shoe to roll forward but not backward.

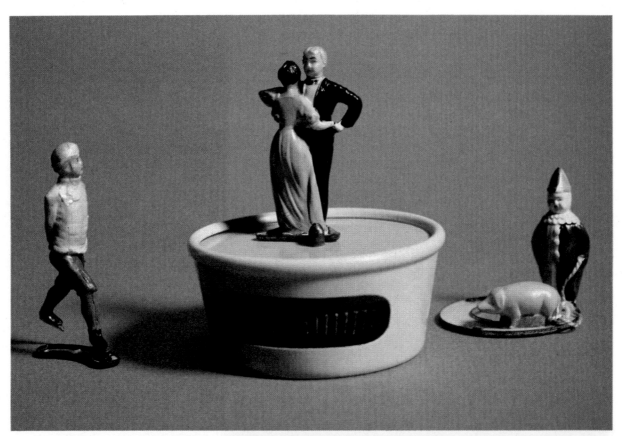

The vertical axis of a spinning flywheel extending from the base of the Nürnberg dancers (above) is a permanent magnet; its rotation causes the iron feet of the figures to perform various motions. A trigger mechanism causes Madeline (right) to spill the stack of dishes that she is carrying. The Yellow Kid (opposite page, top) was based on the first newspaper comic-strip character. Siam Soo (opposite page, bottom) is powered by the rotation of a phonograph record.

weapons by 30 to 40 years. Similarly, Dick Tracy's wrist radio came before the miniaturization of solid-state electronics made beepers and walkie-talkies practical.

Mirrors of the adult world

All toys faithfully reflect the society of their time as a whole. If they did not, they would not sell. Toys reflect the hopes, fears, and prejudices of their times sometimes better than written history. Aeronautical toys symbolize man's aspiration to fly. A witch or jack-in-the-box evokes squeals of terror. The host of toys depicting black dancers and minstrels around 1900 are stereotypes and caricatures.

Famous people celebrated in toys include Gen. Robert E. Lee on horseback; Pres. Abraham Lincoln; and, of course, the Teddy bear, originally Teddy's bear, inspired by Pres. Theodore Roosevelt's bear-hunting escapades. Stage, radio, and comic-page characters also inspired toys. The Yellow Kid toy was based on the first newspaper comic-strip character.

When Thomas Edison's marvelous phonograph was adapted so that it could use flat records instead of cylinders, toy designers quickly saw their chance to add animated figures powered by the rotation of the record. The choice was large, from Siam Soo (1909), who made exotic Balinese motions in time to a fast fox-trot, to Uncle Sam and Mexican guerrilla leader Pancho Villa. In the latter Villa is being punished by repeated kicks from Uncle Sam for instigating a Mexican–U.S. border incident in 1916. Later, when the U.S. entered World War I, Villa was replaced by a bomb-carrying version of Kaiser William II of Germany.

Toys stimulate the imagination and are enormously satisfying because they take the place of the real thing that is unobtainable. They can bring a whole circus onto a little table, and exotic characters can bring the world into your hand. They can do things we cannot do in real life, thus keeping us in touch with fantasy.

All toys are inherently educational. The best teach subliminally—while one is having fun; the worst are labeled "educational" and never get off the shelf.

Just as the toymaker is freed from some of the constraints of real-world engineering, so is the person who contemplates a toy able to forget some of the constraints of the world in which he or she lives. Such a person can, for brief periods, escape murky reality and return to a world of pure fantasy. We learn from toys how little the amusements of children have changed, how little the amusements of adults differ from those of children, and how toys are the additive to preserve our childlike enchantment with magic, wonder, and play. Thus, toys were never just for children.

Although many toys, particularly old and rare ones, command a high price, they are worth only as much as they are cherished and played with. In this way they pay interest daily in the golden coin of joy.

45

PLANTS
THAT EAT MEAT
by Paul Simons

A look at both old and new research suggests that carnivory in plants may be more widespread and more difficult to define than generally thought.

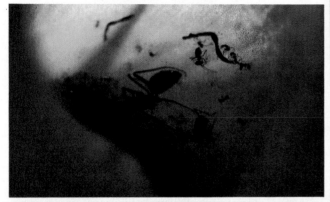

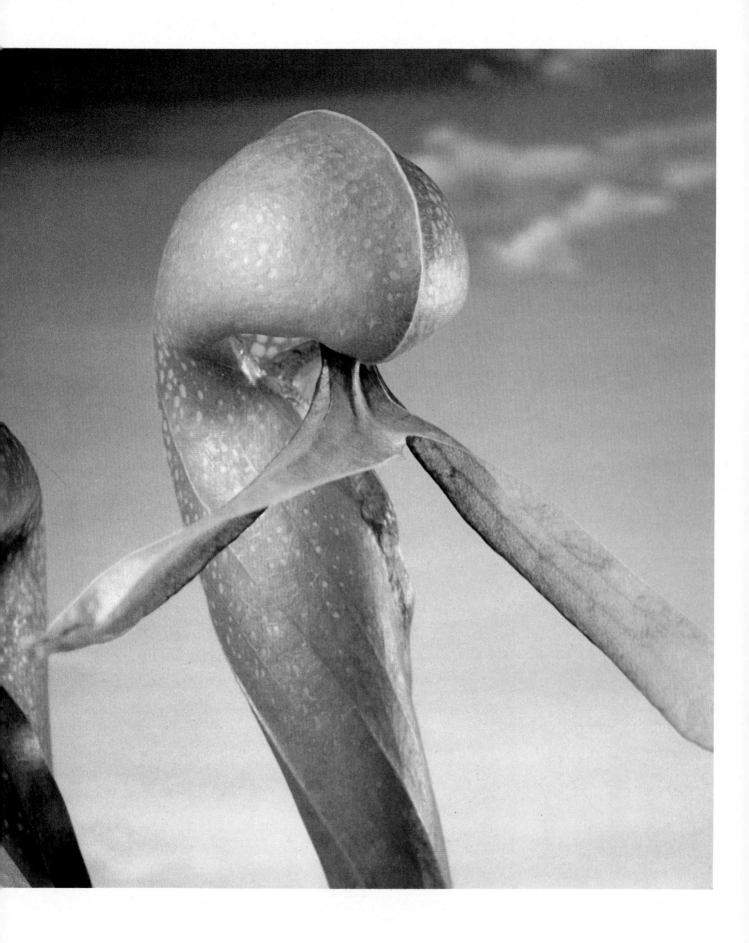

Fictional accounts of man-devouring plants have always held a grisly attraction for their readers. No less fascinating are the hundreds of real plant species capable of capturing and feeding off insects, crustaceans, and other small animals.

Alarming was the discovery that the whorl topping a triffid's stem could lash out as a slender stinging weapon ten feet long, capable of discharging enough poison to kill a man if it struck squarely on his unprotected skin.

—John Wyndham, from *The Day of the Triffids* (1951)

Although there is a morbid fascination for plants that kill and eat humans, the predatory triffids and their kind remain firmly rooted in science fiction. Nonetheless, more than 400 species of real flowering plants are acknowledged to be capable of killing and feeding off animals, mostly insects and crustaceans. This macabre habit, assisted by an arsenal of traps including sticky hairs, watery pitchers, and snapping leaves, is known to be important for fueling their growth and development and has helped elevate the carnivorous plants to an elite group within the plant kingdom—so much so, in fact, that specialist societies around the world are dedicated to growing and studying them.

But carnivory in plants might not be nearly as bizarre and exclusive as is commonly supposed. Evidence from long forgotten literature and recent research together suggests the need to take a fresh look at carnivory in plants and to consider the possibility of degrees of carnivorousness throughout the plant kingdom. This thinking also can help shed light on how and why carnivory evolved in the first place and the variety of ways these plants have adapted to their exotic diet. And although it has overtones of fantasy, carnivory eventually might be bred into crop plants to boost their nutrition and arm them against the ravages of hungry insects.

What makes a carnivorous plant?

Most of the plant carnivores recognized today received their credentials in the last century. A milestone of the old research was Charles Darwin's painstaking studies that culminated in his classic and still highly respected book *Insectivorous Plants* in 1875. His dedication to the work on plant

PAUL SIMONS *is a Botanist and an Assistant Producer with* BBC *Television, London.*

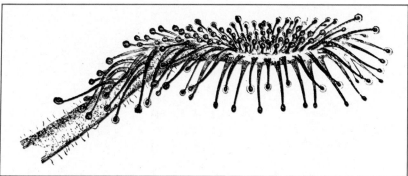

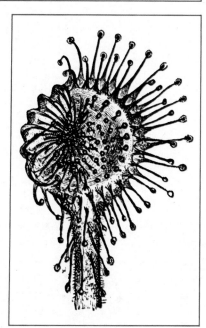

Illustrations from Charles Darwin's In-sectivorous Plants depict the sticky leaf traps of the sundew Drosera. Darwin's studies detailed the ability of the sundew's stalked glands to bend toward a victim once it has been caught.

carnivory was almost obsessional. As early as 1860, the year after publication of the *Origin of Species,* he wrote "I care more about *Drosera* [the sundew] than the origin of all the species in the world." Thanks to his meticulous investigations he detailed the powers of the sundews to trap, digest, and absorb animal matter.

But even Darwin failed to spell out exactly what distinguishes a carnivorous plant from all others. The more familiar carnivorous plants such as the Venus's-flytrap and the sundews, butterworts, bladderworts, and pitcher plants generally lure, trap, kill, and digest animals using specialized trapping organs and then absorb the food into the rest of the plant. One glaring exception, however, is the Sun pitcher, *Heliamphora,* from Latin America. Like other members of the Sarraceniaceae family (the New World pitcher plants) the pitchers of *Heliamphora* are formed from attractively colored tubular leaves, but they lack the enzymatic glands necessary for digesting their prey. Instead, they rely on a "rent-a-gut" system of outside microorganisms to do the digesting for them before absorbing the rotted remains. And yet *Heliamphora* pitchers are so clearly carnivorous in all other respects that they retain their privileged carnivorous status.

Possibilities for sticky hairs

So how well demarcated are the carnivorous plants from the rest of the plant kingdom? Darwin himself mused on the possibilities of carnivorous mechanisms in various unrelated species including the sticky leaf traps of the saxifrage *Saxifraga umbrosa* and of the geranium *Pelargonium zonale* and even the sticky bud scales of the horse chestnut (although he quickly dismissed this particular example). He did not take these speculations further, however, and his contemporaries apparently ignored them. So the relatively small band of established plant carnivores (out of a total of a quarter million flowering species) became firmly entrenched as uncommon and curious oddities of nature, which few scientists took seriously.

49

Table on the opposite page lists the major recognized genera of flowering carnivorous plants grouped by family and showing their geographical distribution. Illustrated above (clockwise from top left) are the Old World tropical pitcher plant Nepenthes gracilis, *a leaf pitcher of a species of* Sarracenia *from North America, underwater bladders of the bladderwort* Utricularia, *a species of sundew (Drosera), and the West Australian pitcher plant* (Cephalotus follicularis).

Major recognized genera of flowering carnivorous plants

family	genus (number of species)	distribution
Nepenthaceae	*Nepenthes* (60), tropical pitcher plants	Old World tropics
Sarraceniaceae	*Sarracenia* (9), trumpet pitchers	eastern North America
	Heliamphora (4), sun pitchers	northwestern South America
	Darlingtonia (1), cobra lily	northern California
Cephalotaceae	*Cephalotus* (1), West Australian pitcher plant	southwestern Australia
Byblidaceae	*Byblis* (2), rainbow plants	western Australia
Dioncophyllaceae	*Triphyophyllum* (1)	western Africa
Droseraceae	*Drosera* (90), sundews	worldwide
	Drosophyllum (1), Portuguese sundew	southwestern Europe, northern Africa
	Dionaea (1), Venus's-flytrap	eastern North America
	Aldrovanda (5), waterwheel plants	southwestern Europe, Africa, India, northwestern Australia, Japan
Lentibulariaceae	*Pinguicula* (30), butterworts	Northern Hemisphere
	Genlisea (15)	South America, Africa
	Utricularia (150), bladderworts	worldwide
	Polypompholyx (2), pink petticoats	Australia, South America

Yet many other plants feature sticky hairs. Long forgotten research at the University of Pavia in Italy in the 1910s and 1920s showed that sticky hairs covering the leaves of *Martynia lutea,* a tropical species; red catchfly (*Lychnis viscaria*), also one of Darwin's suspects; and even two species of *Petunia* had carnivorous tendencies. The scientists conducting this research broadly followed the same procedure of investigation used by Darwin and found, for example, that the protein of egg white was digested and absorbed in true carnivorous style by all four species. Moreover, *Martynia* drew crowds of midges and other detritus-feeding flies with its pungent odor of rotting meat. But although such features are excellent credentials for the accolade of carnivory, these discoveries were lost on dusty library shelves.

Whether this neglect was a deliberate snub or an unfortunate oversight is not clear. Other research has shown, however, that the architecture of sticky hairs like these is remarkably similar to that of many conventional plant carnivores such as sundews. The hairs consist of glands held aloft on stalks and comprise three types of cell masses: a large reservoir that manufactures the glue and digestive enzymes, a selective "filter" (the endodermis tissue) through which the secretions then pass, and a secretory layer through which the deadly juices are pumped to the outside. The liquid remains of the animal are then funneled back through to the reservoir and then into the leaf veins, which pass the food on to the rest of the plant.

These similarities failed to impress U.S. botanist Francis Lloyd in his much-admired review *The Carnivorous Plants*, published in 1942. Lloyd discounted most of the sticky-haired speculations but was equivocal about a few others such as *Caltha dionaeafolia.* The leaves of this member of the buttercup family look rather like the twin-lobed leaf traps of the Venus's-

51

Photos, Peter Parks—Oxford Scientific Films

Flowering carnivorous plants employ a variety of mechanisms for capturing their prey (right). Shown above (clockwise from top left) are the snap leaf trap of a Venus's-flytrap (Dionaea muscipula); the tiny bladder of a bladderwort, which has sucked in a mosquito larva; the adhesive hairs on the leaf of a sundew; and a wasp drowned in digestive fluid at the base of a Sarracenia pitcher.

Trapping devices in flowering carnivorous plants

type	genus
snap trap	Dionaea, Aldrovanda
suction trap	Utricularia, Polypompholyx
pitfall (pitcher) trap	Nepenthes, Sarracenia, Darlingtonia, Heliamphora, Cephalotus
adhesive secretion	Byblis, Triphyophyllum, Drosera, Drosophyllum, Pinguicula
one-way tube ("lobster pot")	Genlisea

flytrap, but they behave more like the sticky traps of the butterworts (species of *Pinguicula*), which roll their leaf margins over insects caught on the leaves. Ironically the butterworts themselves were banished from the carnivorous club at one time, only to be later readmitted.

Such equivocation probably arises from the way botanists have distinguished between sticky glands used for carnivory and those used for defending plants against insect predators. It is quite conceivable that in some cases carnivory evolved from purely defensive sticky hairs and that those plants growing in barren soils experienced evolutionary pressure to develop carnivory for their survival. Yet it also is quite possible that in some species the two functions coexist: plants growing in reasonably nutritious soils might use their sticky glands for defense and also for "nibbling" at their captured bounty.

In fact, several species of sticky-haired wild tomatoes and potatoes grow in particularly fertile soils in Latin America. Their stems and leaves are heavily festooned with glandular hairs that readily immobilize a host of such undesirable pests as mites and aphids. Moreover, W. G. Williams and his colleagues at North Carolina State University identified a powerful insect poison in the mucilage of one species of wild tomato from Peru, *Lycopersicon hirsutum,* and it is noteworthy that the petunias, which are related to tomatoes, also contain an insecticide in their sticky exudates. Furthermore, a digestive enzyme was discovered recently in one type of hair found on the foliage of the domestic potato. Because these hairs are rather sparse, it is not clear what function they serve, but their discovery holds promise for finding similar enzymes in the hairier wild potatoes. To date plant breeders have concentrated their attention on the insect-killing powers of these wild ancestors of cultivated tomatoes and potatoes. But if these plants are also carnivorous, then breeders may be able to endow crop varieties with a valuable additional source of nutrition as well as defensive weapons against pests.

A case for galls and seeds
Other intriguing candidates for plant carnivory also possess sticky traps, but these devices apparently have nothing to do with defense. Many trees become afflicted with unsightly swellings called galls that are caused by certain insects burrowing into the plants. The galls on the Mediterranean oak (*Quercus leptoblanus*), caused by the small gall wasp *Cynips mayri*, are rather extravagant, flower-shaped affairs colored brilliant red. But unlike most other types of galls these particular ones are sticky, and although the larvae of *C. mayri* are quite happy living inside the hollow interior of the gall, other tiny insects come to grief on the tacky surface.

In 1903 Giovanni Mattei of the University of Naples in Italy noticed that these galls give off a smell reminiscent of the garden hyacinth *Hyacinthus orientalis* that attracts even more insects to the sticky surface. Further examination revealed hairs at the periphery of the gall that apparently secrete the mucilage and other types of hairs that Mattei speculated might be able to absorb the rotting (or perhaps digested) remains of the insects.

Possibly even more outlandish than sticky galls, there are strong indications that some seeds might be carnivorous as well. The seeds of many plant

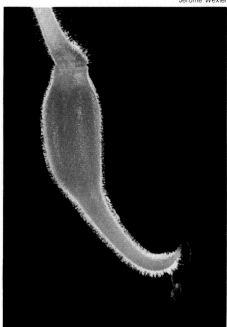

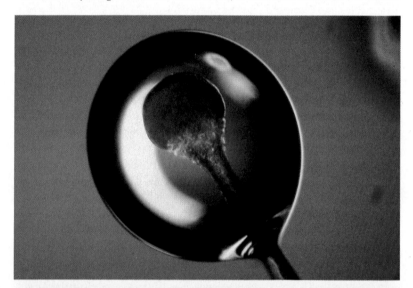

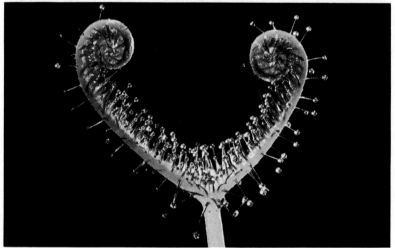

species including mustard and cress secrete mucuslike coats during germination. This goo supposedly cushions the seed against tough environments by holding an envelope of moisture. John Barber at Tulane University, New Orleans, Louisiana, became interested in the stickiness of shepherd's purse seeds (*Capsella bursa-pastoris*) while studying the behavior of mosquito larvae. He noticed that these larvae had a fatal attraction for the seeds and seemed to be lured to the sticky coat, where they became firmly glued by their mouthparts and later died.

This attraction to the seeds was no fancy flight of imagination. Barber separated seeds and larvae in a tank with a barrier that allowed any water-soluble chemicals diffusing from the seeds to pass across to the larvae. After observations and after comparisons with control larvae placed in a tank without seeds, it was clear that the larvae not only swam toward the seeds but also died much faster than the control group of larvae. The seeds thus appeared to launch a two-pronged attack, of an alluring chemical and a poison, on the unwitting insects.

But can anything so small as these seeds, which are less than a millimeter

Species of Martynia *(above),* Petunia, *and many other plants not generally considered carnivorous have sticky hairs, and some of them have been shown to digest and absorb animal protein in true carnivorous fashion. The architecture of hairs found on these plants closely resembles that of the adhesive traps covering many of the recognized plant carnivores such as the sundews (bottom). Each hair (right) consists of a stalk tipped with a gland that both manufactures the adhesive and the digestive enzymes and absorbs the liquefied remains of the victims.*

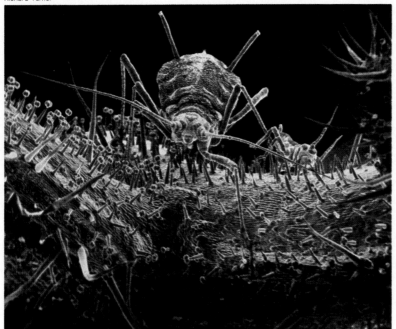

An aphid is immobilized on the glandular hairs of the wild potato Solanum berthaultii. *The leaves and stems of several species of wild potatoes and tomatoes are densely covered with such defensive structures. The hairs of some of these plants may also produce digestive enzymes, holding out the possibility that they are used for both defense and carnivory.*

(0.04 inch) in diameter, actually make a meal out of something comparatively as large as a mosquito larva? Further experiments by Barber showed that the seeds can digest and probably can absorb their prey. Using a chemical dye to highlight protein-digesting (proteolytic) enzymes, he found that the mucilage of the seeds was rich in these enzymes. Indeed, many other enzymes used during germination to release food from their stored reserves could also be turned to meat-eating if need be.

Absorbing the digested remains of their prey should also be fairly straightforward for the seeds. Unpublished results from Barber's laboratory went on to show that shepherd's purse seeds can absorb amino acids (the building blocks of all proteins, which are released by the proteolytic enzymes) from the surrounding water and send them to the young shoots. If amino acids

*The greater butterwort (*Pinguicula grandiflora*) catches insects on its sticky leaves and then rolls them up in the leaf margins for digestion. The butterworts, close relatives of the bladderworts, were once dropped from the rolls of the recognized plant carnivores but later reinstated.*

 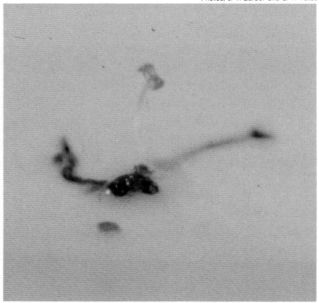

Shepherd's purse seed (above), seen as a small orange oval, is surrounded by six mosquito larvae fatally attached by their mouthparts to the seed's sticky coating. Germinating seed (above right) still carries the remains of two decomposing larvae. Shepherd's purse seeds appear to dispense an insect attractant and a poison to the surrounding medium, and their mucilage has been shown to be rich in protein-digesting enzymes. The seeds also were found to be able to absorb amino acids from the surrounding water and to send them to the young shoots.

can be readily assimilated, it is likely that minerals and other nutrients can also be absorbed. In other words, the seeds have all the attributes of a fully fledged carnivorous plant but without an obvious trapping and digesting organ. This state of affairs is anathema to botanists who would argue that there is hardly any need for carnivory in a seed, which carries its own reserves of concentrated food ready for germination. Barber counters this by pointing out that mucilaginous seeds are generally very small (perhaps to avoid being eaten by large animals), and many grow in impoverished semi-arid environments. Turning to meat-eating could help offset the scarcity of food, just as sundews, for instance, have evolved to cope with the shortage of nutrients in their boggy homes. There are further complications to the carnivorous seed story. Apart from mosquito larvae the seeds also influence far smaller organisms: microscopic nematode worms, protozoans, and even bacteria all were shown to congregate around shepherd's purse seeds but not around inert objects of the same size. All of these organisms can die just outside the seed, providing a useful soup of rotting bodies without trapping them—quite a radical concept in plant carnivory.

Some insights from fungi

The microscopic world of living organisms is worth examining further. Although they have long been recognized, little attention is paid today to meat-eating fungi, living in the rich milieu of decaying compost. The first fungus seen catching its prey was spotted by an Austrian researcher, Wilhelm Zopf, in 1888, who saw living eelworms (nematodes) snared in the tangled network of loops of the fungus *Arthrobotrys oligospora*. Once the worm had poked its head through a loop, it thrashed around violently and finally died some two and a half hours later. Later on the fungus sent probing filaments into the animal's body and literally ate through it.

The network of loops is only one of a variety of astonishing fungal feeding mechanisms. Sticky filaments or club-shaped cells are used by many other

56

species of fungi to capture animals as small as protozoans or as large as eel-worms. In all of these cases the fungi suck the dead carcass of nutrients us-ing probing filaments to puncture the inside of the animal. Some fungal species become parasitic on their eelworm hosts by shedding special cells onto the animals as they pass by. The cell punctures the skin of the animal with a slender tube and then feeds off it. Eventually part of the fungus breaks out through the skin of the animal to deposit fresh spores back into the soil.

Perhaps the height of sophistication in fungal traps is the touchy noose of such fungi as *Dactylella brochopoga*. An eelworm pushing through the trap is bound to rub against at least one of the three cells comprising the noose, which then balloon out in a fraction of a second and pinch the prey with a viselike grip.

Another type of snare overwhelms its prey using a barbed bait. Such fungi as *Zoophagus insidians* hold out tempting clubs for passing protozoans. Once the victim grasps hold of the club the fungus projects a bullet of muci-

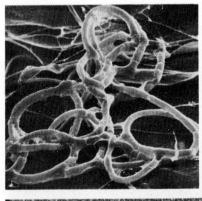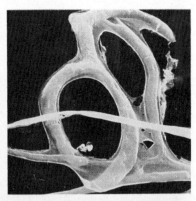

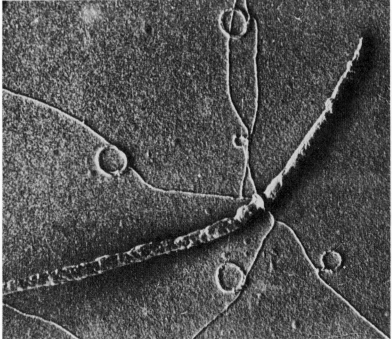

Photos, G. L. Barron

High magnification reveals the tangled network of adhesive loops belonging to the meat-eating fungus Arthrobotrys oligospora (above, left and right). Nematodes become trapped in the loops and are quickly invaded by fungal filaments that drain nutrients from the victims' bodies. A nematode (left) lies caught in a noose trap of the fungus Dactylella brochopoga; touching the noose triggers it to constrict around its prey in a powerful grip.

lage into the open "mouth" of the creature, gluing it in place before growing suckers into its body.

This catalog of quite ferocious fungal traps is worth detailing to emphasize the way in which carnivory has clearly evolved in far-flung corners of the plant kingdom. It is also interesting that the carnivorous fungi normally grow in fertile soils where there is no apparent need to feed off living animals. Furthermore, when there is a lack of living animal life the fungi revert to the more normal method of fungal nutrition, by absorbing the decayed remains of organic material. So carnivory is not exclusive to species that are fighting to survive in inhospitable environments; it can also be used to boost a plant's normal diet.

Liverworts

The leafy liverworts are another intriguing group of primitive plants that also can capture animals, but the presence of carnivory or carnivory-in-the-making here is less clear-cut. These plants are delicate, mosslike epiphytes; they live out of contact with the soil and rely on trees or rocks for support, but not for food. Without roots in the soil, epiphytes are vulnerable to shortages of water, and many leafy liverworts have evolved specialized leaves to collect reservoirs of water. Some of these leaves are shaped like

Many plant species not considered carnivorous possess water-filled leaf pitchers that can catch and kill insects. The common teasel (Dipsacus sylvestris; below) collects pools of water in its cup-shaped leaf bases (below right). These reservoirs trap crawling and flying insects and thus help defend the plant. There is also evidence that the teasel may add an incapacitating drug to the water to drown the insects more quickly.

pitchers, which are ideal for catching water trickling down a tree trunk or rock face.

In tropical species of *Colura* and *Pleurozia* the leaf pitchers are extraordinarily elaborate and formed into twisted slippers with remarkable hinged doors at the entrance to the pitchers. A handsome array of microorganisms lives in these pitchers, but these creatures are evidently trapped by the hinged door. In fact, they can actually be sucked into the trap when a dry pitcher is rewetted and suddenly inflates. Although this seems a perfect capture device for carnivory, there is no hard evidence that captured animals are actually killed. Instead, they may simply die a natural death and their remains may become absorbed into the plant.

Quasi-carnivory

This paradox of a perfect trapping device but no obvious carnivory raises the same nagging question described earlier for the pitchers of *Heliamphora*: can a plant be carnivorous if it lacks its own digestive system or one of the other accepted criteria? Perhaps one should talk of "quasi-carnivory" to distinguish between these and completely self-sufficient carnivores. Epiphytes with pitchers are particularly good candidates for this quasi-carnivorous status since they often supplement their diet with rotting animals. One good example is the pitcher leaves of some species of *Dischidia*, a genus of tropical plants of the Old World. Their pitchers become an organic dustbin of decaying vegetation and animal remains, and they plunder this harvest by growing roots into the compost and absorbing the nutrients and water. Roots may not even be necessary, however, for such plants to take advantage of the rich pickings from the pitcher. There is intriguing evidence that rotting animal matter can simply be absorbed through pitcher walls. This evidence comes from an unexpected quarter–the pitchers of an "ant plant," *Hydnophytum formicarum*.

Many plants hire a mercenary army of ants to fight off unwanted predators, and in return the ants are offered cozy shelters in hollow stems and tubers. Fred Rickson of Oregon State University, Corvallis, recently showed that the ant guardians of *H. formicarum* also feed the plant. First, larvae of fruit flies were fed on a diet containing the radioactive isotope carbon-14. Then the radioactive flies were left near the plant to await collection by the ants, who duly took the food back to their pitcher homes and lined the walls with the flies. Using a sophisticated Geiger counter, Rickson traced the fate of the insect remains and found that they passed through the walls of the pitcher into the rest of the plant. So the ants provided the trapping and perhaps some of the digestion of the animal diet of *Hydnophytum*.

Many other plant species have water-filled leaf pitchers that can catch and kill insects. These traps also lack digestive glands but may qualify as quasi-carnivorous. Francis Darwin, the son of Charles, noted that the pools of rainwater caught in the cup-shaped leaf bases of the common teasel (*Dipsacus sylvestris*) trapped crawling or flying insects. Although these watery pitchers clearly defend the plant from harmful insects, they were also seen to drown beetles more rapidly than in pure water, as if the insects were somehow incapacitated. Although the plant may add a knockout drug to its

Like those of the teasel the leaf bases of bromeliads, members of the pineapple family, also form a water reservoir (right), which assists the plants in times of drought. In some species the rosette-shaped collectors strongly resemble the pitchers of conventional pitcher plants, with slippery inside walls that seem to encourage insects to drop into the watery pool at the bottom where they drown. Such plants shed light on the way some conventional plant carnivores may have evolved—pitchers first employed to collect water may have developed digestive glands and refined their luring and trapping abilities.

watery traps to improve its defense, conventional pitcher plant traps also drug their victims with a powerful narcotic contained in droplets of sugary nectar secreted around the entrance of the pitcher.

The rosettes of leaf bases of bromeliads, which are members of the pineapple family, also collect puddles of water, mainly as a reservoir for overcoming periods of drought. Some species have developed their water collectors to an extraordinary degree; those of *Brocchinia,* for example, look very much like the traps of conventional pitcher plants. The leaves are pressed tightly together into a vase, and on the inside of the pitcher the cells are so flaky that they form a powdery ski slope for an unwary insect to lose its foothold and slip into the watery tank below. Submerged in the water, the walls of the pitcher bear special water-absorbing glands, but these structures are also ideally situated to absorb remains of the dead insects that pile up at the bottom.

These various, possibly quasi-carnivorous pitchers also suggest how traditional carnivorous pitchers may have evolved. The exquisite pitchers of *Nepenthes,* for example, are useful water reservoirs as well as pantries and bear many resemblances to the pitchers of *Dischidia.* So plants starved of a regular supply of water and nutrients could have developed their leaf pitchers further, by evolving digestive glands and such refined attractions as alluring odors and colors.

Some flowers are also powerful pitcher death traps. The flowers of the cuckoopint (*Arum maculatum*) are somewhat small but are wrapped inside a large sheathing spathe, from which protrudes a spikelike spadix, the whole arrangement aiding insect pollination. The rotten stench and warmth of the spadix attracts detritus-feeding flies, which climb down toward the flowers hidden in the bowl at the bottom of the spathe. Once they enter the bowl, the flies pass through a one-way barrier of downward-pointing hairs, and the slippery walls of the pitcher also help prevent the insects from escaping. A modest supply of nectar helps feed the prisoners, and once they pollinate the plant and are dusted with pollen in turn, the prison "gates" wither away and

Photos, G. I. Bernard—Oxford Scientific Films

the prisoners are set free. Meanwhile, however, many of the unluckier insects die from exhaustion and attacks from fellow inmates, and their carcasses accumulate into a rotting pile. Since the flowers can remain intact for several weeks, there is ample opportunity for the insect remains to be absorbed into the rest of the plant.

Considerations for the future

Plant carnivory is nowhere near as cut-and-dried as is often supposed, and apart from some clear cases of radical new types of plant carnivory (for example, sticky seeds) there are many gray areas in need of study. On the whole, plant carnivory in one form or another is probably much more widespread than generally believed, and given the incentive to reduce the financial and environmental costs of man-made fertilizers, it makes sense to explore the practical uses of plant carnivory in agriculture. Were such an application to become widespread, the "day of the triffids," at least for the insects, would indeed have arrived.

The cuckoopint (Arum maculatum; above left) possesses separate clusters of small male and female flowers wrapped inside a large sheath (above, shown sectioned) and topped with a protruding, spikelike spadix. The warmth and fetid smell emitted from the spadix attracts flies, which become temporarily trapped in the bowl-shaped base of the structure while they pollinate the plant and receive pollen in turn. The remains of insects that die within the plant accumulate at the bottom of the bowl. Because the structure remains intact for weeks, there is opportunity for the decaying insects to be absorbed. Whether this actually happens is a matter for future research to decide.

61

THE BEAUTY OF BUTTERFLY WINGS
NATURE'S REMARKABLE MOSAICS

by Charles V. Covell, Jr.

Complex mosaics of scales in more than 100,000 different patterns form the wings of butterflies and moths.

Butterflies and moths are among the most familiar and intriguing living things, inhabiting all but the coldest areas on Earth. They are abundant both in numbers of species (over 125,000) and of individuals; and their broad wings are conspicuous, with a seemingly endless variety of colors and patterns. Images of butterflies were carved into walls of Egyptian tombs more than 5,000 years ago; and by the Greeks and other civilizations the souls of the departed were thought to be reincarnated as butterflies. Among the many Order-level groupings in the insects only the Order Coleoptera, the beetles, is larger, with more than 250,000 species.

Butterflies share with moths several features characteristic of their Order, the Lepidoptera. The name comes from Latin *lepido* (scaly) and *pter* (wing) and brings attention to their foremost characteristic: four broad, membranous wings, covered with tiny flattened scales that are arranged in overlapping rows like shingles on a roof. While scales occur in a few other insect groups such as mosquitoes, they are not as abundant or varied in color as in the butterflies and moths.

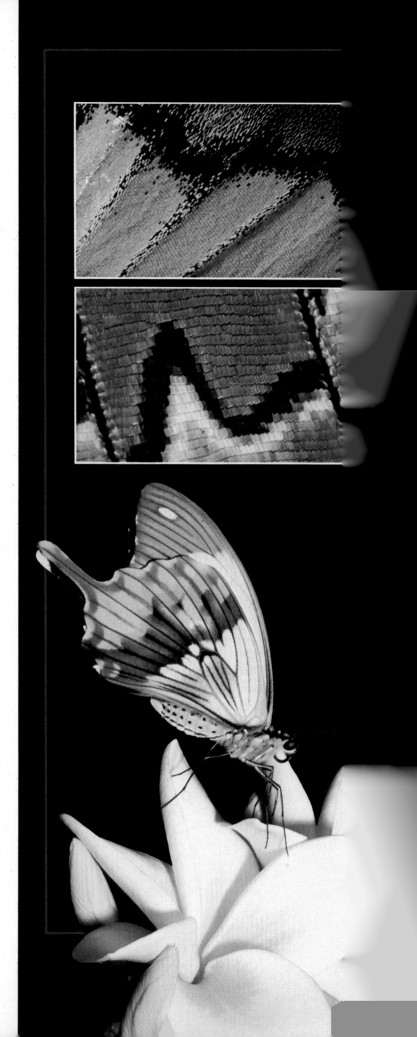

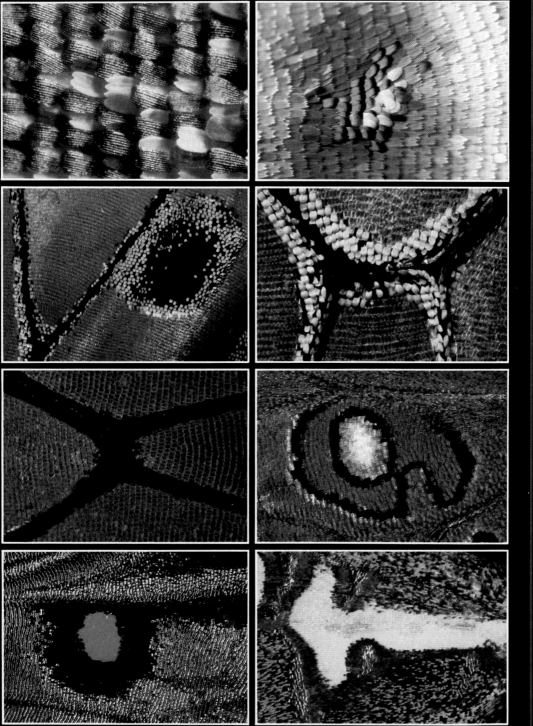

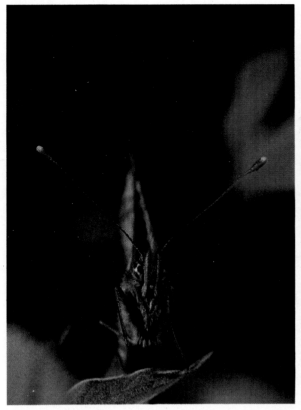

Pearl-bordered fritillary (top left) has threadlike antennae that end in knobs, as do all butterflies. The antennae of the American moon moth (top right) are featherlike, typical of many species of moths.

Butterflies are best distinguished from moths on the basis of their antennae, the two long "feelers" projecting forward from the front of the head. Butterfly antennae are threadlike and end in knobs. Moth antennae are either featherlike or threadlike; if they are threadlike, they do not swell at the end to form knobs except in one tropical family. Finally, butterflies form the pupa in an attached, naked chrysalis; moths normally form the pupa in a cocoon, a cell in the ground, or in plant tissues, and they do not hang it down from an object as do the butterflies. Moths may be active during the day or night, but most are nocturnal; butterflies are almost always active only in the daytime. There are more moth species than butterfly: only 765 of North America's 11,233 Lepidoptera species are butterflies.

Wing structure and development

With the exception of the females of a few moth species the adults of all Lepidoptera are equipped with four wings that arise from the second of three body regions, the thorax. The thorax is located behind the head and in front of the abdomen and is composed of three segments. Each segment bears a pair of legs, but only the two rear segments bear the wings. In Lepidoptera the fore wings and hind wings are usually covered with scales on both the upper and lower surfaces. The actual wings project from the sides of the segments, toward the top.

While not visible at all in the immature stages of butterflies and moths, wings are actually developing beneath the larval exoskeleton. They begin in the first stage after the caterpillar emerges from the egg as thickenings in

CHARLES V. COVELL, JR., is President of The Lepidopterists' Society and Professor of Biology and Chairman of the Division of Natural Sciences at the University of Louisville, Kentucky.

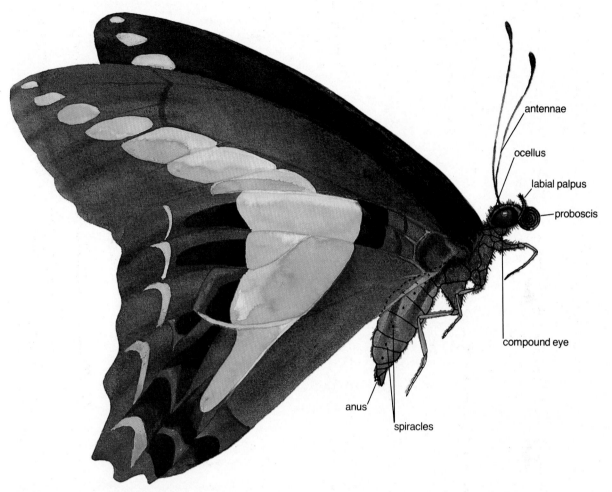

antennae

ocellus

labial palpus

proboscis

compound eye

anus

spiracles

the cell layer beneath the exoskeleton. These lumps are in the thorax where wings would normally be attached and are known to scientists as imaginal disks. As the caterpillar grows, the disks enlarge and then later balloon outward and lie in crumpled form beneath the exoskeleton. When the caterpillar molts to the cocoon stage (chrysalis in butterflies), the out-pocketings are represented as encased in the pupal exoskeleton. Beneath that the final deposition of hollow tubes, or veins, occurs between the two layers of membrane, and the covering of thousands of scales in tiny sockets on the outside surfaces is laid down.

When a butterfly or moth first emerges from the pupal exoskeleton, the wings are small, wet, and crumpled. The insect climbs onto a perch and pumps its watery blood into the wings, blowing them up and flattening them out to their normal size and shape. The wings soon harden, and flight becomes possible. If crowding or some other restriction on free expansion of wings occurs during this critical drying period, the wings become deformed and useless for flight.

Size varies a great deal in the Lepidoptera. The largest butterfly known is the female Alexandra's Birdwing (*Ornithoptera alexandrae*) from Papua New Guinea, with a wingspan of 28 cm; the smallest may be one of several

Adult butterflies and moths, except for the females of a few moth species, are furnished with four wings that extend from the central region of the body, the thorax. In this generalized drawing of an adult butterfly or moth, features of the body are shown. The ocellus is a tiny simple eye with limited functions that supplement those of the large compound eye. The labial palpus is a liplike structure containing taste sensors. Receptors for odors are located on the antennae. The proboscis serves as the mouth of the insect, and the spiracles are openings for the respiratory system.

65

Sequence of development of an adult Monarch butterfly begins with the caterpillar (top left) and then proceeds to the approximately 12-day chrysalis stage (top center). The gradual breaking out of the chrysalis ends with the butterfly hanging straight down (bottom center); at this time it forces its body fluids into the thorax and pumps blood out into the small wing pads, expanding them to form full wings.

blues (Lycaenidae), with a 1.3-cm wingspan (1 cm equals 0.394 in). The variations among moths are even more extreme: the South American *Thysania agrippina* (Noctuidae) may measure 30.5 cm from wing tip to wing tip, while the smallest measure about 1 mm.

Wings are remarkably strong in the Lepidoptera. The double membrane is strengthened much like a wood-and-paper airplane model, with a number of tubular veins extending from the base and branching to the margins. This branching pattern differs among the various groupings of moths and butterflies and thus can help in identifying and classifying them. The membrane between the veins does not lie flat but angles up and down alternately, much as a corrugated Quonset hut, to give it strength. The fore wing and hind wing

66

(Top) Manfred Kage—Oxford Scientific Films; (bottom) Fritz Goro

on each side operate as a single unit and are kept from beating separately by some joining mechanism. Most moths have a curved spine at the base of the hind wing that is held by a catch on the underside of the fore wing. This hook is called a frenulum. A few primitive moths have a thumblike lobe called the jugum on the hind margin of the fore wing that catches on the hind wing. Butterflies have neither but do have the base of the hind wing widened so that it will not pop out from behind the fore wing, for if it did flight would be impossible.

The scales that cover both the bodies and wings of moths and butterflies are remarkable for their wide variety of size, shape, and color. Many moths appear furry because their body scales often take the form of long hairs. These may actually function to preserve heat, especially in cold regions. Although wing scales are normally flat and spatula-shaped, some may be hairlike. Shapes may vary on different parts of a wing, and size varies as well from less than a tenth of a millimeter to several centimeters in length. Scales are hollow and therefore weigh very little. Their colors may be uniform, or they may be striped or tipped with a second color or shade. While they are inserted in sockets like the setae found on caterpillars and on other insects, butterfly scales do not penetrate human skin and cause stinging or nettling as do the sharp, hollow setae found on the caterpillars of some moths. Scales do rub off like colored powder when the wings are handled (especially on a living insect), but the loss of many scales does not cause death, as is commonly believed.

Some Lepidoptera have areas on their wings that appear to be without scales. Examination of the wing surfaces reveals that these seemingly scale-free areas actually do have very tiny hairlike bristles that can be seen only under powerful magnification. The wasp moths (Ctenuchidae), Clear-wing moths (Sesiidae), and some Sphinx moths (Sphingidae) are among the species in which this condition occurs.

As the wings undergo final stages of development inside the pupal exoskeleton, the scales are arranged in patterns determined by genetic mechanisms. In the majority of Lepidoptera the patterns seem not to vary much from one individual to another. There is, however, a certain amount of variability in pattern as well as size that the casual observer will not notice but which a specialist can detect. In other species there is variation to quite a noticeable, even astounding, degree, and different forms of a species are often thought to be different species until rearing or other evidence proves them to belong to the same species.

Sex-linked variation is widespread in Lepidoptera, with males often easy to distinguish from females just by wing pattern. The male Common Sulfur butterfly is yellow with solid black outer borders on all wings. Females, on the other hand, may be either yellow or white, with that color also appearing as spots in the black outer border. A white male is a real rarity, while white individuals make up approximately half of the female population. The male California Dogface butterfly has an iridescent purple dog's-head profile on the fore wing, but the female has only a small dark spot.

There are also differences in pattern in different parts of the geographic range of a given species. This variation may result from genetic factors, but

When greatly magnified, the wings of a butterfly (top) and moth (bottom) are seen to consist of scales of various shapes.

67

(Top) G. I. Bernard—Oxford Scientific Films; (bottom) L. West—Bruce Coleman Inc.

Wing sizes in butterflies and moths vary considerably. The wingspan of the largest moth, Thysania agrippina *(top) measures 30.5 centimeters, while that of one of the smallest butterflies, the Western Pigmy* (Brephidium exilis, *bottom) is about 1.25 centimeters.*

it is likely that such environmental differences as the nutritional characteristics of food plants for larvae play a part. In western North America, for example, several species of *Speyeria* (fritillaries) and *Parnassius* (parnassians) vary perceptibly from one mountain range to another.

Visible differences within a species may occur within populations that fly at different times of the year. Many butterflies and moths have two or more generations annually. The Question Sign butterflies seen in the spring and fall have bright purple edging on an orange-brown hind wing above, while on midsummer individuals this same area is blackish.

The types of variation discussed above tend to be maintained in populations through genetic and environmental controls. They represent what is known as polymorphism ("many forms"). Some are maintained because they help protect the species from predators (*see* below). Others are merely responses to conditions in the environment during immature stages.

Individuals are sometimes found that appear to be outside the range of polymorphism exhibited by that species. Genetic mechanisms sometimes go awry, perhaps through environmental traumas such as extreme cold, and aberrations occur. Spots which are usually sharp may appear smeared. Overall wing color may be quite different from normal. Such aberrations are rare and are treasured by collectors when found. One type of aberration is the gynandromorph ("male and female form"), in which features of both sexes appear on one individual.

Genetic mutations tend to occur in populations of some moths and butterflies rarely but repeatedly over a long period of time. Because the resulting changes in pattern or color may be disadvantageous, they are weeded out by selective forces such as predators. For example, the black-and-white speckled Peppered moth (*Biston betularia*) of the Northern Hemisphere may well be protected from predators such as birds by its pattern, which blends with

68

lichens on tree trunks where daylight hours are spent. Recurring mutations for an all-blackish form have occurred for centuries but were not common until the middle of the 19th century, when the smoke from factories in England's Midlands killed the tree lichens and turned the tree trunks black. As a result of increasing numbers of the dark form in that part of England, noted by H. B. D. Kettlewell from collections made over the previous two centuries, a documented case of natural selection began to unfold. Kettlewell postulated that the normally disadvantageous dark form actually became the advantageous form in the industrial Midlands because it, rather than the normal black-and-white form, blended with the tree trunks. The change in the moth color to match sooty tree trunks became known as "industrial melanism," and the theory was well tested with mark-release-recapture data and films of birds picking conspicuous moths off tree trunks.

Composition of the color patterns

The color pattern of a butterfly or moth is comprised of areas of colored scales. The upper side may be quite different in pattern from the underside. Undersides of moths that normally sit at rest with wings out to the side are usually drab. However, moths and butterflies that sit with wings held together over the back may have colorful underside patterns.

Colors of the individual scales are of two types, pigmental and structural. The pattern may consist of either or both. Pigments are chemical compounds, often complex molecules, that are deposited in the scales during development of the adult within the pupa stage. One of the most widespread and abundant of these is melanin (brown, black), which results from the metabolism of the amino acid tyrosine. Pterines (white, yellow, orange, red) are derived from the conversion of uric acid, the principal nitrogenous waste in insects. Ommochromes (yellow, red, brown) are derived from the amino acid tryptophan.

Pigments are also derived from the larval food that is eaten by the caterpillars and then stored in scales. Green colors are derived from chlorophyll. Carotenoids (yellow, orange, red) come from the carotenes in plants, such as those seen in autumn leaves. Other yellow and red pigments, flavones, are derived from grasses.

At the base of their hind wings most moths have a curved spine called a frenulum that is held by a catch called a retinaculum located on the underside of the fore wing. Below left is a disengaged frenulum on the wing of a pink spotted hawk moth; on the right is an engaged frenulum on the wing of a black witch moth.

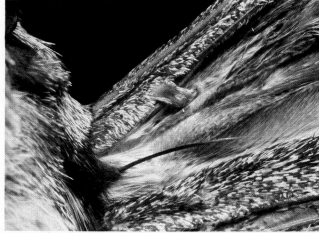

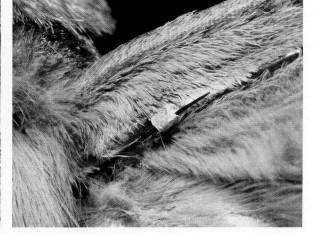

Photos, William E. Ferguson

Photos, G. I. Bernard—Oxford Scientific Films

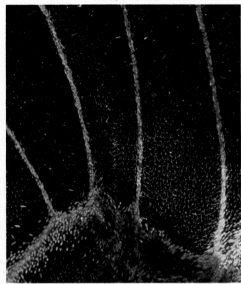

A few species of butterflies and moths have wings that appear to be without scales. Under powerful magnification these wings are revealed to have tiny hairlike bristles that give the effect of translucence. At the top right is a close-up of the wing of a clear-wing butterfly. Such butterflies are also seen at the top left and bottom left. At the bottom right is a clear-wing moth.

The second source of color is called structural coloration. It results from the breaking of light into spectral components by ridgelike blades on the surfaces of individual scales. The size, shape, and spacing of these ridges determines the quality of color reflected and seen by the observer. Most butterflies and moths with structural coloration have at least some pigmental coloration, at least on the underside, where structural coloration occurs less frequently. Usually the structural colors are metallic blues and greens, but some are white, copper, brass, silver, and gold.

Iridescence is the kind of metallic color that seems to change when one looks at the butterfly wing from different angles. Members of the large *Morpho* species of Central and South America are the most famous butterflies that demonstrate this type of color, but it is also found in almost every family of moth and butterfly in at least small areas of the wings. In North America iridescent blue hairstreaks are small but beautiful examples.

70

Functions of wing patterns and shapes

Wings of tropical butterflies and moths are, on the average, much more bright and colorful than those of temperate areas; and those in the cold regions of high elevations and arctic habitats are the most drab of all. In the tropics the energy of life cycles can be employed for reproduction and survival from predators, while in the coldest regions it must also be used for surviving harsh weather. Colors in cold regions tend to be dark, and a fur coat of hair scales on the body is not unusual. Butterflies need a body temperature of about 10° C (50° F), more or less, to fly. Their dark scales absorb sunlight as they sit with wings opened toward the Sun's rays. When enough heat is absorbed, flight is possible, even where the air temperature is well below 10° C (50° F). Heat is lost quickly, however, and butterflies often fly for short hops and then return to the ground to warm up again. An observer on the tundra during the short midsummer flying time of butter-

Photos, William E. Ferguson

Males and females of many species of butterflies and moths can be distinguished from one another on the basis of their wing coloration. At the left are a male Clouded Sulfur butterfly (top) and a female (bottom).

(Top, left and right) Alvin E. Staffan—Photo Researchers; (bottom) William E. Ferguson

The wing coloration of many butterflies and moths differs from one side of the wing to the other and in some species also varies with the season. At the top are the under wings (left) and upper wings (right) of the Question Sign butterfly with its spring and fall coloration. Below, the summer coloring of the same butterfly reveals that the bright purple edging of spring and fall has been replaced by a blackish hue.

flies may see thousands of a few species while the Sun is out but none at all when the Sun goes behind a cloud. Wings probably function to heat the body in other parts of the world as well, but the need is not so critical when the temperature during the day is warm.

In the tropics there are large numbers of species of butterflies and moths but not a great number of individuals of each. Problems of survival and reproduction revolve around escaping predators, finding sources of nectar, and reproducing successfully. Many butterflies and moths can breed continuously throughout the year and have evolved an impressive array of patterns for survival in a dangerous world.

The first line of defense of most insects is to remain motionless unless there is a need to move. Augmenting this behavior is a great variety of camouflage, by which insects appear as part of the background when at rest. Since many predators, such as birds, lizards, and snakes, have vision designed more to detect motion rather than to pick out images of potential prey, camouflage has had high selection value in the Lepidoptera. Most butterflies rest with wings folded together over the back, thus presenting the underside of one pair of wings to view. For this reason butterfly undersides are typically drab, with few sharp contrasts. Some have developed remarkable resemblances to objects such as twigs and leaves. The Asian Dead-leaf butterflies (genus *Kallima*) have a line through the fore wing continuing through the hind wing into a short tail, giving the overall appearance of a dull, dead leaf with midrib and petiole. In the Question Sign and other *Polygonia* species in North America the underside looks like a dried leaf that is somewhat crumpled. The dull coloration combines with a ragged outer margin of each wing to give this effect. Many moths, particularly in the Geometridae, sit on trees during the daytime with wings spread to the side.

72

Their color patterns may be very similar to that of the tree bark. In the genus *Catocala* the moths select some trees to match their fore wing colors. For example, the Birch Underwing, *Catocala relicta,* with white and black fore wing, sits on birch trees, the bark of which it matches so closely as to be virtually invisible until it moves. Some moths roll their wings around their bodies and stand "on their heads," thus resembling short twigs. Some species of several moth families are whitish with brown or black blotches placed so that they appear as bird droppings on a leaf when they sit at rest.

Wing shapes and color patterns, especially on the upper sides, may have the effect of breaking up the outline of the insect, making it unidentifiable by a predator as a potential meal. The wings of the Map butterfly (species *Cyrestis*) of southeast Asia and *Colobura dirce* of tropical America are examples of such patterns.

Some markings on the wings and projections from the hind wings ("tails") seem to act as decoys to direct the eye of a predator away from the vital parts of the body and toward the rear of the folded wings. Round eyespots resemble eyes or heads, and the tails on hairstreak butterflies are hairlike and look much like antennae. Behavior also augments these anatomical adaptations; hairstreaks grind their hind wings up and down while they sit, bringing attention to the tails. In the tropical American hairstreak genus *Arawacus* the undersides have black lines that converge at the place where the tails are attached, also helping direct attention to the false antennae. The spot patterns are widespread in butterflies and moths. Good examples are the buckeyes (*Precis* species), owl butterflies (*Caligo* species), and undersides of *Morpho* species.

One possible purpose for the bright colors of many butterflies and some moths is protection from predators by startling them. When a tropical *Morpho* or hairstreak with an iridescent upperside flies up from its perch, it may glint brightly in the sunlight, momentarily blinding, or at least confusing, a

J. L. Mason—Ardea Photographics

Genetic mutations in the Peppered moth have provided increased protection in a changing environment. Before the mid-nineteenth century the speckled form (left) was most common because it blended with lichens on tree trunks where the moths spent their daylight hours. But with the industrialization of the Midlands in England smoke from the factories killed the lichen and blackened the tree trunks. In that area a mutant black form of the moth (right) gradually became predominant because it blended best with the altered tree trunks.

 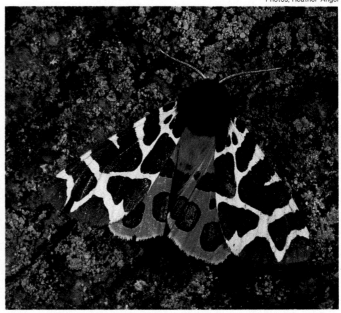

When the Garden Tiger moth is at rest (above), only the comparatively drab upper wings are visible. As it begins to take flight, the brightly colored under wings are displayed (above right).

pursuing predator. In North America the Underwing moths (genus *Catocala*) have fore wings that resemble tree bark. During the daytime the moths sit with their fore wings covering their hind wings and are virtually undetectable on a tree trunk. However, if these moths are frightened, the upper side of their hind wings, having orange or red bands alternating with black (some species), are revealed, again startling predators. Many Lepidoptera could be said to exhibit this phenomenon, which is called flash coloration. Fast flight usually accompanies it.

Another possible protective purpose for bright coloration is called warning coloration. In this case the bright colors (often red or orange and black) are accompanied by slow flight or lack of concealment. These insects, which seem to be daring a predator to attack them, include many caterpillars and other insect orders as well as adult Lepidoptera. Some insect groups have been able to penetrate the chemical defenses of certain plant groups such as the milkweeds and nightshades and can eat them as larvae without harm. The poisons are deposited in the adults, making them distasteful or poisonous to predators, and the latter learn by experience to leave those insects alone. The Monarch butterfly (*Danaus plexippus*) and its many tropical relatives in the family Danaidae are good examples of milkweed feeders; Heliconiidae are nightshade feeders. Their bright patterns seem to warn predators to leave them alone.

An even more fantastic adaptation for protection is the phenomenon known as mimicry. There are two basic kinds, Batesian and Müllerian. In Batesian mimicry (named for a 19th-century naturalist, Henry Wallace Bates, who first discovered it in the Amazon region) one or more good-tasting species of Lepidoptera have evolved appearances similar to a bad-tasting species. Thus in eastern North America the distasteful Monarch is the model for a good-tasting mimic, the Viceroy (*Limenitis archippus*). In the eastern U.S. the bad-tasting, bluish-black Pipevine Swallowtail (*Battus phi-*

74

lenor) is the model for a complex of mimics that includes at least three other swallowtails, including females only of the Tiger Swallowtail (*Papilio glaucus*). Where the Pipevine Swallowtail exists, about half of the Tiger Swallowtail females are yellow and black like the males; the other half are blackish like the Pipevines. In Africa the male Mocker Swallowtail (*Papilio dardanus*) is pale yellow and has tails, and in some parts of the continent the females are similar. However, in various parts of Africa there are about seven different mimetic female forms that are without tails and that have coloration patterned after different bad-tasting models.

Batesian mimics of other undesirable prey exist as well. Some small day-flying Sphinx moths look much like bumblebees, and moths of the families Ctenuchidae and Sesiidae have striking resemblances to various wasps, with largely transparent wings and wasplike bodies and actions.

The second type of mimicry, Müllerian, is named after Fritz Müller, a German naturalist who suggested it after making observations in the Amazon jungle not long after Bates had been there. Because there are so many different species of butterflies in tropical areas, with fewer individuals of each, the many bad-tasting butterflies present a wide array of patterns for predators to learn as undesirable. Müller noted that several bad-tasting species had evolved remarkably similar color patterns, even though both moths and butterflies of different families were involved. This adoption of a "uniform" by bad-tasting species apparently makes simpler the learning task of predators. A common pattern for bad-tasting species in the South American tropics is a combination of yellow, orange, and black bars and blotches.

Features of the wings are very important in the mating behavior of butterflies and moths. The patterns provide a visual cue by means of which males are attracted to females from a distance and by which females recognize males of their species. Reflection of ultraviolet radiation is part of the pattern in many species, and the presence of ultraviolet-reflecting markings may either stimulate or inhibit recognition or mating behavior. However, patterns are only part of the complex picture of successful mating within a species. There are chemical and behavioral aspects as well. On the wings of

Iridescence is a property of the wings of several species of lepidoptera, including the Morpho butterfly (below left) and the Madagascar Croesus moth (below).

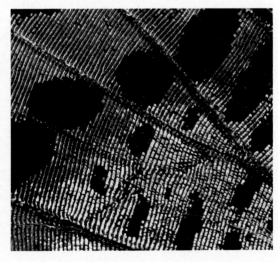

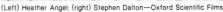

(Left) Heather Angel; (right) Stephen Dalton—Oxford Scientific Films

Many butterflies and moths have wings that are colored so that they provide camouflage against predators. At the top left is a moth of the Amazon region of Brazil, and at the bottom left a Red Admiral butterfly blends with a tree branch. At the right are Asian Dead-leaf butterflies.

many male butterflies are patches of thick, usually dark scales called andro-conia. In many skippers and hairstreaks these can be seen as blackish spots (stigmas) that are located near the front edge of the fore wing. Others, such as the tropical *Agrias* species and many of the swallowtails, have areas of long hair scales along the edges of the hind wings nearest the body. These scales secrete pheromones, chemicals that act like perfume to release mating behavior in females of the same species. In species with long hair scales the pheromones are actually flicked into the air near the female, or even onto her head, where antennae and mouth parts pick up the stimuli. Females usually produce pheromones from the tips of their abdomens, allowing the chemical to evaporate and be carried by the air currents to attract males.

In addition to the chemical activity of mating, special flight and touching behavior are also required as a final check to be sure males do not mate with females of species other than their own. Females can normally prevent unwanted matings by closing their wings over their abdomens or by flying away. Receptiveness is usually signaled by holding the wings to the side and

76

(Top) C. B. Firth—Bruce Coleman Inc.; (center) Alan Blank
for National Audubon Society/Photo Researchers; (bottom) Dr. E. R. Degginger—Bruce Coleman Inc.

Wing shapes and markings of the Map butterfly (left) break up the outline of the insect so that predators can not easily identify it. The eyespots of the Owl butterfly (below) and the hairlike tails of the Great Purple Hairstreak butterfly (bottom) are decoy markings that serve to direct the eyes of predators away from the vital parts of the insects' bodies.

presenting the abdomen to the courting male, often with vibrating wings. Even when many similar species are present in a given area, as in the tropics, interspecies matings are unusual because of the intricate pattern of visual, chemical, and behavioral cues required from both sexes.

Flight

The actual mechanics of Lepidoptera flight are complex and are not covered here in depth. In general, flight depends upon the intricate musculature inside the thorax, the shapes of the tiny bonelike structures at the wing bases

77

Monarch butterfly (right) feeds on milkweed, which makes it distasteful to predators. In an example of Batesian mimicry the Viceroy butterfly (left), though not distasteful itself, is often avoided by predators because of its close resemblance to the Monarch.

that allow both folding and the characteristic figure-eight motion by which the wings "row" the insect through the air, and the strength to withstand the pressure of flight. Flight habits vary considerably in the Lepidoptera. Some of the Sphinx moths (Sphingidae) are among the fastest fliers of the insect world, capable of speeds up to 18 kilometers per hour (11 miles per hour) (without a tail wind) and wingbeats of 85 per second. Those species that depend on flight for protection are usually fast fliers, with zigzag motions that make capture by predators (including collectors) difficult. Butterflies that depend on warning coloration and bad taste, or Batesian mimics of them, may fly languidly into and out of jungle vegetation, speeding up only when threatened directly. Average speeds of these butterflies are represented by swallowtails with wingbeats of from 5 to 9 per second and by the Cabbage butterfly (*Pieris rapae*), which normally travels at a speed of about 9 kilometers per hour. However, these species have different flight habits for different purposes and can move much faster when frightened.

Many butterflies seem rare because of their flying habits. The colorful *Agrias* species of the American tropics can rarely be netted unless attracted to rotten fruit or other bait because they fly so fast and rarely come within reach. The Early Hairstreak (*Erora laeta*) is one of the most prized rarities in eastern North America because it is small, drab, and will not fly up when one approaches closely. When it does fly up, it flits away almost invisibly, its colors blending with the background vegetation.

Butterflies usually alight cleanly when they stop flying. Moths, in contrast, usually blunder into a plant or other object, gain a foothold, then climb to the position they prefer, usually with wings held flat to the substrate. In some moths of the families Geometridae, Lymantriidae, and Psychidae, wings are reduced to short nubs, or lost entirely. This, however, is true only of females, which must put energy into the production of many eggs.

Through sophisticated optical and experimental techniques much has been learned about the wings of butterflies and moths. They are unbeliev-

78

ably varied in design and are necessary in achieving the main goals of adult life: survival and reproduction. Much more is still to be learned, however. In the meantime countless millions of people will continue to enjoy their sheer beauty and fascinating diversity.

FOR ADDITIONAL READING

Jo Brewer and K. B. Sandved, *Butterflies* (Abrams, 1976).

R. F. Chapman, *The Insects: Structure and Function* (American Elsevier, 1969).

T. C. Emmel, *Butterflies* (Knopf, 1975).

Werner Nachtigall, *Insects in Flight* (McGraw-Hill, 1974).

R. E. Snodgrass, *Principles of Insect Morphology* (McGraw-Hill, 1935).

The flight of butterflies and moths such as the Pericopid (top) depends upon interactions among the thorax, the wings, and bonelike structures at the wing bases. Human collectors must be skillful to catch the fast-moving species.

79

THE GREAT PACIFIC MIGRATION

by Peter Bellwood

The expansion of the Austronesians across thousands of miles of land and ocean is unmatched in human history.

Between about 4000 BC and AD 1000 the members of a major linguistic group of mankind, the Austronesians, underwent an expansion and dispersal for which there is no parallel in human history. Their descendants now number perhaps 250 million people and occupy Indonesia, Malaysia, the Philippines, parts of southern Vietnam, Madagascar, and most of the Pacific islands as far east as Easter Island. The American Indians colonized a greater land area and had to pass through more zones of latitude to do so, but their founders faced an empty region in human terms. The Austronesians had to contend with preestablished populations in many areas as well as huge sea distances, and their success in spreading around more than half of the world's circumference in tropical latitudes must stand unchallenged.

The prehistory of the Austronesian-speaking peoples can be approached through the independent results of three major disciplines: archaeology, linguistics, and biological anthropology. Each of these can provide information on Austronesian expansion in terms of date, direction, cultural content, motive, and resistance from preexisting populations. However, each discipline throws light on the above factors in different ways, and it is clear that the basic data for discussing the prehistory of a linguistic category of mankind, such as the Austronesians, are derived first and foremost from linguis-

Moorea, one of the Society Islands of French Polynesia, was settled by Austronesians in the first millennium AD. The achievement of the Austronesians in traveling vast distances across the ocean and establishing colonies on hundreds of islands stands unparalleled in human history.

PETER BELLWOOD is a Senior Lecturer in Prehistory at the Australian National University in Canberra. His books include Man's Conquest of the Pacific (1978) and The Polynesians (1978).

(Overleaf) Illustration by Jane Meredith

tics. The Austronesians are not a clearly visible group in terms of race or of ethnographic or archaeological culture in many areas of their distribution, with the important exception of those Pacific islands which only they settled in prehistoric times. Thus, hypotheses about the ultimate origins and early expansions of the Austronesian-speaking population as a whole can only be supported by the data of biological anthropology and archaeology and not generated from them.

Within the Austronesian region it is clear that late-phase (after 1500 BC) migrations did occur through the Pacific Ocean to uninhabited islands. Therefore, this is an interesting case in which the results of the three disciplines might be expected to be in some accord. The data of these disciplines also can be used to hypothesize about some of the cultural changes which occurred as the expansion progressed, both before and after 1500 BC.

The Austronesians

Present-day Austronesians can be described in terms of genetics and physical appearance, languages, and ethnography. The Austronesians of the past are obviously less visible, particularly in the long-settled lands of Southeast Asia, but they can be described in terms of archaeology, skeletal anthropology, and certain historical and inscriptional source materials. These early Austronesians can also be described according to inferences made from the

82

data on Austronesians of the present; that is, data of gene and language distributions can be analyzed so as to hypothesize how they might have evolved, and then the results can be compared with those from the disciplines in which the past is observed directly, such as archaeology and skeletal anthropology. The environmental sciences must also be considered, for without them all discussion of change and adaptation in the remote past is devoid of context.

The Austronesians of the "ethnographic present" (in practice, on the eve of contact with the Western world) are a large but well-defined linguistic group. However, there is no cultural or physical homogeneity throughout their region. Cultural patterns have been affected by millennia of local evolution and (in the western areas) contacts with Hindu-Buddhist, Chinese, and Islamic civilizations. Physical characteristics have been affected by intermarriage with other residents of the regions, in particular with the Papuan-speaking populations of New Guinea and adjacent islands. But languages, despite millennia of borrowing from unrelated tongues, will generally preserve traces of family history and expansion, which, in the case of prehistoric tribal societies such as the Austronesians, can be assumed to correlate fairly directly with the expansionary history of their human speakers.

The Austronesians of most concern in this discussion are those of Southeast Asia and the Pacific Islands. Madagascar, settled during the 1st millennium AD from Indonesia, is not discussed in detail. The Southeast Asian members of the group include virtually all the peoples of Malaysia, Indonesia, and the Philippines, plus the Chams of southern Vietnam and the non-

Linguistic map shows the areas occupied by the major Austronesian subgroups. Also indicated are the territories settled by Papuan-speaking peoples and the boundaries of the three main geographical divisions of the Pacific islands, Micronesia, Melanesia, and Polynesia.

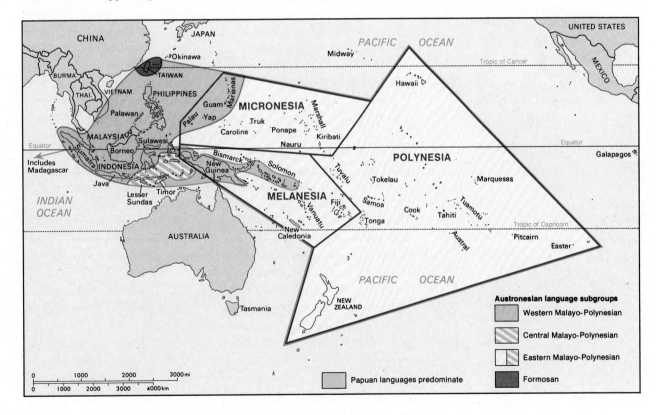

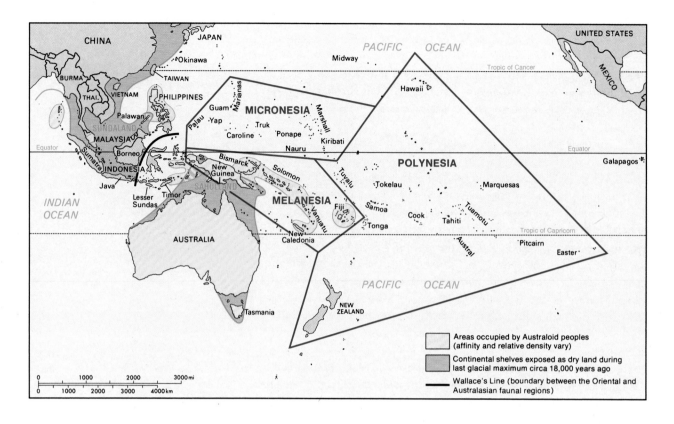

CHINA
JAPAN
Okinawa
PACIFIC   OCEAN
UNITED STATES
BURMA
TAIWAN
Midway
Tropic of Cancer
MEXICO
THAI.
VIETNAM
PHILIPPINES
Marianas
Hawaii
Palawan
Guam
MICRONESIA
Marshall
SUNDALAND
Yap
MALAYSIA
Palau
Truk
Caroline
Ponape
Kiribati
Equator
Borneo
Nauru
POLYNESIA
Equator
Galapagos
INDONESIA
Bismarck
Java
New
Guinea
Solomon
Tuvalu
Tokelau
Marquesas
Lesser
Timor
SAHULLAND
MELANESIA
Vanuatu
Fiji
Samoa
Tuamotu
INDIAN
Sundas
Cook
Tahiti
OCEAN
Tonga
Tropic of Capricorn
AUSTRALIA
New
Caledonia
Austral
Pitcairn
Easter
PACIFIC   OCEAN
Tasmania
NEW
ZEALAND

Areas occupied by Australoid peoples
(affinity and relative density vary)

Continental shelves exposed as dry land during
last glacial maximum circa 18,000 years ago

Wallace's Line (boundary between the Oriental and
Australasian faunal regions)

0   1000   2000   3000 mi
0   1000   2000   3000   4000 km

Map of the Austronesian region shows areas occupied by members of the Australoid physical group. Austronesians are predominantly Southern Mongoloids in regard to physical appearance, but because of increasing intermarriage with the Australoids the island Melanesians no longer fit the Mongoloid generalization.

Chinese aboriginal peoples of Taiwan. Exceptions in Malaysia and Indonesia include the small Negritos of inland Malaya (speakers of mainland Southeast Asian Austro-Asiatic languages) and the Melanesian speakers of Papuan languages in eastern Indonesia and the bulk of New Guinea. All of the Micronesians and Polynesians speak Austronesian as do most of the island Melanesians.

The significance of New Guinea as a bastion of Papuan language-speakers who have clearly resisted Austronesian settlement is great. The Papuan languages may be visualized as forming a resistant massif around which the unrelated Austronesian speakers migrated in a vast swath which extends from Malaya to Easter Island.

In terms of physical appearance the Austronesians are predominantly Southern Mongoloids, having fairly short stature, and slightly darker skin than most Chinese. There has, however, been increasing intermarriage in the Australoid region of New Guinea, and Austronesians in island Melanesia clearly no longer fit the Mongoloid generalization. Polynesians, despite their large body size, are of fairly direct Southern Mongoloid derivation.

In terms of culture the basic Austronesian social formations in those areas least affected by contact with outside civilizations comprise hamlet or longhouse groups based on both paternal and maternal inheritance in many parts of the Philippines and Borneo, unilateral (paternal or maternal) descent groups in and around Melanesia, and stratified chiefdoms in Micronesia and Polynesia. Societies in western Indonesia, perhaps once quite highly stratified, have been transformed by two millennia of powerful Hindu-

84

Buddhist influence and by the tremendous impact of the religion of Islam after 1300.

The linguistic version of Austronesian origins

Linguistic hypotheses concerning Austronesian origins are derived mainly from comparative studies of present-day languages. Ancient inscriptions from about AD 400 onward do occur in western Indonesia and southern Vietnam, but they are too few and mostly too recent to be of great assistance. However, modern comparative linguists are able to compare related languages in terms of phonetics, grammar, and vocabulary; by differentiating shared innovations and inheritances (cognates) from borrowed items, they are able to trace backward through the various forks in a large family tree to a common ancestral node (the basic protolanguage). The languages within a family can be subgrouped according to their shared cognate features in terms of a basic assumption that features widely shared have a greater antiquity than those shared by only two or more neighboring languages. For example, features shared between the widely separated Malay and Tahitian are likely to be from a much older common ancestor than those shared uniquely between Tahitian and neighboring Marquesan. The vocabularies reconstructed for protolanguages are also of great importance for reconstructing cultural backgrounds and geographical origins.

The history of the Austronesian languages has involved considerable dispute in the past, but there is now general agreement about the shape of the family tree and its geographical and time-related characteristics. The linguistic data allow reconstruction back to the protolanguage from which all

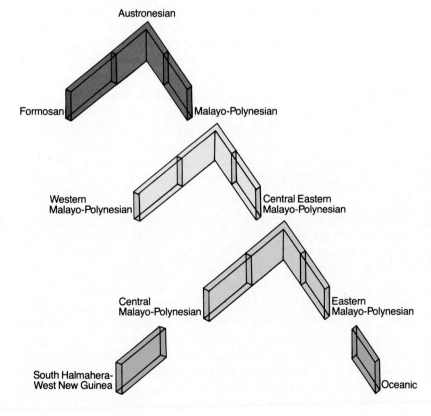

Flow chart reveals the evolution of the subgroups of the Austronesian language family. Founder groups moved from Formosa (Taiwan) into the Philippines to form the Malayo-Polynesian subgroup. From the Philippines the Western Malayo-Polynesians spread south and west into Java, Sumatra, Malaya, and Vietnam, while the Central-Eastern Malayo-Polynesians moved south into eastern Indonesia to form the Central Malayo-Polynesian division and farther east to become the Eastern Malayo-Polynesians. The most widespread division of the Eastern group is the Oceanic, which spread into eastern Micronesia, much of eastern Melanesia, and all of Polynesia.

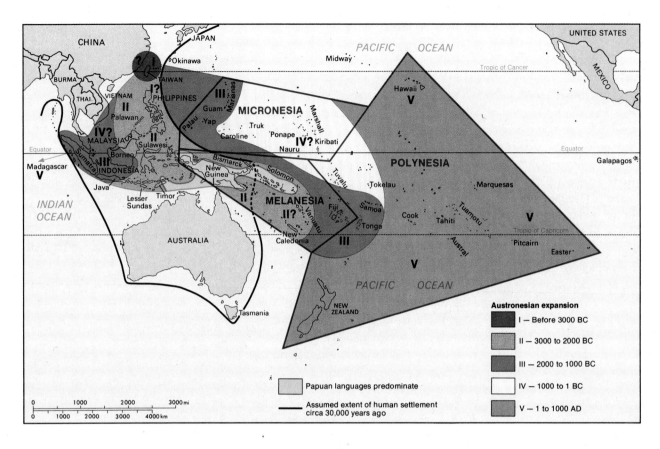

Geographical expansion of the Austronesians from Taiwan across the Pacific to the islands of Polynesia began about 3000 BC and was completed by about 1000 AD. The dates are based on linguistic and archaeological evidence and are considered most accurate for eastern Melanesia and Polynesia. The Papuan speakers of New Guinea and nearby islands lay in the path of the migration but strongly resisted Austronesian settlement.

the present-day Austronesian languages are derived but will not allow any reconstruction of prior stages except through comparison with other languages families that may share a remote common ancestry. Thus, Proto-Austronesian (PAN), which appears to have been located in Taiwan, may have shared a remoter common ancestry with some of the Thai languages, and this suggests an ancestry for the (Pre-) Austronesians on the South Chinese mainland even though no Austronesian languages are spoken there today.

PAN in Taiwan may have been spoken between 3000 and 6000 BC, according to calculations from a range of possible rates of linguistic change. The sequence of linguistic splits (and inferred population movements) following the period of PAN is as follows: (1) Founder groups move into the Philippines, while others remain in Taiwan. The former founded the Malayo-Polynesian subgroup (all languages outside Taiwan); (2) From the Philippines and northern Borneo founders spread south and west into Java, Sumatra, Malaya, and Vietnam (Western Malayo-Polynesian subgroup); (3) Beginning at approximately the same time founders of the Central-Eastern Malayo-Polynesian subgroup move south into eastern Indonesia and east to found the Eastern Malayo-Polynesian subgroup, of which the most widespread division is Oceanic (eastern Micronesia, Polynesia, plus all of Austronesian-speaking Melanesia east of the western end of New Guinea). The most clear-cut long-distance migration of all, that of the Polynesians (see below), began about 1500 BC with descendants eventually reaching New Zealand by AD 1000.

Rough dates for this expansion can be derived from linguistic comparisons. The dates can in turn be sharpened by the use of archaeological evidence with the proviso that many regions, especially western Indonesia, are poorly known archaeologically and future alterations may be required. The order of Austronesian settlement appears to be as follows: (1) Prior to 3000 BC—Taiwan and possibly northern Philippines; (2) 3000–2000 BC—Philippines, northern Borneo, Sulawesi, parts of the Lesser Sunda chain, and possibly western Melanesia; (3) 2000–1000 BC—western Micronesia, central and eastern Melanesia, western Polynesia, and probable continued expansion in Java and Borneo; (4) 1000–1 BC—possible expansion within the above areas, especially western Indonesia, Malaya, and western Polynesia, and first settlement of eastern Micronesia; (5) AD 1–1000—settlement of eastern Polynesia and Madagascar. New Zealand, at about 1,000 years ago, was the last major landmass to be reached, and the 1st millennium AD was the period of the greatest Polynesian migrations.

The reconstruction of parts of the vocabulary of Proto-Austronesian is an exercise of major importance for understanding prehistory. It is clear that early Austronesian societies in Taiwan and adjacent areas belonged to a technological and economic milieu associated with timber and thatch dwellings and community houses; stone tools; the bow; pottery; canoe transport with sails and outriggers; fishing; domestication of pigs, dogs, and chickens; and, most important, agriculture based on the cultivation of rice, millet, and certain tubers such as yams and taro. The importance of these reconstructions for Austronesian societies that existed more than 5,000 years ago cannot be overstressed; the evidence of archaeology alone could never provide such detail nor could it provide the indications for PAN chieftainship that can be detected linguistically. However, the question of general PAN social organization is still under debate. A strong possibility (especially for Oceania) is small stratified chiefdoms of the Polynesian type, in which descent and inheritance are optionally via males or females (with a preference for males in lines of chiefs; anthropologists refer to this kind of descent as ambilineal).

When Austronesian societies are viewed as a whole, the situation in and around Melanesia is revealed to be quite complex, consisting of a great number of highly diversified and rapidly changing languages spoken by small isolated populations. The answer to this diversity, which has produced some of the most intensive linguistic and anthropological research in the world, is that the ancient New Guineans (Australoids who spoke Papuan languages) had already developed population densities high enough to enable them to resist Austronesian expansion and even to "take over" in a cultural sense the Austronesians settling among them. This situation gives rise to two of the great questions of Pacific prehistory: Why were Austronesian speakers so successful in Island Southeast Asia (where there were earlier populations) and the Pacific (where they were first to settle), and why, by contrast, did they clearly meet a population capable of such tough resistance in western Melanesia? The answers to these questions do not lie with linguistics alone, although it is the languages that provide the basic pattern that must be explained.

Viewpoint of biological anthropology

Since the Austronesians are a linguistic and not a racial group, one cannot expect to find them clearly defined in terms of gene frequencies or a skeletal record. In fact, there is no coherent skeletal record for Austronesians with the exception of some material from those Pacific Islands where there were no previous inhabitants. In Southeast Asia and Melanesia the Austronesians look no different in general terms from their non-Austronesian speaking neighbors (such as Thais, Vietnamese, and Papuans), and so it is obvious that linguistic and physical boundaries on this scale do not coincide.

But all is not chaos. First, if Melanesia is temporarily disregarded, all Austronesian speakers are Southern Mongoloids, with varying degrees of Australoid inheritance clearly visible in the Pacific islands and in comparatively remote forested or mountainous regions of Southeast Asia. People in the region who are not Mongoloid and who belong to the Australoid group that once existed there include pockets of Negritos in Malaya and the Philippines, the Australian Aborigines, and the Papuan-speaking peoples of western Melanesia.

Recent analyses of genetically controlled characterisitcs in blood throw much light on population differences. These analyses tend to group all Mongoloids against the Australoids of Australia and the New Guinea Highlands and link the Southern Mongoloids most closely with the other Mongoloids of eastern Asia and the Americas. Specific genetic markers that link these Mongoloid populations are known for some of the serum protein systems (Gm immunoglobulin, group specific component, and transferrin) and also for the Diego red cell and human leukocyte antigens.

The detailed ramifications of the patterning in such complex data are far too extensive to consider here, but some conclusions can be drawn that are in accord with the prevailing views of biological anthropologists. First, the Southern Mongoloids cannot be derived by evolution from Australoid populations as represented by present Australians and New Guineans. The two groups are of quite separate origin, and the question arises as to whether the Southern Mongoloids migrated southward from China or whether they evolved from an ancient (40,000 years ago or more) population located in and around Sundaland, the late glacial continent of western Indonesia. If the latter is the case, then the ancient Sundaland population may have been ancestral to both the Southern Mongoloids and the Australoids. Skeletal evidence does exist in Sundaland, but it does not answer the question unequivocally.

On the other hand, if one only considers such Mongoloid characteristics as light skin and fairly straight hair, then it is difficult to escape the conclusion that they are the results of natural selection in latitudes higher than those of the equatorial regions where the Australoids themselves undoubtedly evolved. Equatorial regions have fostered dark skin and tightly curled hair throughout the Eastern Hemisphere, and so the assumption that the Southern Mongoloids evolved entirely within Indonesia requires some very unusual selective factors for which there is no evidence. It seems most likely that the Southern Mongoloids of Indonesia result from expansion that began in southern China and that these Mongoloids have gradually dominated a local

88

Varied peoples of the Austronesian region include Papuan-speaking tribal dancers in New Guinea (top left), a Polynesian woman of Tonga (top right), Negritos in the Philippines (left), and a Javanese man (above).

Australoid population. The Indonesians are, therefore, the equivalents of the equatorial Indians of South America, who also reveal an unequivocal Asian Mongoloid inheritance despite 10,000 years or more of adaptation to an equatorial region.

The witness of archaeology

Linguistics and physical anthropology provide an important framework in terms of directions of expansion and internal and external population relationships. The explanatory flesh on the skeleton must come basically from archaeology, with the combined support of ethnography and the environmental sciences.

But there are problems with this approach. The populations from which the data of linguistics and genetics are drawn are alive and well and can be sampled across their ranges of distribution. By contrast, the populations of archaeological evidence have been hideously ravaged by time and the tropical climate, and the known samples are spotty in both temporal and spatial distribution. At present, with the important exceptions of the ancestral-Polynesian Lapita culture of the western Pacific islands (1500 BC to early 1st millennium AD) and later Polynesian and Micronesian cultures, the archaeological record for the Austronesians is not clear, particularly for earlier phases in Southeast Asia. It will not speak for itself on the topic of early (pre-Oceanic) Austronesian expansion, although it can speak loudly if asked certain questions of an economic or technological nature. And the answers become even louder as the researcher moves into such well-studied regions as Polynesia.

Because of space restrictions only a brief description of Austronesian expansion and the preceding millennia of human evolution in Southeast Asia can be presented here. It represents a tightening up of the data derived from linguistics and biological anthropology, a result of adding to that information the facts available from archaeology and the environmental sciences. The archaeological record itself is far too detailed to reproduce here, but it does provide a record of Neolithic cultures in the islands of Southeast Asia that may well correlate with early Austronesian societies.

The sequence of human evolution, cultural change, population expansion, and other diverse phenomena in Southeast Asia has the following "best-fit" pattern:

1. Australoid evolution prior to 40,000 years ago was confined mainly to the late glacial Sundaland continent, where a discontinuous skeletal record going back to *Homo erectus* more than 1.5 million years ago has been recorded from Java.

2. Mongoloid evolution took place over the same time span from *Homo erectus* forebears in the Chinese region. Mainland Southeast Asian populations at this time presumably graded from basically Mongoloid in the north to Australoid in the south.

3. About 40,000 years ago (or earlier?) settlers crossed eastern Indonesian sea gaps to settle the single continent of Australia-New Guinea (Sahulland). The indigenous peoples of those areas today are basically the descendants of those founders, and the same may ultimately be the case for the Australian

90

and Papuan languages (although major internal linguistic expansions have taken place in both landmasses).

4. The Australoids who "stayed behind" in Sundaland are represented today by the small gracile Negritos, who most resemble small Melanesians. The expansion of the early Australoids eastward across wide sea gaps into isolation in New Guinea and Australia has led to much differentiation within the group as a whole.

5. The archaeology of this ancient expansion is represented by numerous "core tool and scraper" industries in Indonesia, the Philippines, New Guinea, and Australia. The equatorial regions of Indonesia (such as Borneo) were only lightly settled, and all groups of this time subsisted by hunting and gathering.

6. Following the end of the Pleistocene (about 8000 BC) the continents of Sundaland and Sahulland were broken up by rising seas. The present pattern of land and sea had virtually evolved by about 6000 BC. At this time rice cultivation began in southern China, and in the isolated highlands of New Guinea a separate development of plant cultivation occurred, probably involving tubers. The future seeds of Austronesian and Papuan cultural "competition" are sown.

7. During the 5th and 4th millennia BC early Austronesians with a cereal-based economy (rice and millet) expanded from southern China into Taiwan and the northern Philippines. There, and later throughout most of Indonesia, they had technological and demographic (high population density) advantages that allowed them to replace gradually the indigenous hunter-gatherer Australoid populations, of whom only small-statured representatives survive today in remote inland forested regions. The question of cultural and demographic "advantage" in allowing such a population expansion to take place throughout a previously settled area is of great importance. Such large-scale expansions (as opposed to slow intergroup gene flow) are characteristic phenomena of the Neolithic and later periods.

8. Austronesian expansion into equatorial Indonesia and Malaysia, which took place after 3000 BC, was affected economically by the prevailing non-seasonality and constant humidity of the climate. In those regions the cereal grains were partially replaced in the diet by local tree products such as bananas, sago, coconuts, and breadfruit. Tubers such as yams and taro probably also became much more important. Thus the Austronesian economy underwent an internal economic and geographical shift from cereal to fruit and tuber cultivation, and virtually all Pacific island economies were of the latter type. Many of the native fruits and tubers were undoubtedly exploited by the preceding hunting and collecting inhabitants of the Indonesian region, and many of those groups may have survived relatively unaffected by Austronesian settlement in inland regions of the larger Indonesian islands until less than 1,000 years ago.

9. Austronesians moving into New Guinea and adjacent islands after 3000 BC came face-to-face with an indigenous population far more resistant than that of Indonesia. The New Guineans appear to have been already cultivating a range of local plants, including sago, sugarcane, bananas, and possibly taro. There, around the core region of Papuan-speaking New Guinea, the

Austronesians were dramatically less successful than they had been in the sparsely settled regions of equatorial Indonesia; the results over the millennia have been cultural assimilation and mixing of a most complex order, with a resulting increase in diversity of culture and language.

10. The final Austronesian achievement, the settlement after 1500 BC of the islands of Micronesia and Polynesia, involved long migrations by adept seamen carrying their stocks of tubers, fruits (not cereals), and domesticated pigs, dogs, and chickens. Ultimately, over a 2,500-year period, they settled every inhabitable island through the vastnesses of the Pacific. There the Austronesians finally came into their own, in a region which other peoples could not reach, and created the chiefdoms and monuments that have long fascinated the world since the discovery by Europeans of Tonga, Tahiti, Hawaii, Easter Island, and New Zealand. Periodic contacts with the western coast of South America undoubtedly took place, but there is no longer the slightest doubt that the Polynesians themselves are of Southeast Asian and not American origin.

It is difficult to draw a simple conclusion from such a complex branch of human prehistory. But one point must be stressed. Prehistorians may debate the relative inputs from different disciplines, but the real meaning of the record lies in the achievements of the peoples themselves: achievements, Papuan and Austronesian, that laid the human foundations for a significant region of the modern world.

FOR ADDITIONAL READING

P. S. Bellwood, *Man's Conquest of the Pacific* (Collins, 1978); *The Polynesians* (Thames and Hudson, 1978); "The Peopling of the Pacific," *Scientific American* (November 1980, pp. 174–185).

Robert Blust, "Austronesian Culture History: Some Linguistic Inferences and Their Relations to the Archaeological Record," *World Archaeology* (June 1976, pp. 19–43).

J. J. Fox et al. (eds.), *Indonesia: Australian perspectives* (Research School of Pacific Studies, 1980).

W. W. Howells, *The Pacific Islanders* (Scribner's, 1974).

J. D. Jennings (ed.), *The Prehistory of Polynesia* (Harvard University Press, 1979).

Polynesian double-hulled canoe (opposite page, top), constructed from planks lashed edge to edge through caulked holes, was in common use at the time of the first European contact and probably was the type of craft employed on the earliest Polynesian migrations. A Tongan chief (opposite page, bottom) officiates at a kava-drinking ceremony. (Kava is an intoxicating beverage made from the crushed roots of a shrubby pepper.) On such previously uninhabited islands the Austronesians were free to create a culture that was entirely their own.

WHEN
MAN
CHANGES THE
EARTH

by John Gribbin

Historically the nations of the world have exercised little caution when undertaking large-scale modifications to the environment. Yet people still can act rationally, as some recent examples demonstrate.

More and more, people are waking to the possibility that human activity may be affecting or be about to affect the Earth's environment. Since the mid-1970s much of this concern has focused on two questions: whether the release of chemicals from spray cans is damaging the ozone layer of the stratosphere and whether a buildup of carbon dioxide in the atmosphere from burning fossil fuels will trap solar heat and raise global temperatures through a "greenhouse effect." Because most people who live in the developed countries are directly involved in the activities that these questions address, it may be easier to gain some perspective on the real issues by first examining a situation for which the responsibility is more removed and more clearly defined.

An irreversible mistake?

A Soviet plan to divert the flow of two major Siberian rivers away from the Arctic Ocean and toward new agricultural lands—something in which no Westerner apparently has either involvement or influence—offers an archetypal example of the way human beings are interacting with the environment. At first sight the plan seems wholly admirable and beneficial; only under closer inspection do the potential hazards become clear, hazards that may ultimately outweigh the obvious advantages.

In this case the "obvious advantages" are agricultural. In the past few decades the Soviet Union has been making great efforts to develop the virgin lands of Kazakhstan and Central Asia. The rural population of Kazakhstan has increased by about 1.5 million in the past 25 years. There are more than 36 million hectares (a hectare is 2.47 acres) of arable land in Kazakhstan, but much of it receives no more than 300 millimeters (12 inches) of precipi-

Large-scale irrigation projects have already wrought an agricultural miracle in many regions of Kazakhstan and Central Asia, and even more ambitious plans are in the making. But the continued diversion of such massive volumes of water to farmlands cannot take place without environmental consequences, and as yet those consequences are largely unpredictable.

JOHN GRIBBIN *is Physics Consultant to* New Scientist *magazine, London, and the author of several books on global environmental issues, including* Future Worlds *and* Future Weather and the Greenhouse Effect.

(Overleaf) Illustration by Eraldo Carugati

tation each year. To increase grain production in the region the Soviets have been looking to large-scale irrigation. Water from the Irtysh River, artesian wells, and other sources have already brought an agricultural revolution. When crop failures in such traditional grain-growing regions as the Ukraine forced a massive Soviet reliance on world grain markets in 1972, it was the yield from the "new lands" that prevented complete disaster, enabling the government to meet its commitments to export grain to Eastern European countries even while purchasing grain for home consumption. Throughout the 1970s the plans to improve yields from the new lands gained still more momentum.

These are grand plans indeed, envisaging in their most complete form more than just a little irrigation and a few artesian wells. Although some increased irrigation is already well under way, the ultimate goal of Soviet planners is to divert the flow of the important Ob and Yenisey rivers southward into the Aral Sea, a massive engineering project requiring a canal 2,500 kilometers long (a kilometer is 0.62 miles), 200–300 meters wide (a meter is 3.28 feet), and of navigable depth (about 12 meters). Although few details of the work in progress and planned are known in the West, it seems that within a few years facilities to divert as much as 35 cubic kilometers of water per year could be under construction, with the first southward transfers of water beginning in the mid-1990s. It will be early in the 21st century before the project gains full momentum, with diversions from the two rivers running at 75 cubic kilometers per year. But the 21st century is less than 20 years away, closer than the launch of the first space satellite, and climatologists are beginning to worry over the implications.

To put the plan in perspective, the combined flow of these two great Siberian rivers is nearly twice that of the Mississippi and 400 times that of the

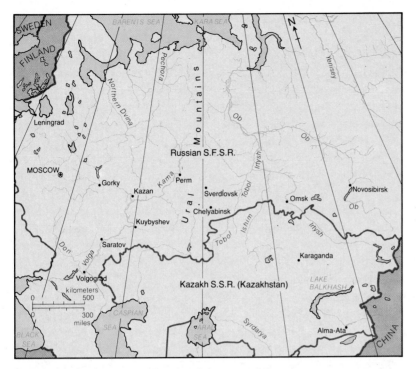

Thames. The Ob alone discharges 400 cubic kilometers of water yearly and the Yenisey 550, and the extent of the envisaged tampering with this natural flow amounts to a 5% reduction in the amount of freshwater discharging into the Arctic Ocean. If the project is developed even further, by the mid-21st century the permanent reduction in freshwater flow to the Arctic could reach 20%. The cause for concern arises because this freshwater flow is a critical factor in keeping the Arctic frozen. Without this freshwater lid the Arctic ice cap would be exposed to an underlying layer of warmer ocean water and become defrosted. Even with a reduction in freshwater flow from the Yenisey and the Ob, changes could well take place in the ocean currents

Tass/Sovfoto

The Ob River (left) discharges 400 cubic kilometers of water a year, and the Ob and Yenisey combined have a flow almost twice that of the Mississippi. Present Soviet plans for agricultural development of the "new lands" envision the southward diversion of as much as 75 cubic kilometers of the annual flow of these two rivers from their natural outlet in the Arctic Ocean.

around the Arctic, affecting the pattern of seasonal breakup and freezing of ice along the Siberian coast.

With further extrapolation the murky forecasts in the climatologists' crystal balls become even more complex. It might well be that such changes would be seen as a good thing in the Soviet Union: less sea ice could make such ports as Murmansk more accessible and more useful. But at the same time scientists now know that the Arctic ice cover somehow controls the whole pattern of atmospheric circulation. If the ice retreats, rainfall belts across the Northern Hemisphere may shift northward, bringing more rain to regions now dry and drought to regions that have come to depend on the rain. No one can yet predict the precise implications—and this is the point. Precisely because the consequences are unpredictable, no action that might turn out to be irreversible should be undertaken. A Soviet climatologist, E. K. Fedorov of the U.S.S.R. State Committee for Hydrometeorology and Control of the Natural Environment, made the following comment at the 1979 World Climate Conference in Geneva: "If the ice cover of the Arctic Ocean were made to disappear, the atmospheric and oceanic circulation would adjust in such a way that the ice would not be able to re-establish itself." This would "lead to considerable changes in climate throughout the world . . . specific, once-only actions could produce irreversible changes."

Just as it is difficult to find out just how far the Soviet authorities plan to carry through their plans for river diversions, so it is impossible to determine whether they are influenced by such an argument. Its message is a reversal of the concept of natural justice: where a potential hazard to the environment on such a scale exists, the only sensible assumption is "guilty until proven innocent." And that assumption has led, rightly, to a dramatic reduction in the industrial use of chlorofluorocarbons (CFC's), even though no one has yet proved that these chemicals are damaging the ozone layer in the Earth's atmosphere.

A case of good sense

Since the early 1970s the role of CFC's in the environment has been the subject of a great deal of scientific research and debate, stimulated by the claims of U.S. scientists F. Sherwood Rowland and Mario J. Molina. The fear

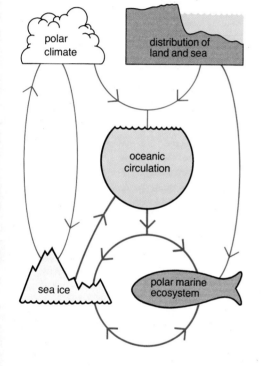

polar climate

distribution of land and sea

oceanic circulation

sea ice

polar marine ecosystem

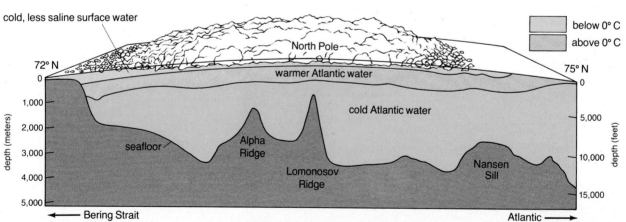

cold, less saline surface water

below 0° C
above 0° C

North Pole

72° N

75° N

warmer Atlantic water

cold Atlantic water

seafloor

Alpha Ridge

Lomonosov Ridge

Nansen Sill

depth (meters)

depth (feet)

Bering Strait

Atlantic

(Top) From *Arctic and Antarctica* by David Sugden. © David Sugden 1982. By permission of Barnes & Noble Books; (bottom) adapted from "Physical Oceanography of Arctic and Sub-Arctic Seas," L. K. Coachman and K. Aagaard, *Marine Geology and Oceanography of the Arctic Seas*, Y. Herman (ed.), Springer-Verlag, New York, pp. 1–72, 1974.

Environmental change need not be viewed in the same regard in every part of the world. Defrosting of the Arctic ice cap could expand the usefulness of such Soviet ports as Murmansk (left) near the Norwegian border. On the other hand it could also alter dry and wet regions throughout the Northern Hemisphere, upsetting the lives and livelihood of millions of people.

was that these materials, widely used as propellants in aerosol spray cans by the mid-1970s, would reduce the amount of ozone high in the atmosphere and thereby allow increased quantities of biologically damaging ultraviolet radiation from the Sun to penetrate to the ground. The topic is complex, involving stratospheric chemistry and the way these CFC compounds circulate through the atmosphere. The issues also were clouded by the emotive introduction of the term cancer into the public debate—solar ultraviolet can cause an increased incidence of skin cancer, although it is by no means clear that this is a real hazard related to use of CFC's in spray cans. What did emerge clearly from the debate stimulated by Rowland and Molina was that nobody had proved that CFC's were safe to release in large quantities. While the controversy continued through the 1970s, industry cut back production of CFC's and found other propellants for its spray cans.

By the early 1980s chemists were becoming increasingly convinced that the risk to the ozone layer was less than initially perceived, but the magnitude of the threat is not the issue. This case is clearly one of "better safe than sorry" and an example of industry reacting promptly and correctly (admittedly under public pressure) to a possible danger as if it were a proven reality. So, in spite of the pessimistic argument that humanity is already too far down the road to self-destruction, polluting the Earth and irreparably damaging the environment, there are signs that people can act rationally, even where major industries are concerned and millions of dollars are at stake. An example from Europe shows that it is even possible for governments to change their minds—and spend more money—to minimize damage to the environment.

The conscience of a nation

Holland's Delta Plan, an ambitious project to dam most of the large sea inlets in the southwestern part of The Netherlands, was prompted by the disastrous floods of February 1953, in which nearly 2,000 people lost their lives. A commission set up three weeks after the disaster recommended closing all

(Opposite page) Cross section of the Arctic Ocean (bottom) depicts its layered structure, in which the main mass of cold Atlantic water underlies a layer of somewhat warmer seawater. Insulating the polar ice cap from this warmer layer is a 200-meter-thick lid of less saline, colder surface water, continually refreshed by the flow from rivers that discharge into the Arctic Ocean. A reduction in this flow could cause changes in the ocean currents around the Arctic and a partial melting of the ice cap. The sea ice and oceanic currents are but two interlocking components in the polar marine system (top; heavy lines) and its major external variables (light lines), all of which in turn figure importantly in the atmospheric and oceanic systems of the entire Northern Hemisphere.

but two of the sea arms, shortening the coastline by 700 kilometers and removing the danger of flooding. In 1958 the plan was incorporated in an act of Parliament, and in its original form the project was scheduled for completion in 1978. But as work proceeded on the plan, public attitudes changed. Memories of the disaster dimmed with the passage of time, and by the late 1960s the question of protection of the natural environment had become a sensitive issue.

With sound Dutch common sense the hydraulic engineers had begun work first on the smaller dams, sluices, and barriers involved in the project, gaining experience to apply to successively larger structures. By the time preservation of the environment had become a major issue, the largest single piece of the project, the damming of the Eastern Scheldt (Oosterschelde) estuary, remained to be slotted into place. After a heated political debate and no less heated technical discussions, the Dutch government decided in 1974 to modify the original plan extensively and to construct—at much greater expense—a storm-surge barrier with steel gates that could be slid into place, like a series of massive guillotines, when storm and tide conditions threatened to flood the estuary. The decision involved adding some two billion guilders (about $740 million in the mid-1970s) to the cost of the project and delaying completion of the scheme until 1985.

The construction has been no easy task. The total width of the estuary at the site of the barrier is nine kilometers, and the storm-surge barrier occupies four kilometers of this in three sections between artificial islands used to dam the channel. Sixty-six concrete piers will support 63 steel gates, each 42 meters long, 5.4 meters thick, and weighing several hundred tons, that must slide precisely into place when required—and all of it built on sandy soil. The technical problems have been so severe that the Dutch minister responsible for the project has called the barrier "the engineering project of the century," and as it nears completion hydraulics engineers from around the world are eagerly monitoring its progress. And all of this engineering expertise is being applied in order to preserve as much of the natural tidal region of the Eastern Scheldt as possible.

The surface area of the region being brought under direct control of the new water-management system includes 45,000 hectares of vegetated mud flats, 24,000 hectares of deep water, and 2,600 hectares of shallow water. Inevitably the new barrier, even when open, will restrict tidal flow into the basin. But two new dams built at the eastern end of the estuary (the land end) reduce the total area of the basin so that even the restricted flow of water produces a tidal range 77% of the original range. The proportion of exposed mud flats will change, but the basic nature of the estuary remains.

This preservation is of key importance to bird life, since the region is the third most important wintering ground for waterfowl in Europe. The estuary also provides a nursery for many species of fish and shrimp that later make their way into the open sea. Ironically, some of the unusual features that environmentalists have been so eager to protect are a direct result of a more casual attitude by previous generations. Quarry stones, dumped to protect the underwater slopes of dikes, have developed rock shoal ecologies, while farmers who have held back silt for their land have ensured that the

FC-11 and FC-12 production, world total
(in millions of kilograms)

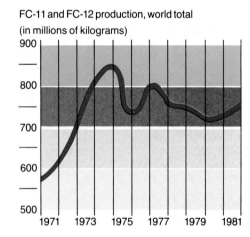

World summary of annual production totals for the two most important chlorofluorocarbons between 1971 and 1981 reveals a dramatic cutback as industry responded to growing public concern about a possible threat to the Earth's protective ozone layer.

Adapted from information supplied by the Chemical Manufacturers Association

100

A system of massive concrete piers and steel gates (above and right) forms the main element in Holland's plan to protect its Eastern Scheldt estuary from flooding. The final design came only after considerable effort to preserve as much of the natural tidal region and its biology as possible.

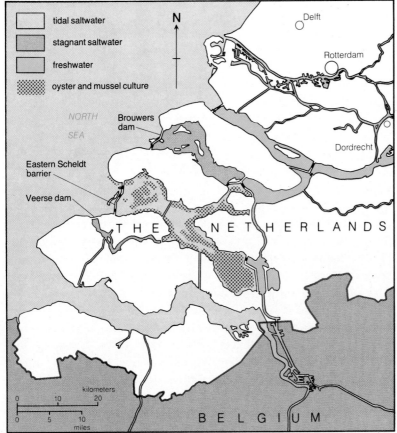

tidal saltwater

stagnant saltwater

freshwater

oyster and mussel culture

N

Delft

Rotterdam

NORTH
SEA

Brouwers
dam

Dordrecht

Eastern Scheldt
barrier

Veerse dam

THE   NETHERLANDS

kilometers
0   10   20

0   5   10
miles

B E L G I U M

N

NORTH SEA

Denmark

England

Amsterdam

The
Netherlands

ENGLISH CHANNEL

Belgium

West
Germany

Luxembourg

France

Adapted from information supplied by the Dutch Ministry of Transport and Public Works

Scientists believe that a major reason for the increase in atmospheric carbon dioxide has been a rise in the burning of fossil fuel since the Industrial Revolution. The foundries of that era demanded the extraction of ever more coal and oil to make steel, which in turn was fashioned into machines that needed still more fossil fuel to power them.

waters are unusually clear. Such an environment encourages species that normally are found only much farther south.

The example of the Eastern Scheldt barrier shows that people can act together to ensure that, while mankind's interests are served by great new projects, the other inhabitants of planet Earth are not ignored entirely. The Dutch project is a national one, not something that is as likely to affect the world's environment even as much as the Soviet river diversions. But it is important because, like the response to the perceived threat to the ozone layer, it offers hope that people can act in time to tackle much bigger issues. Among the most important of these are the twin problems of deforestation and the buildup of atmospheric carbon dioxide.

Some truly big concerns

Just as concern about the "threat to the ozone layer" was the most publicized global environmental issue of the 1970s, so the "carbon dioxide greenhouse effect" seems set to become an issue for the 1980s. For the past several years individual climatologists have been warning that increasing carbon dioxide in the atmosphere will change the climate, acting like a blanket around the Earth and warming the globe. Scientists believe that a major reason for the buildup has been a rise since the Industrial Revolution in the burning of fossil fuel—coal and oil—which puts carbon dioxide into the atmosphere. But until as recently as the 1950s the dominant human source was not burning fossil fuel but cutting down trees to make way for agriculture. Like coal and oil, trees store carbon (in the form of wood), and when they burn or decay the carbon enters the atmosphere as carbon dioxide. In addition, the great tropical forests act as the lungs of the world, taking in carbon dioxide, laying

102

the carbon down as new wood, and releasing oxygen to the atmosphere.

Carbon dioxide is seen as crucially important to climate because, although present only in trace quantities in the atmosphere, it is a very efficient blanket. Outgoing infrared radiation from the Earth's surface (itself warmed by sunlight) is trapped by carbon dioxide and bounced back to the lower atmosphere, making it warmer than it would otherwise be. Estimates vary slightly, but the best evidence is that before about 1850 the concentration of carbon dioxide in the atmosphere was about 270 parts per million, perhaps a little more. By 1980 the figure had passed 335 parts per million and appeared to be increasing by one or two parts per million each year. Many experts believe that doubling the "natural" level of carbon dioxide in the atmosphere will cause a global warming of about 2° C (3.6° F), accompanied by significant changes in weather and sea levels around the world. And this could happen in the early part of the 21st century. (*See* Feature Article: THE PROBLEM WITH CARBON DIOXIDE).

Deforestation is a key issue in the carbon dioxide "problem," because cutting down and burning trees contributes to the buildup of carbon dioxide, even if not on the same scale as burning coal. But the complexities of these environmental issues can be seen by looking at the other side of the coin. Deforestation can also have direct effects on climate, both locally and globally, and these changes may very well be to cool the Earth by increasing its surface reflectivity, or albedo. Climatologist Stephen Schneider of the National Center for Atmospheric Research in Boulder, Colorado, has addressed this problem, paying particular attention to the rapid deforestation now going on in the Amazon basin. As forest is destroyed to make way for farmland and roads, quite apart from the upheaval in the lives of native Amazon Indians, the face of the Earth itself is changing significantly.

Deforestation replaces dark forest with the lighter colors of farmland and urban development. In addition, the rate at which water is evaporated and transpired from the region changes; surface water runoff increases, which increases erosion, and "evapotranspiration" decreases, which may result in lower rainfall nearby. Reginald Newell of the Massachusetts Institute of Technology has considered how these changes may affect the whole circulation of the atmosphere. This weather machine is driven by the effects on water transport of solar heat in the tropics, and evapotranspiration is a key piece of that machinery. With less evapotranspiration and higher albedo, the tropics probably would cool and at the same time heat would be less efficiently transferred to higher latitudes, which would cool even more. Just what the effects will be, however, is not certain. Worse still, the process of deforestation may be irreversible on any reasonable human time scale. Tropical forests do not regenerate in the same way as temperate forests if they are left alone. Erosion caused by increased runoff quickly leaches nutrients and soil itself away from the region, making the jungles literally an irreplaceable asset.

Here is a clear case for the need for caution and in which a few less developed nations, in their eagerness to follow the industrialized countries, may be damaging not just their own environment but that of the whole world. It is unreasonable to suggest that the effects of deforestation and the

The cutting and burning of large regions of the world's tropical forests for wood and new farmland also contribute to the buildup of carbon dioxide in the atmosphere. In addition, deforestation has other effects—both local and global—such as raising the land's reflectivity, or albedo, and changing the rate at which rainfall returns to the atmosphere. These alterations may act to cool the tropics, but the actual outcome can only be guessed at. On a human time scale the denuding of the tropics may be irreversible because tropical forests do not regenerate in the same way as temperate ones.

"greenhouse effect" will cancel each other out. A more plausible view is that with some controls set at "hot" and others at "cold" the weather machine will veer from one extreme to the other. Is it a coincidence that such behavior is just what has been seen in recent years—a run of "freak" seasons, swinging from drought to flood to freeze and back?

Given the political realities of the world, it is unfortunate that so many of these issues concern the "misguided" activities of the less developed nations. In fact the industrialized world made the same kinds of mistakes a hundred years earlier, and it is quite possible that climatic changes in the 20th century have been influenced, for example, by the wholesale deforestation of the northern temperate regions. Those inadvertent changes created a new global balance, one now threatened by the activities of the third world. The detrimental effects of major projects, however, need not be global in order to be significant and perhaps to outweigh the benefits.

The high price of development

The famous Aswan High Dam in Egypt provides an intriguing case study. Hailed on its completion in 1970 as one of the wonders of the age, the $3.6-billion project does indeed provide a hydroelectric output of ten billion kilowatt-hours a year, brings 550,000 hectares of land under irrigation, and ensures two crops of rice a year in upper Egypt. But on the other side of the balance weighs the displacement of 100,000 Egyptian Nubians from the lands flooded by Lake Nasser behind the dam; increased siltation in the lower Nile because of the reduced flow of the river; an increase in the snail-borne parasitic disease schistosomiasis (linked with more sluggish river flow); and loss of fertility in the soils of the delta region, which no longer receive the benefit of rich silt brought down by floods; increased coastal erosion; and reduction in yields from offshore fisheries caused by the reduced flow of nutrients to the sea. Today no one can say whether Egypt is in fact better off thanks to the dam; all that is certain is that conditions there have changed.

104

For a poor nation in the throes of industrial development, the costs of misplaced faith in technological miracles can be crippling. In 1982 the Centre for Science and Environment in New Delhi reported that, over India as a whole, installed hydroelectric generating capacity rose twelvefold between 1954 and 1979 to nearly 40 billion kilowatt-hours, with irrigation increasing comparably to cover 26.6 million hectares. But according to the report, "the expected benefits, in terms of electricity, irrigation and flood control, have fallen short of the planned targets. If we include the costs of environmental degradation such as deforestation, the price we have paid for these modern 'temples' becomes truly staggering." Two case studies from India highlight the problems.

People uprooted by large hydroelectric projects in India have been made refugees in their own land. Rehabilitation programs exist but are generally inadequate in that displaced populations are not treated as living communities but a collection of unrelated individuals. In one project, the Kali Dam in Karnataka, several thousand families face eviction from their traditional lands. Although for every hectare submerged they will be given another hectare of land, because all the good farmland is already under cultivation, what they get as replacement for irrigated lowland farmland is unirrigated hilly land. Dams also can bring increased incidence of some diseases in their wake. The presence of large reservoirs raises the subsoil water level in the vicinity, increasing the concentrations of trace minerals in the drinking water. This may increase the incidence of such diseases as fluorosis, a crippling bone disorder that results from severe chronic exposure to dissolved fluorides. At the same time, irrigation reservoirs are generally surrounded by large areas of weed-infested shallows, which provide a breeding ground for malaria-carrying mosquitoes. V. Ramalingaswami, director general of the Indian Council of Medical Research, has said that "the Raichur district of Karnataka State has become highly endemic for malaria after . . . damming and canal network development."

There are still deeper seated causes for concern. Recently the residents of the Himalayan town of Tehri realized that a project intended to improve their lot might lead to disaster. The project is the Tehri Dam in Uttar Pradesh, a structure planned to stand 260 meters high (the fifth largest rock-fill dam in the world), generate 200 megawatts of hydroelectric power, and irrigate 668,000 hectares of land. But the region is seismically active, and earth scientists have suggested that such a large dam located in such a sensitive area could trigger earthquake activity.

The Himalayas form the youngest mountain chain in the world, still growing and geologically active as the Indian subcontinent is jammed northward into the Asian continental mass by the forces of plate tectonics. The rocks of the mountain gorges that will be flooded by the project are crisscrossed by fractures and fissures produced by this activity. These openings could allow excessive seepage of water that could undermine and weaken the dam structure, causing a collapse much like the failure of the newly completed Teton Dam in Idaho in June 1976, which killed more than a dozen people and flooded 78,000 hectares of land. Indeed, a concrete dam was ruled out early in the planning of the Tehri project precisely because of the

Projects of strictly local effect may also exact a high cost for their benefits. Measured against its hydroelectric output and the ensuing agricultural boom, Egypt's Aswan High Dam is a resounding success. But weighing in the balance are such consequences as the proliferation of regions of sluggish water flow, which appear to encourage the spread of waterborne diseases.

earthquake risk. But according to experts, even if a rock-fill dam is less susceptible to damage by earthquakes, the weight of three billion tons of pent-up water behind it could trigger seismic activity in the region.

Hope for the future

Whether local or global, all of the issues discussed above are complex, but in each case there are some reasons for optimism. No individual farmer or government plans to destroy the world's forests, yet if the piecemeal destruction continues at present rates there could be no tropical rain forest left by

106

Idaho's Teton Dam, an embankment-type structure that collapsed in June 1976, was built against the advice of experts who expressed fears about the porous, fissured nature of the rocks of the canyon that was to hold the impounded lake. The geologic conditions of India's planned Tehri Dam are in some ways similar to the Teton site, and concern has been voiced that water seepage, if not actually triggering seismic activity in the region, may undermine and weaken the dam structure.

the year 2000, with irreversible consequences for world climate patterns. No government or government official plans for an increase in malaria or earthquake activity when giving the green light to a dam project, yet those risks are always present in some parts of the world. If informed public debate can lead to such impressive action to counter a perceived threat to the ozone layer, then perhaps similarly informed debate will set the scene for action to counter the predicted greenhouse effect. If the Dutch can come to terms with the environment while still benefiting people, perhaps the Indians, the Egyptians, the Brazilians, and the Soviets can learn from their example. As human activities begin increasingly to have regional and global effects on the world's environmental systems and as long as those effects cannot be completely seen in advance, then the watchword of everyone involved in such activities and their planning must indeed be "guilty until proven innocent."

FOR ADDITIONAL READING

Knut Aagaard and L. K. Coachman, "Toward an Ice-Free Arctic Ocean," *Eos* (July 1975, pp. 484–486).

Centre for Science and Environment, *State of India's Environment—1982,* distributed by CSE, 807 Vishal Bhawan, 95 Nehru Place, New Delhi 110019, India ($25 incl. air postage).

Lydia Dotto and Harold Schiff, *The Ozone War* (Doubleday, 1978).

Christopher Freeman and Marie Jahoda (eds.), *World Futures: The Great Debate* (Universe, 1978).

John Gribbin, *Future Worlds* (Plenum, 1981).

John Gribbin, *Future Weather and the Greenhouse Effect* (Delacorte, 1982).

Walter Roberts and Henry Lansford, *The Climate Mandate* (W. H. Freeman, 1979).

Stephen Schneider, *The Genesis Strategy* (Plenum, 1976).

WHEN THE RAINS DON'T COME

by Norman J. Rosenberg

Periodic widespread droughts in the U.S. have caused great distress. Efforts are now under way to alleviate the impact of these climatic disasters.

Of the many troubles that weather imposes on humans, drought has probably had the greatest overall impact. The oral and written traditions of most of the world's cultures describe periods when the failure of the rains seriously disrupted life. Joseph in Egypt's prophecy of seven fat years followed by seven lean years may, simply, have been good climatology. Weather varies from year to year, some being wet and some dry.

There are few places in the world where droughts are unknown. One such place is the Sahara desert in North Africa. Where there is essentially no rain and no systems of farming or grazing that depend upon it, there can be no drought. Drought occurs when the expected rains fail to arrive. In Great Britain and Western Europe, for example, an agriculture based on normally ample rainfall and even adjusted to excessive amounts was severely stressed when precipitation was less than 50% of normal during the summer of 1977.

"Drought Stricken Area" (1934) by Alexandre Hogue (American, b. 1898); Dallas Museum of Fine Arts, Dallas Art Association Purchase, photograph by David Wharton

How then should "drought" be defined? There are scores of definitions, which vary in complexity from "lack of rain" to mathematical formulations that consider deviations from normal rainfall, the amount of moisture stored in the soil before the rains became deficient, and the rate at which crops extract moisture from the soil. The hydroelectric industry defines drought in terms that can be translated into kilowatts of power lost. Ski resorts view drought in terms of a poor snowpack and a loss in revenue. For the purposes of this discussion a useful definition of drought is a climatic excursion involving a shortage of precipitation sufficient to affect adversely crop production or range productivity.

While a prolonged or serious shortage of rainfall affects all sectors of society and all human activities, the chain of impacts begins with a reduction of food and feed production. When crop production drops, food prices rise. The farmers directly affected by drought are not those who benefit from increased prices, since they have little to sell. The rate at which such farmers repay loans is slowed, their purchase of new farm machinery is deferred, and fewer items of clothing and other consumable goods are purchased. Thus bankers, implement dealers, and local shops feel the impacts of drought soon after the farmer does.

As the economy of the affected agricultural region weakens, government services dependent upon local taxes also diminish. Taxes going from the affected region into state and federal treasuries also decline, while the demand upon those governments to mitigate the damage done by drought is increased.

Perhaps the most dramatic impact of prolonged drought has been the forced migration of large numbers of people. The last important migration in the United States caused or stimulated by drought occurred in the 1930s. In western, central, and eastern Africa migrations due to drought became serious in the 1970s and continued into the 1980s.

Evidence of drought in North America

Droughts have been a recurrent feature of the climate of North America for as far back, at least, as human beings have inhabited the continent. Evidence for this statement comes from anthropological research and from the science of dendrochronology (the study of tree rings). Regular instrumental observations of weather go back only a little more than a century on this continent, but these records encompass a number of serious droughts.

Jaime Sancho y Cervera, an engineer with the National Water Plan Commission of Mexico, reconstructed a chronology of drought beginning in pre-Columbian times. In the year AD 1400 in the Valley of Mexico (region of modern-day Mexico City) one chronicle tells:

> This year fire rained, that is, there was so much sun that it seemed to rain fire and because of it the tallest *ahuehuetes* [a type of pine] uprooted and the thickest of them dried up.

The Mexican account states that in those years when it "rained fire" the corn harvests were lost, the level of the lake lowered, the floating gardens were grounded, and the crops and harvests reduced. Two or more such years

NORMAN J. ROSENBERG is George Holmes Professor of Agricultural Meteorology and Director of the Center for Agricultural Meteorology and Climatology at the University of Nebraska, Lincoln.

110

meant that there was no seed to be sown; family and state granaries were depleted, and famines followed. In such years authorities of the settlements in the Valley of Mexico prohibited, under penalty of death, the export of corn. Instead, corn was carried in on the shoulders of men from surrounding regions. Inhabitants "... pulled out the roots of the *tulares* (swamp vegetation) for food and caught fish, frogs and shrimps from the big lagoon."

Sancho y Cervera also reported 50 documented cases of drought in the Valley of Mexico in the 300-year period from 1521 to 1821. Seven droughts lasted for two consecutive years, and two lasted for three years. From other records it has been learned that many of these droughts were also occurring simultaneously in the Bajio area north and west of Mexico City.

These Mexican reconstructions are based on documents of ecclesiastical tithes which contained reports on the volume of production. Books on corn prices, municipal acts, and chronicles also served to enrich the evidence. It is even possible from these colonial-period records to determine whether the timing of the droughts affected the seeding, germination, or maturation of the corn plant. Evidence suggests that droughts coinciding with either frosts or hail led to some of the worst agricultural catastrophes of the colonial era (1695, 1785, 1808, 1809).

Mexican records for the period 1821 to 1874 are of spotty quality but are more reliable for the period 1875 to 1910. They show that severe droughts occurred in 1822–23 and 1834–35 in Yucatan and in 1854 in Queretaro. In 1868 an extensive region of Mexico was affected. Additional severe droughts occurred in 1872, 1875, 1884–85, 1891–92, 1896, 1901, and 1908. According to Sancho y Cervera the most severe droughts produced "... the familiar sequence of scarcity and high cost of basic foods, famine, migrations, halts in activities, unemployment, riots in the cities, epidemics and deaths among the poorest sectors of the urban and rural population."

Press accounts are the primary source of information on Mexican droughts in the period 1910–77. Thirty-eight were identified. Consecutive drought years occurred in 1917–28, 1932–35, 1937–39, 1949–51, 1969–72, and 1975–77. Years of particularly severe episodes were 1930, 1935, 1953, 1957, 1960, 1962, 1969, and 1977.

These data suggest an increased frequency of drought in Mexico in the 20th century. It is not certain, however, as to whether this is due to a climatic change, a change in land use that exacerbates the impacts of rainfall shortage, or to improved reporting.

The drought history of Mexico has been emphasized because it provides the longest and most complete record in North America. But there is also good evidence that the land area now occupied by the United States has suffered frequent drought. Much of the evidence is based on chronologies of tree rings that extend as far back as AD 500. Many of these observations were made by Andrew E. Douglass, founder of the Laboratory of Tree-Ring Research at the University of Arizona, and by his successors. In the 1930s Douglass reported analyses of ponderosa pine tree rings which indicated that the Pueblo region of the American Southwest had experienced a catastrophic drought from 1276 to 1299 and another, less severe, one from 1573 to 1593. He identified several others back to about AD 800.

Tree rings provide evidence of climatic conditions in the past. During dry years the widths of the rings decrease.

Harold Fritts at the tree ring laboratory constructed another chronology, which revealed that widespread droughts occurred in the periods 1576–90, 1625–35, 1776–85, 1841–50, 1871–80, and 1931–40. Specimens of red cedar and ponderosa pine found in the Sandhills region of Nebraska were studied by Harry Weakly of the University of Nebraska. In the time span extending back to about AD 1220, he found many short periods of drought, less frequent periods lasting for more than five years, and one such period that lasted 38 years.

David M. Ludlam assembled information on historical droughts in the United States. The first according to his research took place in 1621, when the Pilgrims' first crops were threatened by dry weather. Again in 1623 dry conditions endangered the corn crop. Fields of grain in New England were so dry during 1749, 1761, and 1762 that they caught fire. There were reports of very dry conditions in the eastern states in 1805 and 1822. Rainfall in California was one-third the normal amount in 1850–51. Crops failed for lack of rain from New York state to Missouri in 1854 and in Kansas, Missouri, Iowa, Minnesota, Wisconsin, and Illinois in 1860. A major cattle industry that had been developed in California ended with drought that occurred during the period 1862–64.

In the consciousness of most people in the U.S., the Great Plains region is the one most often associated with drought. Early explorers crossing the Great Plains from the humid east were struck by the dryness of the region. Zebulon Pike, who crossed the southern plains in 1806, described the midcontinent in these emphatic words: "... in time it may become as celebrated as the sandy desert of Africa." Stephen Long in 1822 described what we now call the Great Plains as "almost wholly unfit for cultivation and, of course, uninhabitable by a people depending on agriculture for subsistence." In view of the fact that today the Great Plains is a major breadbasket of the nation, some have suggested that Pike and Long probably passed through the region during periods of drought. University of Texas historian William Goetzmann considers that Pike and Long were reasonable in their views. With the technology then available settlement of the Great Plains region would indeed have been extremely difficult.

University of Nebraska geographer Merlin Lawson studied the Great Plains at a later time when he reconstructed the weather of April to July 1849 from diaries of forty-niners crossing on the Oregon Trail to the goldfields of California. The spring began very wet and cold, and wagon trains were delayed at their starting points waiting for the grass to sustain their animals. The spring continued to be wet, and it was only in mid-July that dust storms were noted as far east as North Platte (now in Nebraska): "... as the argonaut continued west, the roads that had been heavy because of rain now became clogged with sand." While the forty-niners "waded to California in the first months of their journey across the plain—the appearance of the desert was not spared them."

By the 1870s extensive settlement had taken place in the Great Plains. The fear of drought was somewhat allayed by a series of good years. Except for two years in the middle of that decade rainfall was abundant. Science was invoked to explain the good growing conditions. Samuel Aughey, a professor

112

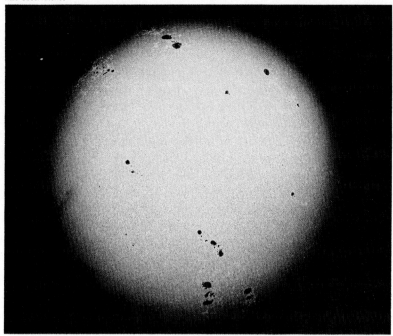

at the University of Nebraska, developed a theory that came to be known as "rainfall follows the plow."

It is the great increase in absorptive power of the soil, wrought by cultivation, that has caused and continues to cause an increasing rainfall in the state. After the soil is broken, a rain as it falls is absorbed by the soil like a huge sponge. The soil gives this absorbed moisture slowly back to the atmosphere by evaporation. Thus year by year as cultivation of the soil is extended, more of the rain that falls is absorbed and retained to be given off by evaporation, or to produce springs. This, of course, must give increasing moisture and rainfall.

Aughey's theory notwithstanding, drought revisited the Great Plains region in the late 1880s and early 1890s. From 1888 to 1892 fully half the settlers of Kansas and Nebraska left the region. The drought became yet more severe in 1893–95. Although these events laid Aughey's theory to rest, it is interesting to note that at the present time there is widespread speculation that irrigation is moderating the climate and increasing precipitation in the Great Plains region.

Serious but short-lived droughts occurred throughout the mid-continent in the years 1910, 1911, and 1913. It was not until the 1930s that the most severe and widespread drought of historic times occurred—from the West Coast to the Ohio River valley and from Mexico to Canada. In the 1950s there was a major drought in the central and southwest United States. It was most severe in the southern plains and southwestern states. The worst drought in the humid northeastern region of the continent took place during 1961–66. Aside from its direct effects on agriculture this drought caused the densely populated region from northeastern Canada to Washington, D.C., to experience severe shortages of water needed for industrial, municipal, and residential purposes. The most recent drought of regional scale occurred

Solar activity, revealed by the appearance of sunspots, may have an effect on rainfall. Cycles of activity from minimum to maximum last about 11 years, and scientists have found that droughts in the western United States have been most severe approximately two years after sunspot activity has been at its minimum.

113

during 1976 and 1977. Most of the U.S. from Illinois and Michigan west to California and Washington state was affected.

Western Canada is also prone to drought. In his journal Alexander Henry, a fur trader with the Northwest Co., mentions a scorched potato crop in the Red River settlement in 1805. Records of the Selkirk settlement in areas near present-day Winnipeg, Manitoba, indicate that severe droughts occurred in 1820 and in 1868. At the end of a nine-year dry period in the 1890s, many farms were abandoned in the Canadian prairies.

The drought of the 1930s led to severe soil erosion in the Canadian prairies. On both sides of the U.S.-Canadian border wildlife was reduced in numbers, and grasshopper outbreaks and forest and grass fires were observed.

Again in 1976–77 drought knew no national boundaries. For eight months from September 1976 to April 1977 precipitation was less than 50% of normal from northwestern Ontario extending west to eastern Alberta and parts of southeastern British Columbia. For most stations in the core area of the drought (Manitoba, Saskatchewan, and Alberta) that period was the driest in a weather record that had, depending on location, been accumulating for 69 to 98 years. As mentioned above, adjacent portions of the U.S. were also affected.

Causes and predictability

As the foregoing historical review has shown, drought is a recurrent feature of the North American climate. Severe and prolonged droughts occur on the continent when large-scale anomalies occur in the atmospheric circulation. High-pressure ridges create "blocking patterns" by remaining stationary and steering rain-carrying storms into directions that are not the usual ones. Meteorologists do not yet know the causes of these large-scale anomalies, and at this writing it is premature to suggest that the skills needed to predict them exist.

As evidenced by the appearance of sunspots, solar activity is roughly cyclical and thus, through its possible effects on the Earth's atmospheric circulation, has been considered a possible cause of drought. Normally a cycle from minimum to maximum activity lasts roughly 11 years, and a complete or Hale cycle lasts roughly 22 years. Periodicity in drought has been difficult to demonstrate, however, because of the relatively short duration of the meteorological data base. For this reason other types of records, such as those to be found in tree rings, have been used.

Using tree rings, J. Murray Mitchell of the National Atmospheric and Oceanic Administration and Charles Stockton and David Meko of the University of Arizona's Laboratory of Tree-Ring Research reconstructed an index of drought severity covering 260 years. Large-scale droughts, they found, recur at roughly 22-year intervals in the western United States. Droughts are at their worst approximately two years after sunspot activity has been at its minimum.

The evidence of a direct link between drought and solar activity remains too meager to serve as a basis for predicting, decades in advance, the onset of future droughts. There is also no evidence that the apparent 22-year cycle

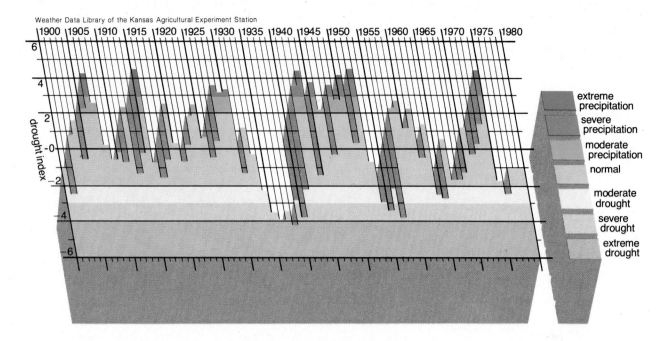

Weather Data Library of the Kansas Agricultural Experiment Station

found in western North America occurs in other drought-prone regions of the world. A weak 11-year cycle is evident in rainfall data from Dakar, Senegal, but so also are 2.2-year and 3.0-year cycles. In data from Central Park in New York City there is some evidence of cycles of 3, 8, 13, and 40 years in an index of drought severity. In analyses from other parts of the world (Madras, India and Fortaleza, Brazil) precipitation cycles of 2–3 years in length and 11.7–13.5 years were detected.

Drought severity

Many mathematical and statistical formulas have been proposed for classifying drought severity on the basis of shortages of precipitation. Droughts begin when rainfall is insufficient for crop growth, but when the soil contains sufficient moisture to support the crops the impact of the dry weather is delayed until after much of that moisture is gone. Wayne Palmer, a grain farmer turned climatologist, devised an index that has come to be widely used for describing drought as well as periods of abnormally wet weather. The Palmer Drought Severity Index (PDSI) treats the soil storage capacity for water as a bank; precipitation is the deposit made into the bank, and evapotranspiration (direct evaporation at the soil surface and transpiration of water by plants) is the withdrawal. When soils are depleted after extended periods of extreme dryness, a value of −6 is assigned regardless of the normal aridity of the region. Conversely, after periods of extreme wetness a value of +6 is assigned.

The PDSI has proved useful as a means of describing the changing extent of drought and its severity. For example, in western Kansas the range of the PDSI from 1900 to 1977 indicates, as is typical for subhumid and semiarid regions, a frequent oscillation between conditions that are too wet and too dry. The index also reveals the unusual severity and duration of drought in the 1930s and 1950s in southwestern Kansas.

The Palmer Drought Severity Index describes periods of dry and wet weather. It is based on the concept of the soil storage capacity for water as a bank, with precipitation as the deposits and evapotranspiration as the withdrawals. When soils are depleted of moisture after long periods of extreme dryness, a value of −6 is assigned regardless of the normal aridity of the area. After extreme wetness +6 is assigned. The above data reflect values for southwestern Kansas.

115

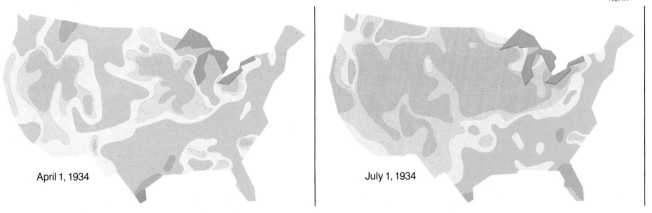

April 1, 1934

July 1, 1934

Palmer Index reveals the severity and extent of the drought in the United States at various times in 1934.

One of the worst years of the 1930s drought was 1934. The PDSI has been calculated for three periods during that year. In the spring after two previously dry years in the upper Middle West, the Southwest and mountain states were experiencing severe moisture shortages. By July 1 virtually all of the United States and parts of Mexico and Canada as well were in severe drought. The drought was most extreme in Illinois and Wisconsin and in portions of the intermountain West. By Oct. 1, 1934, the drought had been alleviated in much of the Middle West, but it had intensified greatly in the upper Great Plains and intermountain West.

The drought of the 1930s coincided with the most severe economic depression of the 20th century, a depression worldwide in extent. After a number of consecutive drought years many farmers were forced to sell out and abandon their land. The images of migration from the Great Plains were captured in the dramatic photographs of Arthur Rothstein and others, in the paintings of Alexandre Hogue, in the songs of Woody Guthrie, and in such novels as John Steinbeck's *The Grapes of Wrath.*

Serious dust storms due to accelerated soil erosion by winds began in the early 1930s. Some attributed these storms to overuse of the land, particularly at the western edge of the Great Plains where annual rainfall is normally only 12–14 inches. Land better suited to grazing had been broken by the plow and intensively cultivated for wheat production. High wheat prices during World War I had strongly motivated farmers to convert this land to grain production.

In response to the deepening drought, soil conservation activities were intensified; a Shelterbelt Project (officially, the Prairie States Forestry Project) was initiated. The intent of this program was to plant tree windbreaks in regular patterns throughout the Great Plains in order to suppress wind erosion. It was thought possible by some that the trees might moderate the climate of the region as well.

Much was learned from the drought of the 1930s. The need for proper management of the soil and water resources, especially in the Great Plains, was a primary lesson. One report from that era stands out, *The Future of the Great Plains*, published in 1936 by the presidentially appointed Great Plains Committee. The committee recommended actions to develop "a type of economy that will withstand the shocks of recurrent periods of severe and

116

extreme precipitation

severe precipitation

moderate precipitation

normal

moderate drought

severe drought

extreme drought

October 1, 1934

prolonged drought." The federal government was urged to conduct necessary investigations and surveys, to acquire land in range areas and to control the use of such land, to introduce measures to increase the size of farms so as to make them more viable economically, to develop water resources, to resettle persons displaced by the drought, to provide compensation to local governments on account of federal land acquisition, to control destructive insect pests, and to develop alternative generators of income for the region. The physical and economic tactics introduced in the 1930s may have had the effect of lessening the impact of later droughts.

In the mid-1950s another major drought occurred in North America. By April 1956 much of the northwest, southwest, and Middle West were experiencing moderate to severe conditions. A band from southern New England into the Ohio River valley was affected, as was the entire state of Florida. By July the drought had broken in the western states; in fact, water was in excess. But conditions had become considerably more severe in the southwest, in much of Great Plains region, and in Florida. The growing season of 1956 passed with little relief in the southwest, mountain, and Great Plains states. Though the area affected by drought was smaller in 1956 than in 1934, in the southwest the drought was more severe than it had been in the 1930s. In west Texas ten consecutive years of drought were experienced, while in Nebraska only 1955 and 1956 were notably dry.

In general, the impact of the drought of the 1950s was less than that of the 1930s. Martyn Bowden and Richard Warrick at Clark University's Center for Technology, Environment, and Development in Massachusetts compared impacts by reference to a number of indicators of stress—wheat yields, population declines, farm transfers, and relief payments. Wheat yields for each major drought were compared with those in the preceding and succeeding good years. The average decline was 35% in the 1930s; in the 1950s drought it was only 10%. However, when the duration and extent of the drought are considered by dividing the yield reduction by the months that all reporting divisions experienced drought, the percentage reductions are nearly identical.

In previous droughts, especially before the 1930s, shortages of food had led to famines and illness on the Great Plains. But during the 1950s, according to the Clark University researchers, there was little impact on health.

117

The severe drought of the 1930s brought great economic hardship to farmers. The dry topsoil eroded and blew away in clouds of dust as in South Dakota (opposite page, top), western Kansas (top), and the Texas panhandle (center). Many farmers were forced to give up their land and migrate under conditions of considerable stress to other parts of the United States (bottom and opposite page, bottom).

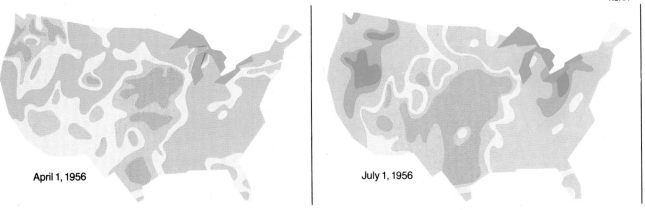

April 1, 1956

July 1, 1956

The extent and severity of the drought of the mid-1950s is revealed by Palmer Index measurements taken at three different dates in 1956.

Records indicate that nearly 300,000 people left the Great Plains during the drought of the 1890s, although conditions then were far less severe than during the 1930s. In the 1910s population displacement was also not small when scattered incidents of drought in the western Dakotas and southern plains caused losses of as much as 25–50% of the population. An extensive outflux of settlers occurred in eastern Montana as well. In the 1950s, however, depopulation was not significant.

Other evidence of the declining impact of drought is drawn from the records of farm transfers. At the peak of the 1930s drought-plus-depression one farm in ten changed hands. Fully half of the transfers were involuntary and came about as the result of forced sales and related defaults. Involuntary transfers were almost insignificant after 1945, even during the droughts of the 1950s and 1970s.

A major outcome of the 1950s drought was the creation in 1956 of the Great Plains Conservation Program, administered by the U.S. Soil Conservation Service. The major aim of the program was to encourage a form of land use that recognized both the region's capabilities and its limitations.

The drought of the 1970s first appeared in the southwestern U.S. in 1974. By August of that year half the western states were affected. In the Middle West the drought had begun with a hot and windy growing season in 1976. In Nebraska, for example, rates of water use by irrigated crops were 30–40% greater than normal. Yields of unirrigated corn during 1976 were severely reduced because of extreme heat and dryness during the critical reproductive stage when the silks appear and pollen is released. The winter of 1976–77 was unusually dry and warm so that by spring a wheat crop disaster was fully expected. The drought in the Middle West was actually most severe in Wisconsin and Minnesota, although the eastern Great Plains was also seriously affected.

The situation was dramatized when, in late February 1977, dust storms began to occur in the western Plains. Two such storms could be seen in a Geostationary Operational Environmental Satellite picture of North America taken in February 1977. Separate storms were seen originating in eastern Colorado and the Panhandle region of Texas. Thus, the great dust storms that characterized the drought years of the 1930s were still a feature of the Great Plains during other droughts.

120

	extreme precipitation
	severe precipitation
	moderate precipitation
	normal
	moderate drought
	severe drought
	extreme drought

October 1, 1956

By mid-August 1977 the drought was broken in the southern and central Great Plains. Moisture was, in fact, excessive in central Nebraska. The drought continued unabated in parts of the Southeast, in the upper Middle West and northern plains, and in the mountain and far western states. In the Far West two winter seasons with little rainfall had already passed. Since winter is the "rainy season" on the west coast, that region had no prospect of relief for some months to come. Serious shortages of water for municipal-

Farmer in Colorado uses two plowing techniques in an effort to protect his soil from erosion during droughts in the 1950s. They are: "listing," the plowing of trenchlike furrows to counteract the wind, and "contouring," plowing furrows at right angles to slopes in order to hold any rain.

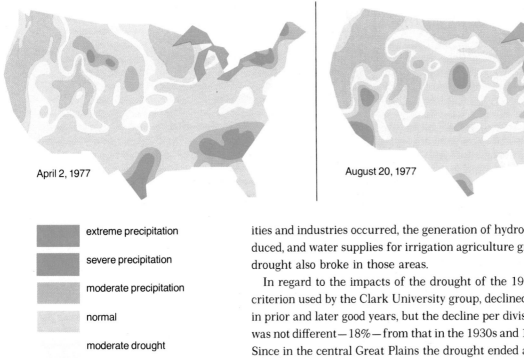

April 2, 1977

August 20, 1977

extreme precipitation

severe precipitation

moderate precipitation

normal

moderate drought

severe drought

extreme drought

Two Palmer Index measurements show the development of the drought in 1977.

ities and industries occurred, the generation of hydroelectric power was reduced, and water supplies for irrigation agriculture grew short. In 1978 the drought also broke in those areas.

In regard to the impacts of the drought of the 1970s, wheat yields, one criterion used by the Clark University group, declined only 10% from those in prior and later good years, but the decline per division-month of drought was not different—18%—from that in the 1930s and 1950s drought periods. Since in the central Great Plains the drought ended abruptly in the spring, the wheat that had survived the dry planting and dormancy periods was actually well supplied with water during the flowering and maturing stages. Thus the overall impact of the drought on wheat production was moderated.

The drought of the 1970s in the Great Plains was of short duration; no starvation or significant out-migration is known to have occurred. Because of the earlier onset of drought in the western states, governmental agencies were already engaged in modest mitigation efforts by the late winter and spring of 1977, when, from the national viewpoint, the drought became more severe.

Technological defenses

The overall upward trend in the yield of wheat since the turn of the century can be attributed to technology—the use of new plant varieties, chemical fertilizers, herbicides and pesticides, and more efficient machinery. The year-to-year variability in yields can be attributed to weather. It is clear that no amount of technology (except, perhaps, for irrigation) can protect crops from significant loss in yield when drought occurs. There are, however, many technologies that appear to be effective in partially mitigating the impacts of drought on crop production.

At the University of Nebraska studies of technological responses to drought have been under way for a number of years. The sought-for strategies should be consistent with the following goals: avoidance of food shortage, maintenance of soil resources, maximum sustained use of natural resources, maintenance of environmental quality, enhancement of the quality of life, and stimulation of a robust and efficient economy.

When a drought is actually in progress, there are a few practical tactics that can be employed. For example, rather than irrigate small acreages

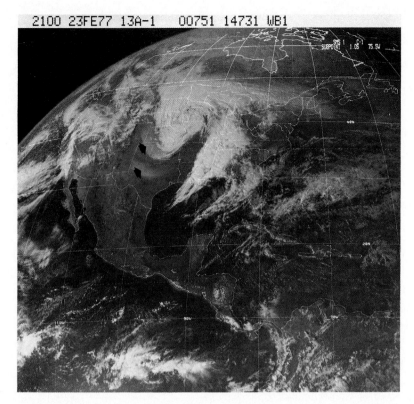

2100 23FE77 13A-1   00751 14731 WB1

Weather satellite photograph taken in February 1977 shows dust storms originating in eastern Colorado and the Panhandle region of Texas. The western end of the Texas storm coincides with an abrupt change in agricultural practice, with rangeland predominant on the New Mexico side of the border and cropland on the Texas side. The heavier white markings are clouds.

intensively throughout the season, irrigators can apply the available water to larger areas at critical stages of growth. Also, populations of crops growing in the field can be reduced to minimize competition of the plants for limited soil water supplies. Fertilizers can be withheld, because when soil moisture is short additional fertilizer actually increases the stress on plants. If conditions are unusually dry before planting, drought-hardy species can be chosen; for example, sorghum withstands drought better than does corn. Since the soybean has a long reproductive period, good yields can be achieved with this crop even after very severe dry spells if water becomes available later in the season.

While the tactics available during a drought are limited in number, there are several long-term measures that have merit. The strategy in these procedures is to increase the supply of water for crop growth or to decrease demand by the crop itself.

Water harvesting is the capture of runoff water, which then is spread over depressed areas in fields or the flood plains of streams. The practice has ancient roots. Water harvesting provided the basis for all food production in ancient settlements in Israel's Negev desert. In North America water spreading has been limited mostly to a few high-value crops grown in the southern Plains region, but the potential exists for greater use. One method of harvesting involves placing small watersheds within fields. These can, however, cause severe flooding of planted areas when precipitation is heavy, and so except in very arid regions this technique may be of limited use.

Methods have been developed to reduce the number of tillage operations needed in crop production. Certain plowing, harrowing, and cultivation op-

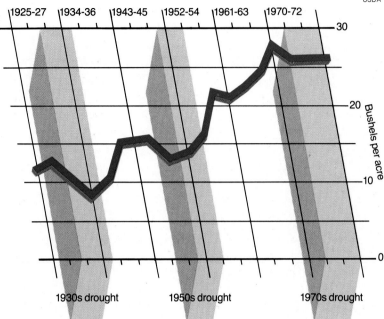

| 1925-27 | 1934-36 | 1943-45 | 1952-54 | 1961-63 | 1970-72 |

1930s drought   1950s drought   1970s drought

Wheat yields in the Great Plains region of the United States from 1925 to 1977 declined during the droughts.

erations can be eliminated for many crops—particularly when chemical herbicides are effective in weed control. About 20% of U.S. crop production took place on minimum or no-tilled land in 1979. Much greater use of this practice is predicted for the future. Some unsolved problems of minimum tillage include uneven seed germination, low soil temperature in spring, possible disease and insect outbreaks, and possible undesirable environmental effects due to reliance on chemical herbicides. Nonetheless, minimum-tillage methods have been shown to improve soil moisture conditions, minimize the loss of topsoil, and reduce the energy and labor costs in crop production.

In the Canadian prairie provinces, the northern Great Plains, and into Nebraska and Kansas a significant portion of the annual precipitation occurs in the form of snow. Unless controlled, snow either blows off or runs off over frozen ground as it thaws. Thus, it generally contributes little to the reservoir of soil moisture available to the crop in the spring. Snow can be controlled and eventually utilized, however, by reducing wind speed near the surface of the ground. This can be accomplished with constructed barriers, tree windbreaks, sown windbreaks, or the stubble of the previous crop.

Systems of reduced tillage that maintain crop residues, reduce evaporation and erosion, and control weeds are important factors in increasing stored soil moisture. Crop residues and other mulches on the soil surface reduce evaporation for one or more of the following reasons: a vapor barrier is created; soil temperature is lowered; and wind speed at the soil surface is diminished. Weed control by mechanical means depletes soil moisture by hastening evaporation from the moist soil exposed. Thus it is clear that reliable techniques of chemical weed control for moisture conservation are needed. Also, winter moisture is stored more efficiently than is summer rainfall so that in the northern plains windbreaks of perennial

124

grasses can be used to increase snow catch and soil moisture storage.

One way to face a problem may be to avoid it. Thus, thought is being given to introduction in semiarid regions of new crops that are less sensitive to moisture stress than those currently grown. Possible new food crops for use in dryland farming or with limited irrigation include pearl millet, amaranth, and guar. Specialty crops considered for introduction include guayule as a source of latex and forage sorghum for biomass conversion. Kochia and fourwing saltbush (*Atriplex canescens*) are potentially useful new plants for Great Plains rangeland.

Strong and damaging winds often reduce agricultural productivity. Cold winds in the spring and fall may cause mechanical damage to the whole plant as well as freezing damage to certain tissues. Winds blowing from arid into semiarid and subhumid regions can also cause mechanical damage. But these winds, because of their high temperature and low humidity, also impose severe moisture stress on the growing crops and cause wilting, desiccation, and the loss of potential productivity. In regions where the land is not well protected by vegetation, wind erosion may occur and initiate a decline in productivity. Young, tender vegetation may be damaged or destroyed by "sand blasting" when soil is eroded by wind.

Center-pivot sprinkling systems provide moisture for crops in areas of low rainfall. These irrigation systems have made land so valuable that farmers begrudge giving up any acreage to tree windbreaks, which had proved their usefulness in conserving soil moisture and preventing erosion.

Grant Heilman

Reducing the number of tillage operations in crop production improves soil moisture conditions and minimizes the loss of topsoil. Top, no-till seeding is taking place between barriers of tall wheatgrass. The barriers act as a windbreak and snowcatch. At the bottom is a close-up of winter wheat that has been no-till seeded in standing spring wheat stubble.

Properly designed windbreaks can aid greatly in stabilizing agriculture in regions where strong winds are common. A windbreak aids in distributing snow uniformly over the fields, thereby increasing the supply of soil moisture in spring. During the growing season windbreaks also have a considerable impact on the crops that they shelter.

Considerable experimentation with tree windbreaks and with windbreaks constructed of such materials as snow fencing, plastic screens, and reed mats has shown that the climate that prevails in a sheltered area is more moderate than that in adjacent unsheltered fields. The air is slightly warmer by day and slightly cooler by night, but absolute humidity is greater by day and by night. The overall effect on the microclimate is to moderate both evaporative demand and moisture stress on the sheltered plants. Since moisture stress leads to wilting, closing of the plant stomates, and cessation of photosynthetic activity, windbreaks permit the achievement of improved crop yields.

126

Corn stubble acts as a windbreak to prevent snow from blowing off the ground and thus allows the moisture in the snow to enter the soil and be used by spring crops.

The effect of shelter on crop growth is now fairly well understood. There is a great need for engineers, foresters, and agronomists to develop and/or adapt windbreak designs that will be most effective in each region. Tall growing annual crops such as corn, sorghum, or ryegrass can be planted in fields of shorter crops in order to provide shelter or to augment shelter provided by widely spaced tree windbreaks.

Despite the proved beneficial effects of windbreaks planted in the Great Plains during the drought years of the 1930s, many of them are now being removed. Changes in agricultural land use that involve larger fields and expensive irrigation systems have increased the value of the land to the point where farmers begrudge its occupation by tree windbreaks. Windbreaks may interfere with the mechanical operation of the large center-pivot sprinkler systems that are revolutionizing irrigation in the Plains. Thus, there is urgent need for windbreak designs that are compatible with current and foreseeable agricultural systems in such regions.

127

Scientists have increased the reflectivity of plants and thereby reduced their need for moisture by coating leaves with kaolinite (right) and breeding soybeans so that they have hairier leaves and stems (below).

Plant physiologists and agricultural meteorologists have speculated that by increasing the albedo (reflectivity) of plants the energy loaded upon them by solar radiation could be reduced, which should result in diminished transpiration. There is good experimental evidence that artificial coatings that increase plant and soil reflection of sunlight actually do reduce water use. Such materials as kaolinite (a clay) and Celite (a diatomaceous earth) have been used in controlled environment studies and also in the field with positive results.

There is one possible drawback in the use of reflectant materials—they

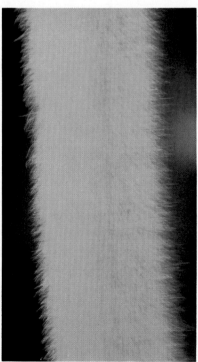

can diminish the amount of photosynthetically active radiation that is absorbed by the leaf. In experiments conducted with soybeans in Nebraska, no major decrease in photosynthesis was anticipated because, under field conditions, for most of the day the soybean has more light than its photosynthetic mechanism requires. Photosynthesis and yield were not reduced at all, apparently because the materials with which the plants were coated increased multiple reflection of light deep into the crop canopy where the plant is usually starved for light.

The application of reflectant materials may be impractical on a large scale. The practice may prove useful as an emergency technique in times of drought, especially where labor to apply the material is available. However, a different approach to increasing water use efficiency has developed.

Evidence indicates that increased reflection by a plant reduces its consumption of water. There are ways by which reflectance can be naturally modified. Reflectance varies from species to species and within species according to age of the leaf, turgidity, presence of waxes or other materials on the surface, and concentration of chlorophyll. Workers in Montana have bred barley plants that appear yellow because of their lower chlorophyll content. These plants reflect more sunlight than do the normal barley plants, and they also yield a bit less. But they require less water. In Nebraska soybeans were tested that had four times the normal number of hairs on the leaves and stems. These hairs increase the reflectance of sunlight, allowing the plants to use about 10% less water than do other soybeans. The hairs also tend to reflect more light into the lower parts of the canopy, and, perhaps for this reason, yields are as good as with the normal plants.

Future prospects

The drought of the 1930s led to the initiation of technological and economic tactics to stabilize the Great Plains in the face of any future occurrences. The subsequent droughts of the 1950s and 1970s caused much less disruption to the region than did that of the 1930s. There is reason to think that soil conservation and other technological, economic, and social measures have succeeded in strengthening drought-plagued regions. But no drought since the 1930s has been so severe or prolonged, and therefore the thesis of a "lessening" drought impact may not yet have been critically tested.

Modern technology is providing new tactics to help the farmer and the land withstand severe drought. Water harvesting, minimum tillage, snow management, evaporation reduction by means of weed suppression and wind shelter, and the use of drought-tolerant varieties and new drought-tolerant species of plants offer practical, attainable improvements. Altering physical characteristics of currently used species is one of the newest opportunities for "drought-proofing" agriculture.

While technology offers some hope that the impacts of drought on agricultural production may be lessened, it would be unrealistic to believe that complete immunity to the severe disruptions of drought can be achieved. Federal, state, and local governments must be aware of the available technological and economic strategies, and orderly ways must be sought to initiate programs when drought comes again, as it will.

THE PROBLEM WITH
CARBON DIOXIDE

by Roger Revelle

It is generally agreed that man's activities have increased the carbon dioxide content of the atmosphere. Scientists are now working to understand the possible consequences for Earth's climate and human society.

Remote site near the summit of Mauna Loa on the island of Hawaii was one of two primary locations chosen in the late 1950s from which to take continuous measurements of atmospheric carbon dioxide. The air sampling tower is visible on the left.

From the standpoint of living things carbon dioxide (CO_2) may well be the most important inorganic substance on the Earth. Carbon compounds produced by the photosynthetic reduction of CO_2 and in other metabolic processes are the principal stuff of which all living creatures are made. Free oxygen, which is required to sustain the high metabolic rates of animals, was produced mostly from carbon dioxide and water in the process of photosynthesis. And the presence of liquid water, which is essential for all forms of life on the Earth, probably depends on the "greenhouse effect" of carbon dioxide; that is, its ability to absorb and back-radiate infrared radiation. In the absence of this effect the oceans could be a solid mass of ice; the average temperature of the Earth's surface might be below the freezing point of water instead of 15° C (59° F), as at present.

Like that of the Earth, the atmospheres of its sister planets, Venus and Mars, also contain carbon dioxide but in very different proportions. On all three planets large quantities of CO_2 were probably emitted to the air from the interior by volcanic activity. Because the Earth has an ocean, nearly all the carbon dioxide that was once in its atmosphere has been transformed chemically into calcium and magnesium carbonates or into organic matter and buried in marine sediment; most of the remainder is dissolved in the oceans. Only about 0.001% is still contained in the air, but this amount is sufficient to give a very significant greenhouse effect. Venus has no oceans and hence its carbon dioxide has remained in the air with the result that the Venusian atmosphere, consisting mainly of carbon dioxide, is heavier than the Earth's atmosphere. On Venus an overwhelming greenhouse effect occurs: the surface temperature is a hellish 400° C (750° F). On Mars, with its relatively low gravity, most of the carbon dioxide and other gases emitted from the interior apparently escaped into space, and its greenhouse effect is much smaller than the Earth's.

Measurements of atmospheric CO_2

During the past few decades a possible increase in the Earth's greenhouse effect resulting from human activity has become an issue of scientific and

ROGER REVELLE *is Professor of Science and Public Policy at the University of California, San Diego.*

(Overleaf) Photographs, Photo Researchers; (left) Robert W. Hernandez, (right) Jerry Cooke

132

Like Mauna Loa the U.S. South Pole station in Antarctica is free from contamination by nearby sources of CO_2, thus offering another good location for atmospheric measurements. The air sampling tower is the tallest stack on the roof.

public concern. To make a start on obtaining the needed geochemical data, a series of continuous measurements of atmospheric carbon dioxide was begun during the International Geophysical Year of 1957–58. These measurements have continued ever since. Two primary measuring sites were chosen: one near the summit of Mauna Loa on the island of Hawaii and the other at the South Pole station of the U.S. Antarctic Program. These sites were not likely to be contaminated by nearby sources of CO_2, and it was thought that they would allow sampling of well-mixed air reasonably typical of the atmosphere in the Northern and Southern hemispheres.

The measurements were begun by Charles Keeling of the Scripps Institution of Oceanography, La Jolla, California, and have continued under his direction in collaboration with the National Oceanic and Atmospheric Administration (NOAA). At both stations the atmospheric carbon dioxide content has increased from year to year. At Mauna Loa the average CO_2 concentration in 1959 was 315.7 parts per million. By 1980 it had risen to 338.4 parts per million. This increase of 22.7 parts per million, or about 7%, represents addition of 48 billion tons of carbon to the atmosphere in 21 years. The South Pole station lags behind Mauna Loa by about one part per million because of the time required for mixing across the Equator.

Since Keeling began his measurements, many other CO_2-measuring stations have been established, ranging in latitude from Point Barrow, Alaska, to the coast of Antarctica and in locations from a mid-ocean weather ship in the North Pacific to high-altitude stations in central Europe. All measurement series show a CO_2 increase of the same magnitude as that at Mauna Loa and the South Pole. A striking characteristic of the data is the existence of seasonal variations: high carbon dioxide values are observed in the spring and low values in autumn. The amplitude of these swings is about 12 parts per million at 50° latitude, about 6 parts per million at Mauna Loa, and 1 to 2 parts per million at the South Pole. They must result mainly from an increase in the rate that CO_2 is removed from the air by growing plants over the rate that it is returned by animals, fires, and microorganisms in spring and summer—and from the reverse case in autumn and winter.

Scientists who first studied the observed increase in atmospheric CO_2 believed it to be due almost exclusively to the rapid rise in the consumption of coal (above and below), oil, and natural gas (above right) together with a small contribution from cement manufacture (right). More recently it has been recognized that CO_2 has been added in significant amounts by other human activities, the most important being the clearing and burning of forests under the pressure of growing populations.

Sources of additional CO_2

Keeling and most other investigators first believed that the carbon added to the atmosphere had come almost exclusively from the combustion of coal, oil, and natural gas, collectively called fossil fuels. Calculations based on United Nations data by Ralph Rotty of the Institute for Energy Analysis at Oak Ridge, Tennessee, show that from the beginning of 1959 to the end of 1980 about 83 billion tons of carbon were released to the atmosphere by fossil fuel combustion and cement manufacture. (The latter source accounts for less than 2% of the total release.) By dividing the measured atmospheric increase by the mass of carbon released by fossil fuel combustion and cement manufacture, one can compute the proportion of fossil fuel carbon that remained in the air—about 58%.

Rotty carried his calculations back to 1860, a date that preceded the modern era in which consumption of coal, oil, and natural gas has been rapidly increasing. He found that the total carbon dioxide produced by fossil fuel combustion between 1860 and 1980 corresponded to 162.6 billion tons of carbon. Assuming that the atmospheric increase was in the same proportion to carbon dioxide produced between 1959 and 1980, one can calculate that the total fossil fuel carbon added to the atmosphere between 1860 and

1980 was 94 billion tons. In 1980 the atmospheric content was about 717 billion tons. Hence, if there were no other sources of atmospheric CO_2, the atmospheric carbon in 1860 was close to 623 billion tons, corresponding to 294 parts per million by volume of CO_2 in the atmosphere.

Recently it has been recognized that CO_2 had been added to the atmosphere by human activities other than fossil fuel combustion, including clearing of forests and brushlands for railway and highway rights of way; increased cutting and burning of forests because of population pressures on shifting cultivators—those practicing "swidden" or "slash-and-burn" agriculture; intensified use of grasslands, brushlands, and woodlands by raisers of livestock; and commercial timbering. The most important human process was the clearing of land for agriculture as populations grew.

The world population in 1860 was about 1.5 billion people; 120 years later it was about 4.5 billion. During most of those years, agricultural yields per unit area of land did not increase very significantly. Consequently, to feed three times as many people in 1980 as in 1860, a very substantial amount of land had to be put under cultivation. A large fraction of this new land was originally in forests, which contained as much as 200 tons of carbon per hectare (about 2.5 acres) in wood and other living biomass. The average carbon content of crop-land biomass is only around ten tons per hectare. Hence, when forests are cleared for agriculture, large quantities of carbon from living organisms are oxidized to carbon dioxide and transferred to the atmosphere. Part of the soil humus in forest land is also oxidized when land is converted to farming, which adds more carbon dioxide to the air.

Estimates by different investigators of the CO_2 produced from the biosphere by human activities differ significantly, but all are agreed that the total corresponds to at least 70 billion tons of carbon. Adding this quantity to the fossil fuel and cement production gives a figure of at least 230 billion tons of carbon injected into the atmosphere between 1860 and 1980. This is more than 37% of the probable amount of carbon in the air in 1860.

How much of this carbon actually remained airborne? Here one must return to the period between 1959 and 1980 when the atmospheric increase was accurately measured. J. S. Olson of Oak Ridge National Laboratory in Tennessee, taking into account both the regrowth of forests and the oxidation of carbon from decay of wood products, land clearing, and changes in soil humus, estimated that the net release of biosphere carbon caused by human activities in one year, 1980, was 0.8 billion tons. The range of estimates by most other workers is between 0.5 and 2 billion tons. On the assumption that the rates of conversion of biosphere carbon were fairly constant between 1959 and 1980, the total released to the atmosphere was between 10.5 and 42 billion tons. Adding these numbers to the fossil fuel production, one arrives at totals of 94 to 125 billion tons. The airborne fraction—that fraction of carbon dioxide produced by human activity which remained in the air—was therefore between 38 and 51%, with a likely value of about 45%. Multiplying this value by the total amount of carbon calculated to have been released from human activities between 1860 and 1980, one finds that the increase in atmospheric carbon due to human activity in the past 120 years was about 104 billion tons. When this figure is subtracted from the measured atmospheric content in 1980, one computes that the atmospheric carbon content in 1860 was probably not more than 615 billion tons. Assuming an influx of 70 billion tons of biosphere carbon between 1860 and 1980, the range of uncertainty of the 1860 atmospheric content for the limiting values of the airborne fraction is only about ±15 billion tons; that is, between 600 and 630 billion tons. Atmospheric carbon dioxide probably increased about 17% during the past 120 years, whereas the release of carbon into the atmosphere from both fossil fuel combustion and the biosphere during that time was probably about 37% of the atmospheric content of 1860.

Processes that remove atmospheric CO_2

Where has the excess carbon dioxide gone? One obvious answer is absorption in the oceans. But oceanographers, basing their computations on estimates of mixing and other physical processes between the ocean surface and deeper waters, believe that ocean uptake could not have removed more than 35% of the total carbon dioxide released into the atmosphere since 1860. Other oceanographic estimates, by Peter Brewer of the Woods Hole Oceanographic Institution in Massachusetts and by C.-T. A. Chen of Oregon State University and F. J. Millero of the University of Miami, are based on measurements and computations of the pre-1860 oceanic CO_2 content. These investigators estimate that the oceans have taken up about 70 billion tons of carbon, or not more than 30% of the influx to the atmosphere.

The remaining 20–25% of the carbon dioxide influx to be accounted for may have been reabsorbed by living organisms on land or in the ocean. This would imply that the mass of that part of the biosphere which has not been depleted by human activity has actually grown.

Direct evidence for such an increase is very difficult to obtain, but it is interesting to note that the amplitude of the seasonal swings in the Mauna Loa record and in other continuous measurements of carbon dioxide in the northern latitudes has increased, probably by more than 10%, during the last 21 years. One straightforward interpretation of this increase is that photosynthetic production of organic matter is increasing because the biosphere is

Plots of continuous measurements of CO_2 made at the Mauna Loa and South Pole sites between 1958 and 1980 provide evidence of its rising concentration in the atmosphere. The seasonal variations—high values in the spring and low values in autumn—result mainly from the net removal of CO_2 by plants during the growing season and a net return by animals, fires, and microorganisms during the rest of the year. The South Pole measurements lag behind those at Mauna Loa by about one part per million because of the time needed for atmospheric mixing across the Equator.

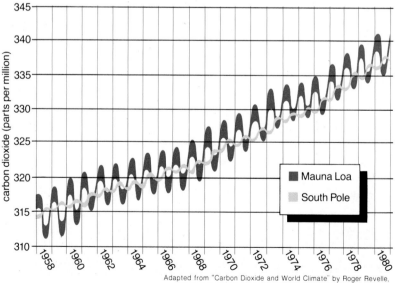

growing in size, at least at the latitude of Mauna Loa and northward. In other words, this part of the biosphere is taking up CO_2 more rapidly than it is being released by forest clearing, timbering, and other human activities.

Growth of the undisturbed biosphere might be expected for several reasons. Carbon dioxide is an essential plant nutrient; in the absence of other growth-limiting factors an increase of atmospheric CO_2 should lead to increased photosynthesis. Plants transpire less water in a CO_2-rich atmosphere; hence, productivity should be less limited by water shortages in semiarid and subhumid regions. Today, because of intensified agricultural practices, more atmospheric nitrogen is being converted to nitrogen compounds that plants can use than in the past. More phosphorus is also available because of increased fertilizer production. Much of this additional supply of nutrients may be entering the "unmanaged" biosphere.

The total mass of the undisturbed biosphere remaining on the Earth, including most of the soil humus, is only about a third of that of the remaining fossil fuels. In the future, therefore, any increases in atmospheric carbon dioxide will be largely the result of fossil fuel combustion.

Estimating future increases

Between 1950 and 1973 the rate of increase of carbon dioxide from use of fossil fuels was 4.6% per year. But since the "oil shock" of 1973 the rate of increase has been only a little more than 2%, about the same as the present rate of growth of the world's human population. The developed countries are growing very slowly in population, and there is good reason to believe that their use of fossil fuels will not rise above present levels, in part because energy conservation measures are becoming more and more effective and in part because alternate sources of energy will be used increasingly. The less developed countries, however, now use comparatively small amounts of energy per capita; if, as they desire, their economies develop, their use of fossil fuels may increase more rapidly than their populations. It is reasonable, therefore, to expect that the use of fossil fuels on a worldwide basis will continue to increase by at least 2% per year for some time to come.

A simple calculation shows that if the rate of increase remains at 2% per year until the year 2050 and fuel combustion levels are constant thereafter, about 1,050 billion tons of carbon will be released to the atmosphere as CO_2 by the year 2065. Adding to that figure a possible 100 billion tons from human activities that deplete the biosphere, multiplying the sum by the probable airborne fraction of 45%, and adding that result to the 717 billion tons measured in 1980 gives an atmospheric carbon content in 2065 of 1,235 billion tons, twice the presumed "preindustrial" value of the year 1860. For a 3% rate of increase in fossil fuel use, sustained until 2025 and succeeded by a constant level of combustion, a doubling of the 1860 atmospheric carbon content would be reached in the year 2040. On the other hand, if the rate of increase were to drop to 1% within the next 35 years, atmospheric carbon doubling would not occur until some time in the 22nd century, one reason being that the oceanic uptake would become larger and consequently the airborne fraction would diminish.

It is obvious that a very large degree of uncertainty exists about future at-

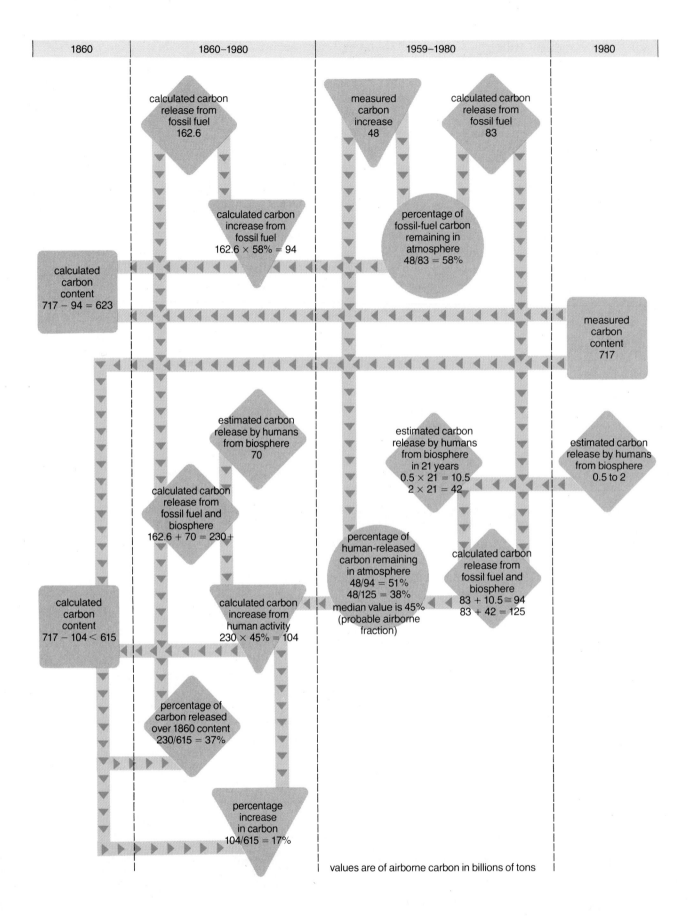

1860 | 1860–1980 | 1959–1980 | 1980

calculated carbon release from fossil fuel 162.6

measured carbon increase 48

calculated carbon release from fossil fuel 83

calculated carbon increase from fossil fuel 162.6 × 58% = 94

percentage of fossil-fuel carbon remaining in atmosphere 48/83 = 58%

calculated carbon content 717 − 94 = 623

measured carbon content 717

estimated carbon release by humans from biosphere 70

estimated carbon release by humans from biosphere in 21 years 0.5 × 21 = 10.5 2 × 21 = 42

estimated carbon release by humans from biosphere 0.5 to 2

calculated carbon release from fossil fuel and biosphere 162.6 + 70 = 230+

calculated carbon release from fossil fuel and biosphere 83 + 10.5 ≅ 94 83 + 42 = 125

calculated carbon content 717 − 104 < 615

calculated carbon increase from human activity 230 × 45% = 104

percentage of human-released carbon remaining in atmosphere 48/94 = 51% 48/125 = 38% median value is 45% (probable airborne fraction)

percentage of carbon released over 1860 content 230/615 = 37%

percentage increase in carbon 104/615 = 17%

values are of airborne carbon in billions of tons

mospheric CO_2 levels and that this uncertainty increases rapidly with the length of time examined. The principal reasons for uncertainty are the wide range of plausible assumptions about future growth in economic productivity and human populations and about the ways in which costs of carbon-based and alternative fuels may be affected by technological change.

The estimated world resources of petroleum and natural gas do not contain enough carbon to produce a doubling of atmospheric CO_2 even if they were entirely consumed. But the recoverable resources of coal, which probably contain more than 3.5 trillion tons of carbon, are more than ample when combined with the remaining oil and gas resources to provide enough carbon dioxide for a quadrupling of the "preindustrial" atmospheric content. Much higher concentrations might be attained if significant portions of the carbon contents of tar sands and oil shales were converted to CO_2.

Effects on global temperature and climate

As was stated above, present scientific concern about "the CO_2 problem" is based on the probable effect of rising levels of atmospheric CO_2 on the radiation balance of the Earth. Molecules of CO_2 in the air absorb infrared radiation from land and water surfaces and from the atmosphere and then reradiate this energy. If the CO_2 content rises, more infrared radiation will be trapped in the lower atmosphere and the proportion emitted to space will diminish. But for the Earth's temperature to stabilize, the quantity of energy emitted to space as infrared radiation must balance the incoming solar radiation. Hence, there must be an increase in infrared radiation leaving the surface and the lower atmosphere. Because infrared emission depends directly on temperature, the temperature near the surface must rise.

There is no known experimental analogue to indicate quantitatively how the temperature and other properties of the surface and the lower atmosphere will respond to increased carbon dioxide. Scientists must resort to theoretical models that take into account a series of potential feedback effects. If the radiation balance were affected only by higher CO_2, the computed average temperature rise for a doubling of CO_2 would probably be less than 1° C (a change of 1° C is a change of 1.8° F). But with higher temperatures, the moisture content of the atmosphere would increase, probably in such a way that the relative humidity remained constant. Water vapor is an efficient absorber of infrared radiation, and consequently more infrared radiation would be trapped in the lower atmosphere. Model computations indicate that with this positive feedback the surface temperature would rise by about 2° C. Several other positive feedbacks are likely. For example, if the clouds rose with increasing atmospheric temperature so that the temperature and the outgoing infrared radiation from the cloud tops remained constant, the temperature near the surface would rise still further. Similarly, the melting of snow and ice caused by CO_2-induced warming would lower the Earth's reflectivity, resulting in absorption of more solar radiation and hence further heating. Computations of the combined effects of direct CO_2 warming and these positive feedbacks indicate that if atmospheric CO_2 doubled, the global temperature would increase between 1.5° and more than 3° C, with a most probable value of about 2.8° C.

Flow diagram on the opposite page provides a summary of the data and calculations presented in the article between pages 133 and 136. Columns reflect the year or span of years to which the values within them apply.

139

To be meaningful to human beings and their societies the projected rise in global mean temperature must be translated into estimated climatic changes in different regions. In principle this can be done by constructing computer models of the atmosphere, called general circulation models, that take into account higher atmospheric CO_2 and use the thermodynamic and hydrodynamic equations that govern the atmosphere. Such models require the use of very large computers, and only a few models have been constructed. Syukuro Manabe, Richard T. Wetherald, and Ronald J. Stouffer of the Geophysical Fluid Dynamics Laboratory at Princeton University were among the first to apply them to the carbon dioxide problem.

The resolution of the present generation of models is too coarse and uncertainties of various sorts are too great to allow detailed regional projections of future climates. Nevertheless, the models do indicate several important features. They show that the temperature increase in the tropics should be relatively small, probably less than 2° C for a doubling of CO_2. The temperature rise at higher latitudes should be much larger, probably 4–5° C at latitude 45° N (about that of Montreal and Venice) and perhaps more than 9° C during winter at latitude 70° N, which is within the Arctic Circle. Precipitation should increase at latitudes above 50° N (near London and Vancouver) and below 35° N (Los Angeles and Tokyo). Between latitudes 35° and 50° N climates may be drier than at present because of both reduced precipitation and increased evaporation. This zone of drying should be most pronounced in the interiors of the continents and may not occur near coasts.

The projected climatic effects will lag behind the increase in CO_2, probably by one to three decades, because the ocean must be warmed as well as the atmosphere. Time will be required for an oceanic temperature increase to penetrate below the uppermost mixed layer of the ocean. On the other hand, when equilibrium finally is attained, the rise in temperature probably will be found to be greater than that estimated from the increase in carbon dioxide. The reason is that several other "greenhouse gases" that absorb and back-radiate infrared radiation also exist as trace constituents of the atmosphere, and their abundances are apparently increasing along with the abundance of carbon dioxide. Climatologically the most important are methane (CH_4), nitrous oxide (N_2O), and several chlorofluorocarbons (*e.g.*, CCl_3F and CCl_2F_2). James Hansen and his colleagues at NASA's Goddard Institute for Space Studies concluded from a study of these gases and their growing abundances that during the decade from 1970 to 1980 the equilibrium greenhouse warming caused by the four gases was about 0.1° C. During this same decade the equilibrium warming that should have resulted from the observed increase in atmospheric carbon dioxide was 0.14° C.

Consequences for human life and society

If carbon dioxide doubles, the average global temperature is likely to be higher than civilized humanity has ever experienced. But the change will not be catastrophic; it will be a slow pervasive shift virtually imperceptible from year to year. Moreover, the resulting climate in any particular region will not be much different from climates that exist today somewhere on the Earth in regions where human beings live without much difficulty. Large popula-

140

tions have migrated over long distances throughout human history. During their migrations they have experienced differences of climate that are larger than the changes projected for a doubling of atmospheric CO_2. On the other hand, extreme variations in climate at mid-latitudes from year to year, particularly extremely hot summers, endanger the health of many people, and these extreme summers are likely to be much hotter if average summer temperatures increase.

The consequences of the projected climatic changes on human concerns are likely to be both positive and negative. Four important activities that would likely be significantly affected are rain-fed agriculture, irrigated agriculture, Arctic development, and the habitation of present-day coastal areas.

At latitudes above 50° N the principal effects on rain-fed agriculture may be a lengthening of the growing season and increased water supply. At low latitudes increased rainfall without much change in temperature would be beneficial in some regions and harmful in others. In mid-latitudes the projected warming and diminished precipitation would be harmful for most existing crop varieties. But if the projected climatic changes did not occur too rapidly, the agricultural research establishments of the developed countries should be able to produce new varieties that are adapted to the changed climatic conditions. The feasibility of such adaptation is well illustrated by the story of hard red winter wheat. This kind of wheat was formerly grown mainly in Nebraska, but new varieties have been created during the past few decades that produce satisfactory yields from crops grown as far north as North Dakota and as far south as Texas.

Aside from climatic changes increased CO_2 should be beneficial to agricultural crops. A good deal of experimental evidence shows that a CO_2-rich atmosphere benefits photosynthetic production. Equally important, most crop plants transpire less water under high carbon dioxide. Consequently, rain-fed crops should grow satisfactorily even though the rainfall diminishes and potential evaporation increases.

The negative effects on agriculture of CO_2-induced climate changes may be much more severe in the presently less developed countries. Few of these countries possess the scientific research establishments that could help them adapt to changing climate.

At mid-latitudes the expected lower rainfall and higher evaporation may affect irrigated agriculture profoundly. For example, in the Colorado River Basin of the western U.S., runoff of the Colorado River system is barely sufficient to support irrigation farming today. Only about 15% of the precipitation in the upper basin of the Colorado enters the river; the remaining 85% evaporates. Runoff is an even smaller proportion of precipitation in the lower basin. With even a slight drop in precipitation and increase in evaporation, the flow of the Colorado could be sharply reduced, and heroic measures might be needed to maintain the present production of irrigated areas. One such measure would be to increase crop yields per unit area of land and to reduce the area under cultivation. Another might be large-scale transfer of water from other rivers in Canada or the U.S. Northwest.

Warmer temperatures would generally benefit the Arctic. There is good reason to believe that the Arctic Ocean would be ice-free in the summer, a

141

condition that would greatly assist commerce in general as well as the exploration for oil and gas and their production and transportation. The old dream of a Northwest Passage would become a reality. Problems of military security in the Arctic would change in character. Higher winter temperatures would ease the problems of working with metals and other substances that become brittle in extremely low temperatures.

Sea level is now rising—at not more than 1.5 millimeters per year—partly because the oceans are becoming somewhat warmer and therefore expanding in volume as carbon dioxide increases and partly because of a slow reduction in the mass of the Antarctic or Greenland ice cap, or perhaps both.

142

The rate of rise in sea level might be greatly accelerated if a large portion of the Antarctic ice cap were to disintegrate. Many glaciologists believe this could happen to that portion of the ice sheet which lies west of 0° longitude and extends south of the Antarctic peninsula. The land underlying this part of the ice sheet is mostly below sea level. Consequently the overlying ice is thought to be unstable, being held in place partly by the Ross and Filchner-Ronne ice shelves, which are pinned by high places on the seafloor and by islands in the Amundsen Sea that block the flow of the glaciers.

Disappearance of the western Antarctic ice cap would cause a rise in sea level of five to six meters (16–20 feet). Interestingly, fossilized coral terraces five meters above present sea level occur in many parts of the world. Radioactive dating indicates that these terraces were formed 125,000 years ago in the warmest part of the last interglacial period. Their existence suggests that the western Antarctic ice cap disappeared at that time.

Climatic warming, which would accelerate disintegration of the ice shelves, could cause the western Antarctic ice cap again to disappear into the sea. Most glaciologists believe this event could not happen in less than 200 years, with a minimum time of 500 years being more likely. If the ice cap did disappear in 200 years, sea level would rise about three centimeters, or somewhat over an inch, per year—roughly 20 times the present rate. Unless high dikes were constructed, The Netherlands, Bangladesh, most of Florida, and other low-lying areas—including London, Washington, D.C., and other great cities of the world—would be inundated within a relatively short time. Research to gain a better understanding of the behavior of the western Antarctic ice cap, particularly to give better estimates of the rate at which it might disintegrate, is clearly of high priority.

Giving some thought to the future

Other than the measurements of atmospheric CO_2 made since 1959, the UN figures on fossil fuel consumption, and the observation that the sea level is rising, there are few real facts to clarify the carbon dioxide issue. Nevertheless, the work that has been done is enough to reveal the need for further research to help forecast the consequences of a continuing CO_2 increase and to suggest the prudence of thinking now about the ways in which humans can best cope with the changes.

For example, drilling through the annual ice layers of the western Antarctic ice sheet to a depth corresponding to 125,000 years may reveal something of the sequence of events that led to its postulated breakup in the past. Isotopic analysis of the fossil terraces from that period may provide information about the rate of the breakup. The movement of the present ice sheet toward the sea could be monitored by satellite; an increase in the ice flow might provide early indications of the disintegration of the sheet. It is also not premature for governments to consider the possible climatic effects of rising CO_2 levels in their agricultural-development and water-resource plans for the future. Finally, because nearly 90% of the recoverable coal is in the U.S., China, and the Soviet Union, these countries need to recognize that they bear the primary responsibility for the way in which a major potential source of future atmospheric CO_2 will be used.

Runoff from the Colorado River system, parceled to the last drop among seven U.S. states and Mexico through a complex of dams, pipelines, and irrigation canals (opposite page, right column), is barely able to support irrigation farming today. Only about 15% of the precipitation in the upper basin (opposite, top left) enters the river; for the lower Colorado (opposite, bottom left) runoff is an even smaller percentage. Only a slight drop in precipitation and increase in evaporation due to CO_2-induced changes in climate could severely reduce the flow of the Colorado and force the implementation of heroic measures to maintain present agricultural production levels.

THE
WEATHER
OF
OTHER PLANETS

by Andrew P. Ingersoll

*Recent observations from spacecraft and
from powerful Earth-based telescopes
are providing new information concerning
the atmospheres and climatic conditions
of other members of the solar system.*

Weather is the state of the atmosphere—the wind, temperature, pressure, humidity, precipitation, cloudiness, vapor, and aerosol content—at a given place and time. Climate is the average weather over a period of time, such as during the ice ages or the climate of Mars. The study of weather and climate is called either atmospheric science or meteorology. Weather forecasting is just one aspect of this science, which also includes studying past climates, the climates of other planets, and the origin and evolution of planetary atmospheres.

There are practical reasons for including remote planets and past climates in this study. Scientists know from the geologic record that the climate of the Earth has changed considerably. Tropical plants once grew at high latitudes in Greenland and Antarctica. Many species of plants and animals became extinct as a result of climate change. Glaciers covered half of North America just 20,000 years ago, which is just a tick of the geologic clock—equivalent to 0.4 second if the Earth were one day old. It is also known that human beings are accelerating the process of climatic change, by adding carbon dioxide, aerosols, and other chemicals to the atmosphere, and by altering the soil, water, and vegetation at the Earth's surface. To assess the climatic impact of human activities, it is useful to understand the extreme cases. That is one way in which other planets and ancient geologic records are interesting.

Studying the weather and climates of other planets also sheds light on the origin of life. Life as it exists on the Earth requires certain elements, principally carbon (C), hydrogen (H), oxygen (O), and nitrogen (N). These are present in all planetary atmospheres in simple compounds such as methane (CH_4), water (H_2O), carbon dioxide (CO_2), and ammonia (NH_3). Liquid water is also a requirement, which implies temperatures somewhere between the freezing and boiling points of water (0°–100° C, 32°–212° F). Such temperatures are found at some times and places on all the planets from Mercury to Neptune but usually not with liquid water present.

Another requirement for the development of life may be peace and quiet. The lifetimes of fragile organic molecules must have been short in the lakes

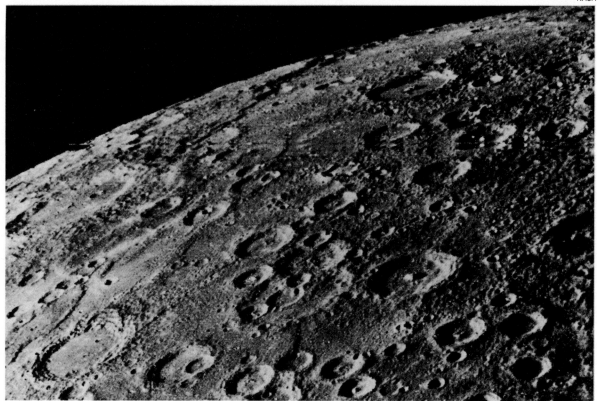

The northern limb of Mercury was photographed from the Mariner 10 spacecraft at a distance of 78,800 kilometers (49,000 miles). Mercury lacks an atmosphere, and so its weather depends entirely on whether it is day or night. At noon on the planet's Equator temperatures rise to 625 K (665° F), and at night they fall to 100 K (−280° F). On the preceding page is a view of Jupiter's Great Red Spot taken from Voyager 2 at a distance of 6 million kilometers (3,730,000 miles).

ANDREW P. INGERSOLL *is Professor of Planetary Science in the Division of Geological and Planetary Sciences at the California Institute of Technology. As a member of the Voyager Imaging Science Team, he is responsible for atmospheric observations of Jupiter, Saturn, and Uranus and the extraction of wind information from these observations.*

(Overleaf) Photos, Jet Propulsion Laboratory/NASA

and seas of primordial Earth. Such lifetimes would be much shorter in a deep atmosphere such as that of Venus or Jupiter, where winds carry molecules down to sterilizing temperatures or up to destructive ultraviolet light. Favorable climatic conditions apparently occurred simultaneously on only one planet in our solar system—Earth.

A weather forecast for the solar system

To imagine what it would be like on the surface or in the clouds of another planet, one might first consider airless bodies such as Mercury and the Moon; then Mars, which has an atmosphere 1% as massive as the Earth's; and then Saturn's moon Titan, Venus, and the gas-giant planets, all of which have massive atmospheres. In so doing it soon becomes obvious that the characteristics of an atmosphere make a significant difference in controlling surface conditions.

For Mercury the "weather" depends entirely on whether it is day or night. At noon on the planet's Equator temperatures soar to 625 degrees Kelvin (625 K), about 665° F. At night temperatures plunge to 100 K (−280° F). One complete day lasts for 176 Earth days because Mercury rotates so slowly. These large temperature changes are regular and predictable.

The Moon's "weather" is only slightly less harsh. The maximum daytime temperature is 380 K (225° F), which is colder than on Mercury because the Moon is farther from the Sun. The 120 K (−245° F) nighttime temperature is warmer than on Mercury. This is because the lunar day is shorter (28 Earth days) and the surface has less time to cool off.

146

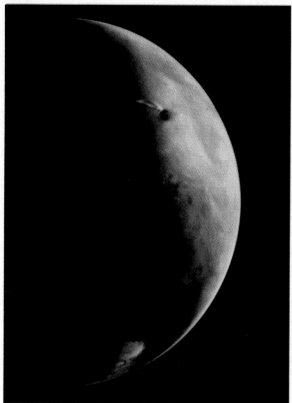

The temperature changes on Mercury and the Moon are large because they lack atmospheres. The Earth's atmosphere stores the daily solar input with only a modest temperature rise, and it continually transports heat from hot regions to cold. Without an atmosphere the Earth's climate would be like that of the Moon.

On Mars as of early 1983 it is late autumn at the second Viking Lander site (latitude 48° N). The Martian day is only 37 minutes longer than that on the Earth. Nights are cold; the minimum temperatures are approximately 150 K (−190° F), which is cold enough to condense both water vapor and carbon dioxide from the atmosphere. Indeed, ice clouds and fog are forecast for this season. Autumn is also a stormy season on Mars. Winds in the atmosphere above the Viking Landers reach hurricane force (116 km/h; 72 mph), and global dust storms take place. The dust will obscure the Sun and will take several weeks to settle. Near the Equator daytime highs range up to a comfortable 280 K (45° F), warm enough to melt ice. But there is no water or ice on that part of the planet; it all lies trapped at the poles. Most of Mars is literally dry as dust.

On Titan, Saturn's largest moon, it is early spring in the northern hemisphere. Indeed, spring will last until 1987, for Titan's year is the same as Saturn's, about 29 Earth years. The weather forecast is for smog—a fine rain of black carbon compounds that are created by sunlight in the clouds 160 kilometers (100 miles) overhead. At the surface the temperature is about 90 K (−295° F), and it varies by only a fraction of a degree from day to night. The mass of the atmosphere is about ten times that on Earth.

Above left, Mars as seen from the Viking 2 spacecraft at a distance of 419,000 kilometers (260,355 miles) reveals bright plumes of water ice extending northwest from the volcano Ascreaus Mons. On the surface of Mars (above) a very thin layer of water ice coats the rocks and soil around the Utopia Planitia landing site of the Viking 2 lander.

147

Photos, Jet Propulsion Laboratory/NASA

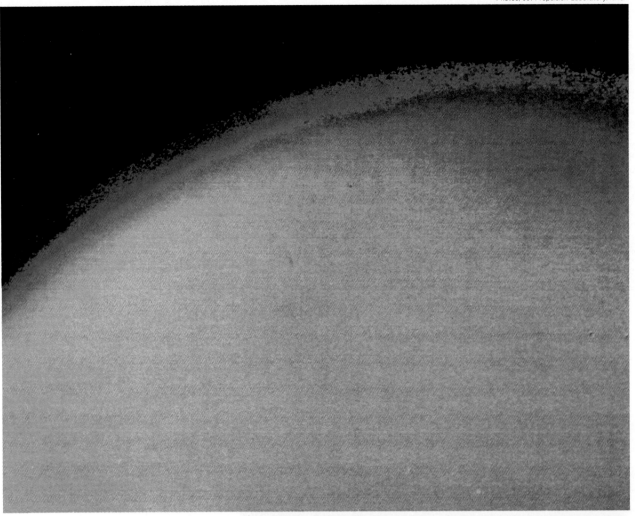

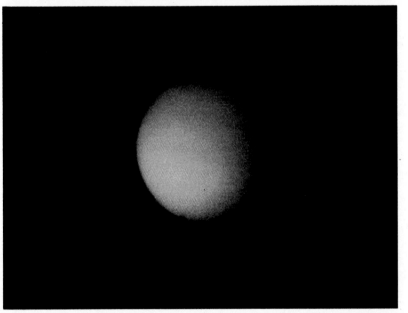

Color-enhanced image of Titan, Saturn's largest moon (above), was taken from Voyager 1 at a distance of 435,000 kilometers (270,000 miles). It shows that Titan is covered with a layer of haze, which consists mainly of fine carbon compounds and which merges with a darker cloud layer at the north pole. At the right the true colors of Titan's haze are seen from Voyager 1 at a distance of 4.5 million kilometers (2.8 million miles).

Other characteristics of Titan are unknown. These include the amount of sunlight reaching the ground and even if there is a ground. The planet may be covered by a liquid methane ocean or a frozen layer of ice. Methane raindrops may fall, and methane rivers may flow, but no one yet can be sure.

Venus is another cloud-covered planet. With an atmosphere one hundred times more massive than that of the Earth, it experiences little daily variation in temperature. At the ground there are gentle winds (a few mph) and red-hot temperatures, about 730 K (855° F). In the clouds at an altitude of 55 kilometers (35 miles) temperatures are comfortable—about 295 K (72° F). Winds there are strong but steady. In a balloon at that altitude one would circle the planet every four days. The balloon would be enveloped in a bright mist of sulfuric acid drops, and passengers would barely be able to make out another balloon floating one kilometer away.

On Jupiter, Saturn, Uranus, or Neptune balloons must be used. These planets have no surfaces and therefore are called the gas-giant planets. A person floating at the edge of Jupiter's Great Red Spot or in one of the wide jet streams that circle that planet would be moving at a speed of 240 km/h (150 mph). The forecast for the Great Red Spot and other storms is that they will persist indefinitely, despite their high peripheral winds and intense small-scale motions. Indeed, this persistence is one of the mysteries about the giant planets. It may be due to the great depth of their atmospheres, but no one knows.

Evolution of planetary atmospheres

The kinds of matter one finds in the inner and outer parts of the solar system are very different. In the outer solar system hydrogen (H) is the most abundant element. It binds to other chemically active elements to form compounds such as CH_4, NH_3, and H_2O. The remaining hydrogen binds to itself to form molecular hydrogen (H_2). These compounds and the inert gas helium are the major constituents of the four giant planets and their atmospheres. In the inner solar system oxygen (O) is the most abundant element. It combines with metals to form metallic oxides (rocks), which are the major bulk constituents of the four terrestrial planets. It also combines with carbon to form CO_2, which is the major atmospheric constituent of Mars and Venus and an important compound on Earth. Hydrogen is present on the terrestrial planets largely in combination with oxygen and is not a major bulk constituent of the inner solar system.

These basic differences between the inner and outer solar system probably are the result of the high temperatures close to the early Sun. Hydrogen was the most abundant element in the primordial cloud of dust and gas that eventually contracted to form the Sun and planets. This inference is based on the facts that the Sun is mostly hydrogen and that most of the solar system's mass is in the Sun. The lightest elements, including hydrogen and helium, were largely driven out of the inner solar system by the high initial temperatures. The heavier dust grains remained closer to the Sun to form the rocky inner planets.

There is evidence that the gases now in the atmospheres of Venus, the Earth, and Mars were chemically bound to the solid particles at the time of

On the surface of Venus (above), as photographed from the Soviet Venera 14 lander, the planet's massive atmosphere has damped out day-to-night swings of temperature. The cloud-covered surface experiences gentle winds and temperatures of about 730 K (855° F).

formation. If these atmospheres were simply a small remnant of the primordial cloud, then their composition should resemble that cloud. In particular, the noble gases neon, argon, krypton, and xenon should be present in approximately equal parts with carbon dioxide, water, and nitrogen. However, the noble gases cannot form chemical bonds, and they are rare in the inner solar system. They were presumably swept away with hydrogen when the Sun was forming. Later internal heating of the inner planets may have released the chemically bound gases, which then became the atmospheres and (for the Earth) the oceans of those planets.

It was known before the space program that the Earth had outgassed huge amounts of water and carbon dioxide. The water is mostly in the

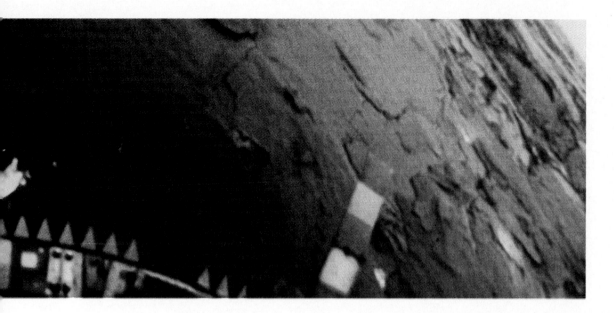

oceans, which have a mass equal to about 300 Earth-atmospheres. The carbon dioxide is now mostly in limestone rocks (calcium carbonate—$CaCO_3$), which formed as ocean sediments from dissolved CO_2 and calcium salts. The total mass of CO_2 is uncertain because some of the limestone has been buried by drifing continents, but estimates range from 40 to 100 atmospheres. The atmosphere itself is approximately one-fifth molecular oxygen (O_2) and four-fifths molecular nitrogen (N_2).

Venus has about 100 Earth-atmospheres of CO_2, but it all resides in the massive atmosphere. The high temperatures on Venus do not allow limestone to form. Venus has about two Earth-atmospheres of N_2, which is also in the atmosphere. Water is a trace constituent of the atmosphere, and there

Ultraviolet photographs of the clouds over Venus (opposite page, bottom and below) were taken from the Pioneer Venus orbiter over a period of 38 hours at intervals of 9½ hours, 4½ hours, and 24 hours (left to right). The clouds of Venus circle the planet completely once every four days.

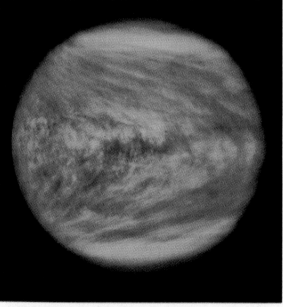

NASA

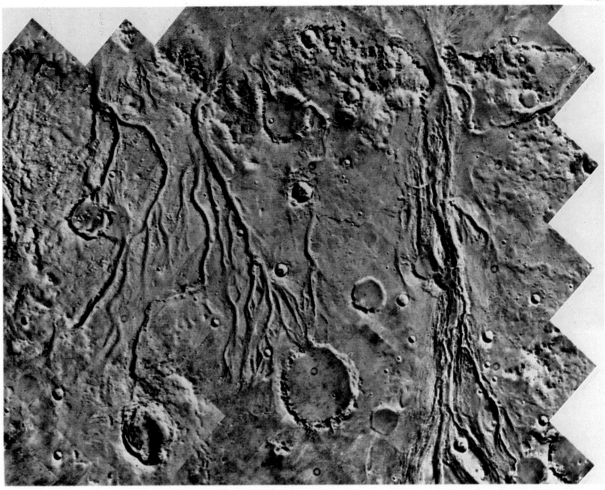

Mosaic of the surface of Mars consists of photographs taken from the Viking 1 orbiter on four separate revolutions. The well-defined channels suggest that the now dry and frozen surface once contained rivers of liquid water.

are no oceans. But recent spacecraft results indicate that large amounts of water have been lost from Venus. The evidence is that the hydrogen of Venus is heavier; that is, it is richer in the heavy isotope deuterium (^2H) than is the hydrogen on Earth. This fact implies that large amounts of hydrogen were lost by evaporation into space, since evaporation favors the lighter isotope and leaves more of the heavier variety behind.

Thus Venus and the Earth seem to have started with approximately the same inventory of volatile compounds. This is not too surprising, since the two planets are roughly of the same size and density. Differences arose later as a result of their different positions in orbit around the Sun. Venus, being closer to the Sun, was, and still is, hotter than the Earth. Therefore, water and carbon dioxide remained in the atmosphere of Venus, whereas on the Earth both substances condensed into the oceans and ocean sediments. Sunlight could have converted the massive water vapor atmosphere of primordial Venus into hydrogen and oxygen. The former evaporated into space, and the latter combined with surface materials to form oxides.

Mercury and Mars represent more extreme examples of Earthlike planets that are either too near or too far from the Sun. At Mercury's orbit gases apparently could not bind to the hot dust grains or could not stay bound to the hot planet once it had formed. Thus Mercury has no appreciable atmosphere. Mars has a thin atmosphere that is mostly carbon dioxide. The low temperatures there limit the amount of water and carbon dioxide that the atmosphere can hold. To a large extent these substances are frozen out at the Martian poles.

Nitrogen and the noble gases provide additional information, some of which seems to contradict the theories that have been discussed above. The low abundance of molecular nitrogen (N_2) on Mars seems to imply either less outgassing of the interior or less initial binding of gas to the dust grains from which the planet formed. The first explanation suggests that Mars had an internal history that differed from that of the Earth and Venus. Yet all three planets resemble each other in bulk properties. The second explanation suggests that less gas was bound to the solid material at the orbit of Mars than at the orbits of either the Earth or Venus. Yet high temperatures on the early Sun imply that more gases would be bound at Mars. The resolution of this conflict probably involves some currently overlooked aspect of planetary evolution.

Saturn's largest moon, Titan, provides a good example of atmospheric evolution in the outer solar system. Neptune's largest moon, Triton, and the ninth planet, Pluto, may provide similar examples, but little is known about these objects. All have weak gravity and cannot retain H_2 gas in their atmospheres. Titan's atmosphere is mostly N_2, as is the Earth's. Carbon is present as CH_4 and as more complex hydrogen-carbon compounds that form the black cloud particles. Water is frozen out of Titan's atmosphere. This last fact accounts for the almost complete absence of oxygen in any form, although both carbon monoxide (CO) and CO_2 have been detected in small quantities.

Titan may, in fact, be a frozen version of the early Earth, which according to some theories once had abundant CH_4 and NH_3 in its atmosphere. Sunlight gradually liberated hydrogen, which escaped into space. Nitrogen accumulated in the atmosphere as N_2. On Earth, with oxygen available as water, the carbon became CO_2. Green plants took CO_2 and water to make carbohydrates and oxygen, which also accumulated in the atmosphere. This evolutionary pathway is apparently blocked on Titan because of the low temperatures. Although temperatures might have been higher when Titan was forming and a climate favorable to life might once have existed, it seems unlikely that life exists on Titan today.

Climate change

The Earth's climate varies on many time scales. The processes that cause the climate to change on these different scales include solar variability, changes in the Earth's orbit, continental drift, erratic behavior of continental glaciers, changes in the deep ocean circulation, biological cycles, and changes in atmospheric composition. In addition, there is a random component to long-term climate just as there is to daily weather. It is possible that the Earth's climate flips spontaneously from one state to another without an obvious external cause.

North polar ice cap on Mars is revealed in photomosaic taken from the Viking 2 orbiter. The translucent streaks of varied tones overlie both the ice and the defrosted layered material and may have been formed by the redistribution of ice and soil particles by the wind. The cap consists of ice formed from water rather than from carbon dioxide, as was previously believed.

Photos, Jet Propulsion Laboratory/NASA

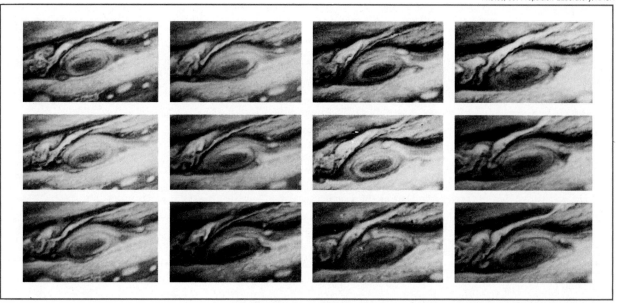

The flow of gaseous fluids circulating around the Great Red Spot on Jupiter is shown in the time-lapse photographs above, taken every odd rotation of the planet; the sequence is from the upper left down each row and ending at the bottom right. Jupiter rotates once every 9 hours 50–55 minutes, while the rotation period of the gases within the Great Red Spot is about six days. At the right is a high-resolution image of the mid-latitudes of Jupiter taken from a distance of 4 million kilometers (2.5 million miles). The pale orange line extending from southwest to northeast (north is at the top) is the north temperate current with wind speeds of about 120 meters per second. Farther north is a weaker jet stream with wind speeds of about 30 meters per second; it is characterized by wave patterns and cloud features that rotate in a clockwise manner.

The history of the Earth's climate is recorded in sediments. In some places the geologic record goes back more than 1,000,000,000 years. One finds evidence of both warm climates and cold climates, but generally the former last longer than the latter. For example, the dinosaurs lived on an unglaciated Earth for more than 100 million years. A slow cooling has occurred during the last 70 million years. For the last few million years polar ice sheets have advanced and retreated across the Earth's surface at intervals of 20,000 to 100,000 years. The most recent advance peaked 20,000 years before the present time and was followed by a rapid retreat that culminated in a warm interglacial period from 5,000 to 7,000 years ago. Since then the climate has become cooler, with minor advances and retreats every few hundred years. During the last hundred years there has been a slight warming.

Photos, Jet Propulsion Laboratory/NASA

Mars and Venus provide other examples of climate variability. The ancient riverbeds of Mars are perhaps the most interesting, since Mars today is dry and frozen. The Sun's lower output in the past only complicates the picture. One possibility is that the atmospheric composition of Mars has changed. An atmosphere with one hundred times more CO_2 than at present could trap the outgoing infrared radiation and warm the surface, allowing liquid water to exist. But accounting for the disappearance of this massive atmosphere of carbon dioxide is a problem: Why did it go and where is the CO_2 now?

By trapping the outgoing infrared radiation, the massive CO_2 atmosphere of Venus maintains the surface at a level hundreds of degrees hotter than a hypothetical airless body at the same distance from the Sun. The sulfuric acid clouds of Venus have two effects—trapping the outgoing infrared radiation and reflecting the incoming solar radiation. The former process leads to a net warming and the latter to a net cooling. On the Earth volcanic aerosols that linger in the stratosphere also contain sulfuric acid. These aerosols cool the Earth, their reflective properties outweighing their effect on infrared radiation.

Like the Earth Mars also has orbital cycles that are regular and predictable. They are probably the cause of the so-called layered terrain in the planet's polar regions. Each layer may be a deposit of dust and ice laid down during part of each climate cycle. As on the Earth the polar climates are warm when the seasonal tilt is large, because the poles then receive more sunlight during the year.

What will happen in the future? The answer for the Earth depends on the time scale. Recent volcanic activity has loaded the Earth's atmosphere with sulfuric acid particles. Therefore, for the next year or so there may be a small global cooling. But averaged over the next hundred years there will be

Changes in the atmosphere of Jupiter are revealed by photographs taken about four months apart. The photograph on the left was taken from Voyager 1 on January 24, 1979, from a distance of 40 million kilometers (25 million miles); on the right is a picture from Voyager 2 on May 9, 1979, from 46.3 million kilometers (28.7 million miles). One of the white ovals located below and left of the Great Red Spot in January had drifted 60 degrees eastward (right) by May, while the bright tongue extending upward from the red spot is interacting with a thin bright cloud that had traveled twice around Jupiter during the four months. The satellite Ganymede is visible at the bottom of the Voyager 1 picture.

155

global warming as a result of increased CO_2 in the atmosphere. If people find ways to avoid burning coal and oil and thereby releasing the CO_2 into the atmosphere, this situation will not come to pass. Finally, over approximately the next 10,000 years the orbital cycles will be driving the Earth into another ice age.

Predictability of the weather

On the Earth it is difficult to forecast the weather more than a few days ahead. In the Northern Hemisphere one can predict with certainty that July will be warmer than January, but it is impossible to predict in January that July 4 will be warmer than July 5. Obviously there is room for improvement, which may be achieved by such means as gathering more weather data and using larger computers. But how much improvement can be expected for a given amount of extra effort? To what extent is atmospheric unpredictability simply something that must be lived with?

The other planets provide some insight in regard to these questions. It appears that the weather on some planets is more predictable than on others. In fact the Earth may have the most unpredictable weather in the solar system. This statement is based on the observed regularity and longevity of flow patterns in other planetary atmospheres. It is surprising that this is the case, since the Earth's atmosphere is neither the least massive nor the most massive, and the Earth's radius, gravity, rate of rotation, distance from the Sun, and average temperature are all intermediate compared with other planets.

The Viking Landers provided a good look at Martian weather. The first data were for the summer season, and it was soon obvious that summer weather on Mars is dull. The variations of wind and temperature are quite predictable and follow a diurnal cycle. As discussed earlier, this diurnal regularity is a general property of planets with thin atmospheres or no atmospheres at all.

Later in the Viking mission the weather became somewhat more variable. On both the Earth and Mars winter is the stormiest season. The storms are driven by the large thermal contrast between the cold winter pole and the warm Equator. The storms on Earth have lifetimes of several days. Old storms are constantly replaced by new ones, which grow unpredictably from small fluctuations. The storms on Mars are more periodic and regular. Wind, temperature, and pressure fluctuations at the Viking lander site are wave-like with a period of about three days. The storms on Mars are apparently less turbulent than those on the Earth. This difference may be due to the more rapid damping of temperature fluctuations in the thin Martian atmosphere. Generally in laboratory fluids the degree of turbulence is inversely proportional to the damping, but the application of this result to planetary atmospheres is uncertain.

Based on the above reasoning, massive atmospheres such as those of Venus and Jupiter should be the most turbulent and unpredictable, since energy is stored for a long time and also because irregular fluid motions are not damped out. But something more interesting happens in these atmospheres. The small-scale motions seem to organize themselves into stable

Color-enhanced photograph of Saturn (opposite page, center) reveals bright spots in the planet's north temperate belt. These may be huge convective storms with upwelling from deep within the planet's atmosphere. The distinct differences in color among the cloud belts of the northern hemisphere may be due to variations in haze layers. The southern hemisphere appears bluer than the northern hemisphere because of the increased scattering of sunlight on that area due to the Voyager 1 spacecraft's point of view. At the top is a color-enhanced picture of Saturn's northern hemisphere assembled from images obtained by Voyager 2. Among the most evident features are three spots flowing westward at about 15 meters per second. A unique red oval is shown in the Voyager 1 photograph of Saturn's southern hemisphere, bottom. The difference in color between the oval and the surrounding bluish clouds indicates that the oval contains a substance that absorbs more blue and violet light than do the clouds.

157

large-scale structures that persist indefinitely, feeding on the energy in the disorganized small-scale flow.

The long-lived ovals in Jupiter's atmosphere are a good example of this organization. These ovals are circulating masses of gaseous fluid ranging in size from less than 1,600 kilometers (1,000 miles) to an east-west distance of about 26,000 kilometers (16,000 miles) for the Great Red Spot. They continue to circulate for years or even for hundreds of years, even though the small-scale eddies nearby have lifetimes of a few days or less. The Great Red Spot, which has existed for more than 300 years, is constantly engulfing small transient spots.

The jet streams on Venus, Jupiter, and Saturn are another example of stable large-scale structures. The upper atmosphere of Venus rotates with a four-day period, moving westward relative to the surface at more than 320 km/h (200 mph). This westward motion is in the same direction but 50 times faster than that of the solid planet. Jupiter and Saturn have multiple jet streams. Each latitude has its own west-to-east rotation, with relative velocities of approximately 480 km/h (300 mph) on Jupiter and 1,600 km/h (1,000 mph) on Saturn. These east-west (zonal) flows coexist with intense small-scale eddies. However, instead of destroying the large-scale structure, the eddies feed additional energy into the zonal flow. This energy transfer has been measured in Jupiter's atmosphere from Voyager images. It appears also to be occurring on Saturn. And it occurs in theoretical models of the Venus atmosphere.

The above processes seem to involve a spontaneous transition from chaos to order, in violation of one of the basic laws of physics. But it is incorrect to think of an eddy that is several hundred miles in diameter as a chaotic structure. Also, several examples of such a transition have been documented elsewhere in nature. This kind of transfer, from eddies to mean flow, seems to sustain atmospheric currents such as the Earth's jet stream, oceanic currents such as the Gulf Stream, and the zonal flows in other planetary atmospheres.

For these undamped planetary flows predictability seems to be related to inertia. The more massive the atmosphere, the more inertia. Therefore, the large-scale zonal flows of Venus, Jupiter, and Saturn are regular and constant in time. The Earth's jet stream is meandering and variable, perhaps because the atmosphere has less inertia. If these speculative ideas are correct, the Earth is in the unpredictable middle range between Mars, where disturbances are rapidly damped, and the more massive atmospheres, where stable flows persist for long periods due to their large inertia.

The lesson for terrestrial weather forecasting is no different from that which has been taught by everyday experience. There is a limit to the predictability of the Earth's weather. Meteorologists may be able to extend their forecasts for a few days, but soon the inherent instability of the Earth's atmosphere will frustrate their efforts. Still, it would be useful to refine the understanding of these limits in order to see where improvement is possible. Studying the weather on other planets is a way to broaden the perspectives of scientists on the Earth and thereby to improve their understanding of the Earth's weather.

158

NASA

View of the Earth from the Apollo 17 manned spacecraft reveals Africa and Arabia at the top and extends south to Antarctica. Perhaps because the Earth's atmosphere is less massive than those of Venus, Jupiter, and Saturn, the flows of its jet streams are more meandering and variable, and its weather is, consequently, less predictable.

FOR ADDITIONAL READING

J. Kelly Beatty, Brian O'Leary, and Andrew Chaikin (eds.), *The New Solar System* (Sky Publishing Corp. and Cambridge University Press, 1981).

A. G. W. Cameron, "The Origin and Evolution of the Solar System," *Scientific American* (September 1975, pp. 32–41).

Richard E. Dickerson, "Chemical Evolution and the Origin of Life," *Scientific American* (September 1978, pp. 70–86).

Richard M. Goody and James C. G. Walker, *Atmospheres* (Prentice-Hall, 1972).

Andrew P. Ingersoll, "Jupiter and Saturn," *Scientific American* (December 1981, pp. 90–108).

Conway B. Leovy, "The Atmosphere of Mars," *Scientific American* (July 1977, pp. 34–43).

John S. Lewis, "The Chemistry of the Solar System," *Scientific American* (March 1974, pp. 50–65).

Tobias Owen, "Titan," *Scientific American* (February 1982, pp. 98–109).

Carl Sagan, "The Solar System," *Scientific American* (September 1975, pp. 22–31).

Gerald Schubert and Curt Covey, "The Atmosphere of Venus," *Scientific American* (July 1981, pp. 66–74).

TWENTY YEARS OF QUASARS

by Maarten Schmidt

When they were first detected in the early 1960s, quasars were mysterious objects, unlike anything else previously found in the universe. Astronomers have since learned much about them, but aspects of mystery remain.

Quasars are astronomical objects so extraordinary that astronomers did not imagine them even in their dreams before 1960. Some quasars are more than a hundred times brighter than even the most brilliant galaxies. Yet in size they probably are a million times smaller than those same galaxies. As a consequence of their high luminosities, quasars can be detected by Earth-bound telescopes out to distances of approximately ten billion light-years. At both X-ray and radio wavelengths some quasars are strong emitters of radiation. In several cases radio waves are ejected by the quasar at almost the speed of light.

Quasars are exceedingly rare: the nearest one is almost one billion light-years away. At large distances their numbers increase dramatically up to a certain point, beyond which they are not seen at all. This apparent limit or boundary is one of the intriguing problems posed by these objects.

The nature of quasars remains mysterious. The most promising explanation of their large output of energy is that it is due to the accretion of gas by a central black hole of about 10^8 solar masses. An alternative hypothesis states that a quasar is a massive, rotating, highly magnetized, compact object.

Since their discovery in the early 1960s quasars have had a profound impact on extragalactic astronomy. At their enormous distances they provide light probes that allow study of gas clouds located in the line of sight from quasar to Earth. Some of these clouds appear to belong to the halos of galaxies. Others, never observed before, are probably dark primordial clouds of gas. In a few cases the light of a distant quasar is bent around a massive galaxy by the latter's gravitational effect. The observer sees two or more images of different brightness but identical properties. This is the first

160

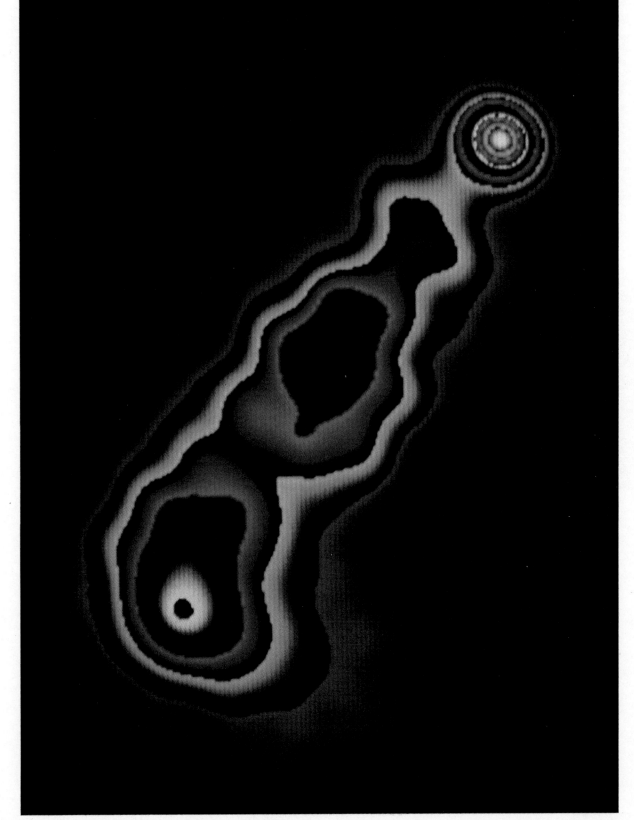

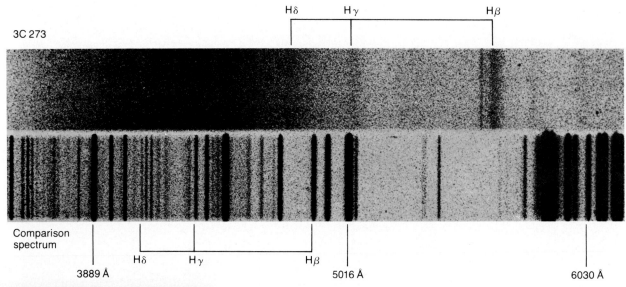

3C 273

Hδ   Hγ   Hβ

Comparison
spectrum

Hδ   Hγ   Hβ

3889 Å   5016 Å   6030 Å

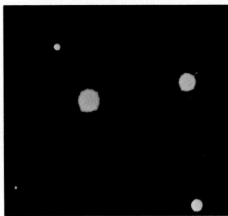

*MAARTEN SCHMIDT, one of the early
discoverers of quasars, is Institute
Professor of Astronomy at the
California Institute of Technology,
Pasadena.*

*(Overleaf) Photograph by Steve
Northup, Discover Magazine, © 1982
Time Inc.*

demonstration of the gravitational lens, which is predicted by Einstein's General Theory of Relativity.

Size, luminosity, and red shifts

Quasars are defined as astronomical objects which on astronomical photographs look like stars and the spectra of which show large red shifts. The red shift is defined as the shift toward the longer red wavelengths of all the lines in the spectrum, expressed as a fraction of the wavelength itself. Thus, for a red shift of 0.10, lines appearing at 5000 and 6000 angstroms in the laboratory will be observed at 5500 and 6600 angstroms, respectively. (1 angstrom, Å, equals one ten-billionth of a meter.) Such a red shift corresponds to the Doppler effect for an object moving away from the observer with a speed of about 10% of the speed of light.

Ordinary stars reveal both blue shifts (due to a velocity of approach) and red shifts, up to a maximum of 0.002, corresponding to a velocity of 600 kilometers per second (375 miles per second). In 1963 the first red shift for a quasar was determined from its spectrum. The quasar, 3C 273, yielded a red shift of 0.16. Such a large shift ruled out the possibility that 3C 273 was a star, even though it looked like one on photographs. Instead, it seemed to belong in the league of galaxies, for which at that time red shifts up to 0.46 had been observed.

The red shifts of galaxies are attributed to the expansion of the universe. Edwin Hubble discovered in 1929 that the red shifts of galaxies are proportional to their distances from the Earth. This led to the "Big Bang" concept of the beginning of the universe, in which all matter started its expansion from a very small initial volume. The proportionality constant between velocity and distance, called the Hubble constant, is probably in the range of 50 to 100 km/sec per megaparsec, corresponding to an age of the universe between 10 and 20 billion years. Assuming that the red shift of 0.16 for 3C 273 is cosmological, that is, due to the expansion of the universe, the distance of 3C 273 from the Earth is the same as that of galaxies of red shift 0.16. How-

162

ever, 3C 273 is four magnitudes (or a factor of 40) brighter than the brightest of those galaxies. Thus, it appears that 3C 273 is 40 times brighter than the most brilliant galaxies. Almost all of the approximately 2,000 known quasars are more luminous than the brightest galaxies, some by a factor as large as 500.

Since quasars reveal a pointlike image on photographs, just as do stars, it is surprising that their luminosities are so much greater than those of galaxies, which have images that are always extended. This difference in size becomes even more remarkable if one considers the variability of quasars. Most quasars vary in brightness by approximately 10 to 50% within a year. Some quasars show much more rapid variations, on a time scale of a week or so. The diameter of such an object cannot be much larger than a light-week, since the light travel time across an object determines how fast a variation can be observed for it. Astronomically speaking, a light-week is extremely small for an extragalactic object. This is especially true if that object outshines luminous galaxies that have diameters of about 100,000 light-years.

It is this combination of relatively small size and high luminosity that makes quasars extraordinary objects. And it was this same combination that led some astronomers to question the interpretation of the red shifts as due to the expansion of the universe.

The red shift controversy

The large distances and the huge luminosities of quasars discussed above are a consequence of the cosmological interpretation of the large observed red shifts. There exist alternative explanations of the red shifts, namely as Doppler shifts of nearby objects or as gravitational red shifts.

Since all spectral shifts in quasars are red shifts, any interpretation of them in terms of the Doppler effect leads to an explosion with all velocities pointed outward. In the cosmological hypothesis this explosion is the Big Bang. In another hypothesis, which puts the quasars at relatively small distances, the explosion has to be local and relatively recent. James Terrell of Los Alamos (New Mexico) National Laboratory proposed in 1964 that quasars are a consequence of a local explosion in our Milky Way galaxy. Accord-

Quasar 3C 273 is seen at the left center in the photograph on the opposite page. In the spectra shown above the photograph three hydrogen emission lines are seen to be shifted toward longer wavelengths (to the right) in the spectrum of 3C 273 in comparison with their normal wavelengths in the spectrum shown below. This red shift indicates that 3C 273 is receding from the Earth at almost one-sixth the speed of light.

Spectra at the right reveal differences between a strong radio galaxy, 3C 79 (top portion of the upper two spectra), and a quasar, 3C 323.1 (bottom portion of the lower two). When their emission lines are compared with the accompanying reference spectra, 3C 79 is found to have a red shift of 0.256 while 3C 323.1 has a slightly greater one of 0.264.

ing to this hypothesis quasars are about 100 times nearer to the Earth than they are in the cosmological hypothesis.

The gravitational hypothesis considers the red shift to be caused by the loss of energy suffered by photons in escaping from the gravitational field of the quasar. For example, light from the surface of the Sun reaches the Earth slightly red shifted, by 0.000002, due to the Sun's gravitational field. Studies of this hypothesis, however, reveal that quasars would be incapable of producing the so-called forbidden emission lines seen in their spectra unless their masses were in excess of those of the largest galaxies.

Since both of the above alternative hypotheses gave rise to a picture of quasars that was even more exotic than that based on the cosmological hypothesis, neither became popular among astronomers. However, yet another local hypothesis has been much discussed for the past 10 or 15 years. This hypothesis, put forward by Halton C. Arp at Mount Wilson and Las Campanas Observatories and G. R. Burbidge at Kitt Peak (Arizona) National Observatory, places quasars at distances much smaller than they are if one accepts the cosmological red shift interpretation. No physical explanation of the red shifts is provided. The main argument for the local hypothesis is based on the purported association of quasars with galaxies of much smaller red shifts. This association can be in various forms such as a luminous connection between quasar and galaxy or an alignment of quasars on either side of a galaxy. If such an association is real, then the distance of quasar and galaxy has to be the same. If that is true, the red shift of the quasar could not be cosmological. The proponents of the local hypothesis believe on the basis of statistical arguments that the evidence for the reality of the associations is solid. These arguments are criticized by the opponents, who believe that the associations are accidental alignments of objects that are at very different distances along the line of sight.

The case for the cosmological interpretation of the red shifts has gradually become stronger. About one-third of the quasars with moderate red shifts have nearby galaxies at the same red shift, showing that they belong to groups or clusters of galaxies. In some cases absorption lines in the spectrum of a high-red shift quasar are seen at a red shift equal to that of a galaxy nearby in the sky. This indicates that the quasar is at least as far away as the galaxy. Also, the double quasar that is known to be gravitationally lensed by a galaxy with a red shift of 0.45 must be at least at the distance of that galaxy.

Further supporting arguments for the cosmological red shift hypothesis are of a statistical nature. It is now known that the observed quasars can account for a large fraction of the observed soft (low-energy) X-ray background. If these quasars are relatively local, then the X-ray contribution from the more distant unobserved quasars in the universe should be added to the local ones, which would result in too large an X-ray background.

Another argument is based on the counts of quasars of different brightness. Quasar surveys indicate that there are 0.007 quasars per square degree brighter than magnitude 16. At magnitude 18 the number has increased to about 0.5 quasars per square degree. The steep increase of the counts, by a factor of 8 per magnitude, can only be understood if the density of quasars in space increases with distance from the Earth. Since this is observed in all directions, the Earth is located at a position in space where quasars are rarer than elsewhere. This, however, is contradictory to the Copernican principle that the Earthbound observer is not located at a preferred or special position in the universe. In the cosmological hypothesis of the red shifts the steep counts are interpreted as a consequence of evolution of quasars on a cosmic time scale.

The main deficiency of the local hypothesis is probably that it does not explain the large observed red shifts, which are the most remarkable property of quasars. While the cosmological-versus-local debate lingers on, most astronomers have adopted the former as a working hypothesis.

Quasars as radio sources

Initially, all quasars discovered were radio sources, and their optical identifications were made on the basis of position measurements obtained with radio telescopes. It had been realized in the 1950s that many radio sources observed outside the Milky Way were associated with galaxies. Optical observations of these radio galaxies supplied their red shifts and hence their distances, which in turn were important for the physical interpretation of the radio observations. Astronomers now know that a substantial fraction of the radio sources are radio-emitting quasars. It appears that radio galaxies and quasars account for essentially all extragalactic radio sources.

The appearance at radio wavelengths of quasars and radio galaxies is fairly similar. Typically, the radio radiation emanates from a small source located at the optical image of the quasar or radio galaxy and often from two large blobs on opposite sides of the central source at a distance of typically 100,000 light-years. In some cases a radio-emitting jet is seen to emerge from one side of the central source.

It has become possible to investigate the structure of radio sources in remarkably fine detail by a technique called very-long baseline interferometry. A given radio source is simultaneously observed by radio telescopes separated by thousands of kilometers. At each location the radio signal is recorded together with accurate time signals. The tapes are played back and correlated at a special computing facility.

The large separation of the radio telescopes allows detection of very fine detail in the source, to 0.001 second of arc or better. Quasar radio maps made by this technique often reveal the central source to consist of several components. For a number of radio quasars the radio map changes on a time scale of only a few months. In most cases one of the components is observed to move away from the others at a speed that appears to be much larger than the speed of light. These so-called superluminal velocities of expansion may be as great as ten times the speed of light. This extraordinary observational result seems to contradict the classical evidence in experimental physics that no velocity can exceed that of light.

The determination of the expansion velocity is based on the angular motion of expansion, which is observed, and the distance that is obtained from the red shift. At first, it might be tempting to question the distance as being responsible for the superluminal velocities. In the local hypothesis there

Alan Stockton, Institute for Astronomy, University of Hawaii at Manoa

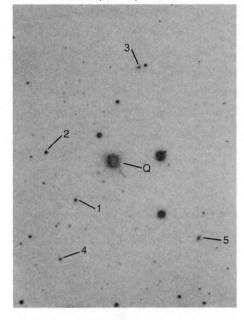

Quasar 3C 273 (Q) is shown in close association with several galaxies of the same red shift (2, 3, 4, and 5; 1 is a background galaxy). Such an association lends support to the cosmological interpretation of red shifts; that is, that they are caused by the expansion of the universe.

Anthony C. S. Readhead, California Institute of Technology

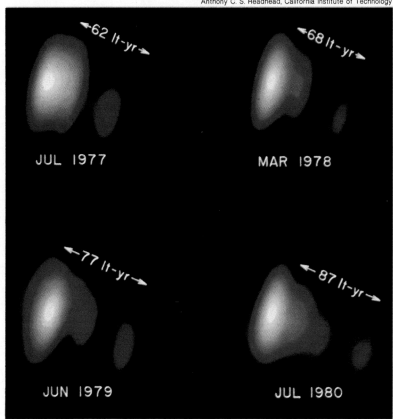

Radio images of 3C 273 achieve a resolution of 0.001 second of arc by means of a synthesis of signals recorded by combinations of either four or five telescopes in California, Texas, Massachusetts, West Virginia, and West Germany. The blob ejected from the quasar appears to have traveled a distance of 25 light-years between July 1977 and July 1980, a "superluminal" velocity 9.6 times the speed of light. This "forbidden" speed was shown to be an illusion created by the fact that the blob is moving almost directly toward the Earth at more than 99% the speed of light.

would be no problem because distances would be 100 times smaller, and the deduced velocities of expansion would be only 0.1 of the speed of light. However, one radio galaxy, the distance of which is not in doubt, also reveals a superluminal velocity of expansion.

The solution to this problem probably lies in the concept of relativistic motion. It is hypothesized that the matter producing the radio emission is ejected with almost the speed of light at a small angle to the line of sight from the Earth. The resulting angular motion is much larger than it would be if the material was ejected perpendicular to the line of sight. When the angular motion is converted into a linear speed, the result appears to be superluminal motion even though nothing moves faster than the speed of light. This interpretation has focused the attention of radio astronomers on the role of beaming of radiation, since matter moving with relativistic speed will beam its radiation mostly in the forward direction.

Among the brightest quasars about one-quarter can be detected as radio sources. This fraction is much smaller for faint quasars. As a consequence the majority of quasars can only be found by optical searches.

Distribution of quasars

Extensive searches for quasars have been conducted over the last ten years. Some studies aim at the discovery of very faint quasars over small areas of the sky, while others cover much of the sky but probe less deeply. All objects

166

have to be confirmed as quasars on the basis of a spectrum that shows red-shifted emission lines. Since the observation of a spectrum at a telescope is time-consuming, astronomers cannot afford to search blindly for quasars by taking spectra of every starlike object in the field. Fortunately, a pre-selection can be made on the basis of color or slitless spectroscopy.

Quasars identified with radio sources show an ultraviolet-intense optical continuum in the sense that the ratio of brightness in the ultraviolet over that in the blue part of the spectrum is larger than for most stars in the sky. This ratio is determined by measuring the star's brightness with filters that transmit the ultraviolet and the blue wavelength bands, respectively. Lists of ultraviolet-intense stars so selected turn out to be relatively rich in quasars. However, this selection technique does not work well for quasars with red shifts larger than 2.2. Because of their spectral properties these quasars are not ultraviolet-intense optically. The best technique for finding quasars with large red shifts is slitless spectroscopy. When a grating or prism is placed in the light path in a telescope, each object imaged at the focus exhibits a short spectrum. While the detail that can be observed in these spectra is usually not great, it does show the strong Lyman-alpha hydrogen emission line at a rest wavelength of 1216 Å. This line indicates the presence of a quasar. Red shifts in the range 1.8–3.5 have been so determined for hundreds of quasars.

Complete surveys, which aim at the detection of every quasar to some magnitude limit in a given area of the sky, constitute a census of quasars from which their density in space can be derived. The results show that the space density increases enormously with red shift. For example, quasars with the same luminosity as 3C 273 increase in space density by a factor of 600 between red shifts 0.5 and 2.5.

The steepness of the density increase depends strongly on the luminosity of the quasar. For quasars of the lowest luminosities there appears to be little or no increase. In interpreting these results one should remember that it takes light a very long time to get from the quasar to the Earth. This travel

In searching for quasars astronomers use the technique of slitless spectroscopy to find those with red shifts larger than 2.2. This involves placing a prism or grating in the light path of a telescope and thereby obtaining at the focus a low-resolution spectrum of an observed object. These spectra are detailed enough to reveal the strong Lyman-alpha hydrogen emission line at a rest wavelength of 1216 Å, indicating the presence of a quasar. Below left is a direct image of a quasar with a red shift of 2.75, and below is a low-resolution spectrum of the quasar obtained by slitless spectroscopy.

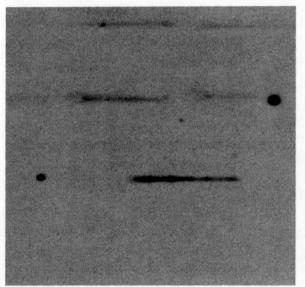

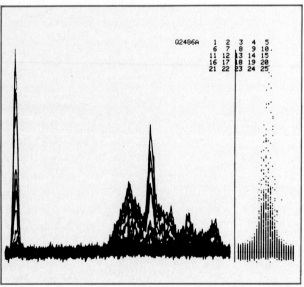

Reprinted courtesy of Tobias J. Kreidl, Norman G. Thomas, Arthur Hoag, and *The Astrophysical Journal*, vol. 261, p. 20, October 1, 1982 published by the University of Chicago Press; © 1982 The American Astronomical Society

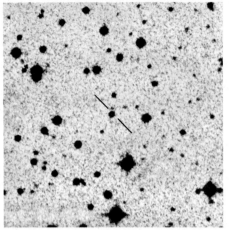

*The object shown between the dashes
is the optical counterpart of radio
quasar PKS 2000-330. With a red shift
of 3.78 it is the most distant known
visible object in the universe.*

time is typically a few billion years for the nearest quasars and more than ten billion years for those more distant. As a consequence observations show the quasars as they were billions of years ago. On the basis of this information the increase of space density with red shift can be reinterpreted. Since light-travel time increases with red shift, the space densities were higher in the past; in other words, the space density of quasars is decreasing as the universe is getting older. Some ten or twelve billion years ago there were many more quasars than there are now. In fact the decline has been so rapid that relatively few exist today.

A red shift limit?

In some of the slitless spectroscopic searches for quasars red shifts of up to 4.7 could have been detected, but none have been found so far. The largest red shift known at present is 3.78, for the radio quasar PKS 2000-330.

The apparent absence of quasars with red shifts larger than 4 has given rise to much speculation. Some astronomers believe that it may have taken quasars a few billion years after the Big Bang to begin radiating. This would show up in the observations as a boundary in red shift or distance that corresponds to the epoch when radiation began. Other astronomers think that quasars may have different properties at large red shifts, which would prevent their detection by the techniques used for the searches. Yet others suggest that the absence may be caused by dust absorption in distant parts of the universe. Much observational work is going on in an effort to clarify the situation.

Intergalactic clouds

The first evidence for discrete absorption lines in quasar spectra was found in 1966. The quasar 3C 191 showed a rich absorption-line spectrum at a red shift slightly smaller than the quasar red shift. In this case the absorbing material is very close to the quasar and probably associated with it. Subsequently, many quasars were found to exhibit numerous narrow absorption lines. These lines exhibit many different red shifts, usually smaller than the quasar red shift. The interpretation is that the line of sight to the quasar cuts through many intergalactic clouds, each at a different distance and thus with a different red shift. In a few cases these clouds may have been ejected by the quasar; those in an Earthbound observer's line of sight would have been ejected toward the Earth, leading to an absorption red shift smaller than the quasar red shift.

Some of the intergalactic clouds show only hydrogen absorption lines, but others also show lines of such elements as silicon, sulfur, and iron. The latter are almost certainly associated with the outer halos of galaxies. The nature of their spectra agrees well with absorption caused in the halo of our own Galaxy. The occurrence of these absorption line systems in quasar spectra is more frequent than had been expected originally, but this is probably caused by the large size of the galactic halos, making it more likely for the line of sight from a quasar to cut through one of them.

The other intergalactic clouds, which display only hydrogen absorption lines, are a new phenomenon. They may consist of primordial material in

168

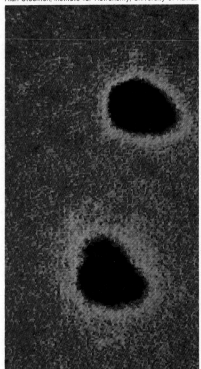 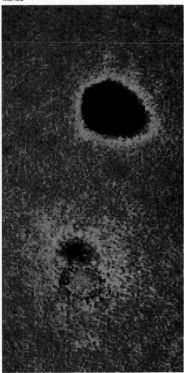

Twin quasars as photographed by a 2.2-meter telescope on Mauna Kea in Hawaii demonstrate the phenomenon known as a gravitational lens. At the left the twins are shown in a display that was generated by a computer program which summed and color-coded many images. The elongation of both in the direction of four o'clock is a result of imperfect alignment of the telescope optics. The northern image (top) was adjusted so that it had the same brightness as did the southern (bottom). At the right the adjusted northern image is subtracted from the unadjusted southern one. This procedure reveals an image of a galaxy one arc second north of the southern twin. The structure of the image shows that the galaxy lies between the quasar and the Earth, providing additional support for the theory that quasars are at great distances.

which no star formation and thus no synthesis of heavy elements through nuclear reactions has yet taken place. There are indications that these clouds tend to cluster together less than is the case for galaxies.

Gravitational lenses

Einstein's General Theory of Relativity predicts that light rays will be bent by a gravitational field. An example is provided by the Sun; during a solar eclipse when stars can be observed near the darkened Sun, their positions show a small displacement radially away from the Sun, in agreement with Einstein's prediction. Under suitable circumstances a large mass can act as a lens, concentrating light from a distant object on the observer. If the object, lensing mass, and observer are perfectly aligned, the observer will see a bright ring. A slight misalignment will break the ring up into several small images. The very long line of sight to the distant quasars makes them particularly good candidates for such a lineup with a galaxy. Several quasars exhibit two or more images, each with an identical spectrum and red shift. In one case the lensing mass has been detected. It is a large galaxy in a cluster of galaxies, the combined effect of which appears to be responsible for the double imaging.

The typical separation of the double or multiple images of lensed quasars is a few seconds of arc. This is about as large a separation as can be expected from lensing by galaxies; there should be many cases where the image separation is smaller than two seconds of arc. However, systematic searches for

Gary A. Chanan, Columbia University

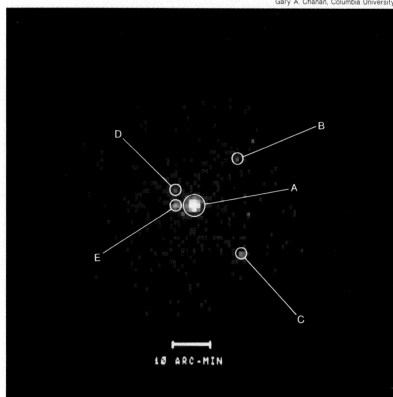

False-color X-ray image taken from an orbiting satellite reveals a region of the sky in the constellation Hercules. Unlike ordinary visible-light photographs it effectively distinguishes X-ray sources (A–E) from other objects. The source A is a previously known quasar 3C 345, about 7.2 billion light-years from the Earth. B, C, and D are quasars that had not previously been detected; B is 9.5 billion light-years, and C is 6.7 billion light-years distant. Source D is the combined emission from two separate quasars, one at a distance of 7.9 billion light-years and the other at 7.2 billion light-years. Source E corresponds with the abnormal galaxy NGC 6212, which is only about 560 million light-years from the Earth.

such double or multiple images have produced few additional candidates.

The rays that form the separate images travel different paths around the lensing galaxy. The light travel times from object to observer along the different paths differ by as much as one or more years. If the object itself is variable, then the different images should show the same variation but displaced in time. One of the lensed quasars is indeed variable and is being monitored regularly. If the time delay between the images can be established, it allows in principle an independent determination of the distance of the object. This would be a valuable check on the Hubble constant.

Quasars as X-ray sources

X-ray astronomy requires observations from high altitude or in orbit to avoid the absorption of this type of radiation in the Earth's atmosphere. Only the brightest quasar, 3C 273, was detected in early rocket flights. During the past few years large numbers of quasars have been observed with the Einstein satellite. These observations have shown that the amount of X-radiation per unit of optical light is highest for quasars of low optical luminosity and high radio luminosity. The deepest surveys carried out with the Einstein satellite have detected some 20 X-ray sources per square degree. Some of these are associated with clusters of galaxies, but it appears that most of them are quasars.

Measurements over wide angles reveal an X-ray background the origin of which is the subject of much discussion. At first it was thought that this background could be caused by hot intergalactic gas, and it appeared that

Reprinted courtesy of J. A. Tyson, W. A. Baum, T. Kreidl, and *The Astrophysical Journal,* vol. 257, pp. L1-L5, June 1, 1982, published by the University of Chicago Press; © 1982 The American Astronomical Society

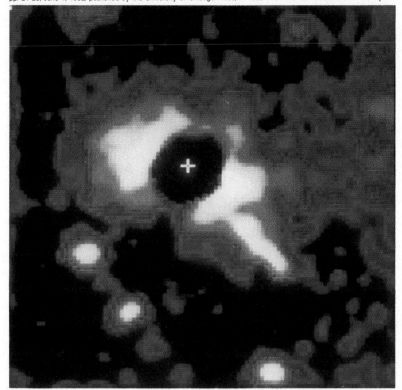

Light from quasar 3C 273 was blocked at the telescope, resulting in the black oval with the cross in the middle. A sensitive charge-coupled device imager was then used to capture the nebulosity surrounding the quasar, which revealed that 3C 273 lies within a galaxy. The surface brightness of the outer blue regions in this color-intensity-coded image is 390,000 times fainter than is the quasar light and would not be visible if the quasar had not been blocked. The color and luminosity of the galaxy favor the hypothesis that it lies at the same distance as 3C 273 and thus does not act as a gravitational lens between the quasar and the Earth.

this gas might have critical cosmological mass density. This critical mass density is the one required to slow down the expansion of the universe to zero at time infinity. It now appears that a substantial fraction of the soft X-ray background is due to the accumulated effect of quasars. This predicted contribution by the quasars depends on the maximum red shift to which they exist. The X-ray background may eventually allow confirmation of, or improvement upon, the red shift limit of about 3.5 or 4 that is suggested by optical surveys.

Epilogue

When first discovered 20 years ago, quasars were objects so extreme in their properties (high luminosities, small size) that they seemed to bear little relation to the universe of objects already known. During the intervening period this situation has changed radically. Even though they are much more powerful, quasars are now considered to be similar to nuclei of galaxies, in particular of Seyfert galaxies and radio galaxies. In fact, low-luminosity quasars and Seyfert nuclei cannot be clearly distinguished from one another and may be identical phenomena. Quasars may well signal the birth of a galaxy or of its nucleus. This would fit in well with the fact that quasars were much more numerous in the distant past, since it appears likely that most galaxies were born within a few billion years after the Big Bang.

FROM
ANCIENT PLANTS
TO
MODERN MEDICINE

by Richard Evans Schultes

Biologically active plant substances have figured importantly in primitive societies as medicines, narcotics, and poisons. Their systematic study, ethnopharmacology, offers science a vast source of new agents for medical therapy and research.

The Earth is home to an estimated 500,000 species of plants, and botanists describe about 5,000 new species and varieties each year. Many of these plants contain substances—alkaloids, aromatic compounds, alcohols, aldehydes, ketones, esters, terpenoids, steroids, flavonoids, and amino acids—that have physical or psychic effects on human beings. Through experimentation over thousands of years various peoples have been able to turn these effects to their use as medicines to alleviate or cure ills, as narcotics in magico-religious rituals, or as poisons for use in killing enemies, euthanasia, hunting, fishing, or the administration of justice. It is impossible even to guess how many plant species have been valued for their biologically active (biodynamic) properties, but every culture has developed its own pharmacopoeia, the size of it depending usually on the variety of available plants. Some of the uses to which plants have been put represent truly ingenious discoveries. The complex formulas for preparing curare, a South American arrow poison (which can involve from 4 or 5 to 20 species), is an excellent example of the perspicacity of humans in primitive societies who live in close association with the local vegetation.

In addition to purely academic or intellectual interest, the study of medicinal plants in aboriginal societies serves a very practical purpose in pointing the way to the discovery of new drugs. Many of the most valuable and widely employed older drugs in today's medical arsenal, of course, have been used for millennia in native practices. But even some of the more recent finds, including most of the so-called wonder drugs of the 20th century, were used in some form by primitive societies. In the 1930s the first of these new agents to be recognized for their medicinal value were the muscle relaxants isolated from the alkaloid constituents of curare. This breakthrough was closely followed by the isolation of penicillin and a host of other antibiotics, primarily from fungi. Although these latter discoveries were made in the

laboratory, ancient Egyptians are known to have used fungi to cure infections, and early English folk medicine recommended plasters of moldy bread for sores. The antibiotics were followed in turn by other new drugs, some of which revolutionized medical practice. They include reserpine, a blood-pressure-lowering agent from *Rauwolfia;* alkaloids from the false hellebore (species of *Veratrum*), which also lower blood pressure; podophyllotoxin, an anticancer and antifungal agent from mayapple (*Podophyllum*); the anticancer alkaloids (vinca alkaloids) from the periwinkle; and cortisone, which can be synthesized in quantity from compounds in a Mexican yam (*Dioscorea*)

E. Wade Davis, Botanical Museum, Harvard University

Huarani jaguar shaman of Ecuador dries poison darts dipped in curare. In the foreground and suspended between two war spears is a palm leaf filter used for crude extraction of curare alkaloids from plant shavings. From 4 or 5 to 20 plant species may be involved in the preparation of curare. (Overleaf) Yarn painting from Mexico depicts a Huichol Indian woman being bewitched by a hallucinogenic Datura plant into tasting its fruits.

RICHARD EVANS SCHULTES is Jeffrey Professor of Biology and Curator of Economic Botany and Director of the Botanical Museum, Harvard University.

(Overleaf) Photograph by Peter T. Furst, State University of New York at Albany

and the tropical African arrow-poison plant *Strophanthus sarmentosus.*

The scientific investigation of many of these plant substances was first suggested by a use in an aboriginal society. Modern technology may not be interested in the aboriginal use, but the fact that a plant is biodynamic indicates that it possesses active principles that may have wholly different applications in modern medicine or industry. Rotenone-rich plants, for example, are widely employed in primitive societies as fish poisons, yet rotenone has become a potent, biodegradable insecticide of incredible value in today's intensive agriculture.

Ethnopharmacology

That branch of science devoted to the investigation of biodynamic plants used in primitive societies as medicines, narcotics, or poisons is now known as ethnopharmacology. It is not a new discipline, notwithstanding the fact that only recently has it been widely accorded systematic research. It is an interdisciplinary field, basically botanical but frequently involving anthropology, plant chemistry, pharmacology, and even such apparently unrelated fields as history, geography, linguistics, and comparative religion. Its growing importance is indicated by the recent appearance of several journals devoted exclusively to this or related fields of research—*e.g.,* the *Journal of Ethnopharmacology*—and the numerous scientific gatherings of interdisciplinary character concerning this topic. It has even developed subdivisions such as ethnomycology, the relationship between fungi and human affairs, a new but extremely prolific field.

There are numerous ways in which ethnopharmacological research is carried out. Archaeology frequently is useful. The interpretation of ancient engravings, monuments, and art forms sometimes sheds light on medicinal plants or sacred intoxicants. The literature is rich in uninvestigated uses of medicinal plants—writings going back to the early Egyptians, Indians, and Chinese. Contemporary reports of anthropologists, travelers, and others often provide valuable hints. In addition, the millions of worldwide dried plant specimens maintained in collections called herbaria contain a wealth of notes on medicinal uses, notes gathered firsthand in the field by collectors, with a specimen to provide an accurate identity of the plant.

It is, however, intensive field work in still viable aboriginal societies that constitutes the best method of uncovering significant information, but the extinction or rapid acculturation of many groups makes imperative an intensification of this kind of research. From a practical viewpoint, tapping aboriginal experience is an unrivaled shortcut to laboratory investigation of the properties of the myriad species of plants in the world.

Archaeology and historical writings

Archaeological discoveries are increasingly enriching man's knowledge of the use of plants in ancient cultures. One recent find, a Neanderthal burial site in northern Iraq dated about 60,000 years ago, contained evidence for the use of eight kinds of flowers. That seven of them are still used today for medicinal or insect-repellent properties raises some interesting questions about their purpose in Neanderthal burial beyond aesthetics or sentimental-

174

ity. Archaeological plant remains or art representations in Peru have helped in understanding the pre-Columbian evolution of societies and the evolution of cultivated plants. Recent studies of plant remains in Egyptian mummies have shed much light on ancient embalming.

It is now known that the Egyptians had an herb garden at Karnak in 1500 BC; their monuments feature engravings of medicinal plants brought from as far away as Syria. Recent excavations in southern Russia of Scythian tombs containing braziers, tents, and remains of the marijuana plant, *Cannabis*, support the story written by the Greek historian Herodotus in 450 BC about the effectiveness of Scythian steam baths, in which these people threw hemp on embers and inhaled the vapors. In 350 BC the philosopher Theophrastus, who is credited with founding the science of botany, was director of a garden in Athens that received medicinal plants sent in by Alexander the Great from regions as far away as Afghanistan and India.

Plants first appreciated for their medicinal qualities by primitive peoples have become sources for many modern drugs. They include (clockwise, from top left) the periwinkle Catharanthus roseus, Rauwolfia tetraphylla, *the Mexican yam* Dioscorea composita, *and the African vine* Strophanthus sarmentosus.

175

When they are critically used, historical writings may provide much valuable information, but they are diverse and of varying reliability. Literature of the Old World, filled with significant and still partly unstudied data, includes the Babylonian Code of Hammurabi; the papyrus scrolls of Egypt, especially the Ebers Papyrus of 1500 BC; the Vedas of India, particularly the Rig Veda, probably the oldest repository of human knowledge; and ancient Chinese writings dating back more than 4,500 years. The writings of classical Greece are rich in still unexamined ethnomedical information, but those of Rome, being primarily compilations of earlier Greek work, are in general disappointingly devoid of originality.

Details of the ancient secret religious ceremony of the Greeks, the Eleusinian Mysteries, have been an enigma for 4,000 years. The identity of the intoxicating plant used in this rite has been especially contested. Recent scientific studies of an interdisciplinary nature—a combination of classical philology, mycology (the study of mushrooms, yeasts, and other fungi), and chemistry—suggest that the holy inebriation was due to the use of a species of ergot, a toxic plant fungus (*Claviceps*) and a natural source of substances related to LSD.

For 16 centuries European literature on folk medicine was enslaved by an authoritarian culture that limited medicobotanical writings to interpretation of the teachings of the ancient authorities of Greece and Rome. But the invention of printing, the discovery of the New World, and the Reformation broke this hold on Western culture. Although the earliest herbals were merely garbled versions of the Greek physician Dioscorides and other classical writers, the herbals of Leonhard Fuchs, William Turner, John Parkinson, Rembert Dodoens, and others, written in the 16th and 17th centuries, are veritable funds of information that should be evaluated in modern studies. It is true, however, that the medieval folk medicine of Europe was—as is its modern counterpart—primarily a remnant of ancient Greek and Roman pharmacopoeias.

In the New World extensive medical literature is limited for the most part

Richard E. Schultes

to Mexico. The earliest herbal in the New World, the *Badianus Manuscript* of 1542, was written by an Aztec Indian and illustrates a large number of Mexican medicinal plants, most of which can be identified from the art. King Philip II of Spain sent his personal physician, Francisco Hernández, to study the medicinal plants and animals used by the Aztecs, with whom he remained for five years. His manuscript, *Rerum Medicarum Novae Hispaniae Thesaurus,* published in 1651, has had a powerful influence on modern ethnopharmacological research. Most of the careful illustrations in this work can serve to identify the species and are accompanied by a wealth of still uninvestigated information. In addition, many reports and surveys written by the Spanish authorities in Mexico contain valuable information on medicinal plants. It is due to this rich post-Conquest literature that ethnopharmacological studies in modern Mexico are so far advanced.

Value of specimen collections

There is no more efficient method of gathering ethnopharmacological data than from direct observation and study of plant lore and use in existing aboriginal societies. This kind of investigation usually has been done by anthropologists, to a lesser extent by botanists, and sometimes by medical scientists, pharmacologists, and chemists. Unfortunately, many interesting observations have turned out to be of limited value because they were not substantiated by identifiable plant specimens. An identification is frequently doubtful because it was made through a vernacular or native name; often no identification is available. The value of filing away an herbarium specimen in a botanical institution for later verification has been widely recognized only recently.

During the last two centuries, plant scientists have avidly studied and collected plants in most parts of the world and have filed them away in herbaria for future study. There are now more than 1,400 herbaria, some of which are very large: Paris, 7,200,000 specimens; Leningrad, Geneva, Kew (England), each 5,000,000; Stockholm and Harvard University, each 4,000,000. The herbarium with dried and pressed specimens from around the world represents not only an essential tool for botanical research but also an untapped source of ethnopharmacological information. Many of the specimens bear the collector's notation of a medicinal use of the plant by primitive societies. This information is firsthand, and the data concerning locality, people, and time are exact. One recent search, for example, through the four million herbarium specimens at Harvard University yielded more than 7,500 such collectors' reports, many of which suggest potential targets for chemical and pharmacological investigation. Likewise a search through the equally rich herbarium of the New York Botanical Garden uncovered more than 4,500 similar reports.

While there have not been enough trained ethnopharmacological personnel to keep up with the preservation of aboriginal plant lore in the face of acculturation or extinction of peoples, a surprising amount of literature has been published in the 20th century. This information is widely scattered in numerous journals, and it is essential that it be gathered together so that it can be fully appreciated. Perhaps the ideal goal should be the eventual

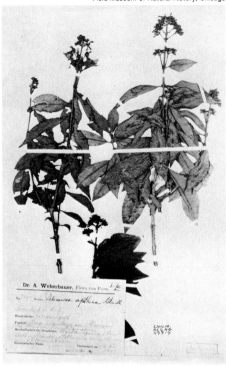

Field Museum of Natural History, Chicago

The collection and filing away of herbarium specimens together with a description of the living plant, the location and circumstances of discovery, and other pertinent information are a valuable part of botanical research. The herbaria of the world represent a largely untapped source of ethnopharmacological information.

computerization of all available data, a project being initiated at Harvard's Botanical Museum on a grant from the World Wildlife Fund.

Field work in the Americas

In North America specialists have recorded the plant lore (comprising in great part medicinal plants) of a number of tribes, including the Blackfoot, Cherokee, Chippewa, Ojibwe, Kiowa, Potawatomi, Miskwaki, Iroquois, Kawaiisu, Yuki, Chimariko, Miwok, and Washo, and have undertaken more specific studies of species valued as curatives by tribes in various geographical regions. Several plants owe their modern application to studies of their use in aboriginal North American societies, including *Lobelia inflata* (commonly called Indian tobacco), which contains an alkaloid used as a smoking deterrent; the false hellebore *Veratrum viride,* with its blood-pressure-lowering and sedative agents; and the mayapple (*Podophyllum peltatum*), with tumor-inhibiting properties.

Due to the virtual extinction of Indian cultures in the West Indies, much information on their plant lore has been forever lost. Recent studies, however, have managed to document the use of several hundred plant species as traditional medicines or charms on a number of the islands.

Mexico has been a source of incredible ethnopharmacological wealth. Its plant life is diverse, and the Indians had developed an intensive use of plants before the arrival of the Europeans. Moreover, the Spanish conquerors made many relevant observations in their writings on the cultural, religious, and medicinal customs of the conquered—observations that have stimulated and oriented the intensive contemporary studies of folk medicine of the country. The pre-Conquest codices of Mexico contain numerous references to medicinal plants, while the rich post-Conquest Spanish reports and writings provide a wealth of information.

The Mexican government at present is supporting an extensive ethnopharmacological investigation through the Mexican Institute for the Study of Medicinal Plants and the National Institute for the Investigation of Biotic Resources. Another agency, the Mexican Academy of Traditional Medicine, also has been set up to further such research. The study of hallucinogenically active plants—the medicines par excellence in Mexico—has been particularly fruitful. One of the hopes underlying this ambitious Mexican program is that of discovering active compounds of use in modern medicine. A recent tabulation showed that of 25 plants used medicinally by the Aztecs, 16 produce the results that were claimed, 4 may be active, and 5 are probably inactive. More research is needed to evaluate the remaining hundreds of medicinal plants of the ancient Mexicans, most of which are still employed by the country folk of that nation.

South America, with its sumptuous and diverse plant life, has been ethnopharmacologically neglected except for a small number of recent and local investigations. Noteworthy among them are studies of the Sibundoy of the Colombian Andes, the Kofán Indians of Colombia and Ecuador, and various other tribes of the Ecuadorian and Colombian Amazon.

The recent discovery of leaves of a holly (*Ilex*) with snuff and snuff-making paraphernalia in a 1,500-year-old tomb in Bolivia indicates for the first

178

time the use of a caffeine-rich plant in snuffing. Moreover, the presence in the tomb of artifacts used for enemas suggests a possible application for this holly in the same way. Surprisingly such work has uncovered the fact that, for reasons yet unknown, certain tribes have exploited only a limited number of species of their exuberant flora. A recently initiated program proposes to collect and computerize all ethnopharmacologically significant information available for Amazonian plant life, which comprises some 85,000 species of higher plants. Notwithstanding its botanical assets and its many wholly or partly unacculturated tribes, the Amazon remains an unexplored ethnopharmacological emporium.

Studies in the Eastern Hemisphere

Africa, floristically and culturally rich, still offers a near virgin field for ethnopharmacological studies, although isolated investigations are numerous. It is noteworthy that several important drugs have come from African plants, among them physostigmine, used in ophthalmology and for other medicinal purposes, from the Calabar bean (*Physostigma venenosum*), one of the ordeal poisons used in Nigeria in trials for witchcraft, and the cardiac drug strophanthine from *Strophanthus Kombe*, source of an African arrow poison.

In the Pacific Islands an extensive literature has grown up on the use of the hypnotic beverage kava, which is made from the root of the pepper plant *Piper methysticum* and drunk ceremonially. Polynesia has been sporadically investigated, while studies on Hawaiian herbal medicine have been extensive.

The luxuriant plant life of southeast Asia has been ethnopharmacologically investigated by numerous specialists, especially by the English and Dutch. A monumental compilation of herbarium and literature reports of the medicinal use of some 6,000 species of eastern and southeastern Asia, the work of many years, has recently been published; when it is put to practical use, investigators will be drawing from an extensive body of knowledge on traditional medical applications from many different cultures, some of them long extinct. The useful plants of Australia, including native medicines, have received attention for many years, and the national government, through the Commonwealth Scientific and Industrial Research Organization, has been active in chemically investigating them.

Ethnopharmacological research is currently so extensive in China and India that any brief summary would be inadequate. Both nations are large and are inhabited by many different groups of native peoples, and both nations have a rich assortment of plant life.

Unlike the Western world China has been inundated with medical writings since earliest times. Whereas the first English-language pharmacopoeia appeared in 1616, the earliest Chinese equivalent is said to date from 2698 BC. Perhaps the most famous of such documents is the *Pen-ts'ao kang-mu*, which was completed in AD 1578; containing 8,160 prescriptions, it is the result of 26 years of scholarly research.

In modern China examination of plants employed in traditional medicine has become an extremely active and serious program. Contemporary Chi-

The medical legacy left in the plant lore of North American Indian peoples includes a smoking deterrent from Indian tobacco (Lobelia inflata; top) and antitumor agents from mayapple (Podophyllum peltatum; above).

179

Photos, Richard A. Howard,
The Arnold Arboretum of Harvard University

Papaya (Carica papaya; top), a plant of Mexican or Central American origin and cultivated throughout the tropics, is a source of powerful protein-digesting enzymes used to shrink ruptured discs and as worming agents. In folk medicine papaya latex is employed as a remedy for a wide variety of afflictions ranging from warts and indigestion to hemorrhoids and tumors. In West Africa the fruit of the vine Mormodica charantia (above) provides a juice used to treat diabetes, while its leaves serve as a remedy for high blood pressure.

nese researchers have enumerated hundreds of plant drugs and summarized much of the knowledge of native Chinese medicines, listing more than 1,700 species and varieties of plants in the process. The U.S. National Academy of Sciences recently published a trip report of the American Herbal Pharmacology Delegation to China, which discussed interdisciplinary studies of approximately 200 species of fungi and higher plants. A major goal of China's active research program is to uncover valuable new compounds for modern medicine, which has already benefited a great deal from China's ethnopharmacological legacy. In the 1920s ephedrine, used to treat asthma and other allergic disorders, was isolated from *Ephedra sinica,* which had been employed in Chinese folk medicine for respiratory ailments since earliest times. Other plant-derived medicinal substances borrowed by the West from the Chinese are castor oil (from the castor bean, *Ricinus communis*), camphor (from the camphor laurel, *Cinnamomum camphora*), and chaulmoogra oil (from seeds of *Hydnocarpus* trees), which was formerly used to treat leprosy.

India similarly is blessed with ancient records of traditional medicines. The Rig Veda was compiled probably between 1500 and 1000 BC; the Ayurveda, *Susruta-samhita,* and *Caraka-samhita,* also repositories of ethnopharmacological information, date from at least the beginning of the Christian era. In all, approximately 1,800 plant species have been recorded in India's medical literature. Many of these plants are listed in specialized dictionaries and summaries from the 19th century, and contemporary writings are numerous. All available ethnopharmacological information has been brought together in the encyclopedic *Wealth of India* published by the Indian Council of Scientific and Industrial Research between 1948 and 1976. In 1980 the Indian Ethnobotanical Society was founded to intensify the study of plant uses among the many tribals in distant parts of the country.

Plants of the gods

Probably no realm of ethnopharmacology more clearly illustrates the strides made in the 20th century in understanding the anthropology, botany, chemistry, and pharmacology of a category of biodynamic plants than the hallucinogenic species, the active agents of which induce altered states of perception, thought, and feeling in human beings. These plants are the medicines par excellence in primitive societies, since according to aboriginal belief all sickness and even death come from intervention from supernatural spirits. Thus, through visual, auditory, or other hallucinations, the medicine man believes it possible to communicate with the sources of the ills. In primitive societies the "power" of those few plants that can cause such unworldly psychic effects is attributed to resident spirits. Consequently they are sacred and are usually employed in strictly magico-religious ceremonies. There has even been speculation that in ancient times the consciousness-altering effects of these plants were not simply incorporated into the rites of primitive religions but actually lay at the basis of the fundamental religious experience itself. They have, therefore, been termed "plants of the gods."

Recent ethnopharmacological emphasis on hallucinogens has been the result of two realizations—that some of the responsible compounds in halluci-

180

nogenic plants might be valuable in experimental or therapeutic psychiatry and that much more remains to be understood concerning their anthropology, botany, chemistry, and biological activity.

A plethora of names for these mind-altering substances has arisen during the last half century: hallucinogens, schizogens, deliriants, delusionogens, eidetics, misperceptionogens, mysticomimetics, phanerothymes, phantasticants, psychotics, psychoticants, psychogens, psychotomimetics, psychodysleptics, psychototaraxics, and psychotogens. Entheogens, a new term meaning "God within us" and referring to the significance to aborigines of these sacred plants, has recently been proposed. The biologically unsound and etymologically incorrect term psychedelic is perhaps the most widely employed word in the United States for these agents.

Hallucinogens have been employed for millennia, but it is only in the past 50 or 60 years that significant strides have been made in their study. This study has been interdisciplinary and has involved many investigators in many parts of the world. Moreover, research in New World hallucinogens has not been confined to the field and laboratory; it has encompassed extensive interpretation of archaeological finds, art forms, and literature. Curiously many more plants are hallucinogenically employed in the New World than in the Old—at least 150 species versus fewer than 20.

Although interdisciplinary discussions of narcotics and stimulants were published as early as the mid-19th century, the modern thrust in ethnopharmacological studies of hallucinogens may be attributed to the appearance in 1924 of the book *Phantastica* by the German toxicologist Louis Lewin. Since this period and greatly aided by writings on peyote that focused attention on the outstanding importance of hallucinogens in New World cultures, the study of ethnopharmacology has come into its own with an increasing number of researchers in a variety of disciplines engaging in field investigations.

Perhaps the most thoroughly studied hallucinogenic plant from many points of view is peyote, the name for two species of cactus of the genus *Lophophora* found in Texas and northern Mexico. Ceremonially employed in Mexico for millennia, peyote is presently the sacrament of an organized

Richard E. Schultes

Leaves of the holly Ilex guayana *(above) were found recently in a 1,500-year-old Bolivian tomb along with snuff and snuff-making equipment. Traditional herbal medicine has been the mainstay of local health for centuries in many parts of Africa. In Ghana a herbalist-teacher and students (below left) complete a traditional medicine training program. The typical "pharmacy" of West Africa (below) is a busy open-air market well stocked with plant substances. Africa still offers a near virgin field for ethnopharmacological studies.*

Photos, Edward S. Ayensu, Smithsonian Institution

Plants employed in traditional Chinese medicine have become the subject of very active and serious investigations by both Chinese and Western researchers. Drawers of a Chinese chest (right) offer a large array of medicinal herbs. Many herbal remedies are now packaged Western-style (below right) to promote the new wave of popularity traditional Chinese medicine is receiving.

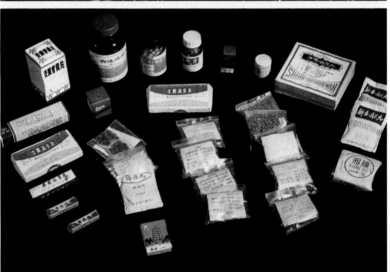

religious movement with 250,000 members belonging to many Indian tribes in the U.S. A number of investigators have ethnologically considered peyote, recent field studies have been done in Mexico, and the chemical investigation of the more than 30 alkaloids in this cactus has been brought up to date. Caches of peyote, mescal beans (*Sophora secundiflora*), and Texas buckeye (*Ungnadia speciosa*), often together, have been excavated from dry caves in Mexico and Texas in contexts indicative of ritual use and dated as early as 8500 BC. The mescal bean, which contains among other alkaloids the toxic cytisine, was employed until the past century as a sacred intoxicant in Mexico and the U.S. Southwest. Texas buckeye is known to be toxic and consequently may have been employed in ancient rituals as a kind of inebriant.

Although early Spanish writings had amply recorded ritualistic use in Mexico of teonanacatl, the intoxicating "magic" mushrooms (species of *Panaeolus*, *Psilocybe*, and *Stropharia*), and ololiuqui, the inebriating morn-

182

ing glories (*Ipomoea* and *Turbina*), their use was rediscovered only in the 1930s. Hitherto, these hallucinogens had been misidentified as peyote and toloache (jimsonweed, or *Datura*), respectively. Intensive research by several specialists has clarified the role of these two hallucinogenic plants in ancient and modern American Indian societies. Other work has elucidated their chemical aspects, which in the case of the mushrooms has resulted in the discovery of two novel indole alkaloids. One, psilocybin, has already found use in psychiatry. If the many umbrella-shaped stone objects found in the archaeology of Guatemala can be interpreted as mushroom icons, they suggest the ritualistic use of these fungi as early as 1000 BC. Although psilo-

Photos, Peter T. Furst, State University of New York at Albany

For the Huichol Indian peoples of western Mexico, eating of the hallucinogenic peyote cactus is a central, deeply sacred element of religious experience. A Huichol peyote pilgrim (above left) shows his harvest of peyote cactuses. Huichol shaman's basket (left) contains two freshly picked peyote plants, prayer arrows, and other sacred power objects.

Stropharia cubensis (above), one of the sacred mushrooms of Mexico, contains the hallucinogenic agents psilocybin and psilocin. Its ritualistic use among the Aztecs was recorded in early Spanish writings. Terra-cotta figure beating on a mushroom-shaped drum (above right) belongs to the Remojadas culture of the southern Gulf Coast plain of Mexico and dates between the first and third centuries AD.

cybin-rich mushrooms are known in Colombia, there is no evidence of their use today in South America, but the presence in the Sinú culture area of human-shaped gold pectorals (chest ornaments) with two round domes on the head has been interpreted as suggesting the use of inebriating mushrooms in religion or medicine in Colombia as far back as AD 500.

In the Andes the recently discovered visionary and folk-healing San Pedro cult is based on the use of a mescaline-rich cactus, *Trichocereus*. Through ceramic and other ancient representations of this plant, it is known to have been ritually important at least 3,000 years ago in Peru.

Ongoing field researches have significantly advanced ethnopharmacological understanding of Andean and Amazonian hallucinogens, including the discovery of six new psychoactive plants. The most unusual is perhaps the finding that a red "resin" in the bark of several species of *Virola*, a genus of forest trees, is employed orally and as snuff. Chemical studies have shown that these plants owe their hallucinogenic activity mainly to high concentrations of chemicals called tryptamines. These indole alkaloids may offer investigators some insight into the activity and function of structurally related compounds such as serotonin, a powerful bioactive tryptamine in the human body.

Interdisciplinary research has added to our knowledge of the narcotic drink of the western Amazon, first identified in 1851 and known variously as ayahuasca, caapi, or yajé. Whereas the primary active agents are indole har-

184

Early illustration of Turbina corymbosa (left), a hallucinogenic morning glory of Mexico, is from the Florentine Codex of the Historia de las cosas de Nueva España, written by the Spanish missionary Bernardino de Sahagún in the mid-16th century. The plant is still used ritualistically in Mexico among Indian peoples today. The mescaline-rich cactus Trichocereus pachanoi (below) lies at the center of the recently discovered San Pedro cult in the Andes.

mines extracted from the tropical vine *Banisteriopsis caapi,* the preparation has a number of variations. Studies in Ecuador reported the use of several other plants as additives (*Psychotria, Brunfelsia,* and *Diplopterys*) that greatly alter the intoxicating effects of caapi; lengthy field research in Peru elucidated the addition of more than 20 other plants to the drink. Extensive field and laboratory studies carried out in the Andes and Amazon have furthered our knowledge of the ethnopharmacology of coca (*Erythroxylon*). This plant, the source of the medically important alkaloid cocaine, is a much misunderstood narcotic still employed by millions of Indians, the use of which goes back at least 3,000 years in the Andes, according to archaeological evidence.

Modern medicine has begun to use some of the hallucinogenic principles of plants, especially psilocybin and mescaline. The desired effect in Western psychiatry is the same as that in primitive societies: altered perception of the outside world as well as of the patient himself. Experimentally induced changes in consciousness and perception have several different applications. In psychoanalysis, for example, it may help the patient escape from a fixation or isolation, allowing better contact between patient and doctor. Hallucinogens also can sometimes call to light forgotten or repressed experiences. Although hallucinogenic principles effect no cures, they may become important tools in psychiatry as well as in research to understand the still mysterious functions of the central nervous system and possibly the causes of certain mental disorders. Some of these agents have even given promise as nonanalgesic painkillers. Recent interdisciplinary ethnopharmacological studies of *Cannabis* have uncovered many new cannabinolic constituents, some of which may be useful in therapeutic medicine (*e.g.,* in the treatment of glaucoma).

A new frontier
The ethnopharmacological study of plants, starting with their use in primitive societies, remains a fertile, almost virgin territory for those interested in the discovery of new psychoactive drugs as well as other types of biologically active compounds. Medical science cannot afford to neglect any longer the

A. Weil

Photos, Richard E. Schultes

hunting ground that until now has provided, mainly through folklore and serendipity, clues that the pharmaceutical industry has turned into products having annual sales in excess of $3 billion in the U.S. prescription market alone.

Peruvian Indian (above left) chews coca leaves mixed with powdered lime. The coca plant (Erythroxylon coca; above), the source of cocaine, has been valued in the Andes for its narcotic effects for at least 3,000 years.

FOR ADDITIONAL READING

S. von R. Altschul, *Drugs and Foods from Little-known Plants: Notes in Harvard University Herbaria* (Harvard University Press, 1973).

G. W. Dimbleby, *Plants and Archaeology* (Humanities Press, Inc., 1967).

D. H. Efron and others (eds.), *Ethnopharmacologic Search for Psychoactive Drugs* (U.S. Government Printing Office, 1967).

R. E. Schultes and A. Hofmann, *Plants of the Gods* (McGraw-Hill Book Co., 1979).

Li Shih-Chên (translated and researched: F. P. Smith and G. A. Stuart), *Chinese Medicinal Herbs* (Georgetown Press, 1973).

N. Taylor, *Plant Drugs that Changed the World* (Dodd, Mead & Co., 1965).

S. von Reis and F. J. Lipp, Jr., *New Plant Sources for Drugs and Foods from the New York Botanical Garden Herbarium* (Harvard University Press, 1982).

R. G. Wasson, *The Wondrous Mushroom: Mycolatry in Mesoamerica* McGraw-Hill Book Co., 1980).

(Opposite page) Recent field studies have shown the forest tree Virola theiodora (top left) to be a source of hallucinogenic snuff, an antifungal agent, and an arrow poison for Indians of the northwest Amazon. Bark of V. theiodora (bottom left) flows red with resin from which the snuff is prepared. Waika Indian of Amazonian Brazil sifts the final preparation (top right), which during an annual religious ceremony is blown through long tubes into the nostrils (bottom right).

LIGHTS
IN THE
SUMMER DARKNESS
by James E. Lloyd

Fireflies create elaborate patterns of flashing and glowing light as signals for potential mates. These patterns vary according to the firefly species and the time of night.

Among the forms of insect behavior most accessible to study is firefly communication. With a penlight and notebook, and after several evenings in the field, a careful observer can: (1) learn to distinguish several species by the flashing patterns emitted by flying males; (2) learn the flash codes of several species by imitating with a penlight the flashing patterns of flying males and looking for the response flashes of females; (3) attract males to the penlight by flashing answers to males like those of their females; (4) find and observe the predaceous fireflies (*Photuris* females) that mimic the females of other species, attract males, and eat them; (5) observe the aerial attacks of *Photuris* females on fireflies and targets that are made to flash and "fly" like fireflies; and (6) determine which species use more than one type of flash pattern for mate searching.

The study of firefly communication has decided advantages over research on insects that communicate by such means as chemicals or sound. Humans have good eyes and can see in dim light; also, their eyes are good analyzers that can detect and discriminate details of color, timing, spatial patterns, and movements. The fast pace of firefly action—entire sequences take seconds or minutes rather than hours or days—makes firefly study more interesting. Expensive equipment is not needed for such research, and, in fact, it can become a distraction. Finally, for people in the United States living east of the Rocky Mountains fireflies may be as near as the front lawn or garden. People living near a cattail marsh have a veritable metropolis of firefly action and interaction.

Fireflies are beetles (Coleoptera: family Lampyridae) and occur throughout the world except in Arctic and Antarctic regions. About 1,900 species have been given scientific names, and there may be a quarter again as many yet to be discovered. Though adults of many species use their own chemically generated light for communication, many others use pheromones, odors that females emit into the air and that waft downwind in invisible clouds

(Overleaf) A male Photinus ignitus flashes a signal to attract a mate. Shown above is the flash pattern of this firefly in flight.

called plumes. Males smell these species-specific aromas, though humans cannot, and fly upwind to the females to mate with them. A number of nonluminescent species in America use this communicative system. If a female of *Lucidota atra,* a day-active firefly found in the eastern half of the U.S., is put in a gauze-covered dish (containing an apple to provide moisture and nourishment), and set outdoors, she will sometimes attract males at a rate of one per minute for several minutes. If the dish she has been kept in overnight is put outdoors, it too will attract males, showing that the female left some of her scent behind.

Glowworms

The simplest form of luminescent signaling known in fireflies is found in several species of the western U.S. and two rare ones in Florida. The females of these fireflies live in burrows, and after dark appear above ground, where they often climb into low vegetation, and glow. Females of such species are sometimes called glowworms. They look quite different from their males because their wings and wing covers are either much reduced or absent altogether. Males of most of these glowworm fireflies do not have lights when they reach adulthood, though as far as is known all fireflies have lights when they are larvae. (Firefly larvae are believed to use their luminescence for protection, warning potential predators away. Adults of some species have been found to have very poisonous blood and to be extremely bad-tasting.) Flying males find the females by searching for their glows, but females of some species also use pheromones to attract males from longer distances than a glow can be seen. Remaining on an advertising station and glowing is dangerous—one female under observation was grabbed and eaten by a toad, and another was carried off by a wolf spider—and so chemical signals that assist the glow and reduce the time a female must be exposed to predation are an advantage. After mating these females return underground, where they lay their eggs and die.

A few species have added male luminescence to this glow system of communication. In the Smoky Mountains of the eastern U.S. *Phausis reticulata,* whose males with their bright green lamps can be seen flying through the forest low over the ground, has modified the glow system and gives females protection against light-seeking predators. *Phausis* females sometimes remain dark until a lighted male flies overhead, and then they light up. Their lights are unusual for fireflies, for instead of being toward the tail there may be four or six glowing in pairs along the back in addition to the two "old larval" lights in the tail.

Precision flashers

But it is the fireflies that control their light with precision and emit it in short flashes or rapidly pulsed flickers that are the most eye-catching and dramatic and have the most complex interactions. There are about 100 species of this type in the eastern half of the United States. One of them, *Photinus pyralis,* is an ideal subject for study because it is so common and widespread (occurring from central Kansas to the Atlantic, and from southern Michigan to the Gulf of Mexico); because it is active at twilight when it is

JAMES E. LLOYD is a Professor of Entomology at the University of Florida, Gainesville.

Photographs by James E. Lloyd
Illustrations by Leon Bishop

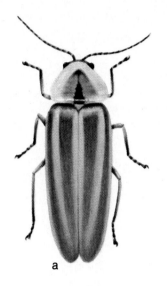

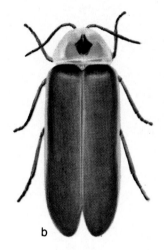

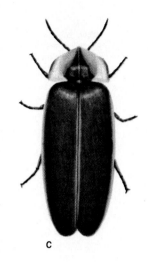

a

b

c

Fireflies from each of five major genera include: (a) *Photuris* (unnamed species), (b) *Photinus pyralis,* (c) *Pyractomena borealis,* (d) *Lucidota atra,* and (e) *Ellychnia corrusca. Lucidota atra* is not luminescent.

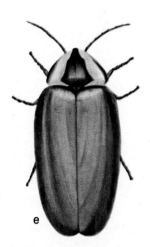

d

e

still quite light outdoors; and because it is so easy to "communicate" with by flashing a penlight.

Pyralis males begin their evening search for mates at about sunset in deep shade, and minutes later they move out into the open. Their flash paths are conspicuous and distinctive. When males emit their half-second, bright yellow flash, they dip and then rise up in flight, making an illuminated, J-shaped stripe in space. At the end of the rise they hover for about two seconds and then fly farther on to flash over another area about six seconds later. It has recently been found that the yellow color of the *pyralis* flashes is important for enhancing their "signal-to-noise" ratio. At twilight there still is considerable ambient light, and much green light is reflected from vegetation. In the past when certain species, including the ancestors of *pyralis,* became active at twilight, they evolved filters in their eyes to remove green light. Then they shifted the color of their light from green, as found in late-active species, to yellow, thus greatly enhancing their vision for receiving yellow signals at twilight. However, this probably makes them almost blind if they fly late at night when there is very little light available.

191

While males search, females perch on grass and low shrubs and herbs. They appear much like the males, for they too have fully developed wings and wing covers. The most conspicuous difference between the male and female *pyralis* is in the size of their lanterns, which in both sexes are located under the tail. The male organ occupies two full segments, but that of the female is usually only a half-moon in the center of one segment. Males and females also differ in the size of their eyes, with those of males being larger. This probably gives them a wide field of vision as is appropriate for the flying-searching activity that is so important for their mating success. One can safely presume that in the past generations of those fireflies it was the males which scanned and aimed better that found and mated with more females, thus leaving more of their genes to future generations.

When a female sees a male's flash or the flash of a penlight or flare of a match that is about the correct duration, her response circuits are activated, and somewhere in her nervous system a timer starts. This counts off about two seconds and then triggers her response flash. This two-second delay is not constant; the timing of flashing in males and females varies predictably with temperature. On cool evenings the flashes, flash intervals, and flash delays are longer than they are on warm evenings. This means that in order to mimic a female flash and attract a male to a penlight, ambient temperature must be taken into account. Temperature curves for male flash intervals and female response delays can easily be graphed by measuring these features at different temperatures with a stopwatch. For male flashes this requires that observations be made over several evenings, thus making use of variations in ambient temperature that occur from night to night. A sample of about ten male intervals at each of three or four temperatures between 18° and 27° C (65° and 80° F) is sufficient. At each timing session air temperature must be taken in the flight space, away from heat-holding structures such as pavement or buildings.

This discussion of temperature raises a question that has not yet been answered by science. It is obvious that the body temperatures of males and females must be about the same if they are to communicate with time-coded flashes. When females of *Luciola lusitanica*, an Italian firefly, were warmed more than 20% above ambient (air) temperature with a small heater, they were unable to attract their males. In nature the metabolism and thus the timing of perched, relatively inactive females may be considerably lower than that of their males, whose wing muscles are generating heat by their activity. If this is the case, it is surprising that the males and females can maintain communication. Perhaps the males lose heat rapidly, or they have thermally isolated their timers from their warm muscles; the males also might measure ambient temperature with a "thermometer" at the remote and cool tip of some part of their body and then feed a temperature correction into their timing circuits.

Male *pyralis* can be attracted to a penlight quite easily. When a male approaches, the penlight is placed at the ground with the tip pointing down against the soil to allow light to escape from around the edges of the "nozzle." Each of his flashes is answered with the temperature-corrected delay and flash. This will vary between 1.8 seconds (85° F) and 2.8 seconds (65°

192

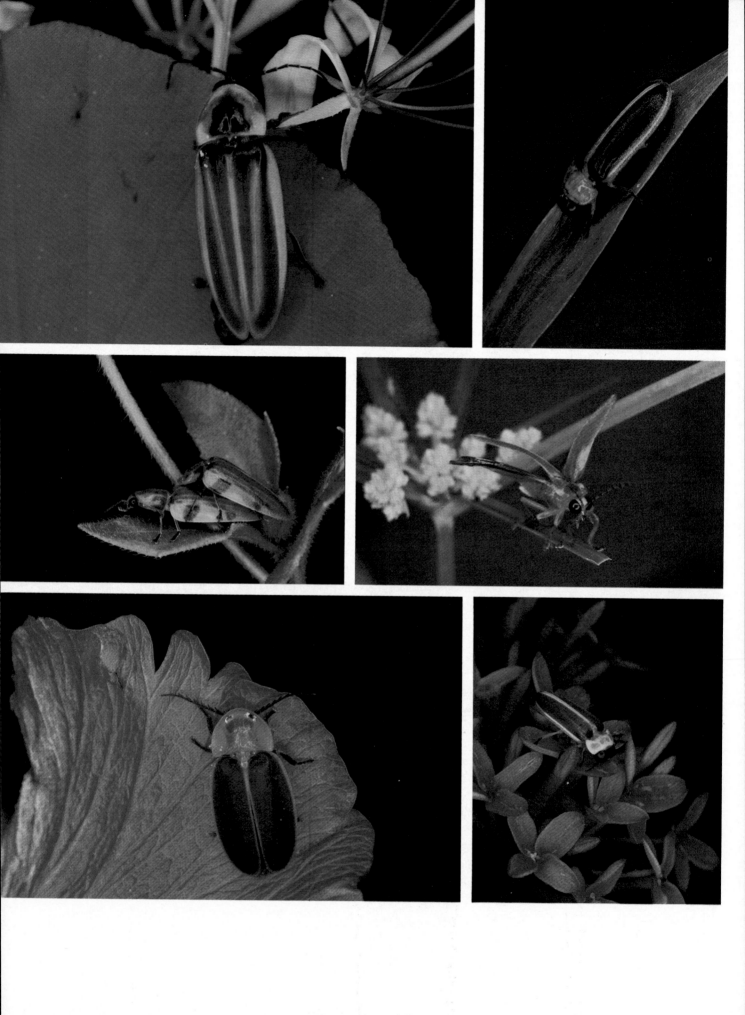

F). The male will eventually land near the light and walk to it, still flashing every few seconds and using the penlight's flash to orient his approach. Another simple experiment assists in the production of the next generation of fireflies. Female *pyralis* sometimes perch in places where males have difficulty finding them. After the penlight locates one of these females, it can be used to attract a male to that place so that the male and female can then see each other's signals and get together.

The J-stroked, yellow flash of *pyralis* is so distinctive that it cannot be mistaken for the pattern of any other U.S. species. Other species have distinctive patterns too. Several in the *Photinus consanguineus* group have two-flash patterns, with each species having its own specific timing. In *P. consanguineus* the two flashes are one-half second apart; in *Photinus greeni* they are slightly more than one second apart; and in *Photinus macdermotti* they are about two seconds apart. All of these species repeat their patterns each 5–6 seconds. About one second after the males' second flash the females emit a short flash. Several *Photinus* species that live in marshes have patterns consisting of three or more (up to 11 in one species) flashes in a series. Perhaps part of the reason that these patterns are used is because they are more easily seen in a habitat of tall grass and cattail stems, but there is more to the answer than that. Another species with a distinctive pattern, and one that is as widespread as *pyralis*, is *Pyractomena angulata*. Its flash pattern is a flicker of 8–10 pulses emitted at a rate of about 9 pulses per second (at temperatures near 70° F). Although the flicker is not very bright, this is one of the most easily recognized signals because of its color, which is a candlelike orange. *Angulata* is one of the *Pyractomena* species whose males do not fly closer to an answering flash but instead drop out of the air and then may not flash again for a minute or more. The reason for this dangerous and slow approach was puzzling for a long time and took nearly 20 years to discover. The answer will become apparent when aerial predation by other fireflies is discussed. *Angulata* males will usually be seen flying singly at the tops of shrubs and trees but occasionally may be found in large numbers low over the grass in damp meadows.

The predatory Photuris

Because the flash patterns of males are often distinctive and easily recognized they have been used by taxonomists to recognize species that are difficult to distinguish by other means. This is especially true with fireflies in the genus *Photuris*, the third and perhaps the largest genus of flashing fireflies in the United States. Although the rule of thumb for the fireflies in *Photinus* and *Pyractomena* is "one species, one flash pattern," the rule breaks down in *Photuris* and many of the species have more than one pattern. This makes the use of their signals for taxonomy or field recognition of species more difficult, but it also makes them considerably more interesting. To understand the multiple-pattern flashing in *Photuris* males, it is first necessary to know something about the mimicry behavior of *Photuris* females. Their predatory behavior has been perhaps the single most important influence on communication among fireflies in the U.S.

Photuris fireflies are in a "class" by themselves. They generally are larger

194

Photinus pyralis male in flight advertises for a mate by flashing its light in a series of J-shaped strokes. It often aims the flashes at foliage, the likely resting places of females.

than other fireflies, have longer legs and more agile bodies, and scramble and fight vigorously when caught in the hand, flashing all the time. When held in the lips so that both hands will be free to get a specimen bottle out of the pack, they will bite, and when put into mason jars, they will run around and flash brightly. *Photuris* use their light like a headlight for illumination when taking off and landing, when walking through tangles of grass or Spanish moss, and when laying eggs. But, most distinctively, *Photuris* females use their light to capture prey. They do this by mimicking the mating signals of females of other species and thereby attracting males. Male fireflies are likely targets for such predation. They are vigorously competing among themselves to find and reach females, which are nearly always scarce (more than 99% of the firefly flashes seen in a field are those of males). An indication of how difficult it is to find a mate and how keen the competition is can be seen in the results of some research that involved following males, counting flashes, measuring distance flown, and recording happenings during each flight. For more than ten miles of flying and 7,988 flash patterns only two females were found by the 199 males that were observed. When females were observed, it took most of them fewer than six minutes to mate and then return to the safety of their underground burrows. *Photuris* femmes fatales that use false signals for predation have tapped a rich and eager source of food.

The male-following study revealed that males were five and one-half times more likely to get an answer from a *Photuris* female than from one of their own, and this observation provided a clue as to how aggressive mimicry

196

can be observed and studied. The same technique is used that worked for finding females of *pyralis* or other *Photinus,* the penlight simulation of male flash patterns in a firefly site. The number of hunting predators in a site varies greatly, and if an evening of search fails, another location should be tried. Sometimes the *Photuris* hunters will be found near each other, perhaps somehow exploiting each other. Sometimes they will perch near or hover near a signaling *Photinus* female. When they flash an answer they can frequently be distinguished from *pyralis* or other females by the green color of their light; however, the apparent color of firefly flashes is greatly influenced by the adaptation to the darkness made by the observer's eyes and mistakes are easily made. After a female has been found and disturbed as little as possible, by checking her identification with a dim or red-filtered flashlight, her responses to passing males and her success rate in attracting them can be observed. *Photuris* females are now known to prey on more than one species and thus to have the ability to mimic females of different species; for example, *Photuris versicolor* females can mimic females of seven species. By simulating the flash patterns of different species, an experimenter can determine the versatility of individual females. The record for a single female to date is four prey signals. Some females can be switched from one mimicry to another without difficulty, but others refuse to change, perhaps influenced by previous hunting successes and failures.

Photuris predators also use another hunting tactic, and they sometimes use it in conjunction with their aggressive mimicry: they attack light-emitting fireflies in the air. In this behavior they resemble the Sidewinder missile that is used to attack airplanes. Such missiles lock onto (aim at) energy that is given off by their target, heat from the engines. Fireflies, similarly, aim at the light that is emitted by their prey. This is easily demonstrated by dangling a tiny light from the tip of a fishing pole and watching the movements of arriving attackers against skylight. If the light is held about three feet from the observer's eyes as he trolls around bushes and along hedgerows in a firefly habitat, attackers can be seen as they move quickly to the target while it glows dimly between flashes; the attacking insects will take longer to strike the light if it merely flashes without a glow. This behavior probably explains why there are so few glowing species in the United States, though on other continents where *Photuris* is not present there are several. *Photuris* females use this tactic of homing in on the light in order to capture males that are slow in approaching their false signals; this method of predation probably explains why certain species, such as *Pyractomena angulata,* drop from the air when they first receive an answering flash and then approach on foot.

Flash pattern variations

Photuris males search for mates under the same sort of intensely competitive circumstances that *Photinus* and *Pyractomena* males do, but they have added a complicating and perplexing element. *Photuris* males use more than one flash pattern in their searches. Their pattern changing is not a "simple" variation such as that described for marsh-inhabiting *Photinus* that may vary the number of flashes in a single pattern; *Photuris* males switch be-

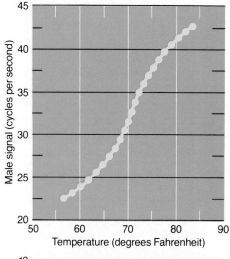

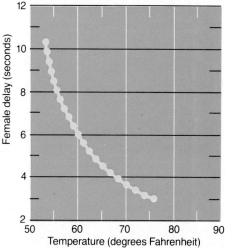

Temperature affects the timing of firefly signals. The frequency of the flickers of a Photuris *species "D" male (top) increases from 26 cycles per second at an air temperature of 58° F (14° C) to 42.5 cps at 82° F (28° C). Females also react to temperature changes (bottom). The response of a* Photinus ignitus *female to a male's signal is delayed more than ten seconds at 53° F (12° C) but is less than four seconds at 76° F (24° C).*

Typical flash patterns and flight paths (left to right) of males of different species of the genus Photinus are shown as they would appear in a time-lapse photograph. From top to bottom the species are: (1) P. consimilis (slow pulse), (2) P. ignitus, (3) P. consimilis (fast pulse), (4) P. pyralis, (5) P. collustrans, and (6) P. granulatus. The species are not all inhabitants of the same areas.

tween or among completely different patterns. One Florida species emits two to six slow flashes in each pattern and then the next minute may begin emitting an eight-to-ten-pulse flicker or a minutes-long glow, still pressing on an obvious searching flight. Another Floridian emits half-second flashes at twilight and then switches to tenth-second flashes when it gets dark, and at both times some individuals emit rapid-pulsing patterns of two to five flashes.

There are many examples of this sort of switching, and in fact it may be the *Photuris* species whose males do not switch that are the rarities. For a taxonomist to be able to use male flash patterns in order to recognize species it is essential to know whether a species changes. The confusion is made even more complete in *Photuris* because most of the species look so much alike, with minor color differences being the primary distinguishing characteristics. When two different flash patterns are found to be emitted by fireflies that look alike, it could either be two species or one species with two patterns. Sometimes individual males can be followed long enough to see them change, assuming that the observer can be sure that a male of a different species has not flown into the airspace being watched during the dark interval. More often it is necessary to do a mark-release study. Males emitting one of the patterns are captured, marked on a wing cover with a tiny speck of airplane dope (yellow, applied with the tip of a toothpick), and released. They will eventually fly off and return to their mate search. Later, males giving the other flash pattern are captured. If they are found to be marked, the question is answered. If no crossovers are found, perhaps there are two species, but there could still be only one.

Why should *Photuris* males use more than one pattern? Several of their patterns are like those emitted by *Photinus* and *Pyractomena* males. That is, *Photuris* males mimic the males of other species. Since they do this during their mating period, it is almost certain that they are seeking mates. Apparently they are mimicking the patterns of their females' prey to locate their females, because even hunters are potential mates. Then they must persuade the females to stop hunting and to mate. Persuasive tactics, the salesbeetleship of courtship that would convert a lethal hunter to a mate, can only be imagined, but it is even possible that males with little chance of finding another female would trade their own bodies for a last mating, "volunteering" for nuptial cannibalism such as has been reported for praying mantids. Forced insemination of a female by a *Photuris* male would seem to be out of the question because the females are larger and presumably stronger.

Behind the development of this mate-seeking tactic is the intense competition that exists among males for mates. Extremism in mate competition is a common pattern in nature. Males of some species grow huge antlers, and others reach huge proportions to enhance their display and fighting. *Photuris* firefly males have become "big" in deception. But *Photuris* males and

Phausis reticulata (below left) is one of the species of fireflies classified as glowworms. The wingless female, at left, lives in burrows and after dark climbs into low vegetation and glows. The male, right, emits a bright green glow in flight. The predatory Photuris versicolor *female (below) eats a* Photinus tanytoxus *male that she has attracted by mimicking the signal of the* P. tanytoxus *female.*

Time (seconds)

	0	1	2	3

Photinus macdermotti
male

female

mimic

Photinus tanytoxus
male

female

mimic

species photuris "A"
male

female

mimic

Photuris congener
male

female

mimic

Photuris versicolor (predator)
male

female

Females of at least 12 species of Photuris *prey on males of other genera and of other Photuris species by mimicking the responses of the prey's own females. The response used by the predator, in this chart the Photuris versicolor, is indicated beneath the female answer that it is mimicking. Females varied in their ability to change their responses rapidly, but some were able to adjust to different stimuli immediately. The flash rate of the Photuris congener female is variable and, unlike other fireflies, does not bear a specific relationship to the flashes of the male. The species-specific patterns of the versicolor male and female are indicated at the bottom of the chart.*

Predatory Photuris females sometimes attack light-emitting fireflies in the air. A print made from two slides shows how a light dangling from the tip of a fishing pole was moved along a roadside in order to attract predators. At the left is the unexpected result: two Photuris "D" females arrived at the light at the same time and attacked one another. The decoy male on the hook is shown below.

Cover, Nov. 7, 1980, "Male Photuris Fireflies Mimic Sexual Signals of Their Females' Prey," James E. Lloyd, *Science*, vol. 210, © 1980 AAAS

Photuris male mimics the signals of males of other genera. At the top of the trees the *Photuris* emits its own species-specific pulses, but as it nears the ground it produces the short flickers (diamond shapes) of Pyractomena barberi *and then glows steadily like* Pyractomena angustata. *This behavior probably evolved as a response to the signals of* Photuris *females, which mimic the signals of other females in order to attact the males of those genera for prey.*

their females are not the only deceivers. The prey of *Photuris,* which have been under constant attack for millions of years, have developed their own communicative signals and systems. For example, when *Photinus macdermotti* males have landed near an answering light, they mimic flashes that their predators emit as they try to determine if the invitation is from a predator or a mate. Because of the high risk of predation *macdermotti*'s communication has become exceedingly complex, having evolved far beyond the simple flash-answer protocol found in some species. As a principle to guide further questions and research on American fireflies, it must be assumed that a great deal of the complexity observed in their flashing signals and systems has evolved to cope with the predations and deceptions of *Photuris,* in a relentless, luminescent arms race.

FOR ADDITIONAL READING

J. E. Lloyd, "Insect Bioluminescence," in P. J. Herring (ed.), *Bioluminescence in Action*, pp. 241–272 (Academic Press, 1978).

J. E. Lloyd, "Sexual Selection in Luminescent Beetles," in M. & N. Blum (eds.), *Sexual Selection and Reproductive Competition in Insects* (Academic Press, 1979).

J. E. Lloyd, "Mimicry in the Sexual Signals of Fireflies," *Scientific American* (July 1981, pp. 138–145).

PHYSICS UNDER PRESSURE

by Peter M. Bell and Ho-Kwang Mao

Scientists are now using sustained pressures of more than a million atmospheres to create conditions that exist deep within the Earth. Their research has led to forms of matter never before observed.

For many years research in the field of high-pressure physics has yielded surprises and fascination for scientists and nonscientists alike. In the mid-1950s diamonds were made synthetically for the first time in the high-pressure research laboratories of the General Electric Co. in the U.S. and of the Swedish Electric Co. (ASEA) in Sweden. Underpinning that achievement, which heralded the beginning of a billion-dollar business in synthetic industrial-grade diamonds, was a century and a half of high-pressure experimentation. Research began with efforts to prove that water could not be compressed (it turned out later that it could), to liquefy gases, and—perhaps most important to basic science—to observe the behavior of matter under ever higher pressures. Numerous, accurate measurements of solids, liquids, and gases form the basis of modern chemical and physical thermodynamics.

In very recent times, actually since the mid-1970s, there has been a technological breakthrough in the physics of being able to generate and indefinitely sustain high pressures in the laboratory. The new techniques hold promise of the synthesis of many more exotic materials like diamonds. Moreover, they may lead to new advances in understanding the laws of physics of condensed matter.

What happens to matter when the applied pressure is raised to one million or more times atmospheric pressure cannot be predicted from current theory. A sufficient increase of pressure on a gas will cause the gas to condense to a liquid even though its temperature remains constant. Still higher pressure will cause the compressed liquid to crystallize to a solid. According to theory, if the pressure on this solid is increased still more, major changes of

202

The manufacture of industrial-quality synthetic diamonds (right, shown magnified) has grown in commercial importance since the technology was first perfected in the mid-1950s. Behind that success lie decades of research experience in generating and controlling very high pressures. (Opposite page) At sufficiently low pressure the atoms or molecules of many simple substances exist as a gas (top), in which the constituent particles move about comparatively free of each other's influence. As the gas is compressed, the particles become more closely crowded together until their forces of attraction overcome their energy of motion to an extent and cause the particles to condense into a liquid (center). At still higher pressure the particles become squeezed so closely together that their attractive forces lock them into a rigid ordered structure, or crystalline solid (bottom). Theory predicts that further increases in pressure on a solid will induce major changes in its intrinsic properties.

General Electric Co., Research and Development Center, Schenectady, N.Y.

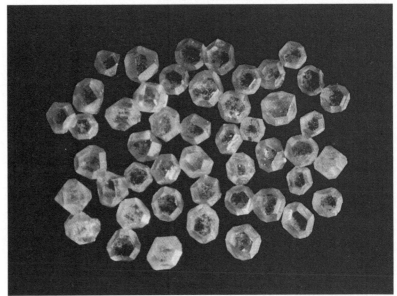

the intrinsic properties of the solid will occur. For example, in a certain range of very high pressure some metals will become insulators. At very extreme pressure (the exact value depending on the specific material) all matter is predicted to change, or return, to the metallic state. Some materials should become superconductors at extreme pressures. In all cases the theory is quite incomplete because the nature of the repulsive forces between atoms as they are crowded very close together in a compressed solid is not yet understood. But now experiments can be done to test theory.

Thinking about pressure

To understand why high-pressure physics is an unexplored field and why it is worthwhile exploring requires knowledge about the concepts of pressure. Nobel laureate Percy W. Bridgman, perhaps the most famous high-pressure physicist in history, referred to his field as "high-stress physics" because he thought the words high pressure deceptively simple. People have an intuitive sense that pressure is a force somehow exerted on a surface. Atmospheric pressure, for instance, is the weight of the Earth's gaseous atmosphere applied to the surfaces of all underlying objects and to the Earth's surface itself. By definition pressure is a force applied to a given unit of surface area. But complexities in grasping the concept arise when one realizes that pressure can be applied in one, two, or three directions or dimensions; hence Bridgman's preference for the term stress. Perhaps the most familiar example of pressure, hydrostatic pressure—the kind that exists in a fluid (a liquid or gas) confined in a container—is really a special case in that the pressure in the fluid and on the inside walls of the container must be everywhere equal in all directions. The principle governing this case was a major discovery of the French physicist and philosopher Blaise Pascal, after whom one of the units of pressure is named.

Pressure is an important and useful variable in that for a substance under pressure, no matter whether the force applied to it is in one, two, or three

PETER M. BELL and **HO-KWANG MAO** are Geophysicists in the Geophysical Laboratory at the Carnegie Institution of Washington, Washington, D.C.

Illustrations by Mark Stearney

dimensions, the pressure is not simply an additive quantity. Pressure is also an important variable thermodynamically as are temperature and other properties. A few examples may assist one's appreciation of these two ideas.

With a hydraulic automobile jack a person can apply a small force by hand to lift a weight of many tons. This device, basically a container filled with liquid and plugged in two places with pistons of different sizes, makes use of Pascal's principle, according to which a change in pressure within one part of the container must be accompanied by an equal change in pressure within any other part. If the second part has an area greater than that of the first, then the force on the second part must be proportionately greater. Thus, if one applies a force of five pounds to a one-square-inch piston connected by an oil line to a 100-square-inch piston, the force exerted on the larger piston is 500 pounds.

Consider a rather different example, in which a person applies the force of a thumb to the head of a thumbtack. In this case the object transmitting the action is a rigid solid, and hence any force applied to one end is sent unchanged to the opposite end. If the opposite end happens to have an area smaller than the first, then the pressure (force per unit area) exerted by the smaller end is proportionately greater. So, if one applies a force of ten pounds to a tack head having an area of a fifth of a square inch, the pressure on the head is two pounds per square inch. If the area of the tack point is 500 times smaller than that of the head, or 0.0004 square inch, then the pressure exerted by the point is 1,000 pounds per square inch.

Similarly the sharp edges of two razor blades pressed together at right angles could intensify an applied pressure of one pound per square inch to 100,000 pounds per square inch, were the edges strong enough. Any rigid object with a tapered shape such as a common pin or the high heel of a shoe can intensify pressures by means of this technique of area reduction. Thus, knowledge of some principles of pressure can be very handy for using small forces to generate large forces or for using small pressures to generate large pressures.

A well-known example of pressure as a thermodynamic variable is the way in which pressure affects the phenomenon of melting. Most substances melt at higher temperatures if the pressure on them increases. Some do not. Ordinary ice, for example, melts at lower temperatures with increasing pressure, and this property provides the mechanism for ice skating. If a person of, say, 150 pounds stands on an ice surface and if the area under his shoes is about 75 square inches, the pressure exerted on the ice is about two pounds per square inch. On the edge of the blade of an ice skate, say, $\frac{3}{8}$ of a square inch, the pressure would be 400 pounds per square inch, enough to melt the ice and greatly increase its slipperiness. In order to raise the pressure on a substance to a million or more times atmospheric pressure, as can be done today, some special applications of these techniques and some very strong materials are required.

Highly compressed matter

To appreciate the concepts of modern high-pressure physics it is useful to have a feeling for what happens to a substance when it is subjected to high

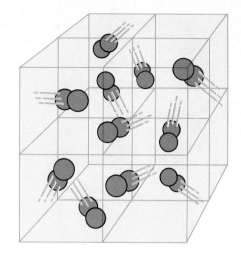

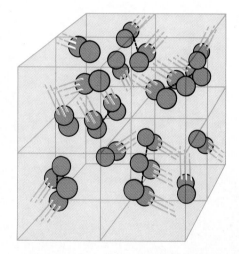

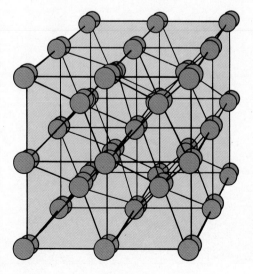

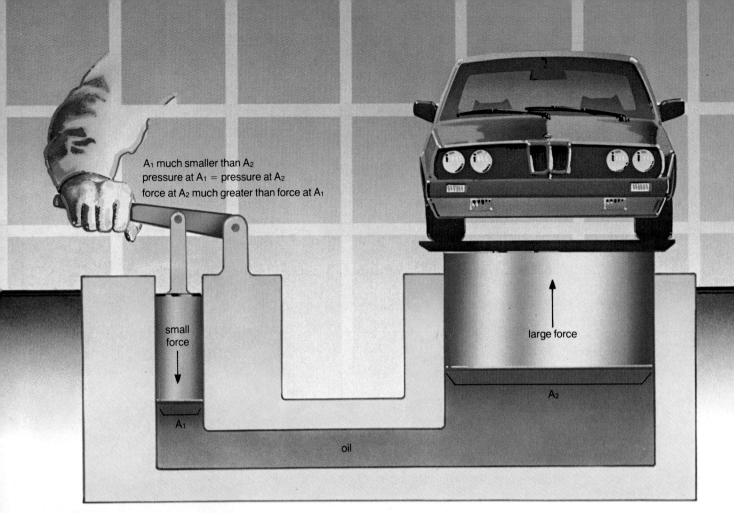

A₁ much smaller than A₂
pressure at A₁ = pressure at A₂
force at A₂ much greater than force at A₁

small
force

large force

A₁

A₂

oil

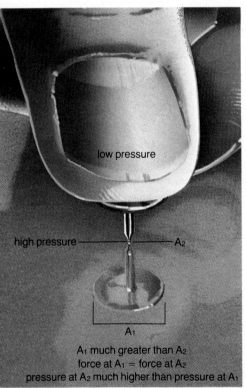

low pressure

high pressure ———————— A₂

A₁

A₁ much greater than A₂
force at A₁ = force at A₂
pressure at A₂ much higher than pressure at A₁

pressure. As a gas is compressed to a liquid, its freely traveling and rotating molecules are crowded together. Some of them form new chemical bonds with their neighbors. Eventually this bonding becomes strong, and the atoms and molecules are crowded so close that they become limited in the spaces that they can occupy. It is during the packing of atoms of different sizes that pressure forces the atoms close enough so that their outer, negatively charged electrons repel each other strongly, and thus a measure of the pressure can be related to the repulsive forces in a solid. It is the interaction of the electrons of neighboring atoms that result in the observed changes in a material at very high pressures. Suffice it to say that at extremely high pressures the compressive forces could presumably tear the atoms themselves apart, but they would also tear apart laboratory apparatus used to test such phenomena. Hence it is unlikely that such a test will be possible to do except by dynamic shock wave experiments, in which the sample and often the apparatus indeed are destroyed.

Today a number of high-pressure experiments are done to study matter as the atoms are compressed together. As is the case for all of physics, high-pressure physics is studied systematically so that observed phenomena can be understood. Even for the physically simplest of molecules, such as hydrogen and helium, the best theories of high-pressure physics are inexact. For more complex substances most theoretical knowledge of their high-pres-

206

sure behavior is quite primitive. Advances in the laboratory should lead to great improvements in theory.

Building better equipment

The most serious limitations in the laboratory for experimenting with high pressures, aside from explosive shock-wave type studies, have been those of engineering. Apparatus to study material at extreme pressures must be able to do quite a bit more than a hydraulic automotive jack, although many of the basic principles involved are the same. For the requirements of particular studies it must be possible to contain a sample under study while applying uniform stress in three dimensions, or perhaps in one or two dimensions. As the sample is thus held, under either hydrostatic or nonhydrostatic (directed) pressure, it must be possible to study the physics of the sample; that is, to make useful physical measurements.

Historically there are numerous examples of laboratory achievements that together have made it possible to accomplish these objectives. Bridgman, for example, is responsible for an advance in leakproof packing called the "unsupported area" pressure seal. In use this seal becomes pressurized higher than the sample and thus precludes the sample's leaking or being squeezed out. Its elegant simple design allowed Bridgman and others to hold samples at pressures above three kilobars for the first time in the 150-year period that high-pressure phenomena had been studied. (One bar is approximately equal to atmospheric pressure, or 14.5 pounds per square inch, measured at sea level. A kilobar equals 1,000 bars.)

In spite of a long career of devotion to high-pressure physics, Bridgman never was able to master the experiment to make diamonds. The first successful conversion of the graphite phase of carbon to the diamond phase—at about 100 kilobars and 1,600° C (2,900° F)—was dependent in part on the gradient pressure seal. This principle is incorporated in current devices that operate at pressures above one megabar (one million bars, approximately equal to a million atmospheres).

Most of the requirements of an apparatus intended to operate at ultrahigh pressures (nowadays arbitrarily defined as pressures above 200 kilobars) have been met with the recently modified diamond-window, high-pressure cell. This device has several advantages. A sample—gas, liquid, single crystal, or numerous crystals—can be held under hydrostatic or nonhydrostatic pressures above one megabar indefinitely. Electrically conducting leads can be introduced to the sample to study changes in conductivity. The diamond windows, which also serve as the pistons or anvils that compress the sample, are relatively transparent to many kinds of radiation; thus many of the state-of-the-art physics techniques that employ laser beams, infrared radiation, X-rays, and gamma rays, and other forms of radiation can be used to study a pressurized sample. Moreover, unlike former designs of high-pressure apparatus, this design allows the scientist to see the sample while it is under pressure (and at high temperature) and to photograph it.

The diamond-window, high-pressure cell satisfies an important requirement of any high-pressure apparatus; namely, that it be constructed of a sufficiently strong material. Diamond is the strongest material known. The

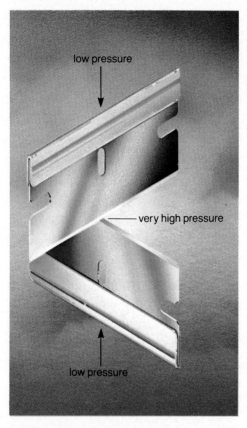

Small forces and pressures can be greatly increased with equipment that exploits the technique of area reduction. In an oil-filled hydraulic jack (opposite page, top) the pressure exerted by the end of a small piston having area A_1 on a contained fluid is transmitted unchanged to the end of a large piston having area A_2, resulting in an amplification of force. A force exerted on the head of a thumbtack with area A_1 (opposite, bottom), a rigid solid, is sent unchanged to its much smaller point (A_2), resulting in an amplification of pressure. Whereas a tack may typically produce a 500-fold increase in pressure, the sharp edges of two razor blades pressed together (above) may intensify an applied pressure by a factor of 100,000.

cell exploits the basic technique of area reduction, so that a relatively small applied pressure can be greatly magnified (typically 500-fold) on a sample within the cell. The cone shape in which most gem diamonds are cut is almost ideal, requiring only some modification to the tip to create a tiny, flat high-pressure surface. Two such diamonds held end-to-end in a device that provides precise alignment are forced together, the sample and sample chamber (basically a washer-shaped gasket) being located in between. The diamonds that are used, frequently stones of one-third to one-half carat, are small primarily because of cost, but one-to-two-carat diamonds have been tried. The high-pressure faces may be no larger than a third of a millimeter across, and observations must be carried out under a microscope.

Although the success of the diamond-window apparatus owes a great deal to Bridgman's ideas, it does not make use of the unsupported area seal. Instead a self-generated gradient pressure seal, in which pressure gradually increases inward toward the center of the opposing faces, effectively keeps the sample and chamber from being squeezed out. In fact, a thin sample of almost any material, weak or strong, held between the high-pressure surfaces of the cell will not extrude much even if a gasket ring is not used. A combination of the friction between the sample and diamond surfaces and the sample's internal friction always allows some sample to remain if the pressure is high enough. Such friction increases greatly at high pressure, although the physics of this unusual increase is not yet predictable or well understood. In laboratory experiments a small amount of sample or metal gasket extrudes as pressure is increased until about 150 kilobars. At pressures above 150 kilobars extrusion usually halts.

If hydrostatic pressure is desired, the hole in the center of a metal gasket is filled with gas, liquid, or a weak solid (such as helium or argon gas solidified at high pressure); the sample is immersed in the fluid or weak solid. For either hydrostatic or nonhydrostatic experiments the sample may be probed with electrical leads to make resistance measurements.

Working through the diamond window
In the early 1960s physicist A. W. Lawson described the outlook of the field of solid-state high-pressure physics with the following statement: "The siren lure of alchemy inherent in the new ultrahigh pressure investigations heralds a renaissance in inorganic chemistry." What had so excited Lawson was

Diagram describes the solid and liquid states of ordinary water for various combinations of temperature and pressure. The sloping line is the melting curve; on the left water exists as solid ice and on the right as liquid. A sufficient increase in pressure (point a to point b) on ice held at a constant temperature causes it to melt. Ice skaters depend on this effect. The blade of a skate supporting a person's weight exerts enough pressure to melt the ice beneath it.

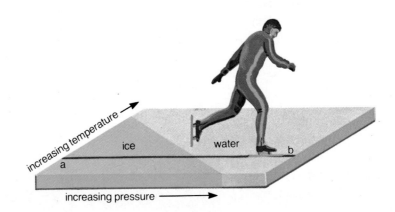

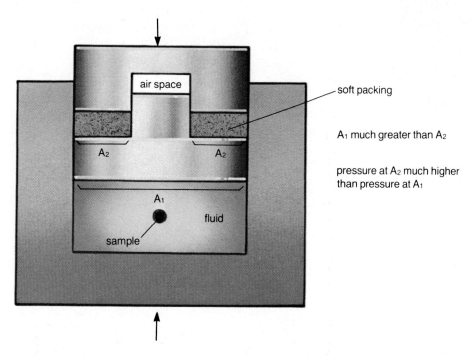

air space

soft packing

A_1 much greater than A_2

pressure at A_2 much higher
than pressure at A_1

A_2 A_2

A_1

fluid

sample

the prospect of being able to conduct experiments in the laboratory at pressures as high as ten kilobars. Today experiments can be done to pressures more than a hundred times higher.

The rapid jump in technology that enabled physicists to produce readily controlled pressures of a megabar and more in solid-state research has been paralleled and assisted by advances in laser technology. Laser beams are used to interact with materials held under pressure in the diamond-window, high-pressure cell. Among the measurements done this way is an accurate determination of the pressure on the sample in the cell. For this task a tiny crystal of ruby is placed in the cell with the sample. When a pressure reading is to be taken, a blue laser beam is focused through the diamond and onto the ruby. The laser light causes the ruby to fluoresce, emitting light at a characteristic wavelength. Previous experiments have shown that the color of ruby fluorescence changes with increasing pressure; this color change has been calibrated against other pressure-measurement techniques, in one case to a megabar and in another to about 1.7 megabars. Just as the diamond window allows a laser beam to enter the cell, it allows the ruby fluorescence to exit. A spectral analysis of the emission is then used to estimate the pressure.

Other lasers are used for heating samples, some of which have been raised to temperatures as high as 4,200° C (7,600° F). The temperature of a sample is calculated from measurements of the thermal (black-body) radiation that it emits. Still other lasers are used for conducting solid-state studies such as Brillouin scattering, a technique employed to measure the elastic properties of a sample at high pressure.

Current research

There are many examples of experiments under way to explore the new dimension of ultrahigh pressures. Geophysicists are studying the physics

The unsupported area pressure seal, invented by P. W. Bridgman, employs the technique of area reduction to pressure the seal higher than the sample and thus prevent the sample from leaking out. The area designated A_1 is the solid face of a cylinder, whereas that designated A_2 is an annular (washer-shaped) surface. Since A_2 is smaller than A_1, when the parts of the pressure cell are forced together the pressure on the packing becomes higher than that exerted by A_1 on the sample and surrounding fluid.

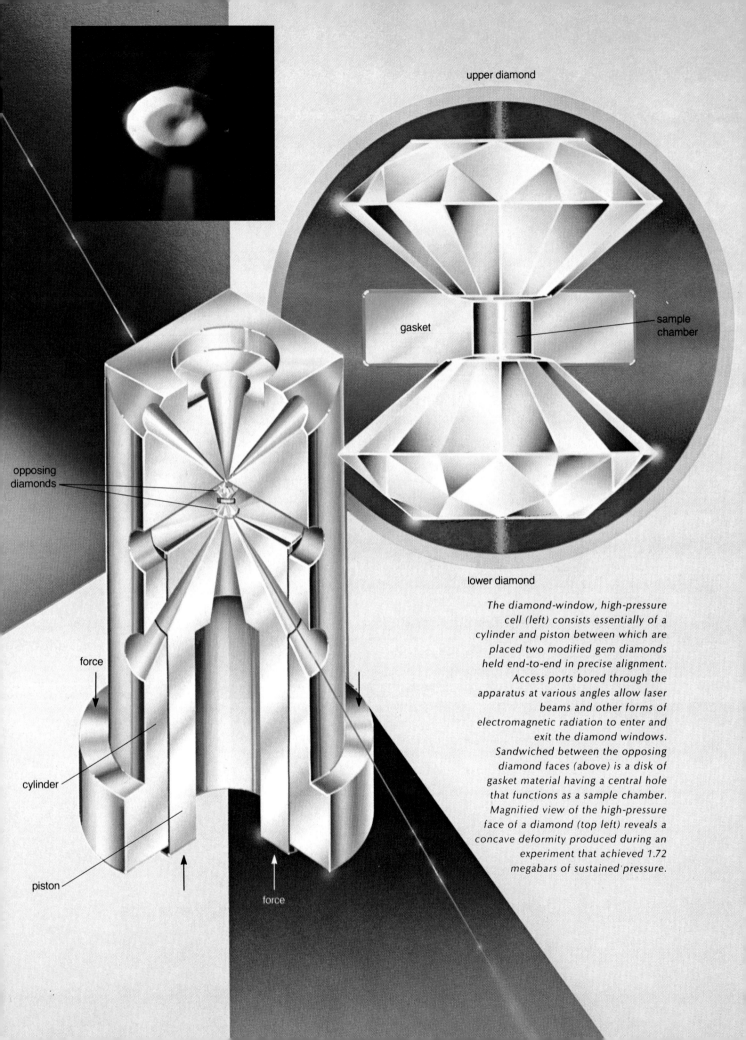

upper diamond

gasket

sample chamber

lower diamond

opposing diamonds

force

cylinder

piston

force

The diamond-window, high-pressure
cell (left) consists essentially of a
cylinder and piston between which are
placed two modified gem diamonds
held end-to-end in precise alignment.
Access ports bored through the
apparatus at various angles allow laser
beams and other forms of
electromagnetic radiation to enter and
exit the diamond windows.
Sandwiched between the opposing
diamond faces (above) is a disk of
gasket material having a central hole
that functions as a sample chamber.
Magnified view of the high-pressure
face of a diamond (top left) reveals a
concave deformity produced during an
experiment that achieved 1.72
megabars of sustained pressure.

High-pressure researcher (top left) examines the alignment of the diamonds in a diamond-window pressure cell prior to an experiment. Blue laser beam is focused through the optics of a light microscope onto a diamond-window cell (top right) during pressure calibration experiments with hydrogen. The cell is mounted on a spring-lever apparatus that presses the piston of the cell into the cylinder with increasing force as the small bolt at the lower right is turned. Two laser Raman scattering studies, one involving a krypton-ion laser beam (above left) and the other an argon-ion laser beam (above right), are conducted on samples pressurized in diamond-window cells.

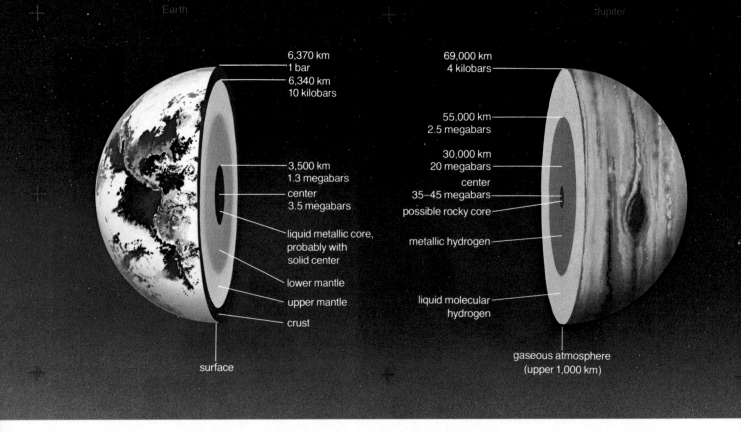

6,370 km
1 bar
6,340 km
10 kilobars

69,000 km
4 kilobars

55,000 km
2.5 megabars

30,000 km
20 megabars
center
35–45 megabars
possible rocky core

3,500 km
1.3 megabars
center
3.5 megabars

liquid metallic core,
probably with
solid center

metallic hydrogen

lower mantle

upper mantle

crust

liquid molecular
hydrogen

surface

gaseous atmosphere
(upper 1,000 km)

Cross sections of the Earth and Jupiter (above) compare their interior structures and indicate the pressures calculated to exist at various distances from their centers. Sample of iron-rich basaltic glass (below) was photographed while under more than 300 kilobars of pressure in a diamond-window cell. Bright spots are beads of metallic iron formed from the breakdown of iron oxides when the sample was heated with a laser. Such results have suggested a geochemical mechanism by which the Earth may have formed its iron core as well as the lighter, oxygen-rich minerals of the upper mantle.

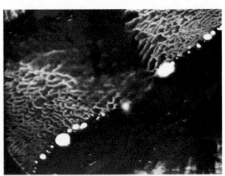

H. K. Mao—Carnegie Geophysical Laboratory

and chemistry of minerals under high pressure so that they can better understand the properties and composition of the Earth at great depths. For example, at the base of the Earth's crust where it joins with the mantle, about 40 kilometers (25 miles) down, the overlying rock exerts a pressure of about ten kilobars. At the mantle-core boundary, 2,900 kilometers (1,800 miles) below the surface, the pressure is about 1.3 megabars, and at the center of the planet the pressure is estimated to be about 3.5 megabars. Such pressures have tremendous influences on the properties of materials and may have been more important than temperature in determining the way in which the early Earth differentiated, or separated into its various chemical components, as it cooled from the molten state.

Complex iron-bearing minerals common in the Earth's mantle have been studied under several kilobars of pressure and subjected to high heat from a laser beam. At conditions equivalent to a depth of 650 kilometers (400 miles) they have been observed to undergo a large, sudden increase in density as they shift from one type of mineral structure to another; in the process they rid themselves of a high percentage of iron in the form of iron oxides. Such changes are consistent with certain density transitions detected in the Earth's mantle with seismic techniques. At higher temperatures and pressures, equivalent to a depth of 1,600 kilometers (1,000 miles), the iron oxides become unstable, breaking down into metallic iron and other oxide forms. This mechanism may be the route by which the Earth formed its heavy metallic core as well as the lighter oxygen-rich materials of the upper mantle. Laboratory experiments at still higher pressures, above one megabar, can now be done and are offering earth scientists a picture of important geochemical events near the mantle-core boundary that could not be observed any other way.

Geophysicists share with solid-state chemists and physicists an interest in determining the properties of such gases as hydrogen, helium, argon, neon, and methane at high pressure. The giant planets are composed of these elements and compounds in the gaseous, liquid, and solid state, ranging from very low pressures in the uppermost atmosphere at the edge of space to many tens of megabars in the interiors of Saturn, Jupiter, Neptune, and Uranus. Since the late 1970s investigators have created and measured the properties of high-pressure forms of many substances. Hydrogen, helium, nitrogen, neon, methane, and ammonia, for example, have been crystallized, some at room temperature. The noble gas xenon has been reported to have been pressured into a conducting metallic form, and sulfur may have been made into a superconducting substance, one that offers no resistance to the flow of electricity.

Molecular hydrogen, being the simplest of molecules, is considered a model for studying the basic laws of physics. It becomes a crystalline solid at room temperature under 57 kilobars of pressure, and its behavior has been studied under pressures as high as 500 kilobars. At a pressure of about 2.5–3 megabars, still a goal in sustained ultrahigh-pressure experiments, hydrogen is predicted to change from an insulator to a metal. As this transition occurs, molecular hydrogen, composed of two protons bonded together by two orbiting electrons, would become a mass of "bare" protons suspended in a sea of freely moving electrons. Some scientists believe that this exotic substance exists deep in Jupiter's interior, and studies have concluded that its creation on Earth could be of tremendous scientific and practical benefit. Like diamond formed at high pressure from carbon, once metallic hydrogen is created it may persist after the pressure is removed. In this state it would have an extremely high energy content per unit volume and may be a useful conventional fuel on Earth and in space as well as a nuclear fuel for fusion experiments. Moreover, some theoreticians have ventured that metallic hydrogen may be a superconductor at room temperature.

There are a wealth of prospects for a room-temperature superconductor. Envisioned are electrical generators that will be able to produce electricity simply by using the temperature differences between day and night; no fuel would be required. Such possibilities stimulate the imagination of physicists, astronomers, nuclear scientists, and crystallographers alike, and it is easy to understand why laboratories around the world are working on the problem.

The problems of making metallic hydrogen and, predictably, many other high-pressure materials that have exotic properties are amenable to experiment, but the experiments are not necessarily easy. Hydrogen, for one, must undergo a huge volume compression—a four-fold factor at least—before it becomes a metal. Currently theory is not even good enough to distinguish whether, for example, superconducting metallic hydrogen will be a solid or a liquid. Of course, hydrogen conceivably may not become a metal at any pressure. Nevertheless, whatever it becomes, its properties will be worth learning about.

Photos, H. K. Mao and
Peter M. Bell—Carnegie Geophysical Laboratory

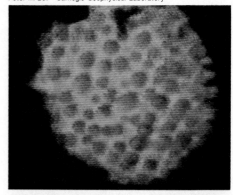

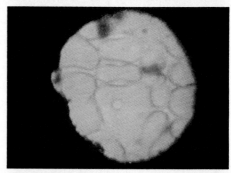

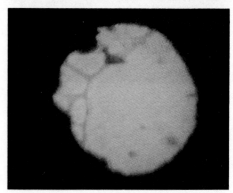

The solidification of hydrogen from the liquid state at room temperature and 57 kilobars of pressure is observed by means of a television camera trained through a microscope on a diamond-window pressure cell. First to appear are numerous tiny hydrogen crystals (top). These merge to form increasingly larger crystals (center and bottom) and finally one large solid mass. The dark grains visible in the images are ruby crystals used for making pressure measurements.

A
MUSEUM
IS TO
TOUCH

by George W. Tressel

Personal discovery, participation, and "hands-on" contact with exhibits distinguish today's science museums, which have far outstripped their traditional role as places for collections and scholarly study.

Every year in the United States roughly 150 million persons pass through the doors of science museums. They come to marvel and wonder and stand in awe, but most of all they come to experience science firsthand—to peer in the window of an Apollo space capsule, to contrast its tiny size with its immense accomplishment, to walk up and actually touch it. Touching is a particularly important part of science museums today. The endless streams of visitors pet horseshoe crabs, sea urchins, and dolphins; moon rocks and spaceships; elephants and snakes; daffodils and orchids; tractors and locomotives. In fact, touching, feeling, and exploring is the principal—and probably the only—common denominator of science museums today.

Even granting that the visitor figures are not accurate and that they include persons who come more than once, science museums are visited each year by a significant portion of the population. Almost as many people attend science museums as all other museums put together, and more do so than the combined physical attendance at football, basketball, and baseball.

Why do they come? It is far easier to read about science and far faster to see it in pictures, but it is not the same. In the science museum you are there. It is not the same to compare pictures of the first airplane and the first space laboratory as it is to stand next to them. It is one thing just to be told that speech is formed by the shape of your mouth; it is unforgettable to actually see a plastic mouth turn the sound of a duck call into human speech.

214

(Overleaf) Two adventurers of different generations share their fascination with the Exploratorium's Sun Painting exhibit, an ever changing projection of reflected and refracted sunlight. Retired locomotives at the Deutsches Museum in West Germany (above) encourage visitors to recall the achievements of a passing era of technology.

GEORGE W. TRESSEL is Program Director of the Office of Scientific and Engineering Personnel and Education, National Science Foundation, Washington, D.C.

(Overleaf) Photograph © Nancy Rodger—Exploratorium

Perhaps this magic of physical presence is why science visitors tend to come in family groups or with friends. Despite the very heavy use by schools, half of museum attendance is by adults, often bringing their children and grandchildren to one of the few places where age does not separate them. We are all childlike in a museum or a zoo; we are all awed by giant machines, dinosaurs, and sharks.

A visit to a science museum is an opportunity to explore exotic worlds that most people have only heard of or read about, a place to experience the pace of science and technology and to remind ourselves that we have had a personal role in its history. The parent who explains the Moon lander to a young child is doing more than explaining a bit of science; he or she is recalling society's magnificent achievements and remembering that "I was there."

The changing role of museums

It is only recently that museums have become such large arenas of popular interest. The name itself might suggest that museums were traditionally places for musing, for quiet contemplation. Until comparatively recently they were a home for collections and a place for study by scholars, curators, and taxonomists. Gradually this role expanded to include displays of the most interesting and outstanding specimens so that students and a relatively sophisticated public could view them. But they were, and many remain, facilities for serious study of systematic collections.

216

Personal contact allows each visitor to a science museum to satisfy an individual need. For one it may be the transformation of a nightmarish fear of monsters to cozy familiarity. For others it may be a unique way of seeing the oneness of humanity through the eyes of people who lived long ago. Still others may stumble upon a scientific principle, thereby laying a firm foundation of attitudes and concepts for the future.

Most of this traditional scholarly activity is unseen by the average visitor. Today, behind the public displays and dioramas many of the finest museums have truly awesome collections and large staffs of curators. Institutions like the Smithsonian Institution in Washington, D.C., the Field Museum of Natural History in Chicago, and the American Museum of Natural History in New York City exhibit only a minuscule part of their collections and employ large numbers of scientists who are responsible for collections that range from plants, animals, fossils, and rocks to clothes, tools, machines, and other human artifacts.

Only occasionally is the public aware of the richness of these collections. Recently the National Museum of Natural History, part of the Smithsonian, opened a major display of artifacts, photos, and notes documenting life among the Eskimos of the Bering Sea and collected by the museum's naturalist Edward W. Nelson well before the turn of the century. For the years between 1877 and 1881 he was assigned to the U.S. Army Signal Corps in Alaska and wandered from village to village, recording customs and life in the most primitive and hostile of environments. Nelson's notes were sent back to the National Museum of Natural History together with tools, clothes, artifacts, and perfectly crafted tiny models of the boats, houses, and other constructions that were too large to ship in any other way. There at the Smithsonian they lay for more than a hundred years waiting to be deciphered, assembled, and placed on display. Nelson and the Eskimos he recorded are long gone; today his collections are both an impressive display and an irreplaceable record of a lost civilization.

Valuable as such exhibits may be for curiosity, they also shed important light on scientific conjectures, theories, and policies. It is from arcane collections of skeletons, for example, that scientists know that tree squirrels are "living fossils" essentially unchanged for millions of years and that primitive humans had healthier teeth than humans do today. When planners are called upon to assess the environmental effect of changes in land use or pollution, they rely upon surveys of fauna, flora, and geology that have largely been documented and preserved in the collections of museums. The National Science Foundation alone provides more than $5 million each year to support such research.

As the educational value and stimulus of public displays were recognized, the roles of archival study and public education became increasingly parallel and separated. In a time before radio, television, and the sophistication of modern media, dioramas and glass boxes were a stimulating experience offering a closer view of nature and science than most people could find in any other way. Film, television, and increasingly realistic special visual effects have robbed a great deal of this excitement, but there remains something special about actually stepping up to meet the looming skeletons of *Triceratops* and *Tyrannosaurus rex*.

In great traditional museums of the U.S. like the Field Museum and the National Museum of Natural History there is still a strong ambivalence between the roles and needs of scholars and spectators. Hence, cases of stuffed birds sometimes will be found side by side with multimedia presentations on ecology and the environment. Although it is popular to consider the former

Today's science museums treat visitors to a broad range of experiences. Young aviation enthusiasts at the Franklin Institute Science Museum in Philadelphia (opposite page, top) work with "flying facts" computers that offer information at three levels of comprehension. Members of a school group visiting the Lawrence Hall of Science in Berkeley, California (bottom), compare the vital signs of an iguana with their own as part of a biometrics workshop.

219

Unseen by the average museum goer is the scholarly role of many of the traditional museums, which house laboratories, libraries, and rich collections of specimens ranging from plants and animals to geological material and human artifacts.

"old-fashioned," it is the visible part of an important scholarly activity that is a national asset.

Two ground breakers

In the early 1900s the Deutsches Museum in Munich, West Germany, added a spectacular change to this pattern, a style that has profoundly influenced almost all science museums since then—participation. The Industrial Revolution was in full swing. Labor, architecture, transportation, and communication were changing explosively. Who could fail to stand in awe of the first steam engines, locomotives, machine tools, and mining and textile machinery? Rich and poor alike gloried in the opportunity to see the new machines, much as people today swarm around Apollo and Spacelab.

But when Oskar von Miller opened this "German Museum for Masterworks of Natural Science and Engineering," he set out to provide more than awe and spectacle; he wanted the visitor to learn and understand. When the museum first opened many of its exhibits in 1906 in temporary quarters, cutaway machines and working models set a standard of visitor involvement and excitement that has been copied and developed throughout the world. Visitors were treated to demonstrations, they walked through a coal mine, they operated machines—all exciting new display techniques that now are taken for granted.

Almost every science museum has emulated this style to some extent. Even the simplest have installed pushbutton question-and-answer displays, while leaders like the Exploratorium in San Francisco feature endless experiments for the visitor to perform and sensory novelties that challenge the visitor's mind and imagination. The Exploratorium, in fact, has become the archetype for the "hands-on," experiential science center. An enormous cavern of lights and sounds, the museum is housed in the hulk of a once-abandoned neoclassical Palace of Fine Arts. Everywhere one turns is a new and exciting experience: something to do, surprising to discover, puzzling to explain. Neighborhood children have found this a marvelous place to play and explore. So have their parents; the Exploratorium has become one of San Francisco's attractions as well as a model for science museums throughout the world.

In today's science museum the visitor is constantly challenged to do something. Visitors can fly a real, working flight simulator, walk through a tropical rain forest with an explorer guide, attend an electricity demonstration by "Michael Faraday," experiment with mirrors and prisms and wave machines, puzzle over optical illusions, and study the behavior of insects, fish, reptiles, and other animals. Dioramas also have become participatory. In the Milwaukee Public Museum, for instance, schoolchildren follow a winding path, turning a corner to come face-to-face with a bellowing elephant at arm's length. The more knowledgeable ones (already having heard from an older sister or brother) run for the concealed button that makes a stuffed rattlesnake come to life.

Even zoos and aquariums are changing to provide opportunities to be close to and even touch the animals, as evinced by the proliferation of children's areas and petting sections in these institutions. In the National Aquarium in Baltimore, Maryland, one follows a spiral ramp down into the center of an enormous tank populated by myriads of fish, sharks, and rays, whereupon a female oceanographer in scuba garb feeds and pets them.

First opening its doors in 1906 in temporary quarters, the Deutsches Museum set a standard of visitor participation that was copied worldwide. People could tour a life-size replica of a coal mine, operate models of mining equipment (below left), and watch machines that demonstrated celestial mechanics and traced the paths of astronomical bodies through the heavens (below).

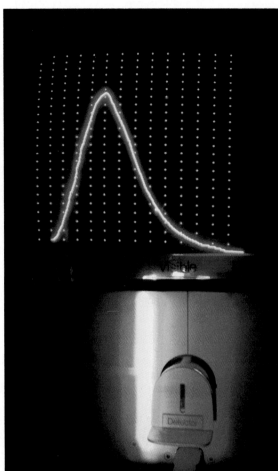

Learning in the museum

Behavioral scientists believe that most understanding is developed gradually over a long period of time. Learning is a process of building and tuning, not stuffing. Hence, educational experts feel that success in mathematics and science is founded on attitudes and concepts that are established very early in life. The process of learning about science is one of development, an accumulation of concepts, skills, and experiences that ultimately contributes to the structured understanding of the classroom. The child who is fascinated by shadows on a wall of the Exploratorium as they shift and merge in every color of the rainbow cannot tell you what he or she has learned. But years later the teacher who explains how colors combine to make white light will find it a little easier, and the student will find it a little less intimidating.

Perhaps more importantly, the student who sees beauty in science and finds the museum a great adventure is a little more likely to persist, despite the acknowledged difficulty and discipline of studying formal mathematics and science. And the 12-year-old girl who watches a female scientist working in the Living Coral Reef laboratory of the National Museum of Natural History knows that all scientists do not have bushy mustaches and long white hair.

Modern museum directors are acutely aware of this influence, and they consciously foster it. In the Exploratorium a black high school student wears

San Francisco's Exploratorium has become the archetype "hands-on" science center, featuring endless experiments and sensory novelties. At the Hot Light exhibit (opposite page, top left) visitors move a sensor through the component colors of the light from an incandescent bulb while a display screen plots the intensity of each color. The Light Island (opposite, top right) allows people to manipulate beams of light with mirrors, lenses, and prisms. Spectators at the AM Lightning tube (opposite, bottom) play with glowing beads of light generated by a radio wave. In the Duck into Kaleidoscope area (this page, below left) people substitute for the conventional bits of plastic. At the Vocal Vowels exhibit (below) participants pump air into plastic models of the human oral cavity to produce some of the sounds of speech.

(Top) Ontario Science Centre; (bottom left) The Franklin Institute; (bottom right) Bruce Roberts, Southern Living, Inc., September 1982, reprinted with permission.

Modern science museums constantly challenge people to do something. Visitors to the Ontario Science Centre in Toronto (top) try their hand at the dexterity and concentration needed by technicians who handle dangerous substances. At the Franklin Institute's museum (above left) one can pilot a working flight simulator, while at Discovery Place in Charlotte, North Carolina (above right), an ersatz Michael Faraday encourages visitors to think about the mysteries of electricity.

a red jacket to label him as an "explainer." As he dissects a cow's eyeball before a somewhat apprehensive but fascinated crowd of young admirers, the image he projects is profound: a not much older, not much smarter, not-too-distant explainer who is both a teacher and a role model. Before long the explainer will know too much for his job and will be replaced by another ingenuous teacher-learner.

It should be recognized that neither children nor adults go to science museums for "education." They go for fun. Museums are a home for recreational learning, for the part of the public that enjoys exploring, adventure, and discovery. Whatever is learned there is informal, impulsive, and unintentional, but it indeed is learning. And as people explore and wonder and think about the things they see, they are contributing to their accretion of experi-

224

ence and ideas. Museum designers are fond of quoting the ancient Chinese adage: "I hear and I forget; I see and I remember; I do and I understand."

The "crisis" in science education

This growing sophistication and interest in informal learning is coming none too soon, for today schools in the U.S. need all the help they can get. Half of all newly hired mathematics and science teachers are unqualified. Not enough people are being trained to replace the teachers who plan to retire in the near future. In 1982 one state reported that it had trained only a single

(Clockwise from top left) Busy museum goers send their voices between parabolic dishes at the Pacific Science Center in Seattle, hold a giant millipede at the Smithsonian's Insect Zoo, watch an Ontario Science Centre demonstrator set a water-filled bronze bowl resonating by rubbing it, and use their shadows at Discovery Place to find hidden colors in white light.

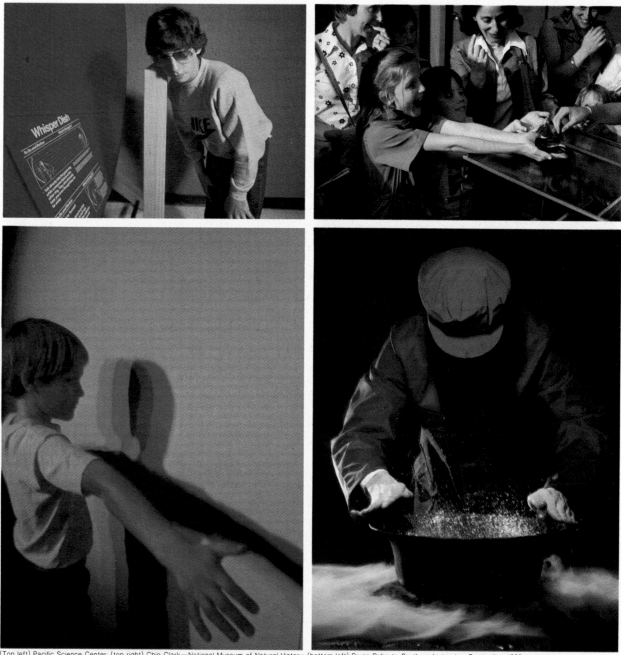

(Top left) Pacific Science Center; (top right) Chip Clark—National Museum of Natural History; (bottom left) Bruce Roberts, Southern Living, Inc., September 1982, reprinted with permission; (bottom right) Ontario Science Centre

Like museums, today's zoos and aquariums have embraced the theme of visitor participation, featuring habitats that bring people and animals into much closer contact. At the National Aquarium in Baltimore (above right) spectators descend a spiral ramp into the center of a 335,000-gallon ring-shaped tank to view a living model of an Atlantic coral reef community. (Above) A diver in the tank gives visitors a better look at a Hawksbill turtle, an endangered species. The facility also features a 260,000-gallon Open Ocean Tank housing several species of sharks and a Children's Cove where children can explore "tide pools" containing periwinkles, starfish, crabs, and clams.

new science teacher, and almost all states report serious or critical shortages of mathematics and science teachers.

Girls and minority children tend to avoid math and science because they are considered "difficult," and well-intentioned but misguided counselors often encourage this view. Both achievement and enrollment in the U.S. are falling below those of other developed countries like Japan and West Germany, and a child who drops out of mathematics effectively precludes most participation in science and technology. Moreover, all this is happening in an era of increasingly exotic technology and intense international competition.

No single institution can change the quality of technical education alone. Children need early and sustained motivation and encouragement; teachers need improved training and compensation comparable to those of industry; schools need costly facilities and specialized personnel; primary and secondary education systems need more coherent early patterns of mathematics and science instruction for all students—to mention only a few of the more pressing problems.

Science museums stand out in this milieu as one of the few places where good facilities, an exciting environment, well-trained science specialists, and a dedication to motivating and encouraging the general student is taken for granted. As a result they serve a unique role in providing basic background experiences that contribute to the success of more conventional education.

Partly in response to this potential, science museums are continuing to evolve. Increasing numbers of museum programs are designed to complement and extend the activities and curriculum of the formal classroom. In the Exploratorium, for example, teachers are helped to organize museum experiences for their students that will relate to classroom activities. In the Lawrence Hall of Science in Berkeley, California, outdoor biology experiments are designed to be administered by Boy Scout and Girl Scout leaders. The Franklin Institute Science Museum and Planetarium in Philadelphia performs science demonstrations in shopping malls where teenagers gather. In Discovery Place in Charlotte, North Carolina, several hundred volunteers

226

provide a constant stream of science demonstrations that most elementary school teachers would find difficult or impossible to duplicate.

Perhaps the most developed of such school-related programs is that of the Fernbank Science Center, which is operated by and for the school system of Atlanta, Georgia. Here the science museum is the focal point of a large nature center surrounded by extensive science classrooms and laboratories where specialized science teachers conduct classes for motivated students using equipment and techniques that would be difficult or impossible to maintain in a typical elementary or high school. Many of the staff at Fernbank are engaged in ongoing research and offer gifted students the use of exotic tools like spectrophotometers, a large professional telescope, an electron microscope, and a variety of computers, not to mention the opportunity to work with a practicing scientist.

In Fernbank's Science Tools and Techniques program, motivated students spend three to six months in a concentrated hands-on course. They learn to program computers, make photomicrographs, test antibiotics, identify and measure trace chemicals, and make field observations in meteorology, biology, and other fields. Each day includes four hours of science and one hour of mathematics, but more important than the direct content of these courses is the unforgettable experience of problem solving and scientific discovery.

Tomorrow's science museums

This constant experimentation with ways to increase the visitor's involvement and refine the museum's role has just begun. In the Smithsonian Institution a Naturalist Center offers a kind of library-workshop where the enthusiastic amateur scientist and curious collector can come to identify fossils and minerals, learn to stuff birds, and, when appropriate, meet with scientists of the Smithsonian's staff. In fields like archaeology and paleontology an overenthusiastic amateur can be an "unguided missile" who damages
continued on page 230

For all the technical capabilities of television and film, museum directors know that there remains something special about actually standing in the shadow of a space capsule or a hulking creature from the Earth's past. Workmen refurbish Dinosaur Hall (above) at the Smithsonian's National Museum of Natural History as part of an extensive project to present the history of life through fossils. A new life-size model of a pterosaur (above left), an extinct flying reptile with a 40-foot wingspread, receives finishing touches before being put on display in Dinosaur Hall.

227

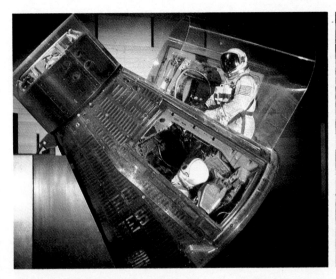

The spectrum of science museums

Science museums reflect the diversity of their subjects and span a broad range of topic, style, purpose, and sophistication. The more than 800 science museums in the U.S. tend to be larger, more adventuresome, and more flamboyant than their nonscience counterparts. Although making up only 18% of the museum world, they spend 40% of its budget and attract 45% of its audience.

Exploring different science museums is an adventure, because no two are the same. A few examples listed below offer an introduction to the range and excitement of the science museum world.

The *National Air and Space Museum* in Washington, D.C., is America's most popular museum and houses a spectacular collection of rockets, space vehicles, and airplanes. Visitors can view an awesome super-size film about flying as well as a collection of "real machines" that includes the Wright brothers' plane that achieved the first heavier-than-air flight, Charles Lindbergh's "Spirit of St. Louis," and the human-powered "Gossamer Condor." This museum presents a powerful and nostalgic reminder of the pace of technology during our lifetimes. (See *1979 Yearbook of Science and the Future* Feature Article: THE NEW MUSEUM OF FLIGHT.)

The *Exploratorium* in San Francisco is less than fifteen years old but is already the world's model of exploratory, discovery experiences. No other museum is truly comparable. Housed within San Francisco's charming old Palace of Fine Arts is an incredible adventure. Every exhibit is a surprise, a puzzle, and a work of art—and every work of art is a study in science. This is the museum for people who think that science is dull, where children explain exhibits to their parents and where "Oh, my!" is a cliché.

The *National Aquarium in Baltimore*, the newest of the great aquariums, takes visitors on a tour of coastal ecology and down into the ocean where they are surrounded on all sides by sharks, turtles, and marine life of every description. One enjoyable experience is watching the fish gather around to be fed and petted like a pack of puppies.

The *National Museum of Natural History* in Washington, D.C., possesses the striking public displays that have come to be expected—about dinosaurs, early man, evolution, and flora and fauna. And like the attractions of the other great natural history museums these are only the surface evidence of immense collections and exotic research across a wide range of specialties. Notable exhibits are the Living Coral Reef, a working marine-biology laboratory with a complete living ecology including several hundred species of coral, fish, crustaceans, and other animals; the Insect Zoo, where children discover a different kind of "zoo animal"; and the Naturalist Center, a "library" of tools and advice for the amateur naturalist.

The *Museum of Science and Industry* in Chicago is America's answer to the Deutsches Museum and the biggest and best of the industry and technology museums. Visitors walk through a working coal mine and a captured submarine, visit a modern farm, and learn about chemicals, nutrition, and endless other achievements of industry and technology. This museum is best at Christmas when Chicago's many ethnic groups stage special displays and programs.

The *Ontario Science Centre* in Toronto, just across the U.S.-Canadian border, is one of the best planned and balanced science centers in the world. It covers a full range of activities and subjects for all ages and all interests, housed in a building that is a model of museum design. The Ontario center is government funded and maintains a consistent quality of design and content that few U.S. museums can match.

The *Fernbank Science Center* in Atlanta, although relatively unknown outside of Georgia, has an attendance of more than 800,000 per year and is a model of complementary museum and school activities. Established and owned by local citizens it is operated by the school system, and half of the attendance comprises students and special education programs. Student facilities include elaborate chemistry, computer, astronomy, biology, and meteorology laboratories. Its planetarium is among the largest in the country. Fernbank's programs are models of science education and an exemplary approach to making the most of limited educational resources.

The Science Arcade (opposite page, top left) at the Ontario Science Centre offers visitors perception games, muscle-powered electrical generators, handles to crank, musical instruments, and other delights. The Gemini 4 spacecraft (opposite, bottom left), from which astronaut Edward White took the first U.S. space walk, is displayed in the Smithsonian's National Air and Space Museum. At the Fernbank Science Center motivated students are given the opportunity to work with an electron microscope (opposite, bottom right) and other sophisticated laboratory equipment. A captured World War II German submarine (above) is open for tours at the Museum of Science and Industry. In the National Aquarium divers feed coral reef fish by hand three times a day (bottom), ensuring the health of even the least aggressive species.

Aware of their unique role in providing basic learning experiences, science museums are ever seeking ways to increase visitor involvement. The Milwaukee Public Museum sponsors Dig-a-Dinosaur field trips (above), while a traveling exhibit brings a piece of the Ontario Science Centre to distant communities (above right). The enormous public hunger to know has been amply demonstrated by such classic institutions as the Museum of Science and Industry (below).

Museum of Science and Industry

continued from page 227

important scientific evidence. Several science centers are experimenting with summer and weekend field trips in which amateur scientists work as assistants to professionals. In the process the motivated individual becomes an asset instead of a liability.

In the Ontario Science Centre in Toronto senior citizens are invited to free movies and encouraged to stay to view the exhibits and mingle with the crowds of excited children. The museum circulates a large number of mobile displays and demonstrations to schools throughout Ontario. And the museum itself is so popular that each year more than 50,000 U.S. schoolchildren are bused across the border to visit there.

When the Voyager 1 space probe began sending back its pictures of Saturn, hundreds of Portland residents brought sleeping bags and containers of hot coffee to the Oregon Museum of Science and Industry, where they spent the evening watching the pictures appear bit by bit on a king-sized television screen. The same pictures would be in the newspaper the next morning, but there was something special about being there to watch the first message arrive across millions of miles of space. In the same museum evening classes of businessmen, students, and housewives are learning the intricacies of home computers and how to make them do their tricks. The classes are so popular that the museum is limited only by the availability of teachers and space.

Gradually such experiments are expanding the role of the science museum, making it a complement to the school and a center for community interest in science and technology. Today's magnificently flamboyant museums like the Museum of Science and Industry in Chicago and the National Air and Space Museum in Washington, D.C., have demonstrated the enormous public hunger to know about science and technology, but they have only begun to explore this greater potential.

Tomorrow's science museums are likely to combine the best features of today's innovations: displays for the general visitor; special classrooms for the gifted and motivated; libraries, workshops, and facilities for amateur sci-

(Left) Jack Fishleder—Lawrence Hall of Science; (right) Bernard Thoeny—Fernbank Science Center

entists; auditoriums for public lectures and debates; collections, curators, and even working research centers open to public view—like the Pacific Science Center's Meteorology Center in Seattle, Washington, and the Smithsonian's Living Coral Reef laboratory.

Science museums will never look like carbon copies. Their diversity and individuality are part of their excitement. But there is today an exciting exchange of ideas, and most museums are busy extending the range of their activities and audiences. The ambivalences—between scholars and showmen; between public playground and classroom supplement; between a home for collections and a public science center—have yet to be resolved. But it is safe to assume that most science museums will provide an increasing variety of activities for every level of interest and participation, where children from 9 to 90 can continue to learn—by "accident."

Young naturalists (above left) dip for specimens in the Nature Study Area of the Lawrence Hall of Science, while late-night students make use of Fernbank Science Center's 36-inch telescope (above). The backup Skylab on display at the National Air and Space Museum (below left) shows people how astronauts lived and worked in space for months at a time. Although every science museum is unique, all extend the same invitation (below).

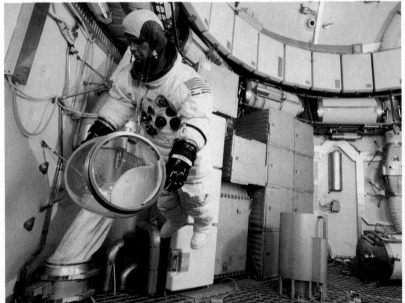

(Left) Smithsonian Institution; (right) Charles Cegielski

SCIENCE
AND THE
PRIVATE
SECTOR

by James Stacy Coles

*Limitations on government support
for basic research are causing
scientists to turn increasingly to private
enterprise—industries and
foundations—for funding.*

Private philanthropy has long been an important
aspect of many religious and philosophical traditions. The rise of civilization was marked by the
development of ethical values, including a concern for one's fellows. With the advent of Chris-
tianity the Church became a center for
philanthropy, and at one time England found
that the ecclesiastical foundations held a significant fraction of the country's total wealth. (By
comparison, foundations in the United States in
1982 accounted for less than 1% of the nation's
assets.) Growing corruption in the use of this
wealth by the Church eventually resulted in the
transfer of its control to secular authority in
17th-century England.

Thus, the first English settlers in America had
an appreciation of the benefits of secular as well
as religious philanthropy. William Penn, Cotton

Mather, and Benjamin Franklin were all involved in some form of philanthropy. In fact, the American Philosophical Society, founded by Franklin, today is still making grants in support of scholarly research. Throughout the 18th and 19th centuries public charities were established in the U.S. for a wide variety of purposes.

Such was the tradition of giving in America at the beginning of the 20th century, the age of the first of the great modern philanthropists, Andrew Carnegie and John D. Rockefeller. From their examples came the frequently quoted adage that private foundations are created by the rich from surplus wealth. (This rule is not universally true. Research Corporation, a foundation for the advancement of science and technology, was created in 1912 by a man of modest means, and some community foundations are supported by many small donors.)

The Carnegie Corporation of New York, the first large, modern foundation for general purposes, was established in 1911 by an act of the New York state legislature. In 1913 the Rockefeller Foundation was organized, again for general philanthropic purposes. It, in turn, was the largest in terms of assets until, through a series of major gifts of Ford Motor Co. stock, the Ford Foundation emerged in the 1940s with the largest corpus of any foundation up to that time.

Many different categories of foundations exist, such as family foundations, company foundations, special-purpose foundations, community foundations, and general-purpose foundations. Most of the largest fall in the last category. Another distinction is made between grants-making and operating foundations. F. Emerson Andrews has perhaps given the most generally accepted and succinct definition of a foundation: "A nongovernmental, nonprofit organization having a principal fund of its own, managed by its own trustees or directors, and established to maintain or aid social, educational, charitable, religious, or other activities serving the common welfare." Federal and state law may define many categories of foundations in more precise legal terms but no more comprehensively than the definition above.

While general-purpose and other types of foundations can and do support scientific research, the most significant nongovernmental support in this area has come from those that are specialized. Foundations that support research in the basic sciences (chemistry, physics, biology, mathematics, etc.), are unfortunately few in number. In the United States they include the American Philosophical Society, the Dreyfus Foundation, the Petroleum Research Fund, Research Corporation, the Alfred P. Sloan Foundation, and the Welch Foundation (the last limiting its support to chemistry within the state of Texas).

Other foundations have given substantial support for medical and agricultural research. Among them are the Commonwealth Fund, the John A. Hartford Foundation, the Henry J. Kaiser Family Foundation, the Josiah Macy, Jr., Foundation, the Rockefeller Foundation, the Markle Foundation, and the Robert Wood Johnson Foundation. Johnson is the largest special-purpose foundation supporting medicine and medical research. Up to the present time it has directed the bulk of its resources to research on the delivery of health care.

JAMES STACY COLES is Chairman of the Executive Committee of Research Corporation in New York, N.Y.

Illustrations by John Craig

234

Foundation-funded achievements

Examples of successful medical research projects supported by foundation grants include the elimination of hookworm, previously debilitating to millions of people in the southern U.S. and to others living in warm climates; the conquering of malaria, long a scourge in tropical countries; and the vaccine to protect against yellow fever. In an allied area Research Corporation's now-terminated Williams-Waterman Fund played an important role in the fight against the diseases of malnutrition in children, particularly in Latin America and the Philippines.

In agriculture the Rockefeller Foundation by means of both its own staff and of grant support sustained over many decades has brought about the Green Revolution, whereby new varieties of wheat and corn developed by plant genetics have resulted in great increases in yield per acre. More recently, Rockefeller joined with the Ford Foundation in establishing IRRI, the International Rice Research Institute, in the Philippines in order to increase the production of rice in those countries dependent on it as the main dietary staple. Somewhat allied with respect to agricultural yields and the control of disease is ICIPE, the International Centre of Insect Physiology and Ecology. Headquartered in Nairobi, Kenya, it is funded cooperatively by several foundations and governments.

Although successful research in medicine and agriculture can have a dramatic, widely perceived impact, the results of fundamental research in the physical and natural sciences underlie all efforts in such applied fields. Often this basic research is highly speculative; it may or may not produce useful results. It is in this area that the private foundation, operating with a flexibility not possessed by government and answerable primarily to its own trustees, can perform a valuable role in advancing science.

For example, the Daniel and Florence Guggenheim Foundation long supported research related to aeronautics, including pioneering work on jet propulsion. Also supported was the early work of Robert H. Goddard on rocketry (leading eventually to satellites and space research), in which Research Corporation also played a crucial role. With respect to the latter, Esther C. Goddard has written that this support provided vital assistance in the 1920s when the Smithsonian Institution could no longer support her husband's work, and prior to resources becoming available from Guggenheim, saying:

"The entry of Research Corporation with help was truly crucial. We both felt that [it] did not receive adequate credit for its . . . generosity at a critical time."

Similarly, E. O. Lawrence at the University of California developed and constructed the first cyclotron with grants from three foundations—Rockefeller, Markle, and Research Corporation. The consequences of this pioneering research are enormous, for medicine and many other fields of science, as well as for such applications as nuclear weaponry and nuclear power.

The growth years

With a few notable exceptions basic scientific research has primarily been conducted in college and university laboratories. Prior to World War II a number of business corporations supported basic research in their own laboratories, though such in-house efforts have dwindled in recent decades. In 1939 only 5 of 77 large foundations made grants for research in the physical sciences; these totaled $208,000. In 1946 six foundations granted $1,883,000, and in 1953 ten granted $1,686,000. Immediately after World War II the federal government, first through the Office of Naval Research and then by means of the newly established National Science Foundation, initiated what was to become a massive program of support for research in the sciences. This effort dwarfed support by private foundations, even though assistance from the latter sector had grown to almost $70 million by 1979. However, no adjustment has been made for inflation in these data; if such were done, it would be clear that the level of real support increased much less over this span of years.

With the launching of the first man-made satellite by the Soviet Union in 1957 government support for U.S. science was itself launched into its own new orbit, spiraling upward for a dozen or more years. This era was especially productive for science in the U.S., as evidenced by the number of Nobel Prizes awarded U.S. scientists and by such feats as landing men on the surface of the Moon.

Federal support for basic research continued to grow, from $715 million to $1 billion in 1960 and to almost $9 billion in 1981; research funding from universities and colleges themselves (including state and local government sources), increased during that period from $72 million to $885 million. Assistance from other nonprofit agencies, including foundations, rose from $68 million to $520 million. The vast and much greater expansion of the role of government forced universities and foundations to reassess their roles in research so as to support those areas where government lacked the imagination, initiative, and flexibility to anticipate and meet new and vital needs.

Alternatives to government support

To the distress of the science community the flow of research support fell victim in the early 1980s to the combined effects of inflation, recession, the energy crisis, and large federal deficits. Government support of basic research in academic institutions leveled off in terms of constant dollars and, to some degree, declined. With real support from government being limited and other urgent demands being made on foundations and internal funding, universities and other nonprofit laboratories were forced to look elsewhere for funds with which to support their ongoing research effort. One such source was industry and the business community. In general this meant soliciting direct grants from industry for research in narrowly defined fields.

Grants from U.S. industry to colleges and universities are not new. Large companies, particularly those involved in chemistry, have maintained support programs of one kind or another for many decades, often through company foundations. These have generally been in the nature of fellowships for graduate students, equipment grants, or general support for science departments. Another facet of this relationship has been the practice by industry of hiring university faculty members as specialized consultants. The total of this industry support of university research in the sciences has been small, however, relative to government aid.

Data from the National Science Foundation for 1979 are illuminating. The amount of support received from industry by 20 of the top 25 universities (those with research and development expenditures ranging from $59 million to $142 million), was relatively minor. Six universities received 3% or less of their total R and D costs from industry; seven had such support for from 3 to 4.5% of R and D costs; six had 4.5 to 10%; and one received more than 10% from this source. For 85 of the top 100 such institutions (some with total R and D expenditures as low as $15 million), 33 received funding from industry for 3% or less of such expenditures, 28 received 3 to 4.5%, 19 gained 4.5 to 10%; and only five had support in amounts greater than 10% of the university's total R and D expenditures. Therefore, while significant, such support has not been overwhelming. The overall average is about 4%. The remaining funding for these expenditures has come from the U.S. government, supplemented by internal institutional funds, foundation grants, and occasional gifts and bequests from individuals.

With the advent of recombinant DNA research and the resulting emergence of genetic engineering as a tool of immense and unknown power, the chemical and pharmaceutical industries found themselves without in-house expertise to rapidly develop research and manufacturing techniques that would enable the exploitation of these new concepts. Industry needs "best science" behind its development of new technologies, and in totally new fields that "best science" is most often found in the universities. The result has been a number of contracts or agreements between companies and universities for the support of on-campus research in some specified area. Examples of such bilateral agreements are shown in the table on page 240.

With respect to university/industry interaction a number of new small companies have sprung out of recombinant DNA research; among them are: Agrigenetics, Biogen, Calgene, Cetus, Genentech, Genex, Hybritech, and Monoclonal Antibodies. Considerable investor interest has been evidenced in such enterprises. The first public offering of Genentech was heavily oversubscribed, even though at the time of the offering the company had yet to turn a profit nor were significant earnings projected for several years. Later public offerings by other small companies did not generate nearly as much interest, as the investing public came to realize the extensive development required in adapting these revolutionary techniques for industrial production. The pharmaceutical firm Eli Lilly and Co. was licensed by Genentech to produce human insulin (in contrast with bovine insulin, which was the only kind previously available) by the use of genetically engineered bacteria, and this came to the market in 1983.

This support of basic research in the university laboratory by industry is not without its difficulties and hazards. While these have always been present to a degree, the massive increases in funding, in interest, and in expectations on the part of industry seriously exacerbate the problem. Basically, industry's goals ultimately revolve about production and return on investment. The university, in contrast, is concerned with education, study, and research. Its "bottom line" is new knowledge and the dissemination thereof. Industry may legitimately enforce secrecy in its laboratories, but the philosophy of the university requires its antithesis—open disclosure.

238

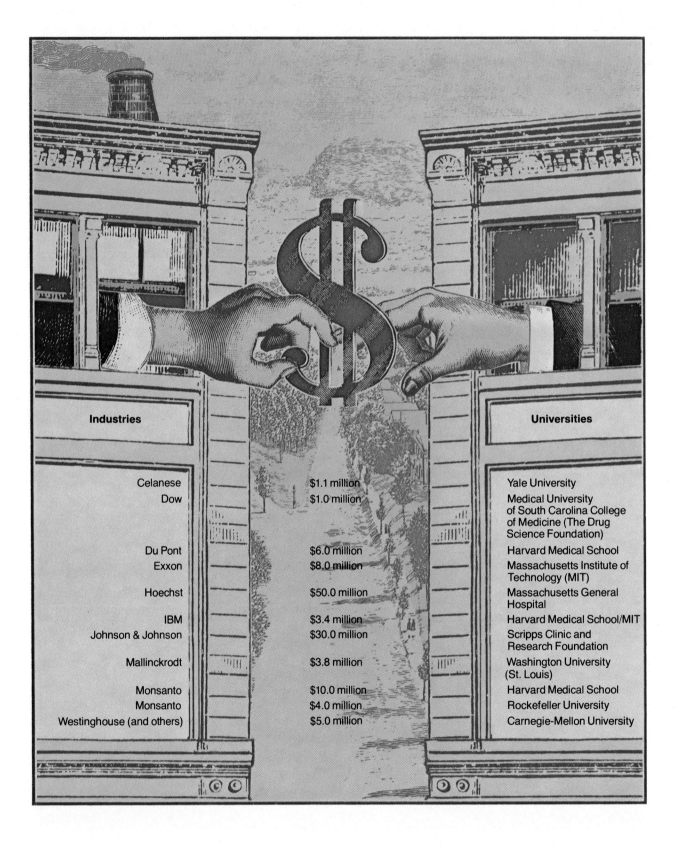

Industries

Universities

Industries		Universities
Celanese	$1.1 million	Yale University
Dow	$1.0 million	Medical University of South Carolina College of Medicine (The Drug Science Foundation)
Du Pont	$6.0 million	Harvard Medical School
Exxon	$8.0 million	Massachusetts Institute of Technology (MIT)
Hoechst	$50.0 million	Massachusetts General Hospital
IBM	$3.4 million	Harvard Medical School/MIT
Johnson & Johnson	$30.0 million	Scripps Clinic and Research Foundation
Mallinckrodt	$3.8 million	Washington University (St. Louis)
Monsanto	$10.0 million	Harvard Medical School
Monsanto	$4.0 million	Rockefeller University
Westinghouse (and others)	$5.0 million	Carnegie-Mellon University

University administrators and business leaders are aware of the hazards of the interface between their two realms. For example, there have been cases of inhibition of free and open discussion among scientific colleagues and peers. Many new concepts, however, have emerged from "corridor" or "lunch table" conversations with one's colleagues. Another example is that of formal agreements in which a given corporation benefits exclusively from the results of research, with no recognition of the involvement of university, foundation, or government funds in providing laboratories, apparatus and supplies, and staff effort. Faculty time has on occasion been devoted disproportionately to industrial contracts at the expense of teaching and of more fundamental investigations into the nature of the world.

These are among the conflicts that can be cited. That the need to avoid such situations is recognized and heeded was demonstrated by the agreement reached in December 1982 between Harvard Medical School, MIT, and IBM. The $3.4 million five-year, three-party contract involves research and development of new diagnostic instrumentation with the following provisions: the two educational institutions will own any patents that might evolve, the corporation will have rights to license the patents on a nonexclusive basis, and academicians will have full freedom to publish their findings without prior approval. It should be noted, however, that this funding is for applied research and development, not for basic research.

Future prospects

What will be the source of funds for the present and growing needs of basic research in university laboratories? The growth of government support is without question limited by political and budgetary considerations. Industrial support not only imposes the hazards previously mentioned but is often constrained by narrowness of purpose. Internal funds for scientific research are available only to the extent justified in terms of the institution's obligation to the humanities, social sciences, and other areas.

Funds from private foundations, which played so important a role in the early years of the 20th century, have certainly not kept pace with government funding, yet all in all are not insignificant and do have potential for growth. During the six-year period from 1977 through 1982 private foundation grants in support of research in the sciences as reported to The Foundation Center ranged in number, annually, from 520 to 848 and in dollars from $16,764,000 to $49,027,000. Those categorized as physical sciences but excluding technology (mathematics, astronomy, Earth sciences, physics, and chemistry) had grants ranging in number from 223 to 571 and in dollars from $7,190,000 to $22,090,000, as compared with life sciences (excluding medicine) with grants numbering 65 to 325, and in dollars, $6,281,000 to $31,027,000. Private foundation grants in the physical sciences numbered roughly two to three times those in the life sciences, presumably because of generous funding of life sciences by such public agencies as the National Institutes of Health.

As evidence of the total effort by private foundations, for all basic research from 1977 through 1982 there were 4,491 grants totaling $219,413,000. The wealthiest of foundations reported few grants (and those limited in amount) in the sciences, which suggests that as the needs and benefits of basic scientific research are perceived by these general-purpose foundations a healthy growth in support could result.

Innovation in technological areas is essential to a vigorous economy and to the continuing advance in the well-being of a society. The U.S. from its earliest days has been generously endowed with innovators, their effort and genius resulting in such inventions as the cotton gin, steamboat, telegraph, telephone, phonograph, motion pictures, automobile, airplane, cyclotron, and television, to say nothing of countless pharmaceuticals. More recently have come the laser, the transistor, solid-state electronics, pocket calculators, and the computer in its several guises. All of the discoveries of more recent origin would not have been possible without the knowledge gained by basic scientific research.

The U.S. productivity in basic research, supported by the encouragement of imaginative concepts and innovative thought, and the high level of education among many groups, has contributed to the advancement of our society. Without the special contributions, at appropriate moments, of individuals, foundations, government, and industry, in support of scientific research, the U.S. would not be nearly so advanced nor would other parts of the world have been beneficiaries.

Science
Year in Review

Science
Year in Review
Contents

Anthropology

The notion that all cultures must be evaluated in their own terms has been an important component of the anthropological approach through much of its history. Cultures, in this relativist view, were championed by ethnographers as psychologically satisfying, internally consistent, and ecologically sound success stories. Values held by the bearers of any culture, therefore, were thought to be valid and treated as uncontestable.

Demise of ethical relativism. In recent years, however, anthropologists have been taking increasingly judgmental positions in regard to their own and other cultures. Tacit acceptance of the status quo, perhaps once acceptable in traditional fieldwork settings among relatively uncontacted groups, was now viewed as a theoretical as well as a practical impossibility. Cautious since the 1940s of passing judgment on other cultures, anthropologists in the 1980s showed an increasing awareness of the need to place their typically small-scale studies within a larger geopolitical context.

Anthropologist Elvin Hatch, writing on the demise of ethical relativism within his discipline, addressed the ironies of a tolerant approach to culture. In *Culture and Morality*, published in 1983, Hatch argued that tolerance implies a moral commitment to the status quo; it is not a neutral stance at all.

Movement away from ethical relativism began in the 1940s as British and U.S. anthropologists, confronted with Nazi atrocities and a world at war, found certain value systems clearly unacceptable. In the 1950s anthropologists joined the quest for international understanding, a goal predicated on the ability to establish ethical guidelines with broad-based validity. This agenda was broadened in the 1960s in the U.S. to include self-reflective indictments of a Western culture torn by racial strife and mired in an unpopular war abroad. For comparisons anthropologists drew upon portraits of societies at apparent peace with themselves and their neighbors.

The anthropology of the 1970s and 1980s seemed primarily to produce studies of peoples caught up in global developments beyond their control. Though anthropologists certainly continued to look for peoples unaffected by external political and economic conditions, these quests were largely fruitless. Most of the subjects of anthropological studies of the last 20 years were inhabitants of less developed countries who clearly lived under undesirable conditions. These peoples were found to harbor feelings of inferiority in view of the displays of wealth and power presented by the industrialized nations. This generated in many of them a desire to westernize, and so anthropologists could no longer assume that the people they studied were resistant to change.

In the wake of these developments anthropologists resisted indiscriminate approval of cultural values

The late anthropologist Margaret Mead became a center of controversy during the last year when Derek Freeman questioned her research methods and conclusions in her 1928 classic book Coming of Age in Samoa.

simply because they were "cultural" or exotic. Flagrant violations of human rights perpetrated by non-Western peoples against other non-Westerners served to reduce anthropological impartiality yet further. Anthropologists in the 1980s wrote critically of violence and infanticide among the Yanomamö of the Amazon region, of honor killings of pregnant unmarried women in the Arab Middle East, and of cannibalism in the Eastern Highlands of New Guinea. Following Hatch's suggestion, anthropologists sought ways to evaluate cultures in moral terms without begging the question—implicitly or otherwise—of the superiority of Western culture over all others. By most accounts the anthropology of the 1980s was better equipped than ever before to be analytic of all cultures encountered, including Western culture itself.

Interpretation of fieldwork. During the past year the notable anthropologist Margaret Mead came under attack as did, by extension, cultural (nonbiological) anthropology. This resulted from the publication of a book early in 1983 that allowed anthropologists to pause and take stock of their accomplishments during the last 50 years.

The book, *Margaret Mead and Samoa: The Making and Unmaking of an Anthropological Myth*, by Derek Freeman (Harvard University Press) questioned both Mead's methods and conclusions in *Coming of Age in Samoa*, her classic ethnography published in 1928. This was not the first time that two anthropologists have disagreed in public on fact and interpretation of data from the same ethnographic locale, nor was Freeman the first to question the quality and comprehensiveness of Mead's work in Samoa. Novel to this issue,

245

In the foreground are fossilized fragments of a skull (left) and part of a thighbone that belonged to hominids, creatures that walked upright like humans but had brains only about the size of chimpanzees'. Found in Ethiopia and with an estimated age of four million years, they are the oldest evidence discovered so far for the existence of hominids. In the background are skulls of a modern human (left) and of a chimpanzee.

however, was its linkage to the nature/nurture issue. Freeman's finding of aggressive behavior among Samoan males supported the sociobiological perspective on biogenetic adaptation applicable to the entire species. Defenders of Mead (who died in 1978) pointed out that neither she nor her famous mentor, Franz Boas at Columbia University, subscribed to the unmediated cultural determinism attributed to them by Freeman.

The crux of the discrepancy revolves around the character of the Samoan personality in the 1920s (when Mead worked) and in the 1940s and later (when Freeman conducted his fieldwork). Freeman's finding that Samoans, especially males, are highly aggressive members of a violent society differed dramatically with the view of Samoans as gentle and completely adjusted, based on Mead's description.

In light of Freeman's attack anthropologists were prompted to reread Mead's work, and despite the obvious differences with Freeman's account they found much to recommend it. Contrary to Freeman's review of Mead's book, it described many aspects of Samoan culture as less than idyllic. While focusing on the positive qualities of Samoan adjustment, Mead also showed its high cost for the Samoans in terms of loss of interpersonal intimacy. Her discussions of "surreptitious rape" and anxieties between males and females provide a balance to summaries of her work which report that there are "no neurotic pictures."

Several of Mead's theoretical contributions have proved to be long-lasting. Her analysis of Samoan dance anticipated the theory of anti-structure developed by Victor Turner in the 1960s, and her analysis of the impact of older children on the socialization of younger ones provided the basis for Robert Levy's fuller treatment of this topic in the 1970s.

Two notable differences are revealed when Mead's work in the 1920s is compared with the standards for the field today. First, Mead showed no inclination to address Samoans themselves in her book. In recent years, however, the subjects of anthropological studies themselves have become consumers and critics of the ethnographies about them. Samoans in 1982 were keenly aware of Mead's book. They were also tiring of so many questions about sex put to them in the wake of two celebrated studies. While anthropologists were debating the nature of Samoan culture, Samoans were also drawing comparisons with Western culture. Samoans might be quick to brawl, they admitted, but they also quickly make up. Anthropological debates, on the other hand, seem to last for decades.

Second, Mead assumed that both the culture she was studying (Samoan) and the culture to which she would draw inferences (U.S.) were static and uncontradictory. Her methodology, however, was far from unsophisticated or unclear. She began with questions derived from her sense of U.S. culture (such as, adolescent turmoil) and allowed them to define the issues she would investigate in Samoa. She then reversed the process, using the resultant Samoan ethnography as a platform for understanding facets of U.S. culture. In this way Mead came to realize, for example, that attitudes about death in the U.S. are learned in the context of the family, making bereavement an unnecessarily highly charged experience.

That her model of culture is static and non-complex makes Mead's work less than fully modern. Her insights into two cultures at once, however, puts her ahead of those contemporary practitioners who have yet to learn that ethnography must necessarily always be comparative.

Roots of language. The publication of *Roots of Language* by Derek Bickerton in 1981 constituted a major development in linguistic anthropological theory. Bickerton proposed major reorientations within three important fields of inquiry: language acquisition, the origin of creole languages (defined as languages that have undergone massive changes due to culture contact), and the origin of human language. Bickerton, a creolist, analyzed all three areas as if they were all part of the same question. While assessment of the overall capacity of Bickerton's theory was slow to emerge—it would take experts in three heretofore different fields to examine the separate components of the argument—no one doubted that this work breathed new life into creole and cognitive anthropological studies.

In his work Bickerton described systems of constraints on language development in individual infants, in language contact situations, and in the original emergence of human language. Consistent with his unified approach, these constraints would necessarily be the same in each of the three areas of investigation.

Bickerton's evidence derives from the study of Hawaiian and other creoles. A uniform syntax seems to have replaced the loose structure of Hawaiian pidgin English, an auxiliary contact language native to no one. Citing similar developments in other parts of the world where creole languages have emerged, Bickerton hypothesized the existence of a genetic "bioprogram" that generates a biolinguistic logic found in all humans. Creole cannot be derived from its pidgin antecedent, Bickerton argued, because the previous generation would have been incapable of transmitting it to them. Rather, the first generation of Hawaiian creole speakers invented their language without the help of the previous generation.

Additional evidence pointing to the existence of a bioprogram comes from similarities in the structure of Hawaiian creoles and in creole languages found in Guyana and elsewhere. Early childhood acquisition of more traditional languages, like English and French, reveals many of the same creole patterns. Evidence is also supplied by an analysis of the "learning trajectory" of children, which shows traces of the bioprogram, or innate biological language, as it is forced to make way

for what Bickerton calls cultural language.

Social scientists found Bickerton's treatment of language origins the most difficult portion of his thesis to prove. Bickerton proposed that the study of the origin of human language must be approached as the study of conceptualization, not communication. He opposed his approach to what he called the "Flintstone approach" in which language is believed to derive from a simpler communicative system of grunts and groans. According to Bickerton, a world view must precede, not follow, communicative capacity. Bickerton cited an array of research studies for support, including chimpanzee communication research and a study demonstrating the universality of basic color terms across languages.

A basic element in Bickerton's overall theory is the separation of biological (or innate, bioprogrammatic) language from cultural language. The latter builds on, then slowly supplants, the former, whether it be in early childhood development, creole language development, or, as it must have been according to Bickerton, when cultural language first emerged as an extension of our species-specific bioprogram. As needs arose for particular historic groups, Bickerton surmised, the cultural language developed accordingly. Thus, in this view, cultural languages arose to address the various ecological circumstances in which humans might have lived; no biological language alone could allow this degree of flexibility.

Bickerton claimed that the original word order was SVO (subject, verb, object) in direct opposition to plausible arguments in favor of SOV. Most language families can be traced back to SOV structure. Other facets of Bickerton's admittedly hypothetical and provisional theory indicated that action words were the first components of original human language and that the formation of questions by moving words in sentences is foreign both to children and to speakers of creoles. No true creole language, according to Bickerton, shows

The figure of a bird, perhaps a great horned owl, was found as one of a series of mud drawings in a cave in eastern Tennessee. The first known prehistoric mud drawings in North America, they were probably made by ancestors of the Creek or Cherokee Indians between the 12th and 16th centuries.

any difference in syntax between questions and statements.

In suggesting that his theory provided "access to the essential bedrock on which humanity is founded," Bickerton raised concern among linguists and linguistic anthropologists of a revival of the concept of "primitivism" in their fields. While he admitted to attacking the widely held belief that all existing languages are at the same level of development, he preferred to think of creoles as "primary" rather than "primitive."

Bickerton himself expressed an awareness of the political implications of his proposal. He voiced a request popular with proponents of unpopular theories, asking that his critics look carefully at the empirical foundation of his argument before deciding the issue on the basis of political commitment alone.

—Lawrence E. Fisher

Archaeology

During 1982 important new discoveries were reported in several areas. These included evidence pertaining to the cultural and evolutionary developments involved in the shift from Neanderthal to fully modern human beings, a breakthrough in archaeological interpretation in the Saharan desert region through the use of space shuttle imaging radar, new developments in the understanding of ancient metallurgy, and a fascinating perspective on the life cycle of a Maya city.

Paleolithic discoveries. It has long been established that human beings of fully modern type were preceded in Europe and the Near East by Neanderthalers, people similar in many ways to modern *Homo sapiens* but set apart by generally more robust skeletons and certain distinctive features of cranial morphology. The

later, fully modern people known after about 35,000 years ago also possessed stone tools of more refined form and greater variety than those of the Neanderthalers. The nature of the relationship between these two kinds of people and their cultures has long been a matter of controversy. One popular view is that the Neanderthalers represent an evolutionary "dead end," a human form that diverged from the main stem of hominid evolution far back in time and persisted for some tens of thousands of years, only to be replaced by an influx of superior and culturally more advanced modern *Homo sapiens.* A competing view has been that the Neanderthalers represent a preceding evolutionary stage in the natural and cultural evolution of *Homo sapiens.* In this view the shift from Neanderthal to fully modern humans came about as a result of gradual change, completed by about 35,000 years ago.

Excavations at the Tabun and Skhul caves on Mt. Carmel in northwestern Israel, conducted by Dorothy Garrod during 1929–34, established a very long archaeological sequence for this region that gave evidence of both Neanderthal and fully modern human skeletons, associated with paleolithic stone tools. Neanderthal skeletal remains were found near the top of a cultural deposit some 25 m (82 ft) deep in the great cave of Tabun, in association with Mousterian tools. Artifacts of the same type were also found at the nearby Skhul cave, but in association with the bones of modern *Homo sapiens.* The fact that the tools from both caves were of the same types suggested that the Tabun and Skhul finds were of roughly the same age, while to some observers the rather robust character of the *Homo sapiens* skeletal remains from Skhul suggested that its people may have evolved only recently from the Neanderthal type. To many, the finds from Mt. Carmel seemed to support the idea that the Nean-

Imagery of the same region of the Sahara was made by a Landsat satellite (right) and by radar on the space shuttle "Columbia" (black and white strip at the far right). The shuttle's radar penetrated the thick layer of sand to reveal dry stream valleys and channels and thereby provided an explanation for the evidences of early human habitation found in now-parched areas of the desert.

Jet Propulsion Laboratory

From "Batán Grande: A Prehistoric Metallurgical Center in Peru,"
Izumi Shimada, Stephen Epstein, and Alan K. Craig, *Science*, vol. 216, pp. 952–959, May 28, 1982, © 1982 AAAS

Small furnaces for smelting copper (left) were discovered near the northern coast of Peru. Found near the furnaces were ceramic tips (above) for blowtubes that supplied forced air to the furnaces. These discoveries indicate that Andean Indians developed a copper-smelting technique about 800–1400.

derthalers and their culture represent not a "dead end" but an important stage in the evolution of modern humans. However, the interpretation has remained controversial.

A recent report on follow-up excavations conducted at Tabun during 1967–72 by Arthur J. Jelinek presents significant new evidence bearing on the problem. A statistical analysis of stone scrapers derived by the new excavations from successive levels of the cave deposits showed that, contrary to previous misconceptions, there was strong continuity in the relative frequencies of these tool types over time. Another analysis showed a smooth and long-continued trend of change in stone flake dimensions—a decrease in the thickness of flakes in proportion to their width—that provides further evidence of unbroken cultural continuity over a long period. A third analysis, of the relative frequencies of flaked stone bifaces and scrapers, showed that the variations previously observed between these tool classes were correlated with climatic shifts: scrapers correlated with warm intervals and bifaces with cool intervals.

The establishment of a correlation with climatic change, as well as a demonstration of the gradualness of the tool-type shifts, makes it much more likely that the changes simply represent modifications in the activities of the caves' human occupants to suit changing environmental conditions. This new information provides much stronger support than had formerly existed for the concept of cultural continuity between the time of Neanderthal and fully modern human populations at Mt. Carmel. This, in turn, bolsters the concept of evolutionary continuity between Neanderthal and modern *Homo sapiens* at that site. Although the issue is not yet completely settled, the simplicity and directness of the evidence from Tabun is very appealing.

Geoarchaeology. Previous archaeological work in Egypt and the Sudan has shown that human occupation of the Sahara occurred with some intensity at widely separated intervals. Artifacts of Late Acheulian type, dating between 300,000 and 100,000 years ago, have been found in a number of localities. Middle Paleolithic specimens, of the period roughly 100,000 to 40,000 years ago, are known from other places, while the latest period of major occupation seems to have bridged the Late Paleolithic and Neolithic stages dating between about 10,000 and 5000 BP (before present). It is clear that no human occupation would have been possible under climatic circumstances remotely like those of the present, and this as well as other evidence establishes the fact that the Sahara has undergone major environmental changes during Quaternary (Ice Age and Recent) times.

The Great Sand Sea of western Egypt and eastern Libya and the Selima Sand Sheet of southwestern Egypt and the Sudan are some of the most barren reaches of the planet. Sand covers everything, and since in the sand sheet rain may fall in any given locality only every 30 to 50 years, there is no vegetation. Yet at many places in this featureless landscape, archaeological sites giving evidence of human occupation are found, miles from the nearest modern oasis. Indeed, the rare modern oases themselves are often a mystery, the sources of their life-giving water unknown.

The flight path of the "Columbia" space shuttle in November 1981 passed over the Selima Sand Sheet, and, incredibly, its shuttle imaging radar produced photos based on the radar reflectance of the bedrock that dramatically portrayed an integrated fluvial landscape completely buried beneath the sand. Major river valleys were revealed, some with floodplains rivaling that of the Nile. When more extensive radar coverage becomes available, it should be possible to map entire

249

Roman woman was trapped in Herculaneum and buried alive when Mt. Vesuvius erupted in AD 79. The eruption destroyed Pompeii, Herculaneum, and other nearby towns, but until recently scholars had believed that most citizens of Herculaneum had escaped the cascades of volcanic debris.

river systems to which the sand surface gives no clue.

Fortunately, previous geologic and geoarchaeological expeditions to the Sahara had traversed paths that lay across the track photographed by "Columbia," and it was possible for the scientists involved to integrate their results with the data provided by the radar images from space. The correlations established between ancient, concealed waterways and archaeological sites makes sense of the previously puzzling distributions of human artifacts in the barren and featureless sand desert. Clearly, the sites mark former sources of water, and future mapping of the ancient drainage systems of the Saharan region promises to lead to many more prehistoric sites than are currently known. The subsurface patterns also provide an explanation for the water sources that support modern oases: ancient drainage channels, now as in the past, are the most likely collecting places for the little ground water that does occur in the region.

Early metallurgy. Artifacts made from alloys of copper (bronze) are one of the defining characteristics of the Bronze Age in Mediterranean prehistory. Archaeologists have long recognized the importance of determining the geologic sources of the copper so used for understanding early cultural contacts and trade, and chemical analysis of bronze specimens has a long history in antiquarian studies. Despite much work, how-

ever, chemical and trace element studies seeking to match bronze artifacts to natural sources of copper have largely failed because copper ore bodies vary greatly in internal chemical composition even over short distances, and primitive smelting methods differentially drove off various chemical elements originally present in the ore.

A promising new method applied by Nöel H. Gale and Zofia A. Stos-Gale to sources and specimens from Greece, Crete, and Cyprus obviates earlier problems by relying on measurement of the isotopic content of lead. Lead often occurs as a natural impurity in copper ores; its isotopic composition tends to be consistent within given localities; and its isotopic composition is not affected by the chemical processes associated with smelting. Although lead was deliberately added to some later Bronze Age specimens because it improved the casting properties of the metal, artifacts containing lead as a result of this practice can normally be recognized because the proportion of lead from natural impurities is much lower.

Gale and Stos-Gale used this method to characterize major ore sources on Cyprus and in Attic Greece and plotted the lead isotopic composition of a large number of Bronze Age artifacts from the eastern Mediterranean. The evidence shows, somewhat surprisingly, that copper from Cyprus—a renowned source of the metal

250

in Roman times—was apparently little used during the Bronze Age, particularly in its earlier stages. Instead, a source in Attic Greece dominated, although some other sources were recognized by the analysis as well. Although a great deal more research needs to be done, the lead-isotope method promises an important advance in the understanding of Bronze Age patterns of exchange in copper ores and finished metal goods.

Recent excavations near Batán Grande, in the Lambayeque Valley of Peru's far northwestern coast, have documented a major copper-mining and smelting complex that used techniques not previously described for prehistoric South American metallurgy. These finds clearly show that Andean metallurgists developed the copper-smelting technique known as prill-extraction to a high level between about AD 800 and Inca times in the 15th century. The production of metals has long been known as a characteristic of ancient Peruvian cultures, but documentation and dating of prehistoric mining and smelting practices have lagged.

Around Batán Grande a major ore body with well-defined veins of copper is known, and prehistoric mining trenches, prospect holes, and tailings piles are numerous. Excavations led by Izumi Shimada at the small prehistoric site of Cerro de los Cementerios, near Batán Grande, revealed some 24 small smelting furnaces made of clay and stone masonry, and it is estimated that at least 100 such furnaces remain to be discovered in the area. Near these furnaces have been found numerous ceramic tips for blowtubes that would have supplied forced air to the furnaces and large shallow stone mortars surrounded by heaps of crushed slag.

The furnaces were very small, probably because of the difficulty of maintaining the 1,100°–1,200° C temperatures required for copper smelting, using only blowtubes and human lung power to supply the forced air. There were, however, a great many furnaces at the site, and despite the small size of individual units it seems clear that Cerro de los Cementerios was a major industrial center where copper was mass-produced for the use of artisans elsewhere.

The techniques used to extract the copper from the ore have been inferred from the physical remains present at the site. Apparently, the slag was not sufficiently heated and liquefied to cause the melted copper to sink through it to form ingots in the bottom of the furnace, as in more advanced systems of smelting. Rather, small pinhead- to pea-sized globules of pure melted copper called prills collected in the viscous slag and were removed by crushing the slag, after it had cooled, in large *batanes*, or shallow mortars. The cold slag was brittle and easily shattered to a fine powder, allowing the prills to be collected readily. This discovery strongly supports the claim of the Andean region as having fostered one of the world's major independent metallurgical traditions in antiquity.

Waxing and Waning of a Maya City. The small Maya city of Cerros on the east-central coast of the Yucatán Peninsula was long considered by Maya scholars as a rather modest and unremarkable site of the Late Classic or Post-Classic period. A recent report by David Friedel and others of six seasons' work at Cerros has resulted, however, in a considerably changed and more interesting interpretation. First, this work determined that the chief occupation of Cerros was much earlier than previously believed, dating to the Late Formative period, approximately 350 BC–AD 100. Second, and the major focus of interest in the present account, extensive excavations and testing revealed a life history of village beginnings, rapid expansion, and equally rapid decline.

During the period 350 to 200 BC Cerros existed as a farming and fishing village, engaged in coastal trade up and down the Yucatán Peninsula. In and around the settlement have been found fragments of pottery made in foreign styles, as well as nonlocal obsidian, greenstone, and hematite, which bespeak a considerable emphasis on long-distance trade. Between about 200 and 50 BC Cerros expanded considerably in area. Raised house platforms, evidencing the growth of a relatively prosperous elite class, appeared in the eastern portion of the settlement, by then grown from a village into a town. Pottery styles from diverse sources continued to reflect wide-ranging trade contacts, which no doubt accounted for the increase in prosperity.

A great and sudden florescence subsequently took place at Cerros; during the brief interval 50 BC–AD 100 the settlement was radically restructured and expanded. Old residential areas were leveled and covered by rubble, and a major complex including four pyramids and associated plazas was constructed over them according to a master plan. Two ball courts were built, and a great canal was dug around the city. This growth corresponds with the burgeoning of Maya civilization all over Yucatán and seems to reflect the degree to which the various Maya centers interacted, with extensive trade and exchange creating new wealth throughout the region.

But the city's moment of glory was short-lived. Even as a planned monumental tomb neared completion, it was abandoned and decline set in. Within just a few years the temples were decommissioned and the population dwindled. The waning of Cerros appears to have coincided with the rise to power of the great Classic period Maya cities of the interior, and it is speculated that as these cities grew and established inland routes for trade and commerce, the basis of Cerros's prosperity in coastal water-borne trade was radically diminished. Though it continued to exist for several hundred years, Cerros never regained the prominence it had so briefly achieved during those heady early years of Maya development.

—C. Melvin Aikens

Architecture and civil engineering

Architecture. Restoration, the fitting of buildings into their surroundings, and the impact of technology and new materials on design appeared to be emerging as the dominant architectural themes of the 1980s. Perhaps the most important of these in 1982 was "fit," according to the *AIA* (American Institute of Architects) *Journal.* "In many cases it is the way buildings fit into their surroundings, in others the way they fit their clients or their clients' needs."

Not only were architects more concerned with making their buildings fit in, but they were increasingly careful to retain and restore the ones that were already there. Perhaps the most inclusive example of fitting in, retaining, and restoring was the headquarters of Levi Strauss & Co. in San Francisco. Built in a four-block area at the base of Telegraph Hill facing the Embarcadero, Levi's Plaza is basically simple but full of complexities and urban wonders. The firm chose Hellmuth, Obata & Kassabaum and landscape architect Lawrence Halprin to design the plaza.

The site is bisected by Battery Street into a two-block rectangle to the west and a triangle of the same size facing the Embarcadero. Already on the rectangular site were Cargo West, a small brick structure where sailors were shanghaied during San Francisco's early days, and a handsome Italian Swiss Colony warehouse.

Both were retained and remodeled and were joined by two new red brick buildings of five and seven stories; the taller of the two featured a soaring glass atrium framed in Levi denim blue.

The most distinctive characteristic of the new buildings is the rounding of their corners, which are set back one bay per floor to create both a low-rise pyramid effect and a series of triangular balconies. On the other side of Battery Street are two additional office buildings and park space described by Halprin as "an abstraction of a water course in the Sierras," where Levi Strauss found his first customers mining for gold.

Another building that fits easily into its surroundings is the Lath House pavilion in downtown Phoenix, Ariz. A 1982 AIA Honor Award winner, the pavilion was added to accommodate the large crowds that gather at the original site of the city—the Rosson House and surrounding barns, bungalows, and gardens. The pavilion is made of pressure-treated wood lath supported by glue-laminated beams and curved purlins. A stucco and wood-frame building containing meeting rooms, a catering kitchen, and a caretaker's apartment sits beneath the lath umbrella. The 2,146-sq m (23,200-sq ft) pavilion and frame building can hold as many as 1,000 persons for dinners, fashion shows, and concerts. The pavilion was designed to provide needed shade on hot summer days but to be transparent enough for people to view the surrounding historic buildings. Lath House was designed by architect Robert R. Frankeberger.

New headquarters buildings of Levi Strauss & Co. lie at the foot of Telegraph Hill in San Francisco. Designed by Hellmuth, Obata & Kassabaum, they are most distinctive for their rounded corners that are set back one bay per floor.

Joshua Freiwald

Lath House pavilion in Phoenix, Ariz., made of pressure-treated wood lath, was designed to provide shade from Arizona's hot sun but also to be transparent enough for visitors to see nearby historic buildings.

In Canada, on the shore of a lake 40 km (25 mi) from the southern Ontario city of Peterborough, architect Jim Strasman designed a $500,000 home comprised of two caves and a glass bridge. Though seemingly a contradiction of the natural and the futuristic, the 560-sq m (6,000-sq ft) summer home matches the tranquillity and simplicity of the landscape. Strasman buried the bedrooms in two rocky "caves" that seem part of the natural topography and bridged them with two glass boxes. Each box contains a living, dining, and kitchen area, and a fireplace. Decking for the box-bridge is pressure-treated cedar planking. Its ceiling is rough-sawn cedar. Log fires and electric floor vents heat the bridge in winter, and sliding doors open at each end to cool it during the summer. Earth and rocks keep the buried bedrooms cool in summer and cozy in winter.

An increasing number of architects found themselves in the restoration business in 1982. Throughout the U.S., in large cities and small towns, museums, opera houses, theaters, concert halls, science centers, city halls, state capitols, and office buildings were being restored and refurbished. An unparalleled example of success in this regard was California's state capitol building at Sacramento. "[The building] was done with such uncompromising accuracy, care, and unrelenting devotion that one finds it difficult to imagine a building in America that has been given more attention per cubic inch," wrote Richard Rush in *Progressive Architecture*. "The task was no more delicate than replacing

the insides of a wedding cake while leaving the icing intact."

The restoration team, led by Welton Becket Associates of Santa Monica, Calif., first had to decide which period of the building's life was to be restored. The team chose 1900–10, a period when the structure had already been furnished with elevators and electric lights but still maintained the glory of the past. The team decided that designers would not be free to fill in the blanks with their own conceptions. Instead, a form of archaeology had to take place. If photographic evidence or written documentation did not exist, the designers had to research the guidebooks of the period and become 19th-century architects themselves. Once the proper design was defined, the technology and craftsmen for its execution had to be found. Anything that was originally done in marble, plaster, wood, iron, or clay tile had to be reproduced exactly in the same material. The result of this painstaking process showed clearly what color, ornament, and detail can do for space.

In direct counterpoint to the trend of buildings designed to fit their environment is the impact of technology and new materials on building design. Structures reflecting such technology and utilizing these materials were rising throughout the world. In many instances they provided welcome relief from overused boxes and rectangles, and often they complemented their environment. For example, when Cummins En-

253

House on a lake near Peterborough, Ontario, consists of two underground chambers and a glass bridge.
In the chambers are bedrooms, while each of the two glass boxes that comprise the bridge contains living,
dining, and kitchen areas and a fireplace.

gine Co. of Columbus, Ind., asked Richard Rogers & Partners of Great Britain to design a new manufacturing center for its Fleetguard, Inc., division in the wooded countryside near Quimper, France, the architect/engineer team decided to hang the roof from a tensile structure outside the building. This ensured that the factory could be adapted to changing needs and could be extended at any time with little internal distur-

bance. The tensile system allowed the weight of the structure to be reduced to a minimum. The result was dramatic: a silver box of corrugated steel sitting inside a delicate cobweb of red tubes and rods. The structure hangs from a grid of tubular steel columns.

Civil engineering. Energy, the environment, and cost-effectiveness continued to shape civil engineering developments in 1982. The Louisiana Offshore Oil

State capitol building of California in Sacramento was restored to appear as it did in 1900–1910.
Considerable attention was devoted to the inside of the dome (left) and to the lobby (right).

Region Operation Control Center at Griffiss Air Force Base in Rome, N.Y., was designed without windows and internal roof drains because it had to be completely secure and dry. Ten aluminum-sheathed nozzles on the sheet aluminum roof serve as skylights for the building's central U-shaped corridor.

Port (LOOP), designed for unloading crude oil from Very Large Crude Carriers (VLCCs) and Ultra Large Crude Carriers (ULCCs), was the major U.S. energy-related project completed in 1982. Winner of the 1982 Outstanding Civil Engineering Achievement (OCEA) award, LOOP was designed to unload crude oil at up to 1.4 million bbl per day and supply 30% of the total refinery capacity of the continental U.S. through connecting pipelines.

The nation's first superport, LOOP was built because the U.S. did not have any natural harbor that could receive VLCCs and ULCCs. Located 29 km (18 mi) off the coast of Louisiana, where water depths range from 32 to 35 m (105 to 115 ft), the superport will be able to handle nearly one-third of present imports to the U.S. Approximately 330 supertankers were expected to unload at LOOP during its first year of operation. Oil for LOOP's system was expected to come from Saudi Arabia, Kuwait, Egypt, Qatar, Abu Dhabi, Algeria, Oman, Libya, and the North Sea. The offshore port pumps oil to refineries located on the Gulf Coast and in the Midwest and Northeast as far north as Chicago and Buffalo, N.Y. Regulated by the Offshore Terminal of Louisiana, LOOP was designed and built by several engineering firms and contractors. Among them were Fluor Ocean Services, Inc., Brown & Root, Inc., McClelland Engineering, and Boh Brothers Construction.

A major portion of the world's largest energy project was also completed last year. Engineers at Itaipú Dam on the Paraná River between Brazil and Paraguay made final tests on its sluice gates in preparation for filling the dam's 3,260-sq km (870-sq mi) reservoir. Builders of the $13 billion goliath have been essentially on schedule since work began on the joint Brazilian-Paraguayan project in 1975. By early 1983 earth and rockfill wing dams were complete, and more than 14 million cu yd of concrete had been placed for the powerhouse, spillway, the main hollow-gravity dam, and the buttressed wing dam. Almost eight kilometers (five miles) of dams rising as high as 189 m (620 ft) were completed. Itaipú was scheduled to begin supplying power in late 1983. Design managers for Itaipú were International Engineering Co. of San Francisco and its Italian partner, Electroconsult, in Milan.

Controlling the impact of construction on the environment stayed high on the list of engineering concerns in 1982. OCEA Award winner Bloomington Lake/Dam on the Potomac River above Cumberland, Md., was a prototype of how a local environment can be enhanced and improved while a project is under construction. Completed in the summer of 1981, the $174 million flood-control and water-quality project involved the relocation of a railroad, highways, and utilities. In May 1971 the first contract was awarded for the relocation of the single-track railroad line of the Western Maryland Railway. Six railway bridge structures varying in length from two to six spans constructed on steep slopes were required for the relocation. "We literally hung this railroad on the outermost edges of the slope," said U.S. Army Corps of Engineers engineer Robert Craig.

An excess of excavated material became a problem as the railroad was rebuilt to clear the crest of the dam. The material was neatly disposed of in several spoil disposal areas that were graded, contoured, and seeded along the route. The nearby quarry that provided nearly eight million cubic yards of rock was restored by grading the side slopes, placing and grading soil material over the quarry floor, and reseeding 40 ha (100 ac).

LOOP Inc., Harvey, La.

LOOP offshore complex in the Gulf of Mexico consists of a large oil pumping platform (seen at the rear) and a smaller platform containing offices and living quarters.

Approximately 15,000 tons of coal were excavated at the spillway site and sold to a coal-burning power plant.

Another environmental winner and 1982 OCEA nominee was the international airport at Orlando, Fla. Billed as the "Airport of the 21st Century," Orlando International will accommodate more than 12 million passengers per year.

A primary design goal for the airport was to build a facility that not only preserved but enhanced the natural surroundings. This required extensive geotechnical work, an innovative water management system, and an ambitious landscaping program. Elevated roadways pass through stretches of prairie range, forests, and wetlands that lead to and from the building. The airport's apron design is unusual in that its configuration allows for easy maneuverability of all types and sizes of aircraft. Coupled with a dual apron-access taxiway system, this design has virtually eliminated the logjams that plague many airports. Lead design firm for the project was Greiner Engineering Sciences, Inc., of Tampa, Fla.

Engineering cost-effectiveness in 1982 was dramatically evident in the new light rail transit system of San Diego, Calif. Built without federal assistance and finished in only 2½ years, the San Diego Trolley is the least expensive mass transit system per mile that any U.S. city has built in the last 40 years. It is a 25.6-km (15.9-mi) line extending from the Santa Fe Depot area in downtown San Diego to San Ysidro at the border of California and Mexico. Part of the line is on city streets, while the remainder uses the tracks of the San Diego and Arizona Eastern Railway. The Trolley provides service every 20 minutes in each direction between the hours of 5:30 AM and 9 PM. Total state and local funds available for the project were about $86 million. This sum funded the complete project plus purchase of the San Diego and Arizona Eastern Railway. The tight budget resulted in a schedule that required the Trolley to be open for service 30 months after construction began. Bechtel Corp. supplied project management.

—John Davis

Astronomy

Among the major astronomical achievements during the past year were the completion of a study of major instrumentation needed to pursue astronomical research, new pictures and data from the surface of Venus, and refinement of knowledge of the Galactic center and the Local Supercluster of galaxies. Sensitive detectors extended the measurement of weak sources beyond the accomplishments of the best photographic efforts. Gamma ray, X-ray, infrared, and radio observations helped the efforts to explain the structure and composition of the universe.

Instrumentation. The Astronomy Survey Committee of the U.S. National Academy of Sciences released its report entitled *Astronomy and Astrophysics for the 1980's.* The survey committee was composed of 21 members chaired by George Field of the Harvard-Smithsonian Center for Astrophysics. Thirteen separate working groups and panels were formed to aid the committee in trying to identify research opportunities in astronomy for the current decade and the equipment, facilities, and support that would be needed to pursue those opportunities. The committee restricted its attention to the remote sensing of astronomical objects by ground-based and airborne facilities or by devices placed in Earth orbit.

The committee assigned the highest priority to the Advanced X-ray Astrophysics Facility (AXAF), which they envisioned as an Earth-orbiting facility containing a grazing incidence reflection telescope with an aperture 1.2 m in diameter and a 10-m focal length. Such an instrument would be capable of providing 0.5-second resolution in the X-ray region from 0.1 keV to 8 keV (keV = thousand electron volts). With appropriate image detectors the AXAF should achieve a sensitivity in detecting point X-ray sources that will exceed that of the Einstein Observatory by at least one hundred times. The system would be able to observe clusters of galaxies at distances corresponding to red shifts as great as ten.

The facility listed next in priority is the Very-Long-Baseline Array of Radio Telescopes (VLBA). The array would consist of ten 25-m-diameter antennae spread across the continental United States and including Hawaii, Alaska, and possibly Puerto Rico. It would act as a huge radio interferometer with a baseline of 7,500 km (4,650 mi). The telescopes would not be physically linked together, however; instead, they would operate independently but in synchronism. The detected signal at each installation would be recorded on magnetic tape along with a precise time signal. The tapes could then be read at a central facility, using the time signals to combine the radio signals as if the telescopes had been physically linked. The VLBA would be capable of obtaining an angular resolution one hundred times greater than that attainable by any facility, optical or radio, now in operation. This ability to see such fine detail would make the instrument invaluable in studying quasars and active galactic nuclei. The VLBA would also be useful in measuring distances throughout our Galaxy and beyond with accuracies exceeding anything now available. In addition, the VLBA will have geophysical uses, including the measurement of continental drift and polar motion. Also, because of its ability to detect small strains in the Earth's crust, it may be able to provide advanced earthquake warning.

The third facility in order of priority was the New Technology Telescope (NTT). This is conceived as an instrument with an effective aperture 15 m in diameter. There are two possible designs capable of giving the desired results. One is a multiple mirror construction similar in concept to, but much larger than, the multiple-mirror telescope at Mt. Hopkins in Arizona. The other is a segmented mirror design being pursued at the University of California, in which hexagonal mirrors are joined to build up the total light-gathering power. Such designs are required because it is not

possible for a monolithic mirror to retain the requisite accuracy of figure as it is pointed toward different parts of the sky. The NTT would be particularly useful in spectrographic studies of faint sources and, through the technique of speckle interferometry, could lead to a resolution capability exceeding that expected for the Space Telescope. (The Earth's atmosphere smears out the image of an object, but a high-speed monochromatic examination of the image shows that it is made up of small segments or speckles. These speckles, in essence, represent the diffraction-limited ability of the telescope and are generated by different turbulent elements in the atmosphere intercepted by the incoming light. It is possible to recombine the speckles mathematically and recapture the resolution removed by the atmospheric disturbances.)

The fourth order of priority went to a large deployable reflector in space. This would be a 10-m-diameter mirror for use in the long infrared and very short radio wavelength regions that are normally obscured by atmospheric absorption. The major areas of study would concern cool stars, interstellar dust clouds, interstellar molecules, and heavily obscured regions of space such as the center of our Galaxy or locations of current star formation.

Solar system. On March 1 and March 5 the Soviet landing craft Venera 13 and Venera 14 reached the surface of Venus. Although the landers were well insulated, the extremely high temperatures on the Venusian surface limited the working lifetime of each to less than 2½ hours.

Venera 13 landed in a highland region expected on the basis of U.S. radar studies to be volcanic in origin. Venera 14 landed 900 km (550 mi) away in a lowland region about one-half kilometer lower in elevation. The

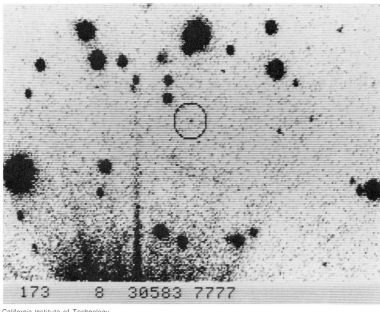

Halley's Comet (within circle) was detected for the first time in more than 70 years by astronomers using the 5-meter Hale Telescope and a sensitive charge-coupled device at the Palomar Observatory in California. At the time the comet was more than 1.6 billion kilometers from the Sun.

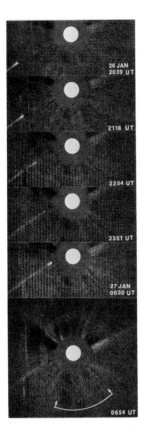
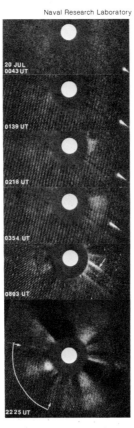

Comets found by a satellite were detected in 1981 by a solar coronograph aboard a U.S. military spacecraft. Each is seen nearing the Sun, and apparently they were then incinerated by it because neither reappeared.

television pictures returned from the two sites showed quite different surroundings. The highland area is a rocky plain, with outcroppings of rock interspersed with areas of dark fine-grained material. In the lowland region no fine dust was evident, but instead a fairly even layer of broken plates of rock extended to the horizon. Each lander was equipped with a sampling device that drilled into the surface beneath the lander. The samples were returned to the interior of the spacecraft through a set of airlocks. Analyses performed aboard the landers showed the samples to be basaltic material, a form of igneous rock extruded from the planet's interior, rich in metals and relatively poor in silicon. The Venera 14 sample was similar to the basalt found on the Earth's ocean floors, while the other sample had a high content of potassium.

Comets will be receiving special attention during the next few years, as astronomers prepare for the return of Halley's Comet to the local region. This comet was detected on Oct. 16, 1982, at the greatest distance ever and for the first time in more than 70 years, by David C. Jewitt and G. Edward Danielson, Jr., of the California Institute of Technology. Accomplishing this task required the use of the 5-m Hale Telescope and the lat-

est in electronic detection devices, a CCD (charge-coupled device) of particularly high sensitivity. (Charge-coupled devices are semiconductor devices arrayed so that the electric charge at the output of one provides the input stimulus to the next.) At the time the comet was more than 1.6 billion km from the Sun. Its apparent brightness was only 24.2 visual magnitude, considerably fainter than can be photographed with the Hale Telescope. The position measured for Halley's Comet shows it to be almost on its predicted course. It should arrive at the point closest to the Sun on Feb. 9, 1986, about one-half day earlier than had been forecast.

The first direct detection of a comet nucleus was accomplished in 1982. Observers from the Massachusetts Institute of Technology (MIT) and the Arecibo radar observatory in Puerto Rico succeeded in making radar measurements of Comet Encke at a distance of roughly 45 million km from the Earth. The measurements were near the limit of sensitivity of the huge Arecibo telescope. By analyzing the width of the radar echo in terms of the six-hour rotation period of Comet Encke, researchers found the diameter of the nucleus to be about 3 km (1.8 mi). This confirmed that the solid cores of comets, which upon heating by the Sun give rise to huge comas and tails, are quite small. In a bright comet such as Halley's the nucleus is probably less than 10 km (6 mi) in diameter.

The first discovery of a comet from a satellite observation was announced in February 1982, even though the comet had ceased to exist on Aug. 30, 1979. Donald J. Michels, Neil R. Sheeley, Jr., Russell A. Howard, and Martin J. Koomen of the Naval Research Laboratory accidentally discovered the comet in images transmitted by a solar coronograph called SOLWIND that was carried aboard a U.S. Air Force space test program satellite. The SOLWIND provided images of the solar corona by blocking out the disc of the Sun and the inner corona out to 2.5 solar radii; it was used for studies of the solar wind. The magnetic tapes that recorded the images on Aug. 30, 1979, were delayed in reaching the investigators, hence the tardiness of their announcement. The tapes showed a comet streaking toward the Sun and eventually disappearing behind the occulting disc of the coronograph. Although the tail of the comet remained visible in the same orientation as on approach for nearly a day, the comet itself never reappeared. The comet must have passed close enough to the Sun to have been completely vaporized, or, as the pictures appear to indicate, it collided with the Sun and was destroyed. Two additional comets having the same paths were seen by SOLWIND in 1981.

Stars. Michael Shara of the Space Telescope Science Institute and Anthony Moffat of the University of Montreal recovered the nova of 1670 recorded by the famous astronomers J. Hevelius and P. Lemonnier. The nova at maximum reached the third magnitude, but CK Vulpeculae, as it was named, disappeared from recognition when it subsided in brilliance. Using the 3.6-m Canada-France-Hawaii reflector with an image tube, Moffat and Shara photographed a stellar image and associated nebulosity at the position given by Hevelius and Lemonnier more than 200 years ago. The nebulae, subsequently observed spectrographically with the multiple-mirror telescope, have expansion velocities near 400 km (250 mi) per second, the velocity associated with ejected material from slow novae. The nebulous clouds appear to be swept up from interstellar material and caused to glow by ejecta from the nova event. CK Vulpeculae becomes the oldest ordinary nova for which its associated stellar object has been positively identified.

Another well-known variable star, T Tauri, was demonstrated to be a double star by H. M. Dyck and Theodore Simon of the University of Hawaii and Ben Zuckerman of the University of Maryland. Using speckle interferometry at infrared wavelengths, they were able to distinguish two stars separated by just 0.7 second of arc. T Tauri has long been known to be a star in the early pre-main sequence stage of evolution. The excess infrared radiation seen from this star had been thought to arise in a cloud of interstellar matter from which the star had formed within the last million years or so. Now it appears that this radiation comes from the newly discovered companion star. But this star itself is just forming inside a dust cloud that totally obscures it in the visible part of the spectrum. Thus T Tauri is not one pre-main sequence star but two; one star has shed the surrounding material from which it formed and can be seen in visible light, but the other is still enshrouded and can be detected only in infrared radiation.

Galactic astronomy. Observations with the 46-m Algonquin and 37-m Haystack radio telescopes in Canada and Massachusetts by Morely B. Bell, Paul A. Feldman, Sun Kwok, and H. E. Matthews of the Herzberg Institute of Astrophysics unearthed the most complicated molecule yet seen in interstellar space. The molecule is cyanodecapentayne, $HC_{11}N$, formed of a chain of 11 carbon atoms with a hydrogen and a nitrogen atom at opposite ends. The molecule exists in the shell around the cool carbon star CW Leonis. It becomes both the heaviest, 147 atomic mass units, and the largest, 15 angstroms in diameter, extraterrestrial molecule known. (One angstrom, Å, equals one ten-billionth of a meter.) It is another proof that so-called organic compounds are not just the products of living organisms on the Earth but exist throughout the universe.

The center of the Galaxy was subjected to increasing scrutiny during the year. The very center cannot be seen in visible light because of obscuring dust, but it is accessible at longer wavelengths and also is the source of intense X-ray and gamma-ray radiation.

Marvin Leventhal of Bell Laboratories and Crawford J. MacCallum, A. F. Huters, and P. D. Stang of Sandia Laboratories reported on measurements of the galactic center that they had made from a balloon-borne gamma-ray telescope above Alice Springs, Australia, in November 1977 and November 1981. The gamma rays were detected at a single wavelength, 0.024 Å, which corresponds to 511 keV, the energy released upon the annihilation of electron-positron pairs. The gamma-ray flux as measured by them and others, using instruments on balloons, rockets, and satellites, has varied remarkably and rapidly in intensity. Leventhal and his colleagues cited this variation as support for an energetic source at the galactic center, the dimension of which must be of the order of one light-year across to correspond with the time scale of the most rapid flux change.

Photos, NASA

Meteorite found in Antarctica (above) came from the highlands region of the Moon, while another Antarctic find (left) contains gases which indicate that it may have originated on Mars.

Robert L. Brown of the U.S. National Radio Observatory imaged the galactic center at 6-cm wavelength with the Very Large Array (VLA) radio telescope in New Mexico. He found an extremely compact and bright core from which two S-shaped jets emerge. The intensity of the core varied greatly over an interval of a day but only slightly over intervals of a few minutes. Brown concluded that the core must lie between a minimum of ten light-minutes and a maximum of one light-day in size, that is, somewhere between the size of the Earth's orbit about the Sun and four or five times the size of the entire solar system. The jets appeared to be gas, as much as 0.001 of a solar mass per year, streaming outward at speeds greater than 350 km (155 mi) per second.

At the same time infrared measurements also pointed to compact sources. In 1982 J. W. V. Storey and colleagues at the Anglo-Australian Observatory reported on measurements made with the 3.9-m telescope using a CCD at a wavelength of 0.9 micrometer. They identified two 19th-magnitude sources only three seconds of arc apart but separated by 4 trillion km at the distance of the galactic center. The sources appeared to be regions of ionized hydrogen requiring an enormous supply of ionizing radiation to keep them shining. Almost concurrently, using the 1.5-m telescope at Cerro Tololo with a CCD, George R. Ricker, M. W. Baatz, D. L. DePoy, and S. S. Meyer of MIT found three other sources at 0.9 micrometer. They concluded that these sources may be ionized clouds or possibly clusters of giant stars.

The gamma-ray, radio, and infrared observations all point to a very energetic source of comparatively small size at the center of our Galaxy. A number of astronomers have proposed in the past that a black hole in the range of one hundred to one million solar masses may be the cause of the activity. An accretion disc around the black hole, fed by infalling matter from the dense region of the galactic center, could easily generate the positrons needed to make the gamma rays as well as the ionizing radiation required to light up the infrared sources and to generate both the radio waves and the high-velocity fields in the jets from the nucleus.

Extragalactic astronomy. David G. Lawrie of Ohio State University and John A. Graham of Cerro Tololo Inter-American Observatory observed NGC 55, a large edge-on spiral galaxy, with the Yale 1-m telescope at Cerro Tololo. They photographed the galaxy with an image tube through a 16 Å bandpass filter centered on the 5007 Å line of doubly ionized oxygen but shifted by 5 Å to correspond to the red shift of the galaxy. They were looking for planetary nebulae but discovered instead a huge shell nebula similar to, but larger than, the Cygnus superbubble in our Galaxy. The superbubble in NGC 55 has a diameter between 4,000 and 6,000 light-years and is much larger than any known supernova remnant. It probably started as an outflow of gas and dust around a star association. The stars themselves may have evolved and disappeared, but the shell continues to expand, driven by the radiation pressure from other stars caught within its volume as it expands.

Not only does our Galaxy belong to a cluster called the Local Group, the Local Group belongs to a larger aggregate called the Local Supercluster. The supercluster is not bound gravitationally and, therefore, the various parts of the aggregate take part in the Hubble expansion. (The astronomer Edwin Hubble discovered that other galaxies are receding from ours at velocities proportional to their distances.) A study of the motions of galaxies in this supercluster by Marc Aaronson of Steward Observatory, John Huchra of The Center for Astrophysics, Jeremy Mould and Paul J. Schechter of Kitt Peak National Observatory, and R. Brent Tully of the University of Hawaii indicates, however, that the gravitational attraction of the Virgo cluster of galaxies has caused our Galaxy and the Virgo cluster to move apart more slowly than the Hubble expansion law would predict.

Two observations were made which favor the argument that quasars are the active nuclei of galaxies. Using the 1.8-m Perkins telescope, J. Anthony Tyson of Bell Laboratories and William A. Baum and Tobias Kreidl of Lowell Observatory observed 3C 273, the first quasar discovered. By blocking out the light of the quasar itself, they detected a faint surrounding light that decreased outward from the center in a manner similar to that observed for giant elliptical galaxies. Todd A. Boroson and John B. Oke of the California Institute of Technology, using the 5-m Hale telescope with a CCD-equipped spectrograph, succeeded in obtaining spectra of fuzzy patches of light around quasar 3C 48. Over the spectral range 5000 to 10,000 Å they found not only the familiar emission lines of the quasar but also a faint continuum and absorption lines due to hydrogen and singly ionized calcium. The relative strengths of the lines indicate that the light came from stars with an average spectral type which indicates that star formation must have occurred in the galaxy associated with 3C 48 within the last billion years. Boroson and Oke propose that the quasar is the active nucleus of a spiral galaxy.

Observations of the southern hemisphere quasar, PKS2000-330, made with the 3.9-m Anglo-Australian telescope, established it as the most distant and luminous object yet found in the universe. A red shift of 3.78, the largest ever, was measured for this quasar. The Lyman-alpha line of hydrogen, which is observed in the ultraviolet region at 1216 Å in the laboratory, was seen in red light at 5825 Å. Thus the light from the quasar was emitted approximately 15 billion years ago.

—W. M. Protheroe

See also Feature Article: Twenty Years of Quasars.

Adapted from information supplied by Mobil Oil Corporation

Chemistry

A large part of chemical research in the past year was directed toward practical needs, much of it relating to the pursuit of alternate sources of energy and of starting materials for basic industrial processes. Antibiotics, powerful toxins, insect hormones and sex attractants, and other natural substances were structurally elucidated, synthesized, and in some cases altered to suit a particular human application. Advances in laser chemistry and new instrumental methods offered insights into the processes of combustion, the complex properties of water, and large biologically important molecules. Other highlights included reports of innovative photographic films and a polymeric artificial skin for burn victims.

Inorganic chemistry

Research in inorganic chemistry in 1982 continued to make significant progress. Many of chemistry's very best graduate students were first selecting problems in inorganic chemistry for their doctoral research dissertations. Later, on their own, they tackled challenging problems that are often of an interdisciplinary nature. Thus the areas of advanced research activity worldwide, carried on mostly by young inorganic chemists, include bioinorganic, organometallic, and solid-state chemistry as well as such energy-related research as homogeneous catalysis and photochemistry. In fact in 1982 the American Chemical Society began its publication of the journal *Organometallics*, destined to become the most prestigious journal in this important area of chemistry. Also during the past year three outstanding inorganic chemists reached retirement age: Luigi Sacconi of the University of Florence and Lamberto Malatesta of the University of Milan, both in Italy, and Sei Otsuka of Osaka University in Japan. All made significant contributions to inorganic chemistry through their brilliant research over many years.

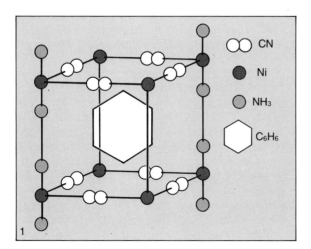

Zeolites: inorganic molecular cages. The area of solid-state chemistry dealing with zeolites has grown continually for many years but currently is experiencing an explosive development. In the past few years zeolites have been the subject of several national and international conferences as well as of a number of significant papers and patents. Before a discussion of the nature and importance of these materials, it will help to mention a related class of substances that has been known for a few decades. These are the clathrate compounds, and a classical example of such a compound is $[Ni(NH_3)(C_6H_6)(CN)_2]$ (*see* 1). The cyanide ions (CN^-) bridge the nickel ions (Ni^{2+}), holding them together in a square-planar layer that is kept separate from other layers to form a structure that has an array of cubic "cages." The cage size in this structure is one that readily accommodates a benzene (C_6H_6) molecule but not a substituted benzene, in which some of the hydrogens are replaced by other atoms or groups. Thus benzene is easily separated from substituted benzenes by allowing the benzene clathrate $[Ni(NH_3)(C_6H_6)(CN)_2]$ to crystallize selectively from a solution containing a mixture of benzene and benzene derivatives. If the crystals are then heated, pure benzene will escape but the cage structure of the clathrate will collapse.

Zeolites, likewise, have open cage structures that accommodate certain molecules selectively, and some

261

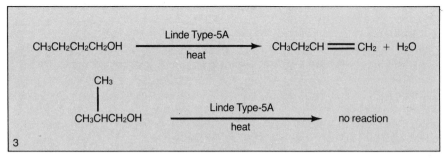

CH₃CH₂CH₂CH₂OH →(Linde Type-5A / heat)→ CH₃CH₂CH≡CH₂ + H₂O

CH₃CHCH₂OH (with CH₃ branch) →(Linde Type-5A / heat)→ no reaction

3

of these structures are stable at temperatures of 500° C (930° F) and higher. A zeolite is a negatively charged aluminosilicate cage, with cations (positively charged ions) and water molecules inside the cage where they have freedom of movement. The negative charge on the aluminosilicate aggregate results from the replacement of Si^{4+} from neutral SiO_2 by some Al^{3+}, and the positive-charge deficiency must be made up by other metal cations (M^{n+}). The basic structural unit of a zeolite consists of corner-linked tetrahedrons of SiO_4 and AlO_4, in which linkage involves a common bridging oxygen; *i.e.*, $-Si-O-Al-$. Other atoms such as Ge, Ga, and P (germanium, gallium, and phosphorus) may replace silicon or aluminum. The metal ions are generally Na^+, K^+, Mg^{2+}, or Ca^{2+} (ions of sodium, potassium, magnesium, or calcium). Joseph V. Smith of the University of Chicago gives the formula for a zeolite as $M_p^+ M_q^{2+} Al_{p+2q} Si_{O_{2p+4q+2r}} \cdot sH_2O$. The tetrahedral structure requires twice as many oxygen atoms as atoms of silicon and aluminum together. Charge balance, described above, requires that the number of Al^{3+} ions be equal to the number of M^+ ions plus twice the number of M^{2+} ions. The structure of a zeolite is shown in (2).

Some 30 different zeolites occur in nature, and only about eight of these have been used commercially. These have a variety of applications as molecular sieves ranging from removal of trace amounts of water from certain solvents to removal of radioactive strontium and cesium from nuclear waste. By far the most important applications of zeolites are as catalysts or catalyst supports in the petroleum industry. For this purpose it generally has been necessary to use tailor-made zeolites with cavities and properties designed to fit the needs of the process.

Inorganic chemists have long been frustrated by the syntheses of zeolites because the reactions are complicated and because there is little rational basis for the preparation of a desired zeolite. The reaction mixtures consist of coprecipitated gels that react at some pH (level of acidity or alkalinity) and age over some period to produce crystalline zeolites. Although the chemist has little control over this process, certain empirical rules of syntheses have emerged that permit reproducible manufacture of a desired zeolite.

One of the most important advances in this regard has been made by Paul B. Weisz and co-workers at Mobil's research laboratories in New Jersey. Into the gelatinous reaction mixture they introduce a molecule of an appropriate size and shape to serve as a template around which the crystalline zeolite forms. The resultant structure has a cavity of the proper size and shape just to accommodate the added molecule. The encapsulated molecules are then driven off at temperatures of about 500° C (930° F), and the stable zeolite maintains the cage structure imposed upon it by the template molecule.

This template method of zeolite synthesis permits one to design different zeolites that are appropriate for the catalytic processes desired. For example, the dehydration of butanol using a zeolite designated Linde Type-5A results in the reaction of only the straight chain alcohol (*see* 3). A branched chain isomer of the alcohol is too large to enter the cavities of the zeolite and does not react. Zeolites with larger cavities cause both isomers to react.

An important commercial development was reported recently by Mobil in which a zeolite designated as ZSM-5 is used to convert methanol into high-octane gasoline in good yield. Methanol is produced on a large scale commercially from syngas (a mixture of carbon monoxide and hydrogen), obtained from the reaction of coal-derived carbon with superheated steam. The Mobil process of producing gasoline from methanol is important because it provides another approach to coal liquefaction (see *1978, 1981,* and *1983 Yearbook of Science and the Future* Year in Review: CHEMISTRY: *Inorganic chemistry*).

A + M →(THF / solvent)→ B

THF (tetrahydrofuran) = [O with CH₂—CH₂ / CH₂—CH₂ ring]

M = Li, Na, K

4

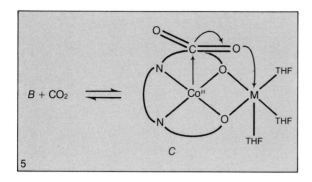

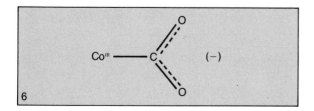

During the past year Edith M. Flanigen and colleagues at Union Carbide discovered a new class of microporous crystalline inorganic solids. These novel materials are aluminophosphates—one of which is designated $AlPO_4{-5}$ and given the trivial name alpo—and are the first family of framework oxide molecular sieves synthesized without silica. The $AlPO_4$ molecular sieves are similar to zeolites in some ways and may find use as adsorbents for separations of molecular species and as catalysts or catalyst supports.

The synthesis of this new family of microporous materials also depends on the use of template molecules to control formation of pore structures of desired size and shape. Without the template molecules, as is well known, trivalent metal phosphates of the type MPO_4 are formed; these are intractable insoluble solids of little utility. With the template molecules added to an appropriate reaction mixture containing Al^{3+} and $PO_4{}^{3-}$ ions, the template molecules become entrapped or clathrated within crystalline products of composition $xR \cdot Al_2O_3 \cdot (1.0 \pm 0.2)P_2O_5 \cdot yH_2O$. The quantities x and y represent the amounts needed to fill the microporous voids within the neutral $AlPO_4$ framework, and R is the template molecule. Heating at 400°–600° C (750°–1,100° F) drives off the water and the template, leaving the properly structured microporous crystalline inorganic solid. The discovery of this family opens the door to a new era in molecular sieve materials. One intriguing possibility is the use of trivalent metals other than aluminum to generate an even larger family of MPO_4 materials.

Carbon dioxide fixation. In the past few years there has been considerable research activity worldwide in what is called C_1 chemistry, and recently a commerical journal was established to publish research in this area. The world of C_1 chemistry deals primarily with carbon monoxide (CO), carbon dioxide (CO_2), and methanol (CH_3OH), the ultimate goal of these investigations being the economical conversion of an abundant resource, coal, into a more useful gaseous or liquid fuel. A tremendous amount of work has been done on CO and CH_3OH chemistry, and important progress has resulted. The same cannot be said for CO_2 chemistry, most of the scant work being plagued with frustration rather than promise.

Recently Carlo Floriani and co-workers at the University of Pisa in Italy succeeded in reversibly adding CO_2 to bifunctional metal complexes containing acidic and basic sites. Clear-cut evidence for bifunctional activation by metal complexes was first provided by Duward F. Shriver and his students at Northwestern University, Evanston, Ill., with the use of Lewis-acid- and proton-acid-promoted reactions of metal carbonyls. Floriani's work represents the first time it has been successfully applied to CO_2 activation.

Early attempts to add CO_2 to metal complexes led to the irreversible formation of various CO_2 derivatives. The metals in these complexes are strongly basic and undergo the well-known oxidative addition reaction with CO_2. This results in the formation of complexes that can react further with CO_2 to give complexes incorporating two molecules of CO_2 as a head-to-tail dimer. Other metal complexes contain acidic or oxophilic metals that attack the oxygen of CO_2 and cause it to disproportionate into $CO + CO_3{}^{2-}$. With all of this information available to him, Floriani decided to try to activate CO_2 by attacking at the carbon with a basic metal, cobalt (as Co^+), and at an oxygen with an acidic metal, lithium (as Li^+), using a bifunctional metal complex.

Used for this purpose were cobalt(II) Schiff-base chelates, represented in (4) by structure A, which react with alkali metals to yield the desired bifunctional metal complexes, represented by B. In toluene solution, complex B readily and reversibly adds and releases CO_2 (see 5). Evidence for structure C in solution is provided by infrared spectra, and in the solid by X-ray crystallography.

Complex C appears to have its $CoCO_2$ component in a form (6) that contains nucleophilic oxygen atoms susceptible to electrophilic attack. Yet reactions with electrophilic alkylating agents (RX, in which X is a halogen) do not alkylate at O, but at Co, perhaps because of the facile equilibrium that makes available Co(I) for ready attack by R^+. It may be that the choice of cobalt was unfortunate; other, more inert metal complexes should be tried. Also instead of a two-electron metal system, Co(I) → Co(III), a one-electron metal complex may be preferred, since it is M-CO_2 interactions involving one-electron transfer that lead to C—C bond formation. Clearly much more research is needed before CO_2 fixation is a reality.

—Fred Basolo

Organic chemistry

A variety of remarkable new organic molecules made the limelight during the past year. Some are man-made wonders; others are of unusual natural origin or exotic structure. Some are suspected causative agents of disease or even weapons of war; others show promise as new drugs or serve to clarify the nature of bonding in molecules. Many of the year's achievements in organic chemistry were made possible by significant advances in analytical instrumentation.

Natural product chemistry. Funguslike bacteria of the genus *Streptomyces* are noted for their ability to make complex antibiotics that challenge the ingenuity of synthetic and structural chemists. Among the year's noteworthy accomplishments are syntheses of bleomycin, a copper-complexing anticancer drug from *Streptomyces verticillus*, by Sidney Hecht of the University of Virginia and Hamao Umezawa of the Institute of Microbial Chemistry in Tokyo and colleagues, and aplasmomycin (1), an unusual boron-containing antibiotic from a marine-derived strain of *Streptomyces griseus*, by E. J. Corey and co-workers at Harvard. Other *Streptomyces* antibiotics for which structures were determined include the novel L-shaped fredricamycin A (2), which is both an antibiotic and an antitumor drug, by Ramesh C. Pandey and co-workers at the National Cancer Institute in the U.S., and the anticancer drug carzinophilin A, which is capable of wedging itself between the rungs formed by DNA base pairs, by J. William Lown and Christopher C. Hanstock of the University of Alberta.

Eclipsing the above compounds in complexity is palytoxin (3), an extraordinarily toxic substance produced by *Vibrio* bacteria growing symbiotically on a ge-nus of marine soft coral. The structural elucidation was completed after more than a decade of work by Richard E. Moore of the University of Hawaii, Yoshimasa Hirata, presently of Meijo University in Japan, and Yoshito Kishi of Harvard and co-workers. Centuries ago palytoxin was used by natives on the island of Maui to tip their weapons when fending off enemies from the island of Hawaii. Recent interest in this toxin has centered on its unique toxicity, structure, mode of action, and natural origin. Palytoxin is more poisonous than any known nonprotein toxin, one ten-millionth of a gram being lethal to a rabbit by causing heart failure. The toxin, which vaguely resembles polyether antibiotics in structure, may function biologically as an ionophore, influencing calcium and potassium ion transport in the nerves and the heart. It is not known how the toxin is made by the *Vibrio* microbe, a distant relative of the organism that causes cholera.

Another unusual bacterial product whose structure was reported in 1982 is the human colon cancer mutagen (S)-3-(1,3,5,7,9-dodecapentaenyloxy)-1,2-propanediol (4), identified by David Kingston, Tracy Wilkins, and co-workers at the Virginia Polytechnic Institute. This air- and acid-sensitive glycerol ether, which is a very potent mutagen, was identified in human feces in populations known to have a high incidence of cancer of the colon and was produced upon culturing the common colon bacterium *Bacteroides* in a medium containing bile.

Fungal toxins of the trichothecene family such as verrucarol (5) were in the news both as naturally occurring toxic contaminants of U.S. and Canadian grain and as constituents of alleged "yellow rain" chemical warfare attacks against villages in Southeast Asia and Afghanistan by Soviet-supplied forces. Verrucarol, the

1   aplasmomycin   2   fredricamycin A

palytoxin

hydrolysis product of macrocyclic trichothecenes, which can cause the devastating and deadly fungal disease stachybotryotoxicosis, was claimed by U.S. State Department officials to have been detected in the hose of a gas mask removed from a Soviet soldier who had died in Afghanistan. Vomitoxin, an oxygenated analogue of verrucarol produced by certain species of *Fusarium* fungi that grow on both wheat and corn, causes vomiting in animals upon consumption of feed containing greater than five parts per million of the toxin. Verrucarol and related compounds were synthesized during 1982.

Natural product chemistry was the basis for the 1982 Nobel Prize for Physiology or Medicine. Sune K. Bergström and Bengt I. Samuelsson of the Karolinska Institute in Stockholm and John R. Vane of the Wellcome Foundation in Great Britain were recognized for their research on prostaglandins, potent naturally occurring fatty-acid substances that control a wide variety of physiologic responses in body tissues. (*See* SCIENTISTS OF THE YEAR.)

While hardly a natural product in the usual sense, the conjugated, highly unsaturated molecule cyanodecapentayne, $HC \equiv CC \equiv CC \equiv CC \equiv CC \equiv CC \equiv N$, was identified in 1982 by radio astronomers at the Herzberg Institute of Astrophysics in Ottawa in the cloud surrounding the carbon-emitting star CW Leonis. This exotic molecule is the most complex organic compound discovered in space to date.

Nonnatural product synthesis. Propellanes, tricyclic compounds in which all rings share a common side, are so called because the three rings flanking the central bond are reminiscent of propeller blades. These unusual molecules are more precisely named [*m.n.p*]propellanes (6), in which *m*, *n*, and *p* refer to the number of unshared ring atoms in each of the three rings. During 1982 Kenneth B. Wiberg and Frederick H. Walker of Yale University prepared the simplest member of this class of compounds, [1.1.1]propellane (7), which holds the distinction of being the most strained organic compound that is stable at room temperature. This compound is notable in that all four bonds to two

human colon cancer mutagen

4

of the carbon atoms are bent back sharply in the same direction, in essence "inverting" the usual tetrahedral arrangement at these atoms. The [3.3.3]propellane modhephene (8), isolated from the toxic plant *Isocoma wrightii* (rayless goldenrod) and notable as the only naturally occurring propellane known, was synthesized by five different research groups.

Another intriguing class of strained hydrocarbons are the fenestranes, named from the Latin word for "window." They are tetracyclic compounds in which all rings share a common vertex, a carbon atom. The central atom of the smaller fenestranes should have severely distorted bond angles. An example of this type of molecule, which has thus far eluded synthesis, is [4.4.4.4]fenestrane (9), the "windowpane molecule"; the numbers in brackets refer to the number of carbon atoms in each of the four rings. During 1982 William G. Dauben and Daniel M. Walker of the University of California, Berkeley, prepared a [4.4.5.5]fenestrane (10), the smallest known fenestrane.

In 1981 Leo Paquette and co-workers of Ohio State University prepared a dimethyl derivative of dodecahedrane, a regular 20-carbon polyhedron with 12 pentagonal sides (see *1983 Yearbook of Science and the Future* Year in Review: CHEMISTRY: *Organic chemistry*). In 1982 this same group prepared dodecahedrane itself in 23 steps starting with a compound containing a single pentagonal ring. Dodecahedrane does not melt at temperatures as high as 450° C (840° F) and dis-

plays very simple spectra, as would be expected for a compound of such high symmetry. The formal name for dodecahedrane is undecacyclo[9.9.0.0^{2,9}.0^{3,7}.0^{4,20}.-0^{5,18}.0^{6,16}.0^{8,15}.0^{10,14}.0^{12,19}.0^{13,17}]eicosane, illustrating the need for colloquial as well as formal names for structurally complex molecules.

In the course of synthesis organic chemists use a variety of techniques including exposure to heat, light, and electrical currents to encourage reaction between sometimes reluctant partners. A new method of promoting reactions through the use of sonic waves was discovered recently by Philip Boudjouk and co-workers at North Dakota State University. Sonication, which employs an ultrasonic bath of the type commonly used to clean jewelry, glassware, and small instruments, has been found to encourage heterogeneous reactions such as that between metallic zinc and organobromine compounds. (See *Applied chemistry*, below.)

New instrumental methods. The development of new instrumental methods for studying organic molecules is a gradual process that requires the talents of physicists, engineers, computer scientists, chemists, and instrument builders. Many of the year's notable achievements in organic chemistry greatly benefited from the use of these new methods.

Before a new compound can be identified it must be rigorously purified and separated from contaminants. With capillary gas chromatography (GC) and high-performance liquid chromatography (HPLC) it is possible to separate quantities of volatile and nonvolatile mixtures (with GC and HPLC, respectively) that weigh less than a thousandth of a gram. In some cases the separated components are passed directly into a mass spectrometer (MS) for determination of molecular ions and ion fragmentation patterns, which provide clues to structure.

New mass spectrometric methods have been developed for the analysis of large, fragile, or heat-sensitive molecules. In the past year a variation of mass spectrometry known as plasma desorption mass spectrometry (PDMS) that uses iodine-127 as an incident beam was employed to produce ionized molecules of insulin. With a molecular weight of 5,730 daltons, insulin represents the largest natural peptide to be seen as a molecular ion. A related technique that uses high-energy inert gas atoms rather than ions to bombard the

verrucarol

5

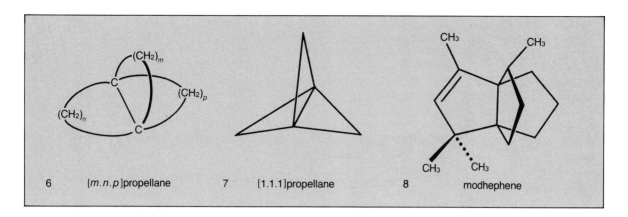

6   [*m.n.p*]propellane   7   [1.1.1]propellane   8   modhephene

sample (fast atom bombardment, or FAB) can generate ions directly from a condensed-state sample, without excessive fragmentation, and was used recently in the structural determination of fredricamycin (2) and palytoxin (3), among other natural products.

Important information can be obtained about the chemical environment of protons (hydrogen nuclei) and carbon atoms in a compound using nuclear magnetic resonance spectroscopy (NMR). Most NMR spectrometers now use the pulsed NMR Fourier transform (FT) technique in which the sample, spun between the poles of a magnet, is briefly irradiated with an intense pulse of radio-frequency energy, and the resulting electrical signal is subjected to special mathematical analysis by a built-in computer to produce the spectrum. The use of computer methods to acquire and manipulate data obtained with high-field NMR spectrometers, which use superconducting magnets to achieve magnetic fields as high as 144,000 gauss, has greatly increased the sensitivity, signal resolution, and ease of assignment of NMR spectra. These new nuclear magnetic resonance methods were of great value to investigators in assigning structures to carzinophilin A, palytoxin (3), and the colon mutagen (4).

— Eric Block

Physical chemistry

Physical chemistry is primarily a basic research activity in which chemists strive to unravel the structures of molecules in solids, liquids, and gases and to probe at the atomic level the details of the interactions between molecules that lead to chemical reactions. Sometimes it is possible to turn the tables, as it were, and use a tool originally developed for research for directing and controlling commercial processes. A form of laser chemistry (the use of lasers to initiate, select the course of, and drive chemical reactions) called laser isotope separation is a case in point. In April 1982 the U.S. Department of Energy selected a process for the separation of fissionable uranium-235 at the Lawrence Livermore National Laboratory to be taken to the pilot-plant stage.

Laser isotope separation is essentially a two-step process. The wavelength of the laser beam is adjusted so that only those molecules containing the isotope of interest absorb the laser light. On the basis of the physical or chemical differences between the molecules absorbing light and those that do not, researchers can collect the chosen isotope. Livermore's laser isotope separation starts with metallic uranium, which is mostly uranium-238. The uranium is vaporized in an

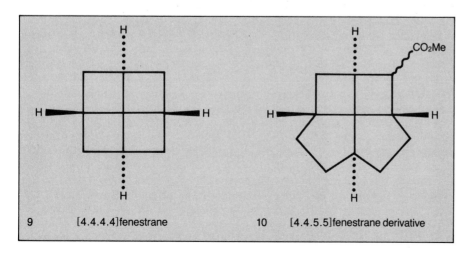

9   [4.4.4.4]fenestrane   10   [4.4.5.5]fenestrane derivative

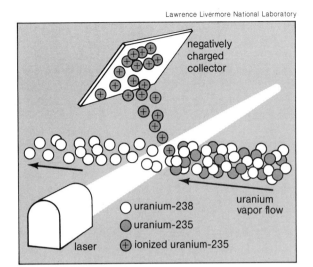

negatively charged collector

uranium vapor flow

○ uranium-238

⬤ uranium-235

⊕ ionized uranium-235

laser

Isotope separation process developed at Lawrence Livermore National Laboratory uses a laser to selectively ionize uranium-235 atoms for collection.

oven heated with an electron beam. Atoms of uranium-235 but not uranium-238 absorb light from several visible-wavelength lasers, which results in ionization of the absorbing atoms. The positively charged uranium ions drift to an electrostatic collection plate and form a liquid there.

The basis of the Energy Department's choice of Livermore's process was the successful operation of a prototype facility by Livermore researchers under the direction of James Davis. A larger facility was under construction at Livermore in 1983, and a $150 million pilot plant was scheduled to be built at the Oak Ridge (Tenn.) National Laboratory by 1988.

Lasers remain expensive to build and operate, however, and for that reason large-scale commercial production of bulk chemicals by laser chemistry is unlikely in the foreseeable future. Isotope production is an exception because isotopes are already expensive and are not needed in large quantities. Other cases in which laser chemistry may be practical include chain reactions, for which the laser may initiate the reaction but not provide the energy to keep it going, and reactions on or near solid surfaces. In 1982 examples of each process came from chemists' research laboratories.

At the Exxon Research and Engineering Co. Mau-Song Chou showed that the chain reaction leading to the production of cumene hyperoxide from cumene [$C_6H_5CH(CH_3)_2$] and oxygen could be either promoted or retarded with respect to the usual thermally initiated reaction by varying the wavelength of an ultraviolet laser irradiating the material. Cumene hyperoxide is useful as a starting material for the synthesis of acetone and other compounds. Ingo Hussla and Joachim Heidberg of the University of Hannover in West Germany were able to selectively desorb methyl fluoride

(CH_3F) from a sodium chloride surface that had molecules of both methyl fluoride and ethane (C_2H_6) on it. They obtained the selective desorption by matching the wavelength of an infrared laser to an internal vibration of the methyl fluoride molecule. The vibration energy excited by the absorption of the laser light migrates to the chemisorption bond between the methyl fluoride and the sodium chloride and breaks it.

In 1982 chemists also continued to exploit lasers as a probe of combustion processes, which are complicated and rapid reactions involving several kinds of molecules. Laser-induced fluorescence, for example, refers to the light emitted by molecules as they relax to low-energy quantum states after having absorbed light from a laser. The intensity of the fluorescence provides information about the concentrations of light-emitting species, and the wavelength of the emitted light provides information about the quantum states involved. At SRI International, Menlo Park, Calif., David Crosley and his colleagues devised a way to use laser-induced fluorescence to make two-dimensional images of the concentration of hydroxyl radical (OH) in a flame. Among other things they found that the spatial distribution of hydroxyl radical in high-energy (excited) quantum states, which are the ones responsible for the color of a flame, is different from that of the low-energy (ground) states, which are the ones undergoing reactions. Thus, the visual flame is not a reliable guide to where the action is, chemically speaking.

Another laser-based technique for investigating flames is laser ionization. Absorption of two or more photons from visible or ultraviolet lasers causes the absorbing species to be ionized. The ions and the free electrons can be collected and provide a measure of the amount of absorption. Kermit Smyth, W. Gary Mallard, and Houston Miller at the National Bureau of Standards in the U.S. used this technique to determine the concentrations of species which are present in very low concentrations or which do not fluoresce readily, such as nitric oxide (NO). Edward Grant, Bennett Rockney, and Terrill Cool of Cornell University, Ithaca, N.Y., used a similar idea to estimate flame temperatures. Finally, with the aid of two lasers of different wavelengths whose beams cross perpendicularly, John Goldsmith at Livermore was able to make spatially resolved measurements of the concentration of hydrogen radical (atom) in a combustion environment.

Chemists, physicists, materials scientists, and biologists all use X-rays for the determination of the structures of crystalline solids by means of X-ray diffraction patterns. X-ray waves have both an amplitude and a phase, and both are needed to reconstruct a structure from the pattern. But general diffraction patterns give information only about the amplitudes of the diffracted X-rays, thus giving rise to the so-called phase problem in X-ray crystallography. To obtain the phases there are indirect methods involving supplementary measurements and sometimes extensive computation. In 1982 Ben Post of the Polytechnic Institute of New York received the Bertram E. Warren Diffraction Award of the American Crystallographic Association for devising a more direct way to obtain phase information.

Post's method requires orienting a crystalline sample with respect to the X-ray beam in such a way that the beam is diffracted in three directions simultaneously. The interaction of the three diffracted beams gives rise to an asymmetry in the angular distribution of the intensity of one (the primary) of the diffracted beams, from which the phases of the three beams can be extracted. The idea is not to use the technique to obtain a phase for every possible diffracted beam but only for a few. These make the assignment of phases to the others much easier. So far, Post's group and a few others have tested the technique on metals and minerals whose structures are already known, such as germanium and zinc tungstate ($ZnWO_4$).

It has always been possible to do time-resolved X-ray diffraction with the use of synchrotron radiation, which is the electromagnetic radiation emitted by high-speed electrons as they travel through curved paths in high-energy accelerators, so that the evolution over time of structures perturbed by some agent could be followed. In 1982 scientists began to take this capability more seriously. Bennett Larson, Woody White, and Thomas Noggle at Oak Ridge and Dennis Mills of Cornell used the CHESS synchrotron radiation facility at Cornell to obtain X-ray diffraction patterns of silicon crystals with a time resolution of a few nanoseconds (billionths of a second). This is possible because the electrons in the accelerator are grouped together in a single "bunch" and come around together, so that radiation is emitted in a very short pulse. The experiment was designed to answer a controversial issue concerning the effect of an intense laser pulse on silicon, which one day may be a processing step in the making of microelectronic circuits. One school of thought is that the surface melts; the other is that it does not. By timing the laser pulse so that it came at various intervals just ahead of the synchrotron radiation pulse, the group could examine the progress of the structural changes following the laser irradiation. They concluded that the surface indeed did melt.

An X-ray diffraction technique designed to be specifically surface-sensitive was proposed in 1979 by William C. Marra, Peter Eisenberger, and Alfred Cho of Bell Laboratories in the U.S. The idea is to have an X-ray beam strike a crystal surface at a glancing angle, so that it does not penetrate far into the sample. The emerging beam will make a similarly small angle relative to the surface, but its direction will be determined by diffraction from surface atoms only. In 1982, Marra, P. H. Fuoss of Bell Laboratories, and Eisenberger used X-rays from the Stanford Synchrotron Ra-

diation Laboratory to observe the melting of a single atomic layer of lead on a copper surface. The details of the way such "two-dimensional" systems melt is of interest to theorists studying phase transitions. The technique seems to be widely applicable. Michael Seul and Harden McConnell of Stanford University, for example, began collaborating with Eisenberger on a project to examine the structure of monomolecular films of phospholipids on solid surfaces. These structures, which are major components of cell membranes, are of interest to those in the field of cellular immunology.

Finally, physical chemists continue to be fascinated by water, the most common yet most unusual of liquids. Many of the unusual properties come from the extensive hydrogen bonding between water molecules in the liquid. During the year two groups used neutron scattering to examine the structure of water. Neutron scattering and diffraction is similar to X-ray scattering and diffraction, but neutrons interact much more strongly with hydrogen than do X-rays and thus make better probes for structural studies of water. At Los Alamos National Laboratory Alan Soper and Richard Silver used neutrons from the laboratory's pulsed neutron source, which obtains neutrons from a high-energy proton accelerator. At Oak Ridge Alfred Narten and William Thiessen collaborated with Lesser Blum of the University of Puerto Rico in the use of neutrons from

Schematic diagram depicts laser-ionization apparatus used to determine the concentrations of various chemical species present in flames.

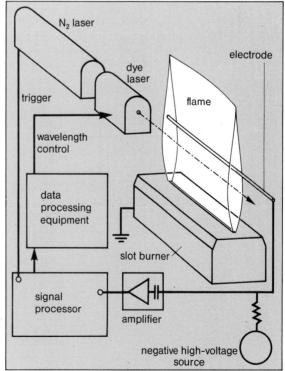

Adapted from information supplied by W. Gary Mallard, J. Houston Miller, and Kermit C. Smyth of the Center for Fire Research, National Bureau of Standards

Oak Ridge's high flux reactor. Both groups obtained so-called radial distribution functions, which give the average distances between hydrogen atoms, between oxygen atoms, and between hydrogen and oxygen atoms.

Meanwhile theorists Alfons Geiger of the Aachen School of Technology in West Germany and Eugene Stanley of Boston University analyzed computer simulations of water and found that the liquid structure includes "patches" in which the density is lower than average, in agreement with earlier X-ray scattering data. The patches are associated with water molecules with four hydrogen bonds. These results are pieces in a larger puzzle that should help eventually to obtain a realistic model of water.

—Arthur L. Robinson

Applied chemistry

As in previous years a major proportion of recent research in applied chemistry was devoted to the search for alternative sources of energy to replace the world's dwindling supply of fossil fuels. In addition to the development of new routes to the production of hydrogen from water, discoveries were made in agricultural chemistry, photography, polymers, and the use of sound waves to accelerate chemical reactions.

Hydrogen from water. Hydrogen, which produces only water when it is burned, has been the focus of much research in recent years (see *1979, 1982,* and *1983 Yearbook of Science and the Future* Year in Review: CHEMISTRY: *Applied chemistry*) and may well be the fuel of the future. According to chemist Howard

D. Mettee at Youngstown (Ohio) State University, the use of hydrogen would reduce the economic effect of a vanishing and largely monopolized fuel reserve, reduce the environmental changes wrought by both the carbon dioxide-caused greenhouse effect and acid rain, and reduce the risk of international conflicts that have come with heavy reliance on petroleum. Electricity produced by sunlight in photovoltaic cells must either be used immediately or stored in batteries, which are only moderately efficient, short-period repositories. Hydrogen, on the other hand, can be stored indefinitely and converted into electricity in a highly efficient fuel cell. In the fall of 1982 two new systems for splitting water into its components, hydrogen and oxygen, by means of sunlight were reported.

Gabor A. Somorjai and Monica Hendewerk of the University of California at Berkeley and Christofer Leygraf of the Lawrence Berkeley Laboratory constructed an electrochemical cell that can dissociate water using only visible light and inexpensive chemicals (most previous systems required ultraviolet light and rare, expensive elements). The system consists of two indefinitely stable disks of iron oxide. One disk is impregnated (doped) with silicon dioxide, an electron donor, making it the electron-excessive or negative terminal. The other disk is doped with magnesium oxide, an electron acceptor, making it the electron-deficient or positive terminal. The two disks are cemented together with a conducting silver epoxy resin to form a diode, which then is suspended in a sodium sulfate or sodium hydroxide solution.

Illumination of the system with visible light pro-

Recently developed light-powered water-splitting system from Berkeley chemists (left) uses doped iron oxide electrodes suspended in aqueous solution. A version from Texas A & M University (right) employs doped silicon electrodes in dilute sulfuric acid plus a battery-supplied external potential.

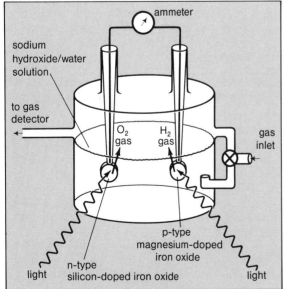
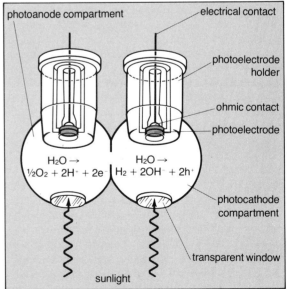

Adapted from information supplied by (left) Gabor A. Somorjai, University of California, Berkeley; (right) John O'M. Bockris, Texas A & M University, College Station

Stink bug attacks caterpillar pest, one of more than a hundred insects on which it feeds including the fall armyworm, cotton bollworm, and gypsy moth. Application of a newly formulated stink-bug sex attractant to crops may increase numbers of the predator among pest infestations.

duces about 10^{15} (a million billion) molecules of hydrogen per minute from a surface area of 0.6 sq cm (0.093 sq in), giving an overall energy conversion efficiency (energy output divided by energy input) of 0.05%. A similar disk one square meter (1,550 sq in) in area should produce four liters (4.23 quarts) of hydrogen per hour, a high yield in light of the low efficiency. After eight hours hydrogen production declines because of reduction of the magnesium electrode, but the hydrogen production can be restored by bubbling air through the system for ten minutes. Improving the efficiency will be an engineering problem rather than a chemical one.

John O'M. Bockris, head of the Hydrogen Research Center at Texas A & M University, and research associates Marek Szklarczyk and A. Q. Contractor developed a system containing silicon electrodes doped with phosphorus and boron—to make them semiconducting anodes and cathodes, respectively—and suspended in dilute sulfuric acid. When the system is illuminated with visible light, the resulting electric current decomposes water into hydrogen and oxygen, but only when a potential is applied across the electrodes with an external battery. The overall efficiency is very high for a photoelectric process—about 13%. According to Bockris, the high efficiency of the cell and the low cost of the electrodes should make it possible to produce hydrogen at a cost equivalent to gasoline at $1 per gallon. While some scientists praised Somorjai's and Bockris's systems, others found the reporting of their results overenthusiastic.

Agricultural chemistry. In recent years researchers have been devoting increased attention to developing insecticides and herbicides that do not have the environmental disadvantages associated with earlier products. According to the U.S. Department of Agriculture (USDA), imported fire ants infest more than 230 million acres in nine southern U.S. states. They can inflict painful bites, and their venom causes allergic, occa-

sionally fatal reactions in humans. The ants attack farm animals and young plant crops, and they build hard mounds that can damage farm machinery and interfere with crop cultivation. Baits treated with Mirex, a product of the Allied Chemical Co., were used for large-scale fire ant control until 1977, when the insecticide's registration was canceled for toxicological and environmental reasons.

In 1982 the Stauffer Chemical Co. introduced Pro-Drone for large-scale fire ant control. The active ingredient of Pro-Drone, called MV-678, is not a poison in the usual sense. First synthesized in 1974 by chemist Meyer Schwarz at the USDA's research center at Beltsville, Md., MV-678 is a synthetic analogue of natural insect juvenile hormones that control larval development. Although it decomposes rapidly in the open air or in soil, it remains active in the ants' forestomachs whereupon it creates a surfeit of idle, sexually mature ants and an ultimately fatal shortage of worker ants.

Pro-Drone contains 98.8% corn grits and soybean oil as bait and 1.2% MV-678. Less than a pound of bait containing only about five grams (0.18 oz) of MV-678 is needed per acre of ground, and in field tests by the USDA and Stauffer fire ant populations were reduced by 80–90%. Stauffer expected to have commercial quantities available in the spring of 1983.

Another potential agent for controlling fire ants is a predatory beetle, *Myrmecaphodius excavaticollis*, which invades the ants' nests. According to chemist Robert Vander Meer and entomologist Daniel Wojcik of the USDA in Gainesville, Fla., the beetle operates by "chameleon-like chemical mimicry" to acquire on its cuticle (outer surface) the blend of hydrocarbons found on the fire ant's cuticle. The fire ant carries both species-specific and colony-specific hydrocarbons, which apparently serve as recognition signals. The beetle can generate both of these types of cuticular hydrocarbons and can therefore move with relative impunity from one nest to another. If the beetle can survive significantly better in real ant nests than in the tests used in the laboratory (only 20% survival rates), it may prove useful in fire ant control.

Another discovery emerging from the USDA at Beltsville is a newly formulated synthetic insect pheromone (chemical sex attractant) that may lure the voracious soldier bug or stink bug (*Podisus maculiventris*) into agricultural service as a pest killer. According to insect physiologist Jeffrey R. Aldrich, the attractant is a blend of five relatively simple, commercially available compounds—(E)-2-hexenal and (+)-α-terpineol, with benzyl alcohol, linalool, and terpinen-4-ol as minor components. The pheromone mixture could be highly successful because the soldier bug, which feeds on more than 100 different insects, prefers to eat them in the larval stage, when insects do the most damage to crops. The soldier bug would be lured into and induced to stay in a field where other insects are already present and about to cause damage.

Another variation on the ecologically sound strategy of using one living organism to destroy another is the discovery of a chemical substance called cyanobacterin that is produced by a freshwater cyanobacterium (blue-green alga), *Scytonema hofmanni*. In 1978 Charles P. Mason of Gustavus Adolphus College, St. Peter, Minn., found that *S. hofmanni* killed other cyanobacteria and green algae growing near it. In January 1982 Mason, along with K. R. Edwards of the H. B. Fuller Co. in St. Paul and F. K. Gleason of the Gray Freshwater Biological Institute in Navarre, Minn., reported the results of their isolation, analysis, and structural determination of the microorganism-destroying chemical. They predicted that cyanobacterin could be used eventually as an algacide to rid lakes of the microorganisms that fill the water with putrid scum and rob other aquatic life of dissolved oxygen. Three or four years may be required to find a suitable synthesis for cyanobacterin, and an additional two to three years may be needed to field test the substance in lakes.

A total synthesis of chorismic acid achieved in the past year by two independent research groups has important implications for agricultural chemistry since it may aid in the development of selective herbicides that do not harm animals. Chorismic acid is an intermediate in the shikimic acid metabolic pathway employed by plants and bacteria but not by animals, and it or its derivatives may kill weeds by inhibiting enzymes (organic catalysts produced by living cells) in the shikimic acid pathway. Glyphosate, a herbicide marketed by the Monsanto Chemical Co. since the early 1970s under the trade name Roundup, apparently functions by blocking one or more chemical reactions in this pathway. Chorismic acid was synthesized first by Glenn A. Berchtold and Donald A. McGowan at the Massachusetts Institute of Technology (MIT) and later by Bruce Ganem, Nobuo Ikota, V. B. Muralidharan, Stanley D. Young, and Warren S. Wade at Cornell University, Ithaca, N.Y.

Photography. At the annual meeting of Polaroid Corp. held in May 1982 the firm's managers demonstrated a new self-developing "instant" color slide system based on Polachrome 35-mm film, the technical details of which were made available in November. Polaroid expected to market the films, developing units, and slide mounters in the U.S. early in 1983 at competitive prices. The new films, which can be used in any 35-mm camera, give excellent color saturation, fidelity, and resolution, and they should find uses in situations that demand fast results and immediate feedback.

The film contains a grid of permanent, alternating red, green, and blue lines, called an additive color screen, aligned parallel to the film length. These lines act as light filters during both exposure and projection of the slides. For development the rewound film cartridge is placed into the developing unit together with a package containing developer solution and a roll of

Screen of alternating red, green, and blue lines that creates the colors in Polachrome 35-mm slide film is visible in close-ups of an eye on a slide of a human face. Each line is only eight micrometers wide.

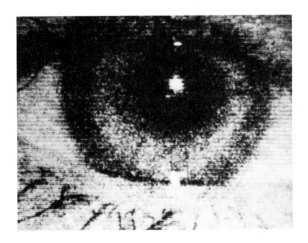 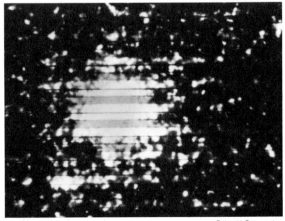

Polaroid Corporation

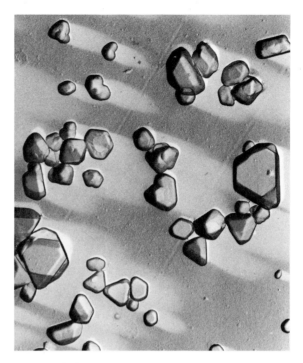

Silver halide grains in Kodacolor VR 1000 film (left) and in conventional film (right) are compared under high magnification. The new T-grain shape raises film speed without increasing graininess.

stripper sheet. The developer reduces exposed silver halide to metallic silver, which remains fixed in place; converts unexposed silver halide to a soluble complex; and causes migration of the complex to an image-receiving layer where it is reduced to metal. The process requires one minute.

A high-speed color print film with an ISO (International Standards Organization) speed rating of 1000 (ten times the ISO 100 rating of the widely used Kodacolor II) would be marketed by Eastman Kodak Co. in 1983 in 35-mm format as Kodacolor VR 1000. The markedly higher speed is a result of a fundamental change in the shape and structure of the silver halide crystals in the film emulsion, developed by Kodak researchers in the U.S. and Europe. To produce faster films researchers have needed larger silver halide grains to capture the light. However, larger grains usually require thicker layers, use more silver, and result in coarser images. By flattening the grains Kodak researchers were able to increase film speed without increasing film graininess or decreasing sharpness. The new silver halide structure is called T-grain because of its flat, tabletlike appearance under the microscope. Conventional grains appear as cubes, octahedrons, or irregularly shaped pebbles. T-grain technology is expected to provide overall improvements in film quality as well as speed.

A problem with "instantly" processed color photographs is the image fading caused by exposure to sunlight and fluorescent lights. Arthur M. Usmani and I.

O. Salyer of the University of Dayton in Ohio found that dinonylphenyl isophthalate incorporated into an "overprint" varnish coating material stabilizes the dyes in Kodak-type instant color prints against the effects of ultraviolet light. The coatings were applied to prints which were then exposed to a UV lamp that produced in 24 hours the equivalent of one year's exposure to natural sunlight. While unprotected prints faded almost completely in 70 hours or less, coated prints showed only minor fading after 170 hours of exposure. Incorporation of the stabilizer into the photographic film itself should produce similar results, and incorporation into fibers or paint pigments should protect wall coverings, fabric, and artwork from fading.

Polymers. About 130,000 persons are hospitalized annually in the U.S. because of burns, and about 10,000 of them die. Once a burn victim reaches a medical facility, the burned area must be quickly covered to prevent infection and fluid loss. In July 1982 Ioannis V. Yannas of MIT and John F. Burke of Massachusetts General Hospital in Boston reported on their progress with two different forms of polymeric synthetic skin. The earlier, simpler version, called stage I, has been used on severe burn patients by Burke and his colleagues as quickly as Yannas and his graduate students were able to make it. Stage I is a highly porous polymer of collagen fibers (obtained from cowhide) chemically bonded to chondroitin-6-sulfate, a major polysaccharide of cartilage, obtained from sharks. The polymer is covered with a sheet of medical-grade silicone rubber,

273

Stage I artificial skin, developed by researchers at the Massachusetts Institute of Technology and Massachusetts General Hospital, is a porous polymer of collagen fibers combined with a polysaccharide and backed with a layer of silicone rubber. When grafted over burn wounds the membrane resists infection and fluid loss while inducing cells and blood vessels to build new skin within the artificial framework.

which presents a barrier to infection and fluid loss and provides mechanical strength when the skin is sutured into place. After the skin is in place, mesodermal cells from the body migrate into it, creating more collagen and synthesizing a new dermal layer—neodermis. Epidermal cells also grow inward from the edge of the graft. Meanwhile the synthetic skin is slowly biodegraded. Burke and his colleagues have successfully used stage I skin on 35 severely burned patients ranging in age from 3 to 85.

The more advanced version of skin, stage II, has the same basic structure as stage I, but in this case Yannas, Eugene M. Skrabut, and Dennis P. Orgill isolate basal cells from a small sample of the patient's skin. These cells, the most immature skin-forming cells, are seeded into the polymer network by centrifugation, and the seeded material is sutured over the wound. Again, mesodermal cells form a neodermis, but the basal cells also form a new epidermis, the outermost skin layer. Stage II skin has been used only on laboratory animals, but Yannas and Burke planned to begin trials on humans in 1983. The MIT patent for stage I has been licensed to Marion Laboratories, Kansas City, Mo., which is attempting to make the polymer in larger quantities and to arrange for the further trials needed for Food and Drug Administration approval.

A new aqueous gel called Pluronic Polyol F-127 with "reversed thermal" behavior can be used as a "pour-on, medicated bandage," according to its developer, Sylvan Frank at Ohio State University in Columbus. Solidifying when heated and melting when cooled, the gel, which is impregnated with a topical drug, can be stored in a refrigerator, where it becomes a syrupy fluid. It can be applied by pouring it onto the skin without rubbing in, an important consideration in burn treatment. As it is warmed by the body, it solidifies to a clear gel that protects damaged tissue and releases medication to the skin. It is easily removed later by washing with cool water. Preliminary tests with animals and humans showed F-127 to be an effective delivery system for lidocaine, a widely used local anesthetic. It will probably first be marketed with anesthetics for local skin therapy, but it should also be used for application of many other drugs. It is possible that the material may eventually be employed to deliver medication that would pass through the skin and travel to other parts of the body.

Sound-wave chemistry. According to Philip Boudjouk and co-workers at North Dakota State University in Fargo, ultrasonic waves (sound waves pitched too high to be heard by the human ear) of the type commonly used to clean jewelry, medical instruments, and small parts may soon be used to synthesize new chemicals and drugs and to detoxify poisons. The waves are believed to remove impurities from the surfaces of solid reactants, thus allowing them to react better and more easily. They also produce short-lived high temperatures and pressures, which markedly accelerate the rate of chemical reactions (pressures as high as 147,000 psi and temperature increases of several thousand degrees are momentarily generated in microscopic regions). These conditions allow reactions to be carried out at lower overall temperatures, which increase the yield of desired products by decreasing formation of by-products. For example, by using the new technique one reaction normally performed at several hundred degrees was accomplished at room temperature, while another normally requiring an entire day was accomplished in only one minute.

—George B. Kauffman

274

Defense research

In the summer of 1981, long before the fighting in Lebanon and around the Falkland Islands reaffirmed the new age of electronic warfare, the U.S. Defense Department's Defense Science Board (DSB) completed a study that underscored how the Pentagon's need to prepare for such warfare had come to influence its selection of research and development priorities. The DSB listed, in order of importance, 17 choice development programs that "could make an order of magnitude difference" in future U.S. military prowess. The list was dominated by technologies having to do, in one way or another, with electronic warfare. At the head of it, topping even the second-ranking Stealth program for making aircraft extremely difficult to detect via radar, was the very-high-speed integrated circuit (VHSIC) project—and justifiably so.

On the success of the VHSIC program will depend to a considerable degree the fruitfulness of a majority of the other technologies on the DSB list. With VHSIC the Pentagon is positioning itself for a quantum leap in integrated circuitry, aspiring to develop silicon-based semiconductor chips not much larger than nail heads and capable of processing signals and data a hundred times faster than existing chips. Just a few VHSIC chips will do the computing job that in the early 1970s required a whole roomful of computer and air conditioning equipment. This will make a world of difference in the sophistication and military application of the technologies of artificial (machine) intelligence (AI), supercomputers, optoelectronics, space-based radars, directed-energy and microwave weapons, monolithic focal-plane sensor arrays, advanced software and algorithms, and microprocessor-based training devices—all of which were on the DSB recitation of elite defense technology programs.

But there is a more urgent reason for the preeminence of the VHSIC program. The Pentagon wants to put those very-high-speed microcircuits to work as soon as possible in a wide variety of existing and gestating military systems that it considers crucial to the efficient execution of electronic warfare missions; these include search and surveillance; communications, command, and control; intelligence through technical means; navigation; target acquisition; fire control of precision-guided weapons and guidance of the weapons themselves; and electronic countermeasures and counter-countermeasures. To all such systems the technologies of electron devices and information processing are the sine qua non and are what the VHSIC program is all about. Indeed, VHSIC microcomputers-on-chips are regarded as the Pentagon's prime prerequisite for automating the battlefield, which now spreads from the seabed to outer space. Destined to provide the keystone technological elements for at least the next two generations of military integrated circuits, the VHSIC program is regarded by many defense research officials as the most important milestone in microelectronics since the U.S. Minuteman missile and space exploration programs gave rise to integrated-circuit technology in the 1960s.

Meaning for industry. The $350-million Army-Navy-Air Force VHSIC endeavor was set in motion at the Pentagon in the late 1970s, but it did not hit its stride until 1981 when six aerospace-electronics companies—Honeywell Inc., Hughes Aircraft Co., IBM Corp., Texas Instruments Inc., TRW Inc., and Westinghouse Corp.—were selected as the principal contractors to design, build, test, and begin producing VHSIC chips beginning as early as 1983. Teamed with other companies and coordinating its research efforts with various universities, each VHSIC program contractor is applying one or more of several different MOS (metal-oxide-semiconductor) techniques, such as combining silicon with sapphire, in developing chips that will embody as many as 100,000 extremely tiny transistors and circuit lines—from 1.25 micrometers (a micrometer is four-tenths of a millionth of an inch) on down to 0.5 micrometers, contrasted with the multi-micrometer dimen-

Metal circuit patterns made of lines a quarter of a micrometer wide and a half micrometer high were fabricated with a double-layer electron-beam resist process developed by Honeywell Inc. to meet the needs of the Department of Defense VHSIC program. The gold lines were built on gallium arsenide substrates.

Honeywell Inc.

sions of the devices in present-day integrated circuits. The densely packed VHSIC transistors, their electron-switching "gates" operating at incredible speeds, will be capable of millions of arithmetical operations per second. Such superabundance of circuitry will provide ample capacity on each chip for self-diagnostic operations and for backup "redundancy" of functions, both signifying high reliability. Moreover, by virtue of its capacity each chip will be extremely versatile, making it possible eventually for the armed forces to standardize on a single family of chips. Thus the VHSIC program also promises much lower acquisition and support costs in military microelectronics.

Stimulated by early signs of success in the Pentagon's VHSIC project, many companies other than those holding Pentagon contracts have embarked on vigorous VHSIC development projects outside of the military tent. Total industry funding of VHSIC research and development is expected to exceed the Pentagon's, and the companies going it alone will be permitted to enter the military market as time goes by. Withal, the Pentagon program clearly will have a major influence on the future shape and well-being of the U.S. electronics industry, with special reference to its competition with Japan.

In 1982 Japan, already far advanced in microelectronics and edging toward remilitarization, launched its National Superspeed Computer Project and its companion Fifth-Generation Computer Project, the latter aimed at transforming computer artificial intelligence from an experimental concept to a fact of life (*see* Year in Review: ELECTRONICS AND INFORMATION SCIENCES: *Computers and computer science*). Both projects will depend in great measure on very-high-speed circuits packaged, or integrated, on a very large scale.

The threat that the projects pose, one of irretrievable Japanese dominance of the worldwide microelectronics market for many years to come, adds urgency to the U.S. VHSIC program and to a parallel and closely akin program being run by the Pentagon's Defense Advanced Research Projects Agency (DARPA). DARPA's goal is to develop supercomputers with very-high-speed, very-large-scale integrated circuits capable of, among many other things, artificial intelligence. The Japanese and U.S. programs have spurred Western Europe into action. In late 1982 the European Communities (EC) initiated what it called the European Strategic Program for Research and Development in Information Technologies (ESPRIT), under which the electronics industries of EC nations will pool their research in order to foster innovation and avoid duplication.

Although the Pentagon welcomes the commercial impetus that its VHSIC program undoubtedly will give to the U.S. electronics industry, it did not initiate the program to that end. Its goal was to lure the industry back into the business of developing advanced microelectronics technologies for uniquely military uses, as had been the rule in the early years of integrated circuits. In recent years the industry had lapsed into a pattern of upgrading its integrated-circuit technologies only as rapidly as, and to the extent that, its commercial markets demanded, for such products as pocket calculators and electronic games. Its mainstream-market semiconductors by and large lacked the speeds and capacities—and such special features as built-in resistance to ionizing radiation from a nuclear blast—that the Pentagon came to desire and that the VHSIC chips, for example, will possess. By the 1980s the Pentagon's share of the total market for U.S.-made semiconduc-

An original B-1 bomber prototype resumed flying in 1983 as part of U.S. Air Force efforts to assess upgraded systems and modifications to be incorporated into the new B-1B multirole aircraft.

TRW, Inc.

Three large telescopes equipped with video sensors form part of the U.S. Air Force's new deep-space surveillance system, which scans the sky beyond 3,000 nautical miles for both natural and man-made objects.

tors had fallen to a miserable 7%. Now, through the VHSIC program, the Pentagon undoubtedly will gain ground in that market. However, it is more concerned with gaining ground on the Soviet Union.

Maintaining the military edge. U.S. military officials are convinced that the expeditious development and deployment of cutting-edge technologies is the only way for U.S. forces to counterbalance the Soviet Union's big and growing numerical advantages of weapons and manpower. This viewpoint crystallized in the late 1970s during the tenure of William J. Perry as undersecretary of defense for research and engineering. By then it was obvious that the Soviets had drawn abreast of, or had slightly surpassed, the U.S. in some critical military technologies such as materials, welding and bonding techniques, propulsion, and perhaps even directed-energy lasers and particle beams. Moreover, intelligence reports indicated that the Soviets were rapidly narrowing the gap in microelectronics, the one technology in which the U.S. had been thought to have an insurmountable, everlasting advantage and the one that may matter the most. Consequently, Perry launched the VHSIC program to redress the situation.

In the autumn of 1981 Richard D. DeLauer, who had succeeded Perry as the Pentagon's research chief, appointed Perry to head a special DSB task force to examine the VHSIC program. In his directive DeLauer wrote that "it is imperative that the program be optimally planned and executed" because "its implications are so pervasive and so important to the defense posture of this country." Among his concerns DeLauer emphasized the urgent need to incorporate VHSIC chips in weapons and other military systems much faster than the seven to ten years that U.S. "technology insertion" usually takes. DeLauer also underlined the need to keep VHSIC technology safe from Soviet pirating. In February 1982 the Perry task force reported that the VHSIC program was proceeding crisply toward the achievement of its technical goals, but that some steps

would be needed to alleviate DeLauer's concerns.

The task force warned that the military services' systems program managers, worried about increasing the development and production costs of their already high-priced, high-technology systems, will be tempted to indulge in "sluggish or incomplete implementation of the [VHSIC] technology," its high promise notwithstanding, unless they were given special VHSIC technology-insertion funding. The Defense Department quickly made plans to provide such funding annually, beginning with $25 million in the fiscal year 1984 defense budget that was scheduled for presentation to Congress in January 1983.

By then each of the VHSIC program prime contractors had selected a particular military system as a starter in which to deploy its chips: Honeywell, an electro-optical signal processor; Hughes, a jamming-resistant communications system; IBM, an acoustic signal processor; Texas Instruments, a fire-and-forget missile with multiple and varied sensors; TRW, an electronic-warfare signal processor, and Westinghouse, an advanced tactical radar signal processor. But those were only a small beginning. One internal Pentagon document detailing "VHSIC Technology Insertion Candidates" showed 19 systems including M-1 tank fire control; TOW antitank missile guidance; a "fiber optics guidance missile"; an extremely high-frequency satellite communications processor; advanced radars for the Airborne Warning and Control System (AWACS) and E-2C surveillance aircraft; and multipurpose radars for the F-15 and F-16 fighters, the B-1B bomber, and the Stealth bomber now being developed under tight security. All told, said still another Pentagon document, VHSIC technology is predestined for "more than 60 systems" that are now in use or are far advanced in development.

In the future there will be no end of VHSIC applications as the demands on signal processors for swift, secure communications and for real-time target recognition by radar, sonar, and optical and infrared sensors become increasingly heavy. For example, VHSIC chips should make astounding advancements in acoustic sensors and associated signal processors that sort out the sounds of submarines from among the surrounding sounds of the seas. Those chips also could be keys to making such directed-energy weapons as lasers practical and effective. Pentagon researchers know various ways to build lasers of sufficient power to destroy targets. The trick in making them into weapons capable of eliminating high-speed missiles in great numbers is to provide them with aiming, tracking, and fire-control subsystems of enormous, computer-managed speed and precision. Satellites, too, stand to benefit from VHSIC chips; eventually they may contain several fault-tolerant microcomputers that will permit them to fix themselves while in orbit and give them prodigious sensing and signal-processing speeds and capacities for photoreconnaissance, electronic intelligence, and missile-warning missions.

Security. It is therefore no surprise that the VHSIC program is under very tight security wraps. Addressing the problem of how to keep VHSIC secrets from falling into unfriendly hands, the DSB task force reported that such U.S. controls as national security classification and the International Traffic in Arms (ITARS), a body of federal arms export regulations, should suffice to protect the critical weapons-related elements of the VHSIC program and the key materials and equipment used in building the microcircuits. However, the task force acknowledged the great difficulty of using those controls to check the dissemination and export of VHSIC technologies that have "extensive non-weapons applications." The Export Administration Act of 1979 sets forth regulations (EAR's) covering the export of such "dual-use" (military and civilian) technologies. These regulations are applied in concert with guidelines laid down by CoCom (Coordinating Committee), a group consisting of Japan and all NATO nations except Iceland. CoCom has no powers of enforcement, however, and U.S. EAR controls "are not adequate," the task force reported.

According to a report by the Senate Subcommittee on Investigations the Soviet Union has managed to breach all such safeguards in acquiring technological know-how in lasers, radars, aircraft catapults, precision ball bearings, and missile-guidance gyroscopes, among others, from U.S. and western European companies. And so, despite objections from some universities and companies that feared the imposition of vise-like controls over flows of research information and products, the Pentagon acted. In January 1983, it set up a technology-transfer "control group" involving the Defense Department and the military services to screen all military and dual-use technologies in critical areas, most especially in microelectronics, with an eye to preventing their shipment to the Soviet Union and to Soviet bloc nations by whatever means necessary.

The security question also bears heavily on DARPA's Very Large Scale Integration (VLSI) program. Working solely with universities, but drawing lessons from the industry-oriented VHSIC effort, DARPA is in the business of designing chips that eventually will incorporate more than a million transistors even tinier than those in the VHSIC chips and capable of performing billions of functions per second. Although the shorter term VHSIC project is dealing in silicon-derived chips because the semiconductor industry knows the properties of silicon inside and out, the VLSI program is increasingly oriented toward gallium arsenide (GaAs) as the medium of choice. GaAs costs a great deal more than silicon, but it offers three times as much electron mobility, requires less voltage, operates at higher frequencies, and tolerates greater heat. Moreover, GaAs chips are 100,000 times more resistant to ionizing radi-

ation, a most important consideration for military systems.

The superswift, vast circuits now being designed in the DARPA program will be crucial to the agency's plans for the "ultimate" computer and for its closely related program to develop machine intelligence. In such great profusion VLSI circuitry should be able to accommodate the highly sophisticated, built-in programming that AI computers must possess in order to conceive and communicate ideas and judgments. What DARPA is striving for, in concert with such universities as Carnegie-Mellon, Stanford, and the Massachusetts Institute of Technology, are AI computers that actually think; for example, in formulating military strategy and tactics on the basis of their analysis and interpretation of intelligence data.

—James W. Canan

Earth sciences

Volcanic eruptions and their effects were major areas of research by Earth scientists during the last year, a result of the considerable amount of volcanic activity that occurred during the period. Atmospheric scientists were concerned with the effects of volcanoes on climate, while geophysicists studied the eruptions and the circumstances surrounding them in an effort to predict future activity. Paleontologists continued to analyze the fossil record, and hydrologists and oceanographers focused on such subjects as the large-scale circulation of the oceans and the flow of water through soil and rocks.

Atmospheric sciences

Atmospheric sciences research advanced on a number of fronts during 1982. Of particular importance were investigations of atmospheric chemistry, of factors affecting the global climate, and of weather phenomena on the scale of individual cyclones and lines of thunderstorms.

Atmospheric chemistry. Broadly defined, atmospheric chemistry deals with the gaseous and particulate constituents of the air, their sources and sinks, the chemical and dynamical processes in the atmosphere that involve the constituents, and, to a certain extent, the effects of these constituents on the weather and climate. Over the last few years there has been a high level of interest in the stratospheric ozone layer and the possible effects on it of nitrogen oxides, chlorofluorocarbons, and other compounds—such as methyl chloroform—that include chlorine. According to a report published in 1982 by the U.S. National Academy of Sciences the reduction in the amount of stratospheric ozone by fluorocarbons that are released continuously at the 1977 rate is likely to be smaller (5 to

Storm lashes the coast of northern California, one of many that affected the West Coast of the U.S. during the winter of 1982–83. According to meteorologists they were part of a system of oceanic and atmospheric events that affected weather throughout the world.

9%) than were calculated in 1979 (15 to 18%). It also was reported that a 30% increase of nitrous oxide (N_2O) over the next century, even with all other factors constant, would reduce total ozone by 5 to 9%. The effects of the various ozone-reducing compounds are not additive. Studies continued on the complex photochemical processes that account for stratospheric ozone and on the dynamical processes involved in its transport. It has been estimated that each 1% reduction of total ozone in a column of air would lead to a 2–5% increase in the nonfatal types of skin cancer.

High-altitude balloons carrying a wide array of instruments have been launched to measure the vertical distribution of important chemical constituents in the stratosphere and the flux of solar radiation. On Sept. 22, 1982, four huge balloons carrying several tons of scientific equipment were launched from the National Scientific Balloon Facility at Palestine, Texas. At the same time measurements were made from an instrumented airplane and from ground stations in New Mexico and Arizona. The program was a joint endeavor of scientists from Belgium, Canada, Great Britain, France, Italy, Japan, and the United States. According to Robert T. Watson of the U.S. National Aeronautics and Space Administration (NASA), "... significant scientific results have been achieved in each flight for the first time in a crucial combination of chemical species in a well defined part of the earth's atmosphere."

Sulfur dioxide (SO_2) and nitrogen oxides emitted into the atmosphere from volcanoes, smokestacks, or tailpipes ultimately leave the atmosphere by direct deposition on the Earth or in rain and snow. The latter is called acid precipitation and during the past year continued to be a subject of considerable attention and debate. The acidity of aqueous solutions is measured on a pH scale that ranges logarithmically from 0 to 14: the greater the pH above 7 the greater the alkalinity; the smaller the pH below 7 the greater the acidity. Because of the formation of carbonic acid by carbon dioxide, precipitation usually has a pH less than the neutral value of 7. By convention, precipitation is called "acidic" when the pH is less than 5.6. In regions of the world with alkaline soils the acidity of rain is neutralized in whole or in part. But in places where the soils are already acidic or are poorly buffered (containing substances capable of neutralizing acids) and that are located downwind of heavily populated and industrialized zones, the acidity of precipitation can have harmful effects on certain types of aquatic creatures, vegetation, and property.

In the northeastern United States, southeastern Canada, and Scandinavia the pH of rain and snow often is about 4 and occasionally is close to 3. Sometimes the acidity of atmospheric water can be extremely high. Jed M. Waldman and his associates at the California Institute of Technology reported in 1982 that the pH of the water in fog droplets over Los Angeles and Bakersfield, Calif., had values of pH between 2.2 and 4.0. (A pH of 2.6 is a thousand times more acidic than the generally accepted 5.6 taken to represent normal acidity of precipitation).

Much remains to be learned about acid rain. Among the critical questions are the following: What are the relative contributions of SO_2 and nitrous oxides by natural sources and by human activities? What are the processes by which these gases are transformed to particles, participate in cloud formation, and are carried out of the atmosphere? How much would the acidity of precipitation be reduced by any specific reduction in SO_2 or nitrous oxide emissions?

Many scientists in many parts of the world are investigating the chemical constituents of air by means of ground-based instruments, airplanes, and balloons. For measuring global distributions of highly variable sub-

Keystone

Attached to the nose of the aircraft is a "weather-sniffler," a device used by the World Meteorological Organization to measure airflow around mountains.

stances it is essential to develop remote sensing techniques that can be used on satellites. Progress has been encouraging in the measurement of ozone and recently in the measurement of carbon monoxide. Henry G. Reichle, Jr., at the NASA Langley Research Center and his colleagues working with scientists at Old Dominion University and at Systems and Applied Sciences Corp. reported 35 hours of measurements of atmospheric carbon monoxide by means of a gas-filter radiometer operating in the 4.67-micrometer band. The initial analysis of observations showed them to be of excellent quality, within about 15% of the accuracy achieved with gas chromatography.

El Chichón and climate. On March 28 and April 4, 1982, the El Chichón volcano in Mexico experienced massive eruptions that introduced huge amounts of ash and sulfur dioxide gas into the atmosphere—amounts that were far greater than those emitted by the Mt. St. Helens eruption. Some of the material, as it was carried by the winds around the Earth, reached into the stratosphere, to heights of more than 30 km (18.5 mi). In the presence of sunlight sulfur dioxide gas is converted to sulfate particles a few tenths of a micrometer in diameter. Since the stratosphere does

not contain precipitating clouds to wash the sulfate particles out of the air, they remain there for as long as two to three years. The particles absorb and scatter solar radiation, thereby reducing the amount reaching the ground. As a result stratospheric temperatures rise, while surface air temperatures fall. Following the eruptions of Krakatoa in 1883 and Mt. Agung in 1963—two volcanoes in the class of El Chichón in regard to the volume of sulfur dioxide emissions—surface air temperatures were reduced by a few tenths of a degree Celsius. It is reasonable to expect that over the next two years the particles resulting from the El Chichón eruption will cause a cooling of the same magnitude. What effects this might have on day-to-day temperatures and precipitation still are not clear.

Various groups throughout the world were measuring the characteristics of the El Chichón emissions into the atmosphere. The cloud of particles was tracked by means of satellite by Charles A. Barth and his associates at the University of Colorado. Ground-based remote sensing devices at the Mauna Loa Observatory in Hawaii maintained by the U.S. National Oceanic and Atmospheric Administration (NOAA) were observing vertical profiles of volcanic material. High-altitude, instrumented airplanes were flown through the stratospheric cloud in order to collect samples of the particles.

Sulfate particles having diameters that are smaller than the wavelength of visible light disperse the various colors in the solar spectrum. The results, spectacularly beautiful skies, are most obvious when the Sun is low on the horizon and the lower atmosphere is cloud-free and clean.

Carbon dioxide and global climate. During recent years there has been a growing consensus that continued increases in atmospheric carbon dioxide are likely to lead to warming of the lower atmosphere. In 1982 the U.S. National Academy of Sciences issued a report concluding that a doubling of atmospheric carbon dioxide is likely to increase globally averaged temperatures by 3° (±1.5°) C. This result, essentially a reaffirmation of an earlier one, was based on calculations by mathematical models of the Earth's atmosphere that incorporate exchanges with the underlying surface.

This view of the effects of carbon dioxide was challenged by some scientists, in particular Sherwood Idso at the U.S. Water Conservation Laboratory in Phoenix, Ariz. He estimated, on the basis of a limited number of observations of incident radiation in the presence of dust and water vapor, that a doubling of·atmospheric carbon dioxide would increase the global temperature by only 0.26° C. Idso's views were criticized on various grounds, most notably that observations in a single region of the world cannot adequately be used to verify a complicated series of processes occurring throughout the Earth's atmosphere. Furthermore it was claimed that Idso's analysis did not adequately take into account the important effects of the oceans. (*See* Feature Article: THE PROBLEM WITH CARBON DIOXIDE.)

Southern oscillation and El Niño. One of the important problems in the atmospheric sciences is to explain, and learn to predict accurately, year-to-year changes in seasonal weather. An examination of weather maps shows that air temperatures and precipitation are governed by the position and the amplitude of the troughs and ridges of atmospheric pressure and the associated wind currents. But the question arises as to how to account for seasonal abnormalities in these features of the atmospheric circulation. For some years a number of meteorologists, among them Jakob Bjerknes at UCLA and Jerome Namias at the Scripps Institution for Oceanography, have maintained that the temperatures of the Pacific Ocean have a critical influence on seasonal pressure, wind, and weather patterns.

In recent years the interactions of the ocean and the atmosphere have been receiving increasing attention. A phenomenon of particular interest has been El Niño, an invasion of warm water that replaces cold, nutrient-rich, upwelling ocean water off the coasts of Ecuador and Peru. An El Niño greatly reduces the fish population and thus causes economic hardship for the fishing industry of the region.

This warming of ocean water off the west coast of South America is related to the wind patterns over the area, but El Niño is only part of a series of changes in atmospheric and oceanic currents that occur over a period of about two years and that are reflected in seasonal weather changes over much of the Earth. The sequence of events, most evident over the Pacific Ocean south of the Equator, is called the southern oscillation. Its existence was first reported in the 1920s by Sir Gilbert Walker, who recognized related increases and decreases of atmospheric pressure over various lower-latitude regions of the Pacific and found correlations of these pressure changes with the weather over North America. Harry Van Loon and Roland Madden at the U.S. National Center for Atmospheric Research (NCAR) provided additional evidence relating pressure changes in Darwin, Australia, with those at Duluth, Minn.

John D. Horel and John M. Wallace at the University of Washington examined the relationship of such variables as sea-surface temperature in the equatorial Pacific, rainfall at selected stations over the equatorial Pacific, and atmospheric pressure distributions over the tropics. They confirmed earlier studies by Bjerknes and others showing how these quantities are interrelated. Horel and Wallace found that warm episodes in equatorial Pacific sea-surface temperatures tend to be accompanied by abnormally low atmospheric pressures over the North Pacific and southeastern U.S. and abnormally high pressure over western Canada.

Squall lines and cyclones. Squall lines are zones of thunderstorms that might be 10 km (6 mi) wide, extend in length for many hundreds of kilometers, and last for many hours. Middle-latitude cyclones, nearly circular regions of low pressure around which there are closed wind circulations, are a few hundred kilometers in diameter and are the principal sources of winter precipitation. Squall lines and cyclones are mesoscale phenomena, intermediate in size between small-scale, ordinary thunderstorms and large-scale wave motions having dimensions of thousands of kilometers.

Mesoscale weather systems are not well observed by the present network of weather stations because the stations are too far apart and because balloon-borne radiosondes used to sound the free atmosphere are launched only twice a day. But this need not be the case; observational techniques exist for achieving more detailed measurements than are made at present. By means of doppler radars it is possible to measure three-dimensional air motions at spatial resolutions of about one kilometer. A new, vertically pointing radiometric method for obtaining nearly continuous profiles of the wind overhead was developed by the Wave Propagation Laboratory of NOAA in Boulder, Colo. Sat-

Flooding in Louisiana in the spring of 1983 was the worst in 25 years. A possible cause was an extraordinarily warm current in the Pacific Ocean.

Chris Harris—Gamma/Liaison

ellites equipped with radiometers operating in the visible, infrared, and microwave bands can measure such atmospheric properties as temperature and water vapor. Computer-based interactive systems were devised for rapidly analyzing large quantities of data and displaying them in easily interpretable formats.

The University Corporation for Atmospheric Research in Boulder, Colo., formulated a plan for a national mesoscale program called STORM (Stormscale Operational and Research Meteorology). It involved a cooperative effort of atmospheric scientists at various universities and at the NCAR. The principal goals of the program were to improve the observation and prediction of small- and medium-scale weather phenomena and to use such capabilities to protect the public from violent weather and to better serve the national economy.

Weather modification. Advocates of weather modification research and operations experienced another disappointment in 1982. Results of the second phase of the Florida Area Cumulus Experiment were released by William Woodley and Ronald Biondini, scientists at NOAA who were responsible for carrying out the experiment and analyzing the data. The aim of the program was to test if the seeding with silver iodide nuclei of carefully selected cumuliform clouds could increase rainfall over an area in Florida. It was hoped that this experiment would confirm earlier results suggesting the rainfall could be increased. The new tests carried out over a three-summer period did not yield such a confirmation. Statistical analyses showed that the results were highly influenced by a single, not-seeded day that had very heavy rain.

Those inclined to the view that cloud seeding can increase precipitation might argue that if that day were ignored the results of the experiment would have been positive, because there would have been 25% more rain on seeded days with only a 13% probability that this was a chance occurrence. But there apparently are no substantial grounds for discarding that one day's data. At best, the results can be said to be suggestive and that additional experiments over a longer period are needed to test whether or not the seeding techniques used in Florida are effective.

—Louis J. Battan

Geological sciences

Paleontology was a major focus of attention during the last year as geologists continued to debate the relationship between the fossil record and theories of organic evolution. Much volcanic activity occurred during the year, and there was considerable research on the eruptions and their effects on the environment.

Geology and geochemistry. *Petroleum exploration.* After a record year in 1981 the search for petroleum declined sharply in 1982. The Petroleum Information Corp. reported that between October 1981 and October 1982 the number of seismic exploration crews in the field in the U.S. declined from 689 to 465. Reflecting a continued interest in offshore prospects, the number of seismic crews operating from marine vessels remained virtually constant during the same period. At the beginning of 1982 there were about 4,500 drilling rigs operating in the United States. By October 1982 the number had fallen to less than 2,500. Continued intense exploration activity on the continental shelves paid dramatic dividends with the discovery by Chevron/Phillips of a major oil field in the Santa Maria Basin off the coast of southern California.

The impact of the decline in domestic exploration activity was felt in the geological community at large. Demand for geologists by the petroleum industry decreased, and this in turn affected Earth science programs in colleges and universities. The director of a major school of geology in the U.S. reported a substantial decline in the enrollment of prospective geologists during 1982.

Most industry analysts expected an increase in domestic exploration activity with the recovery of the national economy. Whether it would rebound to the levels of 1980 and 1981 depended upon national and international developments impossible to predict at this time.

The impact of the decline in domestic petroleum exploration upon geology as a whole should not be exaggerated. Most major fields of geological study are well buffered against short-term economic developments. The intense interest in the physics of the Earth initiated by the geological revolution of the 1960s continued with no sign of abating. Vulcanology was not only much in the public eye because of recent volcanic activity in many parts of the world but was also displaying a renewed theoretical vigor.

Paleontology. It is perhaps surprising in a time when the physics and chemistry of the Earth have received so much attention and publicity that the study of the plants and animals of the past has been experiencing a renaissance of its own. Paleontology has since early in the 19th century served geology by providing the principal means of determining the temporal relationships among sedimentary rocks separated from one another in space. Quite aside from this important function, paleontology has provided important evidence concerning the history of life.

During the past several years there has been a remarkable resurgence of interest in organic evolution. Twenty-five years ago biologists and paleontologists may have supposed that, although much remained to be discovered about the details of the history of life, the main events of evolution had been reconstructed and an adequate explanation of the process had been achieved. Recently, however, there has been a reconsideration both of the history of life and of the theory

A major oil field was discovered from a drilling platform in the Pacific Ocean near Santa Barbara, California.

in terms of which that history may be explained and understood. Paleontology has played a significant role in that intimate interplay of historical and theoretical considerations.

There has always been an uneasy and ambiguous relationship between paleontology and evolutionary theory. Although the fossil record has often been cited as compelling evidence for the occurrence of evolution, it has never served very well as a basis for choosing among different explanations of evolution. Charles Darwin believed that the fossil record presented serious difficulties for his theory of evolution by means of natural selection, which, to him, plainly entailed that evolution proceed by the gradual, almost imperceptible accumulation of adaptive traits. Yet the fossil record reveals striking discontinuities. Darwin devoted two chapters of his *Origin of Species*, published in 1859, to an attempt to accommodate his theory, which required continuity in history, with an historical record that failed to reveal it. Darwin argued that extant fossil collections were a poor sample of the remains of plants and animals that had lived in the past, in part because only a small portion of the Earth's surface had been covered in the search for fossils. Darwin believed that knowledge of the fossil record might improve with time but that it would remain seriously deficient owing to accidental factors involved in preservation. Some organisms left no trace simply because they had no durable parts such as shell or bone. Even in the case of animals whose parts are capable of being preserved, they may have lived under conditions unsuitable for burial. For example, goats, which tend to live in mountainous regions, have poor fossil records because those areas are unsuited to the accumulation of sediments in which the remains of animals might be buried. On the other hand animals that lived on plains, such as horses, camels, and cattle, have rich fossil records. Finally Darwin noted that some sediments and their fossil contents might be destroyed by erosion after they have

formed. Darwin was thus persuaded that the discontinuity of the fossil record did not reflect a fundamental property of the history of life.

Darwinian evolutionists have, by and large, accepted Darwin's explanation of the discontinuity of the fossil record. There were, however, theories of organic succession that did not entail continuity and consequently presented no need to explain away discontinuity. William Smith (1769–1839) is credited with having introduced the method of the temporal correlation of sedimentary rocks by means of their contained fossils. The method rests upon the assumption that each period in the Earth's history was characterized by animals and plants of kinds peculiar to that period, an assumption that Smith justified not by an evolutionary hypothesis but rather by contending that there had been a succession of extinctions and special creations. The discontinuity of the fossil record is theoretically consistent with this view and need not be accounted for as an accident of history.

The "scientific creationists" of our own day often seize upon the gaps in the fossil record as support for their view that evolution cannot explain the origin of species. But also there have been since the time of Darwin those who have accepted the evolutionary hypothesis but have rejected Darwin's gradualist account, often because they refused to accord natural selection the crucial formative role assigned to it by Darwin. Some of these evolutionists supposed instead that species arose in episodes of sudden major change rather than by the gradual accumulation of minor variations.

During the last four decades of the 19th century and the first four decades of the 20th century the search for fossils became increasingly widespread and systematic with the result, as Darwin had predicted, that the fossil record came to appear less fragmented. But so many gaps remained that even thoroughly committed Darwinians were no longer willing to dismiss them

283

An eruption of the Hawaiian volcano Kilauea in January 1983 spews forth fountains of lava approximately 125 meters (400 feet) high.

as accidents but instead came to regard them as theoretically significant features of the history of life. The evolutionist George Gaylord Simpson said in 1953, "It is thus still too soon for the rest of us to take the discontinuities of the paleontological record for granted. Even apart from that, the recognition and interpretation of such discontinuities is interesting and is a necessary, frequently also a practical and useful, part of the paleontological profession. Moreover, it is a fact that discontinuities are almost always and systematically present at the origin of really high categories, and, like any other systematic feature of the record, this requires explanation."

Simpson and other Darwinian paleontologists attempted to account for the systematic occurrence of gaps in the fossil record not by supposing that major evolutionary changes occurred instantaneously, but rather that they took place during episodes in which the rate of evolutionary change was appreciably accelerated for relatively brief periods of time. These episodes could be explained, according to this view, wholly within the confines of Darwinian selection theory. The shorter a period of change, the less chance there would be that it would be detectable in the fossil record.

In a 1972 paper entitled "Punctuated Equilibria: An Alternative to Phyletic Gradualism" Niles Eldredge and Stephen Jay Gould suggested that major evolutionary changes occurred during periods of instability when a population separated from a parent species. These relatively short periods of instability ended with the establishment of a mechanism that maintained stability in the new species for much longer periods of time. Eldredge and Gould cited both theoretical and historical justification for their view. Studies in evolutionary biology had suggested that the fortuitous geographic isolation of populations that had played such a critical role in Darwin's theory might not be a necessary prerequisite for differentiation into species. Instead it was supposed that conditions at the boundary of a species range, where organisms might encounter challenging environmental conditions and where isolation could be quickly achieved, provide ideal circumstances for the origin of species. Under these conditions the evolution of small "peripheral isolates" would, in the fossil record, appear to be abrupt. The paleontological justification for the hypothesis of punctuated equilibria lies simply in the long-recognized gaps in the fossil record. Under this hypothesis many of the gaps are a necessary consequence of the principal mode of evolution, while others remain as accidental features of the record.

Since the publication of the paper by Eldredge and Gould paleontologists have engaged in a vigorous debate about the principal mode of evolution. Almost no paleontologists have denied that both rapid and gradual evolutionary change occur. The point at issue is whether one or the other predominates in the history of life.

During 1982 a number of papers were published in which the issue of punctuated equilibria versus gradualism was confronted directly. But not every paleontologist has seen the resolution of the problem as lying in the acceptance of one hypothesis and the rejection of the other. Writing in the *Journal of Paleontology* J. G. Johnson concluded that it was fruitless to pursue the question of whether gradualism or punctuated equilibria is the principal mode of evolution. Johnson suggested that because evolution is the adaptation to changing environments and because there is no single rate at which environments change, one might expect that the pattern of evolution would vary according to the stability of the environment in which organisms live. He suggested, for example, that gradual change is to be expected in the relatively stable deep-ocean environments, while more rapid change would occur in the relatively unstable shallower waters. Johnson maintained that recent paleontological studies tended to support his view.

Geneticist Doug Petry concluded on theoretical grounds that, "Phyletic speciation is seen to occur over

284

a time span so short as to make observation of the transition in the fossil record unlikely." In a meticulous study of the history of a species of stickleback fish of the Miocene Epoch reported in *Paleobiology* Michael A. Bell and Thomas R. Haglund concluded that most depositional environments cannot produce a fossil record that is up to the task of linking population biology and macroevolution.

The papers of Petry and of Bell and Haglund raised once again the issue that has always been encountered in a consideration of the relationship between paleontology and evolutionary theory. Can paleontology bear the burden of providing information that is relevant to the testing of evolutionary hypotheses? The difficulties that surround the testing of a general hypothesis on the basis of historical knowledge are not unique to evolutionary biology. They arise in any historical science because of two undeniable features of our knowledge of the past. The first is that however scientists may disagree about the adequacy of the fossil record they must recognize that it is incomplete, which is to say that there are events that have occurred in the past about which there is no knowledge. The second is that traces of historical events such as fossils are not, in themselves, historical events but the beginning points of inferences that lead to historical events. It is a truism of scientific methodology that one cannot infer connections among events without accepting general principles to the effect that certain kinds of events are, or tend to be, associated. A difficulty that has plagued historical studies is that sometimes the hypotheses that one wishes to test are just the hypotheses that were presupposed in order to infer the event that is invoked in the test.

Paleontologists sometimes "measure" time, and they do so on the basis of an assumption about evolutionary rates. Thus a gradualist may say that the faunas inferred from the fossils in successive sedimentary beds are so different that some considerable interval of time must have elapsed between their deposition, even in the absence of an intermediate fauna and any physical evidence of such an interval. If the rate of evolution is held to be comparatively rapid, however, there is no reason for one to think that a marked difference between two faunas is indicative of a long interval of time between them.

Usually the relationship between assumed rates of evolution and the estimation of time intervals has been tacitly assumed rather than explicitly delineated, but in a classic paper published in Germany in 1929 Roland Brinkmann maintained that certain time intervals could be measured on the assumption that the rate of morphological change in the Jurassic ammonite genus *Kosmoceras* was uniform. In a paper published in 1982 in *Paleobiology* David M. Raup and Rex E. Crick reported that a reexamination of Brinkmann's data failed to sustain his conclusion. According to Raup and Crick

the irregularity of evolutionary change in *Kosmoceras* is such as to preclude the possibility of using its rate of evolutionary change as a measure of time.

Many of the problems that surround the attempt to infer the tempo and mode of evolution from the fossil record can be solved if duration can be estimated independently of some assumption about rate of evolution. This can be achieved in a number of ways. If fossils are contained in sediments having paired laminations that represent yearly cycles of deposition, rather precise estimates of duration between different faunas may be made. Bell and Haglund were able to measure with some confidence the time interval between depositional events because the remains of the stickleback fish they were studying occurred in such sediments. The occurrence of fossils in sediments of that type is, however, much too rare to be of any general utility.

Radiometric dating provides a method of measuring time intervals, but unfortunately for the paleontologist the rocks that can be dated radiometrically are just those rocks that do not contain fossils. Thus the dates can be only indirectly assigned to fossil-bearing beds. The newly developed technique of magnetostratigraphy offers great promise because it permits the dating of beds that do contain fossils. By this method an attempt is made to match the patterns of reversal of the Earth's magnetic field that are revealed in the remnant magnetism of fossil-bearing sedimentary rocks with a master pattern of radiometrically dated reversals developed from igneous rocks.

With the improvement of currently applied dating techniques and with the discovery of new ones, knowledge of the pattern and rate of evolutionary change will improve. Whether that improvement will be sufficient to resolve some of the issues now facing evolutionary biologists remains to be seen. In any case the vigorous disputes that have marked the relationship between paleontology and evolutionary theory seem likely to continue.

—David B. Kitts

Geophysics. During the past year volcanoes and earthquakes continued to take their toll of human life and to alter the landscape of the Earth. Eruptive activity was reported from at least 40 volcanoes distributed in more than 20 countries. Most of the volcanoes were scattered around the "ring of fire," outlining the margins of the Pacific Ocean, but a few were located in Zaire, and Mt. Etna in Italy also showed signs of activity. An ancient eruption of Italy's Mt. Vesuvius also made news because of the remarkable archaeological discoveries made in Herculaneum, a city devastated in AD 79 by the volcano. The most damaging volcano during the past year was El Chichón (also known as Volcán Chichonal), about 650 km (400 mi) east-southeast of Mexico City in the state of Chiapas. A series of eruptions entirely destroyed or badly damaged villages within a 7-km (4-mi) radius of the volcano. Although many people fled after the first eruption, more powerful ones less than a week later killed at least 200 who had remained in the area.

In the United States Mt. St. Helens in Washington was relatively well behaved. One of the most active developments took place near Mammoth Lakes, Calif., where a number of geophysical and geological studies pointed to the possibility of a volcanic eruption. The town of Mammoth Lakes is nestled against the eastern escarpment of the Sierra Nevada, at the southwestern edge of an elliptical basin about 30 km (18 mi) long by 15 km (9 mi) wide. This basin, known as the Long Valley caldera, was formed by the collapse of the ground after a gigantic, explosive eruption about 700,000 years ago. Subsequently, numerous eruptions have occurred within the caldera and along a chain of craters to the north. At least ten eruptions have occurred during the last 1,500 years, the most recent ones being less than 400 years old.

The recent volcanism and the presence of hot springs and fumaroles (fissures in the ground through which hot gases and vapors are emitted) made the caldera a prime candidate for geothermal energy production, and consequently many geophysical, geological, and geochemical studies were undertaken in the valley. In May 1980, however, an unusual episode of earthquakes as well as measurements of ground defor-

mation turned scientists' attention to the possibility of new volcanic eruptions. Four magnitude-six earthquakes within a 48-hour period took place in May 1980, and many earthquake swarms and an increase in fumarolic activity followed. These swarms are made up of many small earthquakes (in some cases more than 300 events within 1½ hours) and mark a distinct change in the expected seismicity pattern; although the eastern front of the Sierra Nevada has many active faults, earthquakes have been rare in the caldera itself.

The increase in activity has been accompanied by a dramatic increase in numbers of earthquakes in a broader zone in the area. One explanation for the increased activity is that the large earthquakes produced new fractures or reactivated old ones, allowing slivers of magma to be intruded toward the surface. The swarm earthquakes may be the response to this magmatic intrusion. Another explanation is that upwelling of the main magma body produced stresses that were relieved by the large earthquakes. That a magma body lies under the Long Valley caldera is inferred from several lines of evidence. Seismic waves produced by distant earthquakes are slowed down in passing through the caldera. Interpretation of the relative velocities of these waves suggests that a body of low-velocity material lies 7–40 km (4–25 mi) beneath the surface. Consistent with this are distinctive reflections

The most damaging volcano of the past year was El Chichón in southern Mexico. A series of eruptions either destroyed or badly damaged villages within a radius of 7 km (4 mi).

Residents of Dhamar Province in North Yemen carry the body of a victim of an earthquake that struck the region in December 1982.

observed from explosions set off in the caldera during earlier geophysical prospecting studies. Perhaps most convincing (and ominous) is a 25-cm (10-in) bulge of the ground surface during a two-year period. This bulge was found by repeated measurements of geodetic leveling surveys and can be explained by inflation of a magma chamber centered at a depth of 10 km (6 mi).

In view of the considerations above a particularly intensive swarm in May 1982 (coinciding with a meeting of Earth scientists at Mammoth Lakes) prompted the U.S. Geological Survey to issue a formal Notice of Potential Volcanic Hazard. This is the first of a three-stage warning system adopted by the U.S. Geological Survey. It informs officials of the location and nature of potentially hazardous geologic conditions, although sufficient information is not available to predict time or place. The next stage is a Hazard Watch, and the last is a Hazard Warning. Early in 1983 the most intense swarm since May 1980 occurred. During a period of several days thousands of small earthquakes and two magnitude-5½ earthquakes took place in the relatively small southern portion of the caldera. The implications of this increase in seismicity were not yet apparent, but the activity was being closely monitored, both by permanent stations and by portable installations rushed into the field after the start of the activity.

Another unusual swarm that may also be related to magmatic injection was taking place in north-central Arkansas. More than 17,000 earthquakes occurred in an extremely small source volume, 6 by 6 km (4 by 4 mi) across and 1 to 9 km (½ to 5½ mi) deep. Most of these earthquakes were quite small (negative magnitudes and not felt by humans), but one produced the largest ground acceleration yet recorded in the central or eastern United States. There is debate as to the cause of these earthquakes. Some believe that they could be due to a reactivation of preexisting faults by stress that is produced by motions of the tectonic plates. On the other hand the prolonged activity, small source volume, and analogy to a similar swarm in Matsushiro, Japan, led Arch Johnston of the Tennessee Earthquake Information Center to propose that they are related to magmatic intrusion—in spite of the lack of volcanic activity at the surface in that area for 65 million years.

The earthquakes accompanying volcanoes are almost certainly associated with the movement of magma and therefore can be useful in predicting eruptions. Scientists from the U.S. Geological Survey and the University of Washington used various distinctive features of earthquake activity to predict a number of the Mt. St. Helens eruptions subsequent to the devastating blast of May 18, 1980. These features included an increase in the numbers of earthquakes producing ground shaking with lower than usual frequencies of oscillation, the shallow depths of the earthquakes and their location under the mountain, and the presence of harmonic tremors—a train of vibrations recorded up to 100 km (60 mi) from the mountain.

In spite of the successful prediction of a number of the eruptions, such predictions are anything but routine. Considerable experience is needed to recognize that the seismic signals are volcanic in origin, and there is not a set pattern of precursory signals. The main eruption in May 1980 had no short-term seismic precursors. It differed from the subsequent eruptions by being triggered by the decompression of gases, produced by a massive earthquake-caused landslide, rather than being caused by magma-produced pressures overcoming the strength of materials on the surface. This difference may explain why the main eruption had no short-term seismic precursors. Of course, earthquakes, steam eruptions, and the deformation of the mountain in the months preceding the main explosive eruption gave clear warnings of a hazardous condition. In a sense these can be thought of as long-term precursors. The prediction of earthquakes must grapple with the problem of distinguishing between long-term and short-term precursors. Unfortunately, the identification of the short-term precursors has proved to be difficult.

Most damaging earthquakes are not related to volcanoes and occur at the margins of the various tectonic plates moving over the Earth's surface. Occasionally earthquakes also occur in the interior of plates. These quakes are not usually so large as those along plate margins, but because they are not anticipated they can cause considerable damage. This was the case in 1982. Although the earthquake activity was lower than normal, with only about one-half the usual number (19) of events of magnitude seven or greater, the death toll was more than 1,400 and may have been as great as 2,800. Most of the fatalities occurred during a magnitude-six earthquake in Yemen at the southern tip of the Arabian Peninsula. This earthquake was away from plate margins in an area not recognized as being seismically active. As has happened so often, the large number of casualties was due to the shallow depth of the earthquake beneath a region in which economic conditions and lack of adequate building materials make it difficult to construct earthquake-resistant structures.

In spite of its moderate magnitude, the Yemen earthquake provided lessons that are useful in reducing the earthquake hazard in other parts of the world. Early in 1983 a team of seismologists from the U.S. Geological Survey was in Yemen studying the aftershocks of the earthquake. The aftershocks delineate the fault surface that ruptured in the main event, information that can help geologists understand spatial variations in the earthquake damage and can aid in planning resettlement of the region.

Although aftershocks of earthquakes provide important information, the ground shaking from the main earthquakes causes the majority of the damage. The only way to obtain data about ground shaking is to install a permanent network of instruments in regions likely to experience large earthquakes. Seismologists have few recordings from earthquakes greater than magnitude seven at distances within 25 km (15 mi) of faults, yet it is earthquakes in just this range of magnitudes and distances that are of most concern in the design of important structures such as nuclear power plants, high-rise buildings, and dams. For this reason a worldwide effort was underway to install networks of rugged instruments in regions likely to have large earthquakes; such networks were operating or were being installed in most seismically active countries.

There was a trend to supplement the large-scale networks with specialized arrays in which many instruments are placed within small geographical regions. For example, 37 instruments were located within a circle of a 2-km (1.25-mi) radius in Taiwan (the Republic of China). This array has recorded a number of events, and by sophisticated signal processing many characteristics of the seismic waves have been determined. As another example, the analysis of records from a linear array near El Centro, Calif., obtained

during the large earthquake in the Imperial Valley in 1979, has been used to follow the progress of the rupture front. The front traveled at about ten times the speed of sound in the atmosphere. The increasing reliability and decreasing cost of digital electronics and the advent of laser-based digitizing machines for analog records will make the processing of the expected crop of data from the arrays distributed throughout the world much more manageable than it would have been even a few years ago.

—David Boore

Hydrological sciences

The large-scale circulation of the ocean, the flow paths of groundwater, hydrothermal vents in the deep ocean, and mineral deposits in cores from the seafloor were among the subjects under study by hydrologists and oceanographers during the past year.

Hydrology. During 1982 there were a number of important international meetings concerning hydrology. At the first scientific general assembly of the International Association of Hydrological Sciences (IAHS) in Exeter, England, some 530 scientists from more than 50 countries gathered to hear 200 papers. There were six symposia at the assembly having the following titles: advances in hydrometry; optimal allocation of water resources; improvement of methods of long-term prediction of variations in groundwater resources and regimes due to human activities; recent developments in the explanation and prediction of erosion and sediment yield; hydrological aspects of alpine and high mountain areas; and effects of waste disposal on groundwater and surface water. A second major conference in the U.K. took place at Leeds, the annual meeting of the European Geophysical Society. Two symposia of hydrological interest were held there: the state of evaporation research, and the spatial variability of soil physical properties.

The titles of these various symposia reflect the broad scope of current research in hydrology. This brief review will discuss in detail a subject that has implications for many other areas in hydrology, the role of preferential pathways on the movements of water through soil and rocks.

Traditional concepts of the subsurface flow of water have treated soil or rock as a porous medium in which quantities such as moisture content and flow velocity could be averaged over a volume containing a large number of pores ("a representative elementary volume") and treated as macroscopic quantities. This approach circumvents the obvious theoretical and practical difficulties of considering the microscopic flows in individual pores in a medium of complex and, in general, unknown pore structure. There is evidence to suggest that the macroscopic approach is a good representation for laminar (nonturbulent) flows in a saturated

Irrigation jack-gate, developed at the U.S. Water Conservation Laboratory in Arizona, is controlled by a central time clock in order to provide precise water applications.

medium, just the conditions studied by H.-P.-G. Darcy when he formulated his empirical law for water flow in a porous medium, published in France in 1856. Darcy's law states that average flow velocity is directly proportional to the pressure gradient in the direction of flow. In 1931 L. A. Richards extended the use of Darcy's law to unsaturated soils with the proportionality allowed to vary with the degree of saturation of the soil. The assumption that the simple proportionality of Darcy's law is valid for unsaturated soil is a good one in many instances, though it was soon found that the hydraulic conductivity at a given degree of saturation was not a constant but, even for media of simple structure, could vary depending on the history of wetting and drying of the soil.

More recently, a number of research studies have suggested that these traditional macroscopic concepts of soil water flow fail to describe observed patterns of movement in soils with structure. In particular, it has been suggested that large pores that are long in relation to their width may provide important preferential pathways for water flow. These flows will not in general be adequately described by Darcy's law, since water in the preferential pathways may be responding to different pressure gradients and moving at much faster velocities than does the water in the surrounding soil matrix.

The presence of preferential pathways may have important effects on the movement of solutes and pollutants through a soil or rock. Solutes moving through such pathways may have much higher velocities than the average velocity of the bulk flow through the medium. In addition, since the preferential pathways make

up only a small proportion of the total pore space of the medium, the solute within them may have only limited possibilities for interactions with the solid particles.

The importance of such pathways to the movement of water and solutes has been recognized qualitatively since the last century, but only recently has there been any serious research work attempting to quantify their influence. In the last year the results of research projects in Australia, Great Britain, Canada, The Netherlands, New Zealand, Switzerland, and the U.S. have been published.

These preferential pathways result from a number of causes. In many soils wetting and drying sequences gradually result in the creation of structural units called peds that are separated by cracks. The cracks will be widest when the soil is dry but may not close even when the soil becomes wet after prolonged rain. Other important causes of large continuous pathways include the root channels of plants and the burrows of earthworms, ants, and other soil animals. The pores may be interconnected; plant roots, for example, will often follow the cracks between soil peds or the channels where former roots have decayed. It is known that in some cases networks of preferential pathways may extend for more than 10 m in the vertical and for tens of meters down hillslopes. In semiarid climates plants exploit the preferential pathways formed by their root systems. In dry periods the roots shrink, leaving an annular channel around them. When rain falls, it is channeled to the ground by the plant as stemflow; from there it is distributed to the soil immediately surrounding the roots.

Enough is now known about flows through these

Barrier across the River Thames in England was built to protect London from river floods. The largest movable flood barrier in the world, it does not interrupt the normal flow of the river.

preferential pathways in the soil to realize that it is a complex phenomenon, highly variable in space and time. Detailed dye studies carried out by J. Bouma and his co-workers at Wageningen in The Netherlands revealed that at the microscopic scale some cracks show evidence of dye staining while other similar cracks do not. Also, some parts of a crack may be stained, while an adjacent section is not. The researchers suggested that the flow in the preferential pathways is controlled by the narrowest cross-sections (the pore necks) and that if the supply of water is not sufficient to fill a channel the flow pattern may be complex, even spiraling around the walls of a cylindrical pore. It is clear from this work that a knowledge of channel sizes alone will not be sufficient to characterize movement through the preferential pathways; the structure of the channels is also important.

In New Zealand M. P. Mosley reported a study carried out at the macroscopic scale on soil blocks on forested hillslopes. Water was infiltrated above a soil pit, and the outflows at the pit face were observed and collected. It was shown that water could move downslope within the soil at velocities of the same order as surface flows. Mosley noted that the water moved along distinct preferential pathways that ranged in diameter from a few millimeters to a few tenths of a millimeter, suggesting that preferential pathways do not have to be the largest pores. Differences in the response between pits, under similar vegetation covers,

were found to be large. There seemed to be little or no relationship between outflows and such factors as soil depth, slope angle, bulk density, and antecedent precipitation. It appeared, therefore, that there is also complex behavior at the macroscale that currently defies theoretical analysis, at least in the unsaturated soil profile.

The groundwater analogue of a soil with structural channels is a rock with fractures. Many important aquifers are of this type, such as the major Chalk aquifers of southern England and northern France. There are also areas of fractured hard rock that are being considered as repositories for hazardous waste materials; in those regions methods must be developed for predicting flow rates and interactions between the waste and the surrounding rock. Experiments also were made during which controlled explosions were used to fracture petroleum-bearing rocks in order to increase the yields of oil.

P. A. Witherspoon and his group at the University of California at Berkeley have been studying the flows of liquids through fractured materials for several years. In a recent paper they addressed the problem of whether a network of fractures can be treated as an equivalent porous medium. Their results showed that fractured rock does not always behave as would such a porous medium. However, as fracture density or sample volume is increased, or if apertures are constant rather than distributed, or if orientations are distribut-

290

ed rather than constant, then the assumption that the network of fractures behaves like an equivalent Darcian porous medium is more likely to be valid.

From the studies published so far it is possible to conclude that the presence of preferential pathways may in some circumstances have an important effect on water flows and solute transport. Research is still needed to develop a methodology for predicting flow through networks of preferential pathways of generally complex structure, particularly under unsaturated conditions. It may well be that some simple experimental work linked to simple theory may prove more cost-effective than a full analysis of the flow characteristics of a structured medium, particularly where the structure is unknown. Such an approach has been developed by W. A. Jury at Riverside, Calif., for spatially variable solute transport; in this method predictions are based on a set of measurements to characterize the statistical distribution of flow velocities without consideration of the detailed dynamics. As the spatial scale to be considered increases, this type of approach may become increasingly attractive.

—Keith Beven

Oceanography. *Ocean circulation.* A renewed interest in large-scale circulation of the ocean gained momentum as new data were analyzed from global satellite observations and from large-scale ocean chemistry measurements. The results from a large array of data collected in 1978 by the Seasat satellite became available in 1982. The launch of the satellite in June 1978 was a major milestone for the application of microwave sensor technology to the remote sensing of the ocean. The intention of the U.S. National Aeronautics and Space Administration (NASA), which was largely met, was to demonstrate that such properties as ocean surface temperature, wind, and current could be measured accurately and mapped globally regardless of weather conditions. The satellite operated for only three months in 1978 before ceasing because of a short circuit in its electrical system, yet a remarkably complete set of data was made available.

The altimeter from the satellite yielded information on global wave height and wind speed and on the shape of the ocean surface. The wave height and wind speed measurements gave oceanographers for the first time global synoptic (taken simultaneously) views of those ocean processes, which are vital for both understanding and predicting ocean circulation and for practical forecast purposes.

The data on the shape of the ocean surface gave oceanographers a new view of the distribution of eddies in the ocean, previously measurable only by slow-moving ships. These data also revealed large-scale features of the general circulation of the ocean, the first to do so that were not based on measurements made from ships.

The microwave scatterometer and the microwave radiometer worked well, yielding information concerning wind speed and ocean temperature. The radiometer data on ocean temperature showed that sea-surface temperature could be determined to an accuracy of approximately 1° C under favorable surface and atmospheric conditions.

The data from Seasat and satellites now in the planning stage offer a whole new range of pictures of the ocean. As the year ended, physical oceanographers were planning a global ocean circulation study, with satellites as the centerpiece, scheduled to be carried out in the late 1980s.

Data from recent studies showed that the deep water

Acoustic tomography receiver is deployed on a mooring. One of an array of acoustic sources and receivers, it was used to study eddies in the Atlantic Ocean near Bermuda.

Robert C. Spindel—Woods Hole Oceanographic Institution

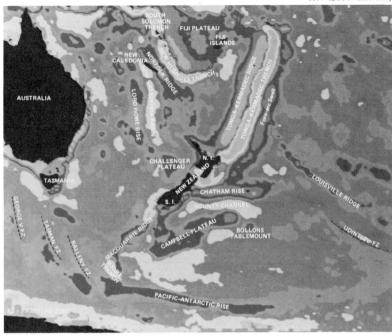

Computer-processed map of a region in the southwest Pacific Ocean was compiled from data gathered by the Seasat satellite. Features of the seafloor are revealed; for the first time the Louisville Ridge was shown to be a nearly continuous chain of seamounts.

in the northern North Atlantic has become colder and less saline; no evidence of previous changes of this magnitude in the deep water had been observed before. It is possible that the shift is climate-related, since reduced salinities were also observed in the upper layers of the North Atlantic and the Norwegian and Greenland seas. The deep water may be a good indicator of previous climate changes.

Marine hydrothermal systems. Direct observations of an active hydrothermal field (an area of very hot springs) on a slow-spreading oceanic ridge showed that mineral deposits could be concentrated by hydrothermal discharges focused through vents. The data suggest occasional bursts of low- and high-temperature discharge from the discrete vents and ongoing slow long-term seepage of hydrothermal solutions through a larger area of the seafloor.

During the year detailed chemical, biological, and geological studies were carried out at the known vents, and anomalies in chemistry and physical properties in the waters surrounding the vents were studied in some detail. One major discovery was that of bacteria that survive in waters as hot as 300° C. These bacteria could be a major producer of methane, a fact important for balancing global budgets of this gas.

It is clear that this research has profound implications for the Earth's thermal regime, geochemical cycles, mass balance of the elements, sustenance of biological communities, and concentration of metallic mineral deposits. The first workshop ever devoted to interdisciplinary consideration of the entire field was held in April 1982 in Cambridge, England; 75 scientists from 15 nations participated.

Biological oceanography. A major multidisciplinary and multi-institutional ecosystem study of the Bering Sea completed its field work during the year. The study was focused on the abundant secondary and higher level fauna of outer Bristol Bay, primarily the early life history of the Alaska pollack, a food fish related to the cod. The results from the field studies were expected to be used to construct numerical models of water circulation and mixing. These models would then form the basis of an overall ecosystem model for management of the Bering Sea and its fauna.

A series of studies was being carried out in the northeastern Pacific to evaluate the production, transport, and cycling of organic matter. Sediment traps and other sampling devices were being used to determine the nature and movement of particles, chemical constituents, and the physical properties of the surrounding water as well as the biological populations.

Observations of organisms ranging from large plankton to small fish that live in water midway between the surface and the bottom were made during the year from a minisubmersible in the Pacific off Santa Barbara, Calif. The submersible was a one-person tethered capsule with the ability to collect samples directly or to take photographs. Since many of these organisms either are destroyed by traditional net collection or escape the nets, the new sampling technique could greatly increase knowledge of the populations in this important region.

The first workshops were held for the analysis of the data from a major experiment on Antarctic krill carried out in 1981. During that experiment in the South Atlantic Ocean 11 countries cooperated in measure-

The Convention on the Law of the Sea, dealing with almost every human use of the oceans, was adopted at a UN conference in 1982.

ments to investigate the growth and mortality of krill in different areas, their spawning success and recruitment mechanisms, stock separation and migration patterns, and survival in and underneath the ice. Krill hold the potential to be a major food resource for the world, and these studies will provide a better understanding of their life cycle.

Information derived from satellites also was proving important in this area. Chlorophyll, as measured from ship and from satellite, was used during the year as a measurable link between physical and biological processes in the study of Gulf Stream "rings," large circular eddies in the North Atlantic. These data provide a new perspective in which to view mesoscale ocean features. The temporal evolution of chlorophyll within and surrounding a specific ring was followed by means of these techniques to show how the rings develop and change.

Seafloor studies. In the general area of geology and geophysics of the seafloor the International Phase of Ocean Drilling continued its successful project of deep sampling with the drilling ship "Glomar Challenger." The schedule for the year took the ship from the equatorial Pacific to the northwest Pacific off Japan to study the ocean bottom in the Nankai Trough and the Japan Trench. The ship then moved to the southwest Pacific to collect cores that contain paleoceanographic records expected to help researchers understand past climates. During 1983 the ship was to work around the

hydrothermal springs area in the eastern tropical Pacific and then to move into the Atlantic Ocean.

The equatorial Pacific work involved both hydraulic piston coring and rotary drilling. An important result of this work was the possibility of using acoustic techniques to identify carbonate depositional changes associated with the middle and late Miocene Epoch and of seismically tracing this geological boundary over much of the central equatorial Pacific. If the boundary can be mapped in a verifiable way, then the new data will allow construction of paleoceanographic regimes not previously possible.

The primary objective of the work in the northwest Pacific was to recover a north-south profile of cores across the Kuroshio current system in order to unravel the preglacial and Quaternary Period paleoceanographic history of the system. This objective was largely achieved.

Discussions continued throughout the year on plans for continuation of the Deep-Sea Drilling Program. A report from the U.S. National Academy of Sciences emphasized the need for ocean drilling by pointing out the uses of such data for understanding climate and climate change and for guiding the search for mineral and petroleum resources. The report noted that the new knowledge gained has been important not only in basic science but also in employing the plate tectonics model to determine the location of resources. Noting that the oceanic crust is the site of fundamental Earth processes that control or affect mountain building, earthquakes, ocean chemistry, ocean circulation, and the placement of ore deposits, the report concluded that "another decade of ocean drilling holds promise of new contributions as important as the discoveries of the past ten years." The report urged continuation of the drilling program.

As of early 1983 plans for transferring the program to a drilling vessel larger and more capable than the "Glomar Challenger" were under discussion. Decisions on continuation of a drilling program were expected to be made during the year.

Law of the sea. On April 30, 1982, the Convention on the Law of the Sea was finally passed (over the objections of the U.S.). Eventually 60 nations must ratify the treaty for it to enter into force. The new regime for the ocean resulting from these negotiations will change markedly the way in which marine scientists and marine scientific research operate. The new treaty recognizes several distinct juridical regions of ocean space, including internal waters, territorial seas, straits used for international navigation, archipelagic waters, exclusive economic zones, the continental shelf beyond 200 mi, and the high seas.

The treaty states that "marine scientific research shall be conducted exclusively for peaceful purposes . . . shall be conducted with appropriate scientific methods . . . [and] shall not unjustifiably interfere with other legitimate uses of the sea." Likewise, nations shall support, promote, and facilitate the development of marine scientific research in accordance with the convention and "shall endeavor to adopt reasonable rules, regulations and procedures to promote and facilitate marine scientific research . . . beyond their territorial sea and to facilitate . . . access to their harbours and promote assistance from marine scientific research vessels." These provisions are supportive of marine research but do not bind the signers to accept them.

According to the treaty, a nation wishing to conduct research can begin its project six months after submitting a request if the appropriate coastal nation has not denied consent within four months after receiving the information. It seems evident that additional administrative and funding considerations will be required for U.S. marine scientists to be able to continue their activities in the world ocean. Scientists will need to test and challenge strict or arbitrary interpretations of the convention, and their governments must be prepared to support their efforts. It appears that the legal problems facing those marine scientists who plan to work in foreign waters during the next few years may be as complex and as difficult to resolve as the scientific problems they intend to attack.

—D. James Baker

See also Feature Articles: WHEN THE RAINS DON'T COME; THE WEATHER OF OTHER PLANETS.

Electronics and information sciences

The increased use of low-cost and miniaturized microprocessors continued to be a major development in the area of electronics and information sciences. From video games to interconnected office communications systems these devices found many applications during the last year. At the other end of the scale, firms in the United States and Japan were introducing new giant supercomputers.

Communications systems

From home telephones to satellites hovering thousands of miles above the Earth's surface, the communications industry is undergoing a technological and commercial revolution that is expected to meet future demands for quick, efficient, and relatively low-cost means of exchanging voice conversations, video images, and information of various kinds throughout the world. Some experts have referred to the coming decade as the Information Age in the belief that an explosion of new communications equipment and services will dramatically change life-styles and business practices just as the Industrial Revolution altered human existence in the last century.

The Information Age envisions the installation and use of new, sophisticated equipment in homes and businesses, allowing individuals and commercial concerns to have access to large volumes of data on almost any subject—from shopping lists to stock portfolios—via high-speed facsimile devices, fast-typing automatic printers, or devices resembling television screens known as cathode-ray tubes (CRT's). One specific application for this technical upheaval has been designated as the "office of the future." It encompasses a wide array of systems which would allow white-collar workers to improve their communicating ability and productivity.

The forces behind these changes include the rapid introduction of small but powerful computers into communications systems, the use of low-cost memory and microprocessor devices, and, especially in North America, relaxed regulations which have opened up markets to many new competitors. In a trend that is expected to continue for some time the communications industry over the past year grew impressively in the number of new products for home and business communications as well as new services for local and long-distance communications.

Telephones. Viewed as part of a total public communications system, the home telephone may emerge as an important link to the Information Age. Firms such as Western Electric Co., International Telephone & Telegraph Corp., General Telephone & Electronics

Teleconferencing allows people in widely separated locations to meet with one another by attending studios equipped with television cameras and linked by long-distance facilities.

Corp., Northern Telecom, and many others are producing wide varieties of home telephones with functions that allow users to put calls on hold, forward a call to an alternate telephone, or automatically dial a regularly used, preprogrammed number with the push of a single button.

In addition, telephone lines into the household television set are essential components in what are known as videotext and teletext systems. Via a combination CRT/keyboard or small keyboard attached to a television receiver teletext and videotext systems can give consumers instant access to local, county, state, national, and international news; restaurant menus; grocery store sales and prices; product information; and educational material. Many of these systems remain in the experimental stage, with charges and types of services yet to be determined. Nevertheless, telephone companies, newspapers, television stations, and other concerns actively are exploring possible implementation of videotext and teletext systems for the home.

In Ridgewood, N.J., approximately 200 homes were being provided with information services on a test basis in a program cosponsored by CBS and American Telephone & Telegraph Co. (AT&T). In other countries home information systems well under way included the Telidon system of Canada, Antiope system of France, and Prestel system of the U.K. Efforts were being made to establish technical standards for videotext and teletext, which would allow communications over telephone lines and broadcast air waves between different types of systems.

In the office, meanwhile, microprocessor and computer technology was making its way into the basic telephones and communications systems used by businesses throughout the world. New electronic desk-top telephones feature automatic dialing and other advanced functions as well as small displays, comparable to those on handheld calculators, which provide the ability to leave messages, recall telephone numbers, and learn the status of a telephone call without the need for handwritten notes and card files.

In telephone company operations the large central office exchanges that switch voice and data calls from town to town and state to state were becoming more powerful and intelligent through the use of computers. The use of digital signals as well as stored program control—operation of a central office switch by computer—were making their way into the public telephone networks of the U.S. and many other nations.

Optical fibers, the strands of glass that resemble cable, were being used increasingly in local and long-haul communications systems. In comparison with underground copper cable, optical fibers are less expensive, use less space, and carry more communications signals. Improvements in the strength and flexibility of the glass itself and the development of devices that reduce noise loss have combined to make fiber optics more attractive in recent years to U.S. telephone companies.

Private branch exchanges. The hub of many business telephone systems is the private branch exchange (PBX), a box the size of a file cabinet that switches telephone calls and controls the entire system for one or more buildings. Full of microprocessors, memory, and computer power, the modern PBX handles tasks other than just switching telephone calls, including the management of energy-consuming equipment such as lighting, heating, and air conditioning; the automatic listing of telephone-call information such as the time and duration of calls; and the storing of "missed" telephone calls on computer disks in the same way that an answering machine tape-records a voice message. One

295

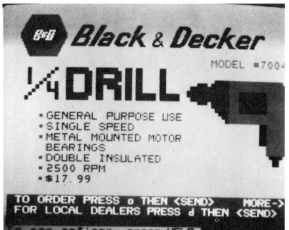

Videotext system developed by CBS and AT&T was tested during the year in homes in Ridgewood, New Jersey. The system consists of a small keyboard that is either attached to a television receiver or combined with a cathode-ray tube and connected to the outside world by telephone lines.

of the most significant potential uses of the PBX involves its ability to store and route data communications between computers and data terminals. Many PBX's introduced recently switch all voice and data signals into what is called a digital format; that is, all the communications traffic is converted into a binary or numerical code as in a computer. With the addition of software—computer instruction language—and other hardware the PBX's will provide a communications mix consisting of many types of CRT terminals, printers, computers, facsimile machines, video cameras, and telephones.

Interconnected systems. The linking of telephones, PBX's, office equipment, data terminals, and computers together into one system is a costly task since manufacturers and large corporate users must develop the software, hardware, and applications that interface many models of equipment and office tasks. Canada's Northern Telecom, for instance, disclosed in 1982 that it planned to spend at least $1.2 billion over the next five years on research and development in that field. Several companies also began marketing desk-top systems, which simultaneously act as a telephone, CRT, and keyboard.

At the same time other research and development efforts were aimed at improving communications links within a building to allow many of the new systems to work together. Generally known as local area networks, these links may enhance the capability of a copper wire already used for telephones or make use of new coaxial cable or fiber optics.

Xerox Corp., one of the first firms to work on local area networks, unveiled products for its Ethernet system, which was designed to provide intra-office links for office equipment. Many other firms were making similar equipment.

One group of firms known as value-added network carriers—GTE Telenet, Tymnet, and Graphnet Systems among them—were offering businesses new ways of transmitting data. In one such method, called packet switching, bits of data are bundled into packets and burst into communications lines simultaneously for later unbundling and distribution. During 1982 both AT&T and IBM were among the firms to begin offering corporate users data communications networks, which are expected to allow incompatible terminals and com-

Scanset XL personal information station developed by Tymshare combines the telephone and computer terminal into one compact device.

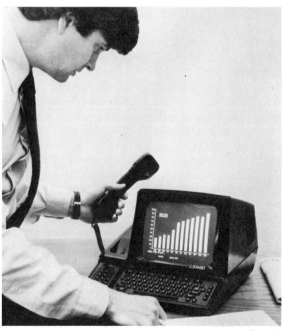

Tymshare

296

puters to communicate and to allow small companies to share time on communications lines.

To implement advanced communications networks, telephone companies, specialized carriers, and private interests began deploying equipment throughout the nation in so-called nodes. These nodes may consist of powerful computers and disks to control and store information, processors for additional control and routing functions, and modems and multiplexers, which produce common speeds and signals for all communications traffic. One goal was to develop an international standard known as the x.25 protocol, which will allow data devices and computers to speak the same language.

Radios. Microwave radios utilizing binary-digit technology increased in popularity during the last year, while radios that employ so-called data-under-voice techniques were being used to carry computer and human communications simultaneously. Microwave radios were also expected to be the key elements in what the U.S. Federal Communications Commission (FCC) designated as the digital terminal system (DTS), intracity communications links that will consist mainly of rooftop transmitting and receiving equipment. A group of firms completed a test of a DTS project during 1982, and many other companies received FCC approvals to develop DTS networks in the future.

In 1982 the FCC also began accepting applications for licenses from companies that wanted to operate "cellular" radio telephone systems, which people use to make calls from vehicles. Such a system divides an area into different frequencies and then allows a computer to switch frequencies as vehicles travel among the "cells."

—Frank Barbetta

Computers and computer science

Computer projects in Japan. Ever since the beginning of the computer age in the mid-1940s, the United States has been the leader in the development of electronic computer technology. During recent years Japan caught up with and even moved ahead of the U.S. in some aspects of microelectronics, but in regard to very large computers and in most areas of research and development the U.S. remained the leader. A number of developments in 1981–83, however, indicated that Japan was preparing to challenge American leadership in those areas.

The only vector supercomputers installed up to the end of 1982 were those manufactured in the U.S. by Cray Research Inc. and by Control Data Corp. (A vector is a list of numbers of the same kind; a vector of length 25 might consist of the numbers stored in 25 consecutive memory locations. Vector-processing units provide vector arithmetic operations that correspond to the conventional arithmetic procedures provided for

single numbers.) In 1982, however, two Japanese manufacturers, Fujitsu and Hitachi, announced new vector supercomputers that they expected to have available for delivery before the end of 1983. These new machines were competitive in speed with the Cray and Control Data systems. An attractive feature of the Japanese supercomputers is the fact that they were designed as extensions of the popular and widely used IBM 370 system.

In 1982 six major Japanese computer manufacturers announced that they were engaged in a joint project to advance the state of supercomputer technology, with the goal of producing a computer by 1990 that would be 1,000 times as powerful as any now available. While most experts did not believe that such an increase in computing power could be achieved so soon, an increase by a factor of 100 did seem to be possible. This well-funded, well-supported Japanese project may indeed succeed in reaching that goal.

The Institute for New Generation Computer Technology was established in Japan in June 1982 to proceed with the implementation of the major research and development project for fifth-generation computer systems. Planning for the project started in 1979, and the planning phase culminated in an international conference held in Tokyo on Oct. 19–22, 1981. Tohru Moto-Oka of the University of Tokyo was program chairman.

Many of the goals of the fifth-generation systems are closely related to those that have been pursued for many years in an area of research generally referred to as artificial intelligence. Thus, the ability to learn by associating and inferring is an important defining characteristic of a fifth-generation system. The ability to organize and search large amounts of information so as to provide expert guidance in such specialized fields as medicine, engineering, and law is another feature of these systems. The limitations of the present generation of computers in this area are apparent, and such systems can reach their potential only in a radically different and more advanced computer organization. The fifth-generation project will probably not achieve many of its ultimate goals, but the existence of such a program with its massive support from government and industrial sources may indeed shift some of the focus of computer science research from the United States to Japan.

Reactions in the United States. Interesting questions of policy and strategy are raised concerning a possible U.S. reaction to the Japanese competitive challenge. The U.S. government has no development goals for American industry. The companies that make up the computer industry do not normally work together to develop new technologies or new products. That type of activity would appear to be contrary to the competitive traditions of U.S. industry and might even be forbidden by the antitrust laws.

UNIX® operating system in 1982 won two prestigious prizes for its developers. Among its most important features is its ability to provide tools for producing computer software.

Of the U.S. firms, IBM Corp. has the resources to compete in any computer-related area, even against government-sponsored cooperative projects in other countries. However, no other computer manufacturer in the U.S. can compete at that level, and it has been suggested that either a government initiative or a cooperative corporate effort will be necessary to maintain the position of the U.S. in the computer field.

A panel on large-scale computing in science and engineering was convened in the U.S. by the National Science Foundation and the Department of Defense in cooperation with the Department of Energy and the National Aeronautics and Space Administration. These are the organizations that provide funding for most of the scientific research activities carried on in the U.S. Consisting of 15 leading scientists from universities and national laboratories, with Peter D. Lax of New York University as chairman, the panel published its recommendations in a report dated Dec. 26, 1982. This report, referred to as the Lax report, may have considerable influence on government policies with respect to the use and the development of supercomputers in the United States. The Lax report recommended "the establishment of a National Program to stimulate the development and use of advanced computer technology." The proposed program would have four major components: to provide increased access to supercomputers for the scientific and engineering research

community; to provide for increased research in computational mathematics, software, and algorithms; to provide for the training of personnel in scientific and engineering computing; and to support research and development leading to the design of new supercomputer systems.

Several efforts were under way to set up organizations for cooperative research and development in the computer field in the private sector of the U.S. economy. Control Data Corp. was instrumental in the formation of the Microelectronics & Computer Technology Corp. This was intended to be a joint effort by computer companies and companies in the field of microelectronics. Its aim was to carry out advanced research and development projects at a level that could not be supported by individual firms.

A somewhat different approach was adopted by Semiconductor Research Corp., which enlisted major U.S. electronic companies in a cooperative research financing effort. The goal was to establish "centers of excellence" around selected U.S. universities by funding appropriate research activities of interest to the electronic industry.

UNIX® operating system. At a conference in Washington, D.C., in September two Bell Telephone Laboratories scientists, Dennis M. Ritchie and Kenneth L. Thompson, received the 1982 Emanuel R. Piore award for their work on the UNIX® operating system. This

298

prestigious prize is awarded annually in recognition of outstanding achievement in the field of information processing. In the issue of Oct. 20, 1982, the editors of *Electronics* magazine announced that their 1982 Achievement Award had been presented to the same scientists, Ritchie and Thompson, "for their work in developing the transportable operating system UNIX® and the high-level language C."

It is impressive that these two major awards honored the originators of the same software system. It is especially noteworthy in view of the fact that UNIX® is not a new system. Development on it began in 1969, and a mature version was described in a paper published in the *Communications of the Association for Computing Machinery* in July 1974. That version was developed to run on the most popular of the large minicomputers, the PDP-11/70 of the Digital Equipment Corp.

Even noncomputer people now know that a computer, except possibly for the most trivial ones, must run under the control of an operating system. An operating system consists of an integrated set of programs that control the allocation of memory and other resources, that control input and output, and that provide for the orderly execution of the tasks (the programs) that constitute the workload of the computer. UNIX® is one of a large number of operating systems that have been developed. The design of such systems usually reflects their orientation toward use by large organizations rather than by individuals. Ritchie and Thompson, however, set out to build an operating system that would provide a productive computer environment for an individual research scientist.

One of the features of UNIX® was its emphasis on providing tools for producing computer software. A number of these tools were collected into a subsystem called the Programmer's Workbench, a feature of more recent versions of UNIX®. Another important feature was the development of tools for producing technical documents. The UNIX® programs nroff and troff permit the user to create a document and to convert it into output that goes directly to a phototypesetter. These, along with such features as a spelling checker and a style analyzer, were collected into a subsystem called the Writer's Workbench.

Many of the features of UNIX® were available in other systems. It was the consistent and elegant structure of the system, the synthesis of so many features, and the presence of so much useful software that made it especially attractive and useful.

UNIX® was originally developed for use within Bell Laboratories, but other organizations became interested, and arrangements were made to license the system for use by others. License fees generated considerable revenue for AT&T, but the company adopted a policy of free licenses for educational institutions for instructional use of UNIX® systems. Most major UNIX® users were linked together in a telephone network, and there

was active communication and cooperation among UNIX® installations.

The programming language C was developed as part of the UNIX® project and provides an excellent language for system implementation. Essentially all of the UNIX® operating system is written in C, and the fact that the system is written in this type of higher level language makes it relatively easy to move UNIX® to computers other than the one on which it was originally written. Versions of UNIX® now exist on many different types of computers, even on some large mainframe models.

A large part of the recent upsurge in interest in UNIX® was due to the rapid introduction into the computer market of microcomputers based on the powerful 16-bit microprocessors such as the Motorola 68000 and the Intel 8086. These microprocessors can support, and may indeed need, more powerful and sophisticated operating systems than were common in the earlier generation of 8-bit microcomputers. A number of versions of UNIX® were written for these microprocessors, and a number of microcomputers now on the market offer UNIX® as their standard operating system. In 1982 Hewlett-Packard Co. announced that the UNIX® system was available for its HP-9000 system, which was based on a powerful new 32-bit microprocessor chip. Also in 1982 Digital Equipment Corp. announced a new microprocessor version of the PDP-11, equivalent in power to the PDP-11/70. UNIX® will almost certainly be widely used on the computers based on these microprocessor chips.

University computing environments. Batch processing and the use of punch cards typified the university computing environment of the 1960s. By 1965 several universities had developed prototype time-sharing systems, and between 1970 and 1980 there was a gradual shift from the use of cards to the use of terminals on time-sharing systems. Some universities moved faster than others and many card systems remained in use, but by the early 1980s the typical university computing environment was based on large numbers of terminals through which students and staff could gain access to one computer or to a network of time-sharing computer systems.

The transition from the punch-card environment to the time-sharing terminal environment continued into 1983, but another equally revolutionary change in the university computing environment may already have begun. There are disagreements about how soon such changes will take place, but it does seem inevitable that the existence of the powerful personal microcomputers will have a major impact on the way computers are used for instruction and research. Some small universities announced that all of their students would be required to purchase personal computers.

A number of universities were engaged in ambitious projects to install campus-wide communication networks that would provide personal computer users with access to varied computer resources. The most ambitious of these projects is one at Carnegie-Mellon University. On Oct. 20, 1982, Carnegie-Mellon University and IBM announced that they had entered into an agreement for the joint development of a distributed computing system on the university's campus that would be a prototype for a "comphrehensive computing environment." Richard M. Cyert, president of Carnegie-Mellon, stated, "For example, in 1991, we expect to have about 7,500 personal workstations, each with its own powerful computer and graphics display, all interconnected. . . . In addition to communications between every workstation, there will be a unified data file system and a central computing facility available to all workstations." The jointly developed workstation computers are expected to be more powerful than the super-minicomputers of the present generation.

—Saul Rosen

Electronics

The breathtaking growth in electronic products, from video games to circuits that permit the physically disabled to walk, has stemmed from the development of the integrated circuit (IC). The IC has its roots in the invention, some 35 years ago, of the transistor. A transistor is a tiny device, typically made of silicon, that can amplify weak signals or process the digital (ones and zeros) signals that are the lifeblood of computers. In an integrated circuit it is possible to form tens of thousands of transistors in a silicon chip equal in area to a commemorative postage stamp.

There are two kinds of transistors used in integrated circuits: the bipolar junction transistor (BJT) and the metal-oxide semiconductor field-effect transistor (MOSFET). The amplifying and switching actions of the BJT are controlled by a minute base current, whereas the MOSFET's ability to process signals is influenced by a tiny gate voltage. In general the BJT can be switched on and off at a faster rate and also amplify higher frequency signals than can the MOSFET. However, more MOSFET's than BJT's can be embedded in a unit area of silicon (called the packing density). As the packing density in a chip increases, however, heat buildup may become a serious problem.

The MOSFET is available in two forms: the p and n channel. A positive supply voltage is required for the operation of an n-channel MOSFET, and current flow is by electrons. For a p-channel MOSFET a negative supply voltage is needed, and current flow is by positive charges, or holes. If n- and p-channel MOSFET's are connected in series, the resulting structure is called complementary MOS, or CMOS. A significant advantage of CMOS over the BJT and the p- or n-channel MOSFET's operating singly is that the CMOS structure consumes little power. Consequently, heat buildup is

Compact Disc Player developed by Sony Corp. plays music recorded digitally, as a series of ones and zeros.

not a serious problem. Thus, CMOS technology is being employed in high-density chips, such as semiconductor memories and microprocessors.

Manufacturing an IC may be viewed as "lithographing" an electronic circuit on a silicon chip. In the past, optical lithography, using an ultraviolet source of light, was the only method employed in the manufacture of integrated circuits. Recently, electron beams (electron beam lithography) were being used by many IC manufacturers. This technique allows circuit geometries of very minute dimensions to be formed, thereby achieving circuits with higher densities. In 1982 Honeywell Inc., in cooperation with the University of Minnesota obtained line widths of less than one-tenth of a micrometer (a micrometer is one-millionth of a meter) with electron beam lithography. The realization of smaller circuit dimensions and greater packing densities is a continuous pursuit in the semiconductor industry.

Gallium arsenide devices. Although silicon has been the workhorse in the manufacture of transistors, integrated circuits, and other semiconductor devices, gallium arsenide (GaAs) may soon replace it in very-high-frequency communications and superspeed computer applications. The majority of gallium arsenide devices used for these purposes have the structure of the n-channel MOSFET. High-speed operation is achieved because electrons in GaAs move much faster (have a higher current mobility) than do electrons in silicon. In addition, GaAs devices require a smaller gate voltage than do the conventional MOSFET's and display a high resistance to radiation. The latter characteristic is particularly advantageous for electronic equipment confined in space vehicles, where radiation can be a problem.

A goal of computer companies in the U.S. and in Japan is to build a superspeed computer that is capable of executing 10 billion arithmetic operations per second. (This is about ten times faster than current superspeed computers.) Because individual traveling electrons are scattered by the crystal lattice structure of GaAs, their speed becomes limited. One approach used in an effort to solve this problem was the development, by Thomson-CSF of France, of a GaAs transistor in which current flows as a thin layer of electrons. The device is called a two-dimensional electron gas field-effect transistor (TEGFET).

In addition to their use in superspeed computers, GaAs transistors and integrated circuits find wide application at microwave frequencies (hundreds of billions of cycles per second) in satellite communications, radar, and electronic warfare weapons. For this reason the U.S. Department of Defense provides a major share of funding for gallium arsenide technology. Companies engaged in the development of GaAs devices and circuits include Bell Laboratories, IBM Corp., Texas Instruments, RCA Corp., Westinghouse Electric Corp., and Rockwell International Corp. in the U.S. and Nippon Electric, Fujitsu, and Toshiba in Japan. (*See* Year in Review: DEFENSE RESEARCH.)

Consumer electronics. Stereo AM (amplitude modulation) at last may become a reality. Delco, a division of General Motors Corp. and the largest maker of car radios in the U.S., chose the AM stereo system pioneered by Motorola Inc. Other approaches to AM stereo included those developed by Magnavox Co. and Harris Corp. Currently, however, there is no standard for the industry. Because listeners to AM car radios constitute a large audience, Delco may force the issue and make the Motorola system the standard for AM stereo.

AM stereo receivers have some features that make them superior to FM stereo for a car. FM signals travel in straight lines, and, typically, the useful range of an FM signal is between 40 and 80 km (25 and 50 mi). AM signals, on the other hand, can follow the curvature of the Earth and may travel in excess of 160 km (100 mi)

before fading occurs. FM, however, still enjoys the advantage of being less susceptible to man-made and natural static.

It is estimated that U.S. consumers spent twice as much on video games in 1982 than on movies. With such a huge market it is not surprising that competition in the field is increasing and that products with expandable features are being marketed. One example is the ColecoVision video game console made by Coleco Industries of Hartford, Conn. If an appropriate conversion module is used, games designed for the Atari video computer system (VCS) can be played on ColecoVision. In the near future Coleco planned to introduce a module that converts its unit to a personal computer.

Individual components that can be arranged to form an overall system, long traditional in stereo sound equipment, recently became available for those purchasing television sets. A consumer can now choose individual modules, such as a tuner, amplifier, monitor, and speakers, to fashion a TV system. In addition the system can be made to accept such components as video games, video cassette recorders (VCR's), and tape decks.

The U.S. Federal Communications Commission (FCC) approved rules for direct broadcast satellite (DBS) television stations. Operating in the frequency range of 12 gigaHertz (GHz), signals transmitted from the satellites will be received by an inexpensive dish antenna less than 1 m (approximately 3 ft) in diameter. (A gigaHertz is a billion cycles per second. In comparison, TV and FM signals are in the range of 50 to 200 million cycles per second, or megaHertz. At the other extreme alternating-current electric power in the U.S. is 60 Hertz, a Hertz being defined as one cycle per sec-

To treat motor disorders of the nervous system four electrodes are implanted in the spinal cord in the patient's neck (right). Pressing buttons on the transmitter (below) activates the electrodes and stimulates the spinal cord, allowing the patient to walk.

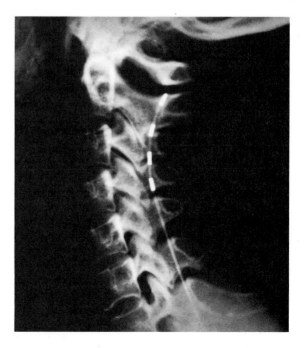

ond.) Stations operating in the gigaHertz range of frequencies can broadcast their programs with greater bandwidth, resulting in high-definition television.

Recording music digitally, that is, as a series of ones and zeros, provides the advantages of virtually no noise and excellent dynamic range. A system of digital recording developed by Sony Corp. and Philips resulted in the Compact Disc. Having a diameter of approximately 12 cm (4¾ in), it has the capacity to record an hour of music. Because the disk is read optically, the record never wears down.

Medical electronics. An interesting application of electronics to a medical problem permitted a woman confined to a wheelchair to walk. The woman, suffering from a muscular disorder (dystonia musculorum deformans) first lost control of her limbs and then of the upper half of her body. She consulted Joseph Waltz, director of neurological surgery at St. Barnabas Hospital in New York City. In response Waltz invented a system in which four small platinum electrodes are implanted along the upper spinal cord of the patient. The electrodes are connected to a microprocessor-based receiver, which is implanted beneath the skin in the patient's side.

The receiver is activated by a compact battery-operated transmitter worn by the patient. When the appropriate buttons on the transmitter are pressed, the receiver is activated and stimulates the spinal cord, allowing the patient to walk. Over a period of four to six weeks an attending physician tries different levels of current and voltage combinations to obtain optimum results for the patient.

Personal computers. The market for personal computers continued to grow rapidly with sales exceeding $6 billion in 1982. Nearly 200 companies were competing for a share of this huge market. Digital Equipment Corp. (DEC) of Maynard, Mass., a leader in minicomputers, introduced three personal computers in 1982. Its Professional Models 325 and 350 contain a 16-bit microprocessor that can use the software developed for DEC's popular PDP-11 series of minicomputers. The Rainbow 100 model uses software written either for an 8- or a 16-bit microprocessor. The 8-bit chip is the Z80, and the 16-bit chip is the 8088—two widely used microprocessors for which much software was available.

Hewlett-Packard Co. of Palo Alto, Calif., introduced the first 32-bit personal computer. The heart of this machine is a microprocessor chip that contains 450,000 transistors and performs the basic arithmetic and logic operations in the computer.

Most personal computers process data, or words, that are 8 bits (zeros and ones) long. (Eight bits are called a byte.) The advantages of a 16- or 32-bit word is that greater precision and faster operating speeds can be achieved. These features are often desirable in business and scientific applications.

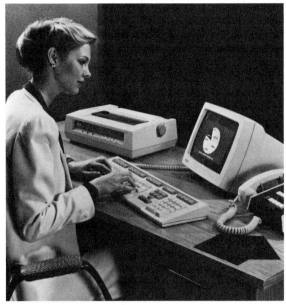

Digital Equipment Corporation, Maynard, Mass.

Professional Model 350, a personal computer containing a 16-bit microprocessor, was introduced by the Digital Equipment Corp. in 1982.

Innovations in mainframe and minicomputer designs also were made during the past year. Efforts were directed to achieve the sharing of information resources, increased operating speed (throughput), and fault-tolerant systems. An example of the last was the Stratus/32 minicomputer manufactured by Stratus Corp. of Natick, Mass. With the use of redundant (spare) hardware the logic operations of this computer can be continuously monitored. If a defective circuit board is discovered, the board is removed and a spare board is automatically substituted before errors appear in the result. Other companies that have been developing fault-tolerant computers include Synapse Computer Corp. of Milpitas, Calif., and August Systems Inc. of Salem, Ore.

Electrical power transmission. Electrical power in the U.S. is generated and transmitted in alternating-current (AC) form. To reduce power losses in transmission lines, the power sent from the power station is high-voltage AC. The maximum value used in the U.S. is 765 kilovolts (kv), where one kilovolt is 1,000 volts. Ultimately, the voltage is reduced (stepped down) with efficient transformers so that when it reaches the consumer it is typically 120 volts AC.

Transmitting power in high-voltage direct-current (HVDC) form has some definite advantages over high-voltage AC transmission of power. More DC power can be transmitted over a given transmission line, and power losses are less than for AC. While popular in Europe, HVDC has not been used much in the U.S. There is concern that the magnetic fields produced by HVDC may affect animal life. Recent tests, however, do not appear to support this fear.

Because power is inherently generated as AC, to obtain DC power it is necessary to convert, or rectify, the AC to a unidirectional form. Semiconductor diodes are used for rectification. At the receiving end thyristors (semiconductor devices used, for example, as lamp dimmers) are employed to convert the unidirectional voltage to AC. Improved thyristors now permit this process to be achieved with good efficiency.

—Arthur H. Seidman

Information systems and services

Information is a valuable resource, but its control and dissemination pose a dilemma for both governments and scientists. In the U.S., for example, government officials are concerned that other nations are gaining military advantages from American research and that the free availability of scientific information in even unclassified fields such as cryptology, high-speed integrated circuits, and artificial intelligence could pose a threat to the nation and should, therefore, be restricted. Most scientists and engineers, however, believe that open communication is essential for creativity and that restrictions on the free exchange of information will inhibit research and ultimately retard the U.S. defense effort. The National Academies of Sciences and of Engineering and the Institute of Medicine convened a special panel made up of educators and executives from industry and government to study, identify, and clarify the principal policy and operational issues concerning the free flow of information and to develop an appropriate balance between policies that stimulate and those that inhibit technological developments.

Arthur C. Clarke, an author and now chancellor of the University of Moratuwa in Sri Lanka, predicted that by the year 2001 larger and more powerful communications satellites would provide less developed countries with a variety of communications facilities, leading to what he calls "an open world." He predicted that by the year 2001 there would be portable libraries consisting of many books, films, and music in a package no larger than one ordinary hard-covered book. He also stated that pocket translators would in the future be able to speak and provide students everywhere with electronic tutors.

Machine translation was already a reality in 1983. The SYSTRAN translation system was originally developed for the U.S. Air Force to translate Soviet space literature into English. Accurate translations can be produced automatically by using an extensive comput-

Schoolchildren in Roseville, Minnesota, were among many throughout the United States who were benefiting from programs designed to familiarize them with computers.

er-stored dictionary and programmed grammar rules. An independent evaluation of SYSTRAN concluded that even its raw translations—those not edited by a human translator—are intelligible, useful, and cost-effective when compared with human translations. This system, which was continually being improved, was adopted by the Commission of the European Communities for the automatic translation of European languages. Versions of the program were completed for English-to-French, French-to-English, and English-to-Italian translations. Work was under way to develop a module that would translate English and French into German for the fields of economics, agriculture, and technology.

U.S. information systems. In addition to being a national resource, information is an important industrial asset used by corporate managers for long-range planning and ongoing performance control and review. Effective information management can have significant financial impact by helping control sales expenses and improving cash flow. Business and industrial organizations recognized the value of management information systems and were making extensive use of computers, information data bases, and telecommunications.

The number of data bases that were becoming publicly available was continuing to grow at 40–50% per year and in 1983 consisted of approximately 1,500 data bases offered by more than 200 online service organizations in the U.S. and Europe. Of even greater significance than the absolute number of data bases was the increasing breadth of their coverage.

The Department of Defense (DOD) sponsored and operated a large number of computer-readable data bases containing scientific and technical information. Indeed, there were so many data bases on such a variety of subjects that it became necessary to create a data base of data bases, which in effect was a computerized directory of all DOD-sponsored research and development activities. Recently developed data bases included: the Manpower and Training Research Information System, which contains information about planned, ongoing, and recently completed people-related research done by or for DOD agencies; Manufacturing Technology, a data base designed to provide improved research management and more effective transfer of information concerning DOD's manufacturing technology program; and a journal data base for the ordering, check-in, circulation, and control of each journal and serial publication received by the Defense Technical Information Center library.

The National Highway Traffic Safety Administration was expanding its consumer program of automobile safety information and provided a toll-free number that may be used to request fuel economy and tire quality ratings, crash test results, maintenance cost comparisons, and publication lists. The program was designed to make available information gathered from both the private sector and the agency's own publications and included bibliographies to assist consumers in locating additional resources.

The Conservation and Renewable Energy Inquiry and Referral Service was established as a clearinghouse for information about energy conservation and solar, thermal, wind, and ocean energies. Sponsored by the U.S. Department of Energy, it maintains contact with a nationwide network of public and private organizations specializing in energy technologies. The clearinghouse's technical staff was prepared to answer energy-related questions and, when necessary, refer the caller to other sources that could provide the desired information.

The Environment Information Center created a data base for locating and disseminating genetic engineering information. Gathered from more than 7,000 primary scientific and general interest sources from around the world, the data base includes information on social and ethical issues, regulatory guidelines, and applications in such diverse areas as pharmaceutical manufacturing, pollution control, crop enhancement, and livestock breeding.

A bibliographic data base and clearinghouse for the Health Standards and Quality Bureau of the Department of Health and Human Services was designed to collect information and reports on standards for health facilities, medical care, and the qualification of health professionals. The document collection dates back to 1973 and contains monographs, journal articles, technical reports, and official bureau documents.

State governments were also providing online data base services to their constituents. For example, anyone with a personal computer or terminal could call the State of Oregon Data Center and obtain the latest information on every bill under consideration by the state legislature. The information retrieval system allowed both legislators and the public to look up any state law, administrative rule, attorney general's opinion, or appellate court decision. To use the service one must pay an initial connect fee and a small monthly charge.

The Kentucky Economic Information System contained time-series data on the state economy and its various governmental divisions and programs. It was available to state agencies, universities, and the private sector on the payment of an annual subscription fee.

A sophisticated hospital information system was installed at the New York University Medical Center. The system, which replaced numerous manual procedures and forms, speeded up the processing time of medication orders, laboratory tests, and X-rays and contained comprehensive patient data from admittance to discharge. A physician using the system must first enter a personal code at a terminal, causing a list of his or her patients to appear on the video screen. On selecting a patient's name the doctor immediately could view all essential data, from medication to vital signs, covering the last 24 hours. The physician could also request and receive a full clinical summary of a patient's hospitalization since the time of admission and could enter diagnostic and therapeutic orders such as tests, laboratory work, and medication; these orders were printed automatically in the appropriate departments within seconds.

International information systems. The international regulation of transborder data flow and communications services can result in the creation of barriers to the export of telecommunications, data, and information services. Public communications services in most countries were controlled either by a government-owned or a publicly regulated monopoly. Some governments, adopting a protectionist policy, took the position that data and information services should be provided only by the domestic communications entity. This eliminated all outside competition but at the same time restricted the flow of information across national borders. A study prepared by the U.S. Trade Representative for Policy Development expressed the concern that these potentially discriminatory policies would increase the cost of exporting information services and cause disruptions and distortions in telecommunications, data processing, and data base services.

An Electronic Materials Information Service data base was developed in the U.K. It contained information on the properties of electronic materials, particularly silicon, gallium arsenide, indium phosphide, and lithium niobate, and also indicated the availability and suppliers of those materials. Access to this information was available on computer terminals by using a simple coding system.

TEXTLINE, an international business data base, covered the business activities of companies, industries, governments, and the European Economic Community. Information was gathered from major newspapers in the U.K., France, West Germany, and Japan. Significant items were abstracted, indexed, and prepared for computer storage and retrieval.

Another business-oriented data base available for online searching via the Euronet telecommunications network was the Fine Fintel Company NEWSBASE. This service contained data on 25,000 companies worldwide. The information was abstracted from the London and international editions of the *Financial Times* newspaper and arranged for easy use.

A data base on animal disease occurrence was compiled by the Commonwealth Agricultural Bureau under contract to the Commission of European Communities. In addition to the usual bibliographic references to articles dealing with animal diseases, the data base contained tables of factual data and provided worldwide coverage of information on disease outbreaks in an easily usable form. It, too, was available for online searching through Euronet.

Information science research. It was Thomas Jefferson who wrote, "Where a new invention is supported by well-known principles and promises to be useful, it ought to be tried." Computerized information sys-

"Whither goeth literature, Emily, there also must I go."

Drawing by Jack Ziegler © 1983 The New Yorker Magazine, Inc.

tems have demonstrated their usefulness in government and industry; they are now being tried in the arts and humanities. At Princeton University historian Charles Cullen was using a computer to edit Jefferson's papers and correspondence. The work was expected to consist of some 65 volumes and was scheduled to be completed in about 20–25 years. Because of the meticulous scholarship involved only one volume could be produced every other year, but without the computer, which enabled Cullen to arrange the material exactly as he wanted it to appear on the printed page, the work would take much longer.

The U.S. Library of Congress during the year was engaged in the research, development, and testing of a computerized information system that would preserve its holdings of illustrations and text materials on optical-disk storage devices and reproduce them on demand using high-quality laser printing. (An optical disk system uses laser scanners to read a document and transmit the image in digital form to a storage device or to display the image on a cathode-ray tube.) In addition, the Library of Congress planned to store its master catalog cards on optical disks, a single disk being able to store the images of more than 200,000 cards. One disk thus would be the equivalent of 140 card catalog drawers, and individual images could be retrieved and printed at the rate of 12 copies per second.

Another research project using optical-disk technology was a joint venture involving the National Museums of Canada and Control Data Corp. to create a large data base of information on the holdings of art objects at all Canadian museums. Also under discussion were plans for a microcomputer network in which the information in the data base could be called up by regional computing centers.

The exchange of information by the use of electronic networks is well within the current state of the art. However, research is needed to determine the effectiveness of electronic communication (as compared with the written or spoken word) and the attitudes of people toward using such systems. To study these problems two universities in the U.K. were conducting experiments on the ways in which electronic communication systems might better meet the needs of users. Loughborough University was investigating the problems of creating and maintaining an electronic journal in which the writing, refereeing, editing, and publishing of scientific articles would be mediated by computers. That is to say, an author would prepare the text of an article at a computer terminal (rather than a typewriter) and then would send it via a communication network to a computer located at the University of Birmingham, where it would be reviewed by an editor and transmitted to a referee for evaluation. The referee would read the article at a terminal, make comments and suggestions, and send them back to the editor. If the article is accepted, subscribers would have access to the text at their computer terminals. The article, and the entire journal, would exist only in electronic form and not on paper. Researchers at Loughborough and Birmingham universities were investigating the costs of producing such a journal and the attitudes of users to this form of communication.

—Harold Borko

Satellite systems

Earth-orbiting satellites that utilize their vantage points in space for economic benefit and military purposes are termed applications satellites. There are three basic classes of such satellite systems: communications, Earth observation, and navigation. Satellite systems are developed and operated by individual nations, groups of nations, and by private industrial concerns.

The U.S. and the Soviet Union continued to dominate such activities because of their large booster rockets. Both nations launched satellites for other countries.

The European Space Agency (ESA), representing 11 countries of Western Europe, was expected soon to become the third competitive source of space launch vehicles. In September 1982, however, an attempted launch of two commercial satellites with ESA's Ariane booster failed in midair. Thirty-five satellite flights have been scheduled for Ariane over the next three years. The ESA booster is in direct competition with the U.S. launch vehicles Delta and Atlas-Centaur and the piloted (reusable) space shuttle.

During the year the U.S. National Aeronautics and Space Administration (NASA) launched 11 satellites (by Delta and Atlas-Centaur) and three flights of the space shuttle "Columbia." The "Columbia," in turn, launched two commercial satellites carried into orbit in the shuttle payload bay.

Communications satellites. Among the most common satellites are those providing international and domestic communications. The International Telecommunications Satellite Organization (Intelsat) is a consortium of 108 nations, including two recent additions, Uruguay and Cape Verde. The Communications Satellite Corp. (Comsat) is the U.S. member.

Two Intelsat 5 satellites were launched in March and September. Each had a capacity of 12,000 telephone circuits plus two television channels. The satellite launched in September (in operation over the Indian Ocean) contained a Maritime Communications Subsystem (MCS). Intelsat 5 satellites equipped with the MCS can voice transmissions between the satellite and coastal stations on the Earth and between the satellite and stations aboard ships. The MCS was designed to supplement the earlier Marisat and Marecs maritime communications satellites. MCS packages will be

Intelsat 5 communications satellite was launched in September and went into orbit over the Indian Ocean. The four-element helical array in the foreground comprises an antenna that expands the satellite's ability to provide communications services to ships throughout the world.

aboard future Intelsat 5s placed in orbit over the Atlantic, Indian, and Pacific oceans.

On July 11 global transmission of the World Cup soccer finals by Intelsat broke all records for worldwide coverage of a televised event. The estimated audience was 1,300,000,000. Intelsat provided more than 5,000 viewing hours of the tournament to 92 nations.

The U.S. Postal Service was using Intelsat in a developing enterprise, Intelpost. Facsimile mail sent via satellite from Washington, D.C., may be picked up within one hour or delivered overnight to the cities of Buenos Aires, Toronto, Frankfurt, Amsterdam, and London. Other countries planning to join the service include Australia, Brazil, and France.

A counterpart of ESA was the European Telecommunications Satellite Organization (Eutelsat). With its plans to operate a regional, international communications system, Eutelsat was seeking to compete with Intelsat within a few years. Representing 20 European nations, the Eutelsat organizational pattern was similar to that of Intelsat.

National communications satellites were being built to begin operating in 1984–86 by Australia, Great Britain, Italy, Japan, Luxembourg, and Switzerland. They were designed primarily for national domestic use, but there were clear implications that communications with a bordering nation might evolve.

Indicative of the explosive growth of domestic satellite communications enterprises was the authorization by the U.S. Federal Communications Commission (FCC) of eight direct broadcast systems (television and radio). Satellite Television Corp. was the first approved to develop satellite broadcasting to home receivers. The others included CBS Inc., Direct Broadcast Satellite Inc., Graphic Scanning Corp., RCA Corp., United States

Satellite Broadcasting Corp., Video Satellite Corp., and Western Union Telegraph Co. Other applications were pending. Authorization to proceed, however, awaited the assignment of frequencies and orbital positions by the International Telecommunication Union conference in mid-1983. Nevertheless, financial negotiations and stock offerings were proceeding to raise the necessary billions of dollars required.

Four other national communications satellite systems were functioning in the U.S. They were operated by Western Union, AT&T, RCA, and Satellite Business Systems (SBS). Two RCA Satcom satellites were launched by NASA, on a cost-reimbursable basis, in January and October. The traffic capacity of the latest Satcom was doubled by a design change in which traveling-wave electron tubes were replaced by solid-state amplifiers. The in-orbit lifetime was expected to be ten years, compared with about eight years for previous Satcoms.

Other communications satellites launched by NASA included Westar (Western Union), SBS satellite, and Canada's Telesat satellite Anik; SBS and Anik were launched from the payload bay of the space shuttle "Columbia" during the STS-5 flight. SBS was granted international common carrier status by the FCC. Initial service was planned in 1983 between SBS and British Telecom International.

In April NASA launched Insat 1, a multiservice Indian satellite with the capability of radio and television broadcast for news, educational programs, and weather observation. Failure of the satellite occurred about five months after launch. A second Insat (built by U.S. Ford Aerospace & Communications Corp.) was scheduled for launch by the space shuttle in mid-1983.

A consortium of 22 member nations of the Arab

307

League proceeded with plans for a regional communications satellite system. Under construction by Aerospatiale (France) and Ford Aerospace (U.S.), two Arabsat satellites were scheduled for launch in 1984, the first by Ariane and the second by the space shuttle.

Earth observation satellites. This category of applications satellites includes meteorological (weather), Earth resources, and military reconnaissance.

Weather satellites. In June two eruptions of the Mexican volcano El Chichón threw great quantities of ash into the stratosphere. (*See* EARTH SCIENCES: *Geophysics.*) Geostationary and polar-orbiting satellites tracked ash clouds around the world, obtaining images in both visible and infrared light. Soundings from orbit showed that some ash reached altitudes of about 9,100 m (30,000 ft).

In November 1982 the U.S. National Weather Service lost the use of one of the two operational Geostationary Operational Environmental Satellites (GOES). Designated GOES West, this satellite monitored and relayed to the U.S. Weather Service half-hourly transmissions of cloud cover, storms, and other meteorological data on much of the Pacific Ocean as well as the western United States. Forecasters lost this continuous view of some 60° of the Earth's surface, critical to weather watch of storms approaching the Pacific coast. Substitute data were obtained temporarily from GOES East and two polar-orbiting National Oceanic and Atmospheric Administration (NOAA) satellites. Subsequently GOES 1, which had been placed in standby status, was moved out of its "parking orbit" to a position where it could observe the West Coast. Partially inoperative, GOES 1 was to be replaced by a new GOES satellite scheduled for launch in 1983.

Earth resources satellites. Joining the ailing U.S. Earth observation satellite, Landsat 3, the improved-design Landsat 4 was placed in polar orbit in July. This spacecraft incorporated two sophisticated sensors, the multispectral scanner (MSS) and thematic mapper (TM). The MSS subsystem was flight-proved on earlier Landsats; the TM was new. The MSS measures radiant energy reflected from the Earth's surface in one near-infrared and three visible wavelengths. Ground scanning by MSS yields information that allows the spectra of different materials to be determined. Applications are broad, ranging from spotting healthy or diseased crops to detecting polluted water, snow and water run-off, mineral deposits, and ocean thermal currents. The TM is similar to the MSS but collects data in seven narrow spectral bands and with a resolution about three times better than that obtained by MSS.

NASA and a California firm initiated a study of existing hazardous waste disposal sites north of San Francisco Bay. Using TM data and ground knowledge of toxic waste locations, scientists were studying the effects of such waste on bay water. Data under study included Landsat images indicating turbidity, chloro-

SBS 3 spacecraft, launched from the space shuttle "Columbia," springs from its protective covering.

phyll concentration, and distribution of heated waters entering the bay.

In December China signed a contract to install a receiving station for Landsat data. Uses for the data would include farming, forestry, mining, road planning, and long-term weather prediction.

Military reconnaissance satellites. The U.S. and Soviet Union continued launching reconnaissance satellites to observe and remotely sense military movements, electronic transmission, nuclear explosions, and for early-warning tracking of (high-temperature) rocket exhaust plumes of ballistic missiles. During the dispute between Argentina and Great Britain over the Falkland Islands and also during the Israeli invasion of Lebanon, the Soviet Union placed in orbit a record number of observation satellites; at least eight were launched. It was reported that two ocean-watching radar satellites were launched within a two-week period. Because of the high power required, a nuclear electric-power generator is carried in such satellites. At the conclusion of its mission the Soviets normally boost such a satellite to a higher orbit, where it is safe from atmospheric drag and reentry. However, Cosmos 1402 with some 45 kg (100 lb) of enriched uranium fuel reentered the Earth's atmosphere in two pieces. Fragments of a structural segment, weighing four tons initially, landed in the Indian Ocean on Jan. 23, 1983. The second fragment, containing the fuel core of the power plant's reactor, burned up in the atmosphere and fell harmlessly into the South Atlantic on February 7. Some radioactive dust was left in the atmosphere, and scientists were divided as to whether it would have any harmful effects.

Image produced by the thematic mapper of Landsat 4 reveals the Detroit, Michigan/Windsor, Ontario, region. Sediment turbidity in Lake St. Clair (top right) and in the Detroit River and Lake Erie (center and bottom) is clearly shown. The mapper achieved a resolution about three times better than did similar sensors aboard earlier Landsats.

Navigation satellites. The U.S., Soviet Union, France, and Canada began tests of a global program using satellites to locate and aid aircraft and ships in distress. Signals from beacon transmitters activated either by a crash or manually by a person in a craft in distress may be received by polar-orbiting satellites and relayed to the Earth. Analysis of the signal frequency shift in relation to the satellite's orbital track can pinpoint the signal location to within a few miles.

Designated COSPAS/SARSAT, the Soviet spacecraft Cosmos 1383 launched July 1 carried SAR (search and rescue) beacon-receiving and transmitting equipment. Within the first month of operation Cosmos 1383 had located four accident sites and saved seven lives. The U.S. counterpart to the Soviet satellites will be SAR equipment on board the NOAA-E weather satellite to be launched in 1983.

The Navstar global navigation system under development by the U.S. obtained approval for the advanced Block 2 design, a follow-on to the eleven Block 1 satellites already built. The initial launch of the series of 18 operational spacecraft was scheduled for 1986. Equipment on board aircraft or at sea will receive signals from four satellites. An onboard computer will calculate the user's position, in three dimensions, within an accuracy of about 15 m (50 ft).

—F. C. Durant III

Energy

The disappearance of energy as a visible public issue accelerated in 1982. The principal policy efforts continued to be those of the members of the Organization of Petroleum Exporting Countries (OPEC). OPEC continued to prevent massive oil price drops but was unable to stem the slow price erosion that had persisted since mid-1980. In the United States and other Western countries, concerns over rising unemployment and how to combat it without rekindling inflation dominated policy debates. Energy issues in the U.S. were pushed aside by the protracted debates over spending and tax policies.

U.S. energy market trends. In the marketplace 1982 was another year of declining consumption with the effects of rising prices accentuated by the impacts of recession. Through September 1982 U.S. energy use was more than 3% below the level of the same period in 1981. It was likely, therefore, that the total for 1982 would also be below that of 1981. As a result U.S. energy use would have declined for the third consecutive year.

As has been true in recent years, overall consumption involved the net impact of quite different trends in various sectors of the energy market. Coal consumption, which had risen annually from 1979 to 1981, was below 1981 levels during the first nine months of 1982. While coal use for electric utilities was roughly equal to its 1981 level, other markets, particularly for making coke for pig iron manufacture, were depressed. Natural gas and oil consumption both declined in 1980 and 1981. Through September 1982 consumption of both fuels was below the levels of the comparable 1981 period, and the declines were greater than that for coal. (Coal consumption was down 2.5%; oil, 4.8%; natural gas, 6%.)

Oil imports continued to be hit heavily by the combined effects of falling consumption and rising domestic output, dropping from a peak of 8.8 million bbl per day in 1977 to just under 6 million in 1981. The rate for

Small Particle Heat Exchange Receiver (SPHER) uses soot to absorb heat from the Sun and convert it into useful energy. An array of mirrors below the metal cylinder focuses the sunlight and passes it through a window into a chamber. There, carbon particles have been mixed with air to form black smoke. The smoke absorbs nearly all the energy of the solar rays entering the chamber. The carbon particles then transfer this heat to the air in which they are suspended, causing the air to expand and drive the turbine of an electric generator.

the first ten months of 1982 was 5 million. Purchases directly from OPEC countries dropped sharply from 6.2 million (in 1977) to 2.2 million bbl per day in 1982. During the same period there was a slight rise from 2.6 million to 2.8 million bbl per day for non-OPEC suppliers. This increase was due largely to a sharp rise of imports from Mexico and a modest increase from Great Britain.

Most of the non-OPEC sources were Caribbean islands with little or no domestic oil production. These islands supplied the U.S. largely with petroleum products refined from OPEC crude. While historically most of this crude oil came from Venezuela, changing U.S. air pollution regulations had necessitated increased substitution of low-sulfur African crudes for the high-sulfur Venezuelan oil.

The decline in consumption also interrupted the expansion of coal output that had persisted during recent years. Preliminary estimates for 1982 suggested that coal output would be little different from the 1981 levels. Oil production rose about 1%, while natural gas data (available only through August) indicated that output was running almost 7% below that of 1981.

A major effect of these trends was a large-scale retreat from the effort to develop such alternative energy sources as oil shales, gaseous and liquid fuels from coal, and solar energy. Many oil-shale and coal-synthe-

sis projects were canceled in 1982. Higher prices seemed to have reduced the growth in demand for energy and also stimulated production from traditional sources to such an extent that the development of alternatives became unattractive.

Nuclear problems. Nuclear power continued the pattern of the post-1975 period. Nuclear capacity continued to expand but only through the completion of units ordered before 1975. In fact, most of the units likely to be completed had been ordered in the late 1960s. Nuclear power generation, however, still had not recovered to the high level attained in 1978. Capacity utilization slipped from the 64% rate of 1978 to about 55% in 1982.

Defenders of nuclear power contended that these developments were caused by ill-advised government policies. Opponents of nuclear power argued that the developments were inevitable given the inherent defects of nuclear power.

However, another consideration in regard to the decline in nuclear power generation was the lack of growth of the electric utility industry. Nuclear and coal-fired power plants were planned in the late 1960s and early 1970s to meet demands that did not materialize. Cancellations and delays of those plans were not in time to prevent generating capacity from expanding ahead of demand. Some of this capacity was used to

310

Table I. World Crude Oil Production
(000 bbl per day)

Country	1973	1980	1981	Aug. 1982
U.S.	9,208	8,597	8,572	8,701
U.S.S.R.	8,465	11,773	11,909	12,000
Saudi Arabia	7,596	9,900	9,815	5,920
Iran	5,861	1,662	1,380	2,200
Iraq	2,018	2,514	1,000	800
Kuwait	3,020	1,656	1,125	920
Libya	2,175	1,787	1,140	1,300
Nigeria	2,054	2,055	1,433	1,105
Total OPEC	30,989	26,890	22,624	18,045
OPEC less Saudi Arabia	23,393	16,990	12,809	12,125
Mexico	465	1,936	2,313	2,795
Non-OPEC Total	24,685	32,648	33,164	34,495
World	55,674	59,538	55,788	52,540

Source: U.S. Department of Energy

substitute for oil, but additional opportunities of that nature appeared to be limited. Therefore, the need for new nuclear and coal-fired plants declined. Observers of state regulations of electric utilities feared that resistance to higher rates would also curtail expansion of capacity.

OPEC in 1982. OPEC behavior in 1982 followed the pattern that emerged in mid-1980. An accord to stabilize or even increase prices eluded the members of the organization, but they restrained themselves from actions that would produce significantly lower prices. Nevertheless, Western observers increasingly speculated about the possibility of a major price break. Such conjectures generally were expressed in cautious terms. Discussions were limited to appraisals of what might happen if prices fell. Great care was taken to avoid indicating why this possibility was worth an appraisal. Readers were left to infer that some anonymous second party had made the prediction. (Conveniently, it was also possible to cite the reports OPEC itself commissioned to warn its members of the need for unity to prevent price collapse.)

Underlying the concern was recognition that historically cartels have broken up because conflicts of interest among members caused them to ignore the benefits of cooperation and to proceed to undercut one another. For the past decade OPEC has managed to limit conflict so that at worst only minor price erosion occurred. Many views exist about why this has been possible.

Some assert that OPEC was not responsible for world oil price rises or at least that much of the rise would have come even without OPEC. These observers suggest that a tightening of world oil supplies was developing. Some would add that attitudes toward saving oil for future generations changed as nations assumed greater control of their supplies. While the private companies were interested in producing rapidly to get out as much oil as possible before being nationalized, the governments could take a longer term perspective.

Both of these views are arguable. Much of the supply tightening may have been engineered by the OPEC countries. Also, the Middle Eastern governments were more expansion minded than the oil companies until the benefits of raising prices by lowering output became evident. Such counterarguments imply that OPEC was responsible in some fashion for the higher world oil prices.

The conjectures about an OPEC collapse generally start from the premise that the organization by operating as a cartel did at least partially control the world oil market. The further premise is made that the strains that previously have been avoided are now becoming severe enough to weaken the cartel. Another interpretation is that OPEC countries have lost their wisdom about adequately saving oil for future generations.

Five wind turbines, each taller than a ten-story building, went into operation near Byron, California, in 1982. They were designed to produce approximately 1,250,000 kilowatt-hours of electricity annually, enough to supply 175 homes for a year.

UPI

Rotary drilling hose is part of the Murco 58, a huge oil rig that was designed to drill as deep as 16,300 meters (54,000 feet).

This last view is as questionable as the earlier vision that OPEC actions reflected a sudden acquisition of sagacity about future needs.

Conflicts were emerging among the OPEC countries themselves. In particular, downward pressures on Saudi Arabian production emerged. Prior to 1981 declining output elsewhere in OPEC allowed the Saudis to ensure price stability by limiting their increase of production. Average Saudi output rose from 7.6 million bbl per day in 1973 to 9.8 million in 1981. Over the same period average output for OPEC as a whole declined from 30 million bbl per day to 22.6 million. By March 1981, Saudi output, then at 10.1 million bbl per day, started a declining trend that brought it down to 5.9 million bbl per day by August 1982. Continued market shrinkage and less willingness by other OPEC members to reduce their outputs necessitated the Saudi declines.

Since March 1981 output in most OPEC countries has displayed considerable gyrations. For example, Iran's revolution and war with Iraq at first accelerated an output decline trend in that nation that had begun in the middle 1970s. Output in Iran had averaged 6 million bbl per day in 1974 but had dropped to 3.2 million in 1979. By January 1980 output was down to 2.3 million, and it hit a low of 600,000 in October of that

year. A rebuilding phase then raised output to 1.7 million bbl in February and March 1981; another decline then lowered production to 920,000 bbl in October; and still another rise put output at 2.5 million bbl in May through July 1982.

Saudi strategy seems to have aggravated the problem. As of 1983 it appeared to be attempting to maintain prices of $34 per barrel on long-term contracts despite the ample availability of cheaper oil elsewhere. This produced the usual response to an unfavorable contract—efforts to alter the terms. Nevertheless, the basic situation in 1983 remained about the same as in late 1981. The tensions did not yet seem severe enough to alter the prevailing condition of only moderate weakening in prices.

The discussions of price declines had two curious features. First, price collapse was almost invariably defined as a decline to $20 per barrel, the level prevailing prior to the 1979–80 price increases. Some might consider this a correction of price rises that could not be sustained rather than a real collapse. Second, considerable concern is expressed over the alleged harm to the world economy that would result from these price declines. In some cases the fear comes from those who believe that oil price rises were a socially desirable warning of impending energy cost increases. Most observers, however, seem to look only at the losses to lenders to countries such as Mexico that borrowed heavily against anticipated high oil revenues. This approach ignores the benefits that will accrue to countries such as Brazil and Argentina, which have had difficulty repaying debts because of high oil import bills. These cries of alarm are diametrically opposed to the frequent assertions that the rise in oil prices was a major cause of inflation and unemployment.

U.S. energy policy. In regard to energy the U.S. remained largely locked in the policy paths established in the 1970s. The administration of Pres. Ronald Reagan began its term of office by exercising its discretionary

Table II. Consumption of Major Fuels in the United States
(000,000,000 BTU's)

Year	Coal	Natural gas	Petro-leum	Water	Nuclear	Total
1947	15,824	4,518	11,367	1,326	0	33,035
1960	10,119	12,385	19,919	1,653	6	44,080
1970	12,664	21,795	29,522	2,654	239	66,828
1973	13,300	22,512	34,840	3,010	910	74,609
1974	12,876	21,732	33,455	3,309	1,272	72,759
1975	12,823	19,948	32,731	3,219	1,900	70,707
1976	13,733	20,345	35,175	3,066	2,111	74,510
1977	13,964	19,931	37,122	2,515	2,702	76,332
1978	13,846	20,000	37,965	3,141	3,024	78,175
1979	15,109	20,666	37,123	3,141	2,715	78,910
1980	15,461	20,391	34,202	3,107	2,672	75,910
1981	16,118	19,911	32,113	2,970	2,901	74,123
1982	15,655	18,305	30,400	3,462	3,013	70,923

Source: U.S. Department of Energy

One of the world's largest hydroelectric projects, the Itaipú Dam on the Paraná River between Brazil and Paraguay, was inaugurated in October 1982.

power to accelerate removal of oil price controls, and the U.S. Congress in late 1981 repealed the requirement that electric utilities cease using natural gas. Subsequently, little has happened.

The administration has been unable to make major changes. A primary problem has been that existing law severely limits administrative discretion. However, instances can be noted where available discretion has not been exercised. President Reagan seems, for example, to have failed to appoint members of the Nuclear Regulatory Commission fully committed to speeding decision making. The critical problem remains an unwillingness of Congress to modify significantly either legislation directly regulating energy or the environmental laws that have profound effects on energy use.

The result is policies that are unsatisfactory to all sides. Energy legislation provides neither the freer market that the Reagan administration (and a broad bipartisan group of economists) advocate nor the strict controls advocated by critics of the energy industries. Similarly, Reagan's desires to loosen some aspects of environmental policies conflict with desires of environmental groups to extend controls.

As long as no visible major problems are produced by this inaction, it is likely to continue. This will probably impose many billions of dollars in economic waste. This waste will be spread out so broadly that no one will notice. The effects will not produce even visible discomfort and certainly not the threats to life that provoke vigorous action. A major disruption in oil supplies could cause difficulties and inspire a revival of intervention. Many advocates of immediate policy changes hope that a better response can be devised in the present period of tranquillity than could be achieved under the pressure of a disruption. However, it is unclear either whether a policy broad enough to handle every contingency can be designed or whether planning truly will preclude ill-advised additional actions when a crisis occurs.

Even more than in 1981 the important aspects of energy have been actions in the market. These actions are difficult to appraise because the effects of a worldwide recession have been superimposed on those of higher energy prices. Nevertheless, the evidence suggests that the long-run impact of higher prices on both consumption and production is greater than the formulators of U.S. energy legislation of the 1970s believed.

—Richard L. Gordon

Environment

During 1982 there were a number of incidents which had important implications for major environmental controversies. At the beginning of May Exxon Corp. decided to discontinue funding of the Colony shale oil project in Colorado, on the grounds that costs of project completion had risen from $2 billion–$3 billion to $5 billion–$6 billion. At the same time, Shell and Gulf Canada Ltd. pulled out of the $13 billion Alsands project, intended to make fuel from the Athabasca tar sands in Alberta. These decisions, considered in context with the virtual nonexistence of oil and gas discoveries in the Baltimore Canyon and the high cost of electricity from wave power in British experiments, challenged the conventional wisdom about future energy scenarios.

At a superficial level of analysis these incidents argue collectively that, while there is plenty of energy on the Earth, much of what is left will not be available at prices consumers are currently prepared to pay. The deeper message supports the views of Howard Odum and others: the net energy return on remaining energy sources will be considerably lower, on average, than in the past. That is, from now on, the energy that has to be spent to capture a unit of energy will climb ever closer to one unit. Society will be confronted with a choice: alter the design of every aspect of modern life from

313

city layout to the thickness of roofing insulation, or suffer mysterious and insidious inflation as higher energy costs are passed all through the economy.

Natural disasters. The year was notable for volcanic activity. On March 28 and April 4 El Chichón ("The Lump") erupted in southern Mexico. This eruption was unlike that of Mt. St. Helens in Washington State in 1980. In the case of Mt. St. Helens the main force of the blast was directed laterally at the surrounding countryside. Instead, El Chichón shot its dust and rocks 9,150 m (30,000 ft) straight up. While these materials dropped back to Earth within a week, the associated sulfur dioxide gas underwent reaction to form sulfuric-acid aerosols. These tiny droplets spread out to form a cloud that encircled the globe and could reduce temperatures by as much as 1° C (2° F) for up to three years. The theory of the effects of volcanoes on weather is still embryonic, but from previous incidents of this type it is reasonable to expect some depression of crop production worldwide. However, El Chichón is a much smaller volcano than Tambora (1815) or Cosigüina (1835), which had startling global effects on food production.

Mt. Galunggung in Indonesia erupted more than 340 times in 1982, and 250,000 people were put at risk from 42 million cu m (1.5 billion cu ft) of debris that could become mudslides in the monsoon season. These incidents are important reminders of the evidence for catastrophism as opposed to uniformitarianism (relatively unchanged conditions over very long periods). The catastrophic view of geologic history would help to explain apparent changes in rates of evolution. It also suggests how relatively sudden environmental changes could have been an important influence in shaping the direction of evolution.

On November 23 Kauai, one of the Hawaiian Islands, was hit by Hurricane Iwa, with waves at least 9 m (30 ft) high and 175 km/h (110 mph) winds. Property damage was estimated at $200 million, although later figures could be much higher. This incident, like a number of other floods in 1982, was a reminder of the wisdom of avoiding construction projects on dangerously low ground. However, the most important lesson to be learned from the Kauai experience concerns the evacuation of the population from coastal areas in hastily arranged bus trips.

It turned out that evacuation via the main roads was impossible, since they were littered with downed trees and utility poles. The buses could leave the low-lying areas only by going cross-country through fields. In a densely populated urban area, if rapid evacuation were necessary and roads were impassable, there would be no such alternate escape routes, and the bulk of the population would be trapped. This incident, therefore, raises serious questions about current plans to evacuate metropolitan-area populations in the event of nuclear attack.

Ash from El Chichón accumulated in nearby towns in southern Mexico after the volcano erupted in March and April 1982.

"Greenhouse" controversy. A controversy was developing among scientists concerning the severity of the threat from the "greenhouse effect." The majority view has been that, with the increase of fossil fuel combustion, the concentration of carbon dioxide in the atmosphere worldwide would continue to rise. (There was no question but that this concentration had increased already.) Furthermore, it was projected that this concentration would be sufficient to hold back enough of the heat radiating outward from the Earth to raise the temperature of the surface by a few degrees. This, in turn, would melt glaciers, raise the average ocean level, and in general prove unfavorable to the environment. The controversy arose for several reasons. One objection to the greenhouse theory is that the increased concentration of carbon dioxide already observed has been associated with a decrease, not an increase, of temperatures in many parts of the Northern Hemisphere. Also, given the likely future rises in the prices of all fossil fuels, a probable scenario is for combustion products to decline rather than increase in concentration.

A new book, *Carbon Dioxide: Friend or Foe?*, by Sherwood Idso was certain to add to the controversy. In it, he demonstrates that (1) since 1945, during the period of most rapid increase of carbon dioxide in the atmosphere, Northern Hemisphere temperatures have fallen, not risen, and (2) higher concentrations of carbon dioxide in air typically result in a large increase in plant productivity. Also, the mechanisms by which increased carbon dioxide concentration would affect air temperatures are many and complex, and some of them would produce a cooling rather than a warming. For example, evaporation increases rapidly with rising temperatures over water or moist soil, and evaporation, in turn, decreases temperature (the latent heat of vaporization, or refrigerator principle). Idso agrees that the carbon dioxide phenomenon is important for mankind but views it as a gift, not a threat.

Soviet agriculture. Two new papers (*Six Steps to a Sustainable Society* and *U.S. and Soviet Agriculture: The Shifting Balance of Power*) from the Worldwatch Institute made important points about world and Soviet commodities production. World per capita production of wood, fish, beef, grain, and oil peaked in 1964, 1970, 1976, 1978, and 1973, respectively. For every category of Soviet agricultural production the peak years occurred in the late 1970s. There are several explanations for the difficulties with Soviet agriculture. Centralized planning removes the responsibility for making such decisions as when to plant from the person in the best position to make a correct judgment—the farmer on the site. Instead, they are handed over to a bureaucrat far away who cannot possibly be familiar with local weather everywhere. A more interesting explanation of the problem has to do with the semipermanent devastation of genetics and the breeding of farm plants and animals during the period when T. D. Lysenko dominated Soviet biology and the inheritance of genetic traits was repudiated as a matter of public policy.

The United States, by contrast, has had a continuous, long-standing program of selection for strains of livestock and crop plants that make the most efficient possible use of fertilizer and feed. One observation is illustrative. Grain use for livestock feed is about the same per capita in the Soviet Union as in the United States, but the U.S. produces more than twice as much meat per person. Soviet farmers are also plagued with an inadequate selection of specialized equipment, and what they do have often breaks down because of manufacturing defects. Curiously, the fates of the two countries are becoming more and more intertwined as far as agriculture is concerned. The Soviets need to buy food from the U.S. to feed their people, and the U.S. needs to sell it to them to raise foreign exchange with which to pay for imported crude oil from the Organization of Petroleum Exporting Countries (OPEC).

The environment and society. A number of books appeared emphasizing the connection between environment, economics, politics, and value systems. In *The Politics of Mistrust* (1981) Aaron Wildavsky and Ellen Tenenbaum point out that conflicts over energy have not been influenced by data. Furthermore, there is no reason to believe that continuous improvement in the quality of data on oil and gas reserves would lead to a political consensus; legislators have voted on the basis of their ideology, not the data. Rather, the authors argue that trust between constituencies could be developed more effectively by shifting the roles of government and the private sector. Under their proposed programs oil and gas industries would give up abatement of taxes for drilling and depreciation; more generally, they would be encouraged to make money at home and develop new sources of supply abroad. The industry would be totally deregulated. Government would be the sole importer of oil and gas, and there would be a substantial tariff or tax on gasoline. The government would also foster the development of other sources of energy (in contrast with present govern-

Hurricane Iwa batters palm trees on the coast of the Hawaiian island of Oahu in November. Winds in the storm reached 175 km/h (110 mph).

UPI

ment policy, which has backed away from support for various forms of solar energy).

Another book, *America's Impasse* by Alan Wolfe (1981), points out the link between a deteriorated political party system in the U.S. and various environmental problems. The two major parties discovered that they lost adherents whenever they tried to make real political choices. Accordingly, the broad goal for both Republicans and Democrats became economic, rather than political: the promotion of rapid economic growth. The reasoning was that if growth were rapid, all constituencies would benefit, and this would do away with the need to make hard political choices. Also, both parties pursued a policy of stimulating economic growth by increasing demand, rather than by management of supply (production and productivity). Because of this failure to attempt management of production, the nation is increasingly bedeviled by the inevitable consequences. For example, many cities have a sprawling, low-density pattern of land use viable only when energy is cheap. Productivity, along with efficiency of resource use and pollution, will improve only if government makes hard political choices that result in the fostering of new industries such as mass transit and solar energy. This means that both political parties will have to enlarge their spheres of concern to include supply as well as demand.

For 14 years the Stanford Research Institute (now SRI International) has sponsored a futures research group of 21 distinguished scholars. During the year an important book was published by three members of the team, in effect representing the culmination of the work by the entire group. This book, *Seven Tomorrows*, contains seven plausible scenarios for the future of the U.S. Which scenario becomes reality will be affected in part by choices that are made now. The book also explores the linkages between environment, the economy, and politics. The authors argue that there is need for a new economic theory that relates economy to ecology. They point out that present theories do not measure the energy efficiency of production. However, this energy cost of production is precisely what must be analyzed and managed if the U.S. is to deal with its national productivity problem, a central issue for the nation. A Japanese-style consensus is needed to stimulate productivity without resorting to socialist bureaucracy. However, U.S. society does not currently prize unity; rather, it values diversity. The result is a system characterized by confrontation and stalemate among various interest groups.

Another important book emphasizing the relationships between environment, the economy, politics, and values was *Making it Happen: A Positive Guide to the Future*, published in 1982 by the United States Association for the Club of Rome. This book also argues that a new body of economic theory is needed, based on the assumption that resources are finite, not limitless. One of the authors, Hazel Henderson, points out that the industrial economies must now divert more and more of their wealth to the extraction of energy and other raw materials from lower-grade and ever more inaccessible or scarce resources. Unless the problem is solved, this will inevitably result in declining productivity of capital and higher rates of inflation.

This theme of the declining productivity of capital was appearing in research from many disciplines and

Pyramid-shaped device weighing 350 tons and measuring 30 by 30 meters is towed into the Pacific Ocean and lowered to the bottom in order to capture oil and gas seeping from the seafloor.

from many countries, including Hungary, Britain, and the United States. One solution might be a switch from a society based on fossil fuels to one based on solar energy, in which the cost of the basic input does not increase as the cumulative amount used increases. Such a strategy would imply a change in the pattern of social organization, from centralization to decentralization. Such a change would be necessary as society shifted from dependence on energy produced in vast quantities at a small number of points (refineries, electrical generating plants, coal mines) to energy produced in small quantities everywhere (sunshine, wind, waves, ocean thermal energy gradients).

Ecological communities. One of the sciences basic to an understanding of environmental phenomena and issues is ecology, which deals with the interactions between organisms and their environments. A new focus for research in this field was the community level of organization, where the worker attempts to understand the processes that determine the relative and absolute abundance of different species of plants and animals. A great deal of experimental, field, and theoretical work has been done on this question, and in 1982 in an article published in *American Scientist* Thomas Schoener reviewed the available evidence to determine what generalizations emerged.

Schoener points out that three theories have become popular for explaining interactions within communities in nature. These might be characterized as the competition theory, the predation theory, and the limited environmental suitability theory. The competition theory argues that the locations where species are found and the number that are found in each place are determined by competition between species. This competition might be for limited resources or it might take the form of interference, as when one species takes over a resource from another.

The predation theory holds that the intensity and selectivity of predation shapes the relative abundance of species in communities. This can happen in a number of ways. For example, a predator species might systematically select the herbivorous species that usually wins in competition for resources with other species. Alternatively, the predator species might always shift to the herbivorous species that was most abundant. In either case, the function of the predator is to allow weak competitors or less abundant species to survive. Experiments show that the removal of one or more predator species results in a decline in the number of prey species present. Thus, heavy predator pressure on a community can operate as a force to foster a high level of species diversity. It is noteworthy that tropical coral lagoons, which may have 150 or more species of fish in a body of water 135 by 45 m (150 by 50 yd) and 1.5 m (5 ft) deep, are combed day and night by a wide variety of fish-eating predators (morays, jacks, barracudas, etc.).

The theory of limited environmental suitability holds that, much of the time, the environment is so cold or dry or short of food that species cannot build up their numbers sufficiently for competition to occur. According to this theory it is fluctuations in the physical environment that determine the density and variety of species populations.

Schoener considers the issue of where these three mechanisms operate. Both theory and experiment support the following generalization. Of the three mechanisms competition is more important for large organisms. Because of their size such species can escape attack by many or all predators. Further, the heat loss by organisms per unit of weight decreases as organisms become larger (surface area increases as the square of the radius of a sphere, the volume or mass as the cube). Thus the largest species can better maintain internal body temperature and chemical balance in extreme environments. The same line of argument suggests that predation and/or the physical environment tend to be more important in determining species diversity and relative abundance of small organisms.

Schoener advances a hypothesis to account for changes seen during fluctuations between lean times and times of plenty, when different types of resources increase differentially in abundance. Under conditions of scarcity each species will focus on those types of resources that it is best adapted to exploit; competition pressure for resources attractive to and suitable for many species will be intense, and those resources will be depleted quickly. During times of abundance many species will find it profitable to exploit resources that have become exceptionally abundant and that are suitable for all of them. Thus, the intensity of competition fluctuates as conditions fluctuate.

—Kenneth E. F. Watt

Food and agriculture

World output of agricultural products during 1982 was slightly less than the record high of 1981 but 1.1% above the average of the past three years. Each of the major regions of the world produced less in 1982 than during the previous year; however, the 1982 level was well above the average of the three preceding years except in the Soviet Union. The 1982 U.S.S.R. production level was about 16% lower than the 1978 record. Japan and Oceania had experienced slightly reduced agricultural outputs over the past three years.

Agriculture

The use of food as a tool of foreign policy was once again a topic of debate and, once again, became an issue between the two superpowers, the U.S. and the Soviet Union. Although the blanket grain embargo im-

Science and Education Administration—USDA

Intermittent plant sprayer uses less insecticide than do continuous-spray models. Three spray nozzles are activated when a plant interrupts an infrared light beam. A photoelectric transmitter and receiver to control the operation are mounted slightly in front of the nozzles.

posed by U.S. Pres. Jimmy Carter in 1980, after the Soviet invasion of Afghanistan, was lifted, the Soviets remained angry about what they considered a breach of contract. During the embargo the U.S. sold the U.S.S.R. only the amount of grain that was obligated under a long-term agreement; all other contracts were canceled. In retaliation the U.S.S.R. determined to buy only a small percentage of the amount the U.S. would like to sell and to purchase the rest of its grain needs elsewhere. An additional reason was Soviet annoyance over the U.S. attempt to stop construction of a natural gas pipeline from the Soviet Union to Western Europe. For the 1983 marketing year total Soviet Union purchases of U.S. wheat were not expected to be much above the eight million metric tons specified in the long-term agreement.

Production and farm economics. During 1982 cereals accounted for about 30% of the world's agricultural production. Four countries, the U.S., China, the Soviet Union, and India, produced approximately 55% of all cereals. The Soviet Union led in wheat production, the U.S. in corn, and China in rice. Wheat production, accounting for about 25% of the world's cereal output, increased at an annual rate of 2.2%.

During the past decade oilseed production, with an annual growth rate of 3.2% worldwide, outpaced all other agricultural categories. Most of the gain was accounted for by soybeans in the U.S., the top producer with nearly 63 million metric tons in 1982. Brazil had increased soybean production from 1.5 million to 12.3 million metric tons over the decade, while Argentina, which had grown very few soybeans ten years earlier, now ranked fourth in the world. China, traditionally a large soybean producer, ranked third with nearly 10

million metric tons. World meat and poultry output fell 3% in 1982, and little if any recovery was likely in 1983.

Net U.S. farm income declined to an estimated $19 billion from $19.6 billion in 1981, $24.4 billion in 1980, and $26.7 billion in 1979. After gaining for 12 years, U.S. farm exports dropped to $39.1 billion from the record $43.8 billion in 1981. A further decline was expected in 1983. The historic "parity ratio" between farm commodity prices and expenses was at its lowest point since 1933. Loan foreclosures, bankruptcies, and delinquencies reported by the Farmers Home Administration climbed further as farm borrowers were hard pressed to meet payment schedules. Finally, the national average value of farmland fell for the first time since 1954.

Depressed markets and hard times for farmers brought about a reduction in the food cost spiral for the consumer. Weak consumer demand and the easing of inflation also were major factors. Retail food prices in 1982 rose an estimated 4.5% and were expected to go up an additional 4% in 1983, although the range could be between 3 and 6%. This would represent the smallest average increase since food prices rose 3.1% in 1976.

The year marked a turning point for dairy farmers as Congress reduced milk price supports. The reduction was included in the budget measure passed in August, which authorized the secretary of agriculture to charge dairy farmers fees when milk output was too great. The first stage of the fee system, a 50-cent charge on every hundred pounds of milk sold, went into effect Dec. 1, 1982. A second 50-cent fee took effect on April 1, 1983.

318

Dramatizing the plight of the farmer, in 1982 the actual farm value of wheat in a one-pound loaf of bread in the U.S. was less than five cents. Wheat plus five other key farm ingredients that go into bread accounted for about five and one-half cents. Nonfarm ingredients added at the bakery were worth another penny. Processing costs added about three and one-half cents and baking and wrapping a little more than three cents. Then came the cost of transportation and display and a "wholesale to retail" price spread of just under ten cents. The total cost of the loaf of bread was approximately 52 cents.

Agricultural policy and world tensions. The Soviet Union's increasing need to import more agricultural products and the need of the U.S. to export more was creating an economic link between the two superpowers that could ease international tensions, according to the Worldwatch Institute. A report issued by the institute recognized that there had been a shift in the world's agricultural balance of power in favor of the United States.

By the end of the 20th century the world may need to feed as many as two billion additional people. Most of them will be born in less developed countries with marginal land ill suited for food production. In addressing the scientific, social, and ecological issues attendant upon this development, the International Agricultural Research Centers were particularly interested in issues raised by the introduction of high-yielding varieties of crops into countries with fertile land and in how varieties can be tailored for introduction into marginal areas. Such efforts, if combined with humanely oriented government policies, could help substantially in reducing world tensions. The picture was complicated by such issues as cash flow, credit policies, fossil fuels, and historical relationships between nations. Nevertheless, the possibility of reducing world tensions through agricultural research existed.

Genetic engineering. Although most of the publicity surrounding genetic engineering concerned its use in the field of medicine, the technique has important applications in agriculture. A number of pairs of twin calves have been born as the result of splitting an embryo with a newly developed microsurgical technique. The embryo is divided into three and even four pieces, each of which can produce a genetically identical calf when reimplanted in a cow. The benefit of this technique for researchers is that it eliminates genetic differences as variables in the study of nutritional, environmental, and disease-related problems. This will allow scientists to conduct experiments that would be too costly if genetic variability had to be accounted for.

The transfer of cattle embryos between cows has been expanded by the use of frozen fertilized embryos.

Genetically identical twin calves were produced by splitting an embryo by means of a newly developed microsurgical technique. Both halves were then transferred to the uterus of a foster mother.

Ken Williams—Colorado State University

Vehicle operation simulator was built by the farm equipment manufacturer Deere & Co. in order to help the firm's engineers design more productive and safer machines.

When only fresh, live, fertilized embryos were used, both cows had to be in the same phase of the estrus cycle, and the embryo had to be moved quickly from the donor cow to the host cow. With the new technique the estrus cycle of the host cow does not necessarily have to be in synchrony with that of the donor cow, or true mother. A research team at Rio Vista International Corp. of San Antonio, Texas, reported a one-step "soda straw" method of inserting frozen embryos of expensive prize-winning cattle into host cows. All the ingredients needed for implantation are contained in a 12.7-cm (5-in) plastic straw, including the embryo floating in its freezing agent and a sucrose mixture that instantly bathes the embryo as it is inserted into the host cow. Air bubbles pumped into the straw from a syringe form an easily broken barrier between the solutions.

The gene-splicing technique was used to develop a new vaccine for foot-and-mouth disease, announced by the U.S. Department of Agriculture (USDA) in 1982. The first chapter of the story involved research conducted in the 1950s and 1960s at the Agricultural Research Service-USDA Plum Island (N.Y.) Animal Disease Center, where the virus was isolated and scientists learned to grow it in tissue culture. A second chapter was the discovery at Plum Island that one of the four proteins that coat the viral RNA is an effective antigen in producing immunity to the virus. This knowledge led to the application of recombinant DNA techniques to produce the new vaccine. The results earned an American Association for the Advancement of Science–Newcomb Cleveland Prize jointly for scientists from Genentech Laboratories and the USDA.

Genetic engineering also had become a reality in crop breeding. Tissue culture was being used in several laboratories throughout the world to allow the selection of crop varieties that will withstand specific nutrient, disease, or environmental stresses. The first step in this work involves a tissue-culture technique in which single plant cells or small groups of cells are allowed to grow on a synthetic medium through several stages to a complete plant. Initial work was done with the tobacco plant because it adapted better to synthetic media than many other plant tissue materials. Subsequently, the work was expanded to include many agricultural crops such as corn, wheat, barley, oats, and rice. For example, in 1982 a salt-tolerant variety of oats was developed that can survive the salt concentrations found in the Colorado and Arkansas River valleys and other high-saline soils.

National Plant Germplasm System. Germ plasm is the genetic raw material required by breeders for the development of new, superior crop varieties that can ensure a stable and plentiful supply of food, feed, and fiber that have desirable qualities. Acquisition, preservation, evaluation, and distribution of germ plasm resources in the U.S. were being coordinated by the National Plant Germplasm System (NPGS). The NPGS was designed to provide, on a continuing, long-term basis, the plant genetic diversity that was needed by farmers and plant scientists to improve crop productivity and minimize the vulnerability of crops to biological and environmental stresses.

The genetic vulnerability of crops becomes crucial when an out-of-the-ordinary range of stresses from diseases, insects, drought, or temperature extremes exceeds a crop's range of tolerance. The results can vary from noticeable yield reductions in localized areas to disastrous crop failures over entire continents. Preventing crop losses through control of biologic and environmental stresses is far more difficult and costly than increasing genetic diversity among varieties of a given crop. Therefore, one NPGS objective was to broaden the genetic diversity of a crop throughout its production area by introducing an array of varieties, all productive but each differing from the others in its range of tolerance for one or more potential stresses. This reduces the likelihood of catastrophic losses.

The NPGS maintained more than 400,000 stocks propagated both vegetatively and from seed, many of them from foreign sources. A few working collections in the National Seed Storage Laboratory in Fort Collins, Colo., also maintained some stocks. New stocks were being added to the system at the rate of 7,000 to 15,000 per year. The system was managed through the USDA, with the primary coordinating function residing with the Agricultural Research Service. The system, however, involved cooperative efforts from all regions of the country through the land-grant universities and their agricultural experiment stations.

The National Seed Storage Laboratory (NSSL), a USDA/Agricultural Research Service facility, was the nation's only long-term seed-storage facility. The laboratory maintained plant germ plasm as a base collection for the U.S. and served as a backup base in support of the global network of genetic resource centers. In addition, 12 clonal repositories were planned, 5 of which were in operation during 1982: Corvallis, Ore. (pears, hazelnuts, small fruits, hops, and mint); Davis, Calif. (grapes, stone fruits, and nuts); Miami, Fla. (subtropical and tropical fruits and sugarcane); Indio, Calif. (date palm); and the Mayaguez Institute of Tropical Agriculture, Puerto Rico (tropical fruits and industrial crops).

Other current research. The Forest Products Laboratory of the U.S. Forest Service, in cooperation with the University of Wisconsin, introduced a new construction system, the "truss-framed system," as an alternative to the conventionally built home. The system uses up to 30% less structural framing lumber than conventionally built houses, requires fewer skilled laborers, and can be built in much less time. Since the trusses can span the entire width of most houses, supports and load-bearing walls are unnecessary. This permits almost complete freedom in designing the layouts of the rooms.

Plant scientists at the New Jersey Agricultural Experiment Station were puzzled as to why certain herbicides affect some plants and not others. Their studies of the herbicide Propanil, used on rice, turned up an enzyme in the rice plant that detoxifies the herbicide as it enters the plant cell. This same enzyme is not active in pest weeds. The scientists succeeded in locating the enzyme in the plant and purifying it for further study. This discovery could lead to the identification and breeding of plants that are suited for pest control

by particular herbicides. Using genetic engineering technologies, scientists might be able to add specific pesticide resistance to the cells of critically important crop plants.

Agricultural engineers at Georgia's Agricultural Experiment Station developed a sprayer capable of putting out very small spray droplets with a negative electrical charge. Since the ground and plants are positively charged, the droplets are attracted to crops, literally enveloping them with spray. Four times as much spray falls on plant leaves with this method as with conventional sprays. The amount of pesticide sprayed on cotton, for example, can be cut as much as 50% below the recommended rate with no loss in insect control. Widespread use of the electrostatic sprayer could reduce the amount of chemicals necessary for pest control, resulting in greater savings for farmers and less pollution of the environment.

Louisiana agricultural scientists developed successful double-cropping systems using rice and crayfish on the same land during the same year. Field waste from the rice harvest is used to feed crayfish in the winter and spring. Following crayfish with rice the second year cuts down on fuel consumption by about 30% because traditional soil preparation is unnecessary. The crayfish keep weeds and grasses under control by eating them, thus reducing the need for herbicides. The system also prevents soil erosion and conserves water, with rain providing the water needed for the crayfish and for early rice growth.

Wisconsin Agricultural Experiment Station scientists succeeded in perfecting a frozen milk concentrate to be marketed like frozen orange juice. The reconstituted product tastes like fresh milk, has lower shipping costs, longer storage life, and results in less waste from spillage. By using this technique it is also possible to manufacture lactose-free milk, making the benefits of milk available to those who cannot tolerate lactose.

Laser leveling of land is a promising technology first used in agriculture in the mid-1970s. A laser beam is set dead level or a specific grade is transmitted by a rotating command post placed on or near the field. The beam is picked up by a receiver attached to a tractor-mounted scraper. The receiver automatically operates hydraulic control valves that raise and lower the tractor's scraper blade, keeping it at the desired grade.

The USDA Economic Research Service reported that women were the sole or principal operators of 128,000—or just over 5%—of the nation's farms. The number had roughly doubled over the last decade. This does not count farms managed by a husband and wife team. Women constituted 13% of farmers in Hawaii, 10% in Florida and South Carolina, and 8 to 9% in several other states. There were more women farmers who were blacks or members of other minority groups than there were white women farmers.

—John Patrick Jordan

Nutrition

Some major physical aberrations may be induced by alcohol (ethanol), particularly when intake levels are high and prolonged, according to Albert B. Eisenstein of the Veterans Administration and the Downstate Medical Center, State University of New York. Ingestion of food and alcohol together results in slower absorption of the alcohol into the bloodstream and delays peak concentration in the blood, as compared with equal amounts of alcohol consumed in the fasting state. Absorption is also affected by the composition of the food and by the amount eaten. Contrary to popular belief, soluble carbohydrate causes a greater delay than either protein or fat. Absorption is more efficient from the first portion of the small intestine than from the stomach.

Definitions of heavy drinking include the intake of one ounce or more of absolute alcohol (two drinks or more) per day or five or more drinks during a single episode. Binge consumption often results in such physical symptoms as cramps and diarrhea, attributed to disaccharidase deficiency resulting in lactose or other carbohydrate intolerance, and impaired water, electrolyte, and vitamin absorption. Certain fatty acids also are not absorbed. Folacin and other vitamin deficiencies are attributed to low intake as a result of poor dietary practices, malabsorption, impaired utilization, or excessive excretion, especially in chronic diarrhea. Malabsorption of thiamin, vitamin B_{12}, and other vitamins may result from damage to the intestinal mucosa. Serious enzyme distortion occurs both in the liver and in other tissue cells, and the malfunction increases with continued alcohol consumption.

When food intake is limited, alcohol can induce hypoglycemia within 6 to 36 hours, resulting in blood glucose levels as low as 40 mg per deciliter (normal is 90–100 mg). If the person is treated with insulin or other medications that depress blood glucose levels, the result may be fatal. Excessive intake of alcohol also affects protein and fat metabolism, resulting in hypertriglyceridemia and elevated cholesterol levels. Clinical examination of the liver and pancreas of heavy drinkers shows damage and acute changes that may prove fatal. Enzyme production is abnormal and, in advanced cases, irreversible.

Recently, fetal alcohol syndrome has received considerable attention, with the focus on pregnant women who are heavy drinkers. Among numerous studies was one by researchers at Boston University, who interviewed 578 postpartum women about their food and alcohol intakes. The data showed that 82% of the women drank alcohol at least once during pregnancy, and more than 10% had maximum single-episode intakes of three ounces or more—a level reported to carry a risk of adverse effects on the fetus. Since only 30% of the women had diets that provided at least two-thirds of the pregnancy-recommended daily allowance for 11 nutrients studied, the influence of alcohol could be even more damaging. Zinc and magnesium, necessary for fetal development, were the nutrients most often deficient in the diets. Since alcohol affects electrolyte absorption, blood levels of those nutrients would be further depressed by drinking.

Based on computerized medical record research, R. J. Sokol and others identified 204 cases of alcohol abusers among 12,127 pregnant women. Other research indicated that 5 to 9% and perhaps as many as 13% of pregnant women are heavy drinkers, whereas 50 to 60% of pregnant women are abstainers. Significantly, records show that when women become pregnant they tend to lower the frequency and amount of their alcohol intake.

Diet, nutrition, and cancer. In June 1982 the National Academy Press released the report *Diet, Nutrition and Cancer*. Two years in preparation by a panel of experts, it had been supported by a grant of almost $1 million from the National Cancer Institute to the National Research Council of the National Academy of Sciences. The aim of the project was to assess available data in order to develop dietary recommendations that would be helpful for reducing cancer risk in the U.S. and to identify research needs. An "Executive Summary" of the report was published in *Nutrition Today* (July/August 1982).

The panel acknowledged that no precise estimates exist of the contribution to cancer by various factors, but it considered that some evidence was strong enough to justify a few dietary guidelines. These included: reduce fat intake from both saturated and unsaturated types to 30% of the total calorie consumption (fat intake had the strongest association with cancer); eat fruits, vegetables, and whole grain cereal products, especially those high in vitamin C, carotenoids, and vitamin A and particularly vegetables of the cabbage family; eat little salt-cured, pickled, or smoked foods, including those preserved with sodium nitrite; drink alcohol in moderation.

The major criticism of the report was that epidemiologic data do not provide an adequate basis for recommending a major change in a nation's life-style. Overall age-adjusted cancer rates have remained stable for the past 30 to 40 years except for respiratory tract cancers attributable to smoking. In summarizing the current status of cancer and food, the *New York Times* noted: "Those who choose to incur the known risk of smoking need hardly worry about the lesser risks of foods." The association of cancer with most ingredients in foods is still tentative. The report concludes with the contention that most common cancers are potentially preventable and that these are related less to genetic influences than to habits and diets.

Diets and weight loss. Consumers often seek advice and help from the Office of Consumer Affairs of the

U.S. Food and Drug Administration (FDA) concerning the reliability of information in various diet books, some of which are best-sellers. Although the FDA is responsible for assuring the safety of foods and their appropriate labeling, it does not assure the safety and appropriateness of claims made in articles or books. Under the protection of the First Amendment to the Constitution, which guarantees freedom of speech and the press, any author can make dietary claims that may appear to be reasonable, and no one can be sure whether his main concern is with truth or profit. Thus consumers must protect themselves by asking an authority such as a physician, dietitian, or nutritionist, by reading references available in libraries, and by utilizing analytical thinking rather than indulging in wishful daydreaming.

The following weight-reduction diets were the subjects of popular books:

The Cambridge diet consists of three daily portions of flavored powder mixed with water, providing 330 calories per day. Nutrition experts agree that less than 800 calories daily should not be attempted without medical supervision. Total dependence on 330 calories daily for an extended period can have very adverse effects, more critical at some ages.

The Stillman diet is high in protein and very low in carbohydrates. It is claimed that this will cause the body to burn more calories than are supplied by the diet, resulting in weight loss. Actually, the weight is lost as a result of water excretion and is regained when regular food is eaten.

The Pritikin weight-loss plan is a 1,000-calorie diet with very limited protein content and is low in fats, cholesterol, sugars, salt, coffee, tea, and alcohol. This leaves only complex carbohydrates, chiefly low-calorie plant foods, which make up most of the diet. Professionals do not agree on its safety for long-term use.

The Beverly Hills diet is a low-calorie fruit diet based on a theory that digestive enzymes for protein and carbohydrates do not work together. The diet recommends that proteins should be eaten alone, as should fats and carbohydrates. The American Medical Association notes that no evidence supports this theory.

Illustrating the amazing popularity of diet books, more than 1.5 million copies of Nathan Pritikin's *The Pritikin Program for Diet and Exercise* had been sold as of 1982. The October 1982 issue of *Consumer Reports* analyzed the claims of Pritikin's book. Some of its advice is generally regarded as sound; for example, regular daily exercise and elimination of smoking. The rigorous dietary regime is extremely low in fat and animal proteins and consists largely of whole grain foods, legumes, vegetables, and fruits. It eliminates sugar, fatty poultry and fish, egg yolks, dairy products, and plant foods that contain fat, such as nuts and some soybean products. Pritikin's promotion for his program and for his three "longevity centers" is threatening; *e.g,* "Clogged arteries with cholesterol plaques, cancers, diabetes, and other diseases threaten life if action is not taken promptly." The program is increasingly emphasizing "approved foods" sold under the Pritikin name.

Pritikin compares his program with the life-style of the Tarahumara Indians in Mexico, who are said to have the longest life span of any people and to have good endurance. Their diet is known to consist of about 12% calories from protein and fat and 75% from carbohydrates other than refined sugar. However, other reports on the Tarahumara Indians—for example, in the *National Geographic Magazine*—indicate that they consume quantities of an indigenous beer and have a mortality rate of 80% for children under age five.

Sodium labeling. The secretary for health and human services and the commissioner of the FDA announced new labeling rules to designate the salt and sodium content of processed foods, thus enabling persons with high blood pressure to reduce their salt and sodium intakes. The rules were intended to encourage and guide food processors in taking voluntary action. Where warranted, the label was to include terms such as "unsalted" or "no salt added" and, under specified conditions, could use "sodium free," "low sodium," and "reduced sodium."

The American Dietetic Association supported the proposed sodium and potassium labeling of processed foods based on the needs of three population groups: the 60 million people in the U.S. who are estimated to have hypertension; those persons who, because of disease or medication, must monitor potassium intake; and the 47,000 dietitians who are instrumental in translating information about sodium and potassium content of foods into appropriate diet choices. Many other people are also vitally interested in controlling their intake of these mineral elements. Tolerance for sodium intake has been lowered by changes in cultural patterns affecting perspiration, such as air-conditioning and reduced manual labor.

Low-birth-weight infants. Dietitians and physicians at the Indiana University School of Medicine assessed early feeding and growth outcome of 207 very low-birth-weight infants (less than 1,500 g [3.3 lb] and not over 35 weeks gestational age). As a group, the infants lost 13% of birth weight, reached low weight by 9 days, and regained birth weight by 18 days of age. The initial sustained weight gain of 19 g (0.67 oz) per day resulted from feedings of 100 calories per kilogram of weight per day (1 kg = 2.2 lb), 31% of which was derived from parenteral nutrition (directly into the bloodstream). A mean weight gain of 24 g (0.84 oz) per day was achieved from 108 calories per kilogram. There was a high correlation between severity of illness in the infants and early growth outcome in terms of (1) age to initial lowest weight, (2) percent weight loss, (3) age to initial sustained weight gain, and (4) age at which birth weight was regained. The study supports the importance of early nutrition for the survival of infants.

—Mina W. Lamb

Life sciences

To many life scientists the past year was remarkable in its profusion of surprising finds and significant achievements. Perhaps most exciting for molecular biologists was the discovery of an RNA molecule that can cut out an unneeded segment of itself and splice itself together again without the help of enzymes. Investigators studying the molecular basis of cancer identified genes in normal human cells called proto-oncogenes whose activation or modification appears to be a major step in the transformation of normal cells into certain kinds of tumor cells. Lotus seeds 400 years old were found to be still alive and able to germinate, while the discovery in Antarctica of the fossilized jawbone of a marsupial offered support for a theory of early animal migration from South America to Australia. Biomining, the use of microorganisms to extract metals and other substances from ores, received growing attention as the energy costs for conventional recovery methods continued to rise.

Botany

Progress in learning about plant structure and function continued steadily in 1982. Interesting and important information was published on the topics of paleobotany, genetics and reproduction, physiology, ecology, and forestry.

Old plants. Mordechai Kislev of Bar-Ilan University in Israel recently reported the discovery of preserved wheat rust possibly 3,300 years old. Buried in a jar protected by a thick layer of charred debris at Tel Batash, Israel, fragments of wheat plants (*Triticum parvicoccum*, or *T. turgidum*) were found to be infected with pustules of the parasitic rust *Puccinia graminis* f. sp. *tritici* with filaments of the fungus and spores in various stages of germination. Such fungal remnants are rare archaeological finds. Some authorities believe that this rust is mentioned in the Hebrew Bible, and the philosopher Theophrastus wrote of it in Greek classical times.

Not as old but perhaps more remarkable were the findings of two investigators working in The Netherlands. David Priestley and Maarten Posthumus received four seeds of the aquatic East Indian lotus (*Nelumbo nucifera*) from an ancient lake bed in southern Manchuria. Radiocarbon dating of two of the seeds placed their age at about 400 years. Three of the seeds were induced to germinate, and samples of their endosperm, the seed tissue that serves as the first food of the germinating plant, were studied for lipid content. A high degree of polyunsaturation (an abundance of double or triple carbon-carbon bonds) was noted and credited to the thick seed coats, which keep out oxygen that would facilitate saturation of the lipids. These investigators believed that saturation of lipids is somehow related to the loss of viability in such seeds.

Hybridization. In the interest of producing better crop plants agronomists long have wished to bring together desired features of two or more species into one. Traditional practice has been to attempt to hybridize such species and then to select the desired progeny for

From "Stem Rust of Wheat 3300 Years Old Found in Israel," Mordechai E. Kislev, *Science,* vol. 216, pp. 993–994, May 28, 1982, © 1982 AAAS

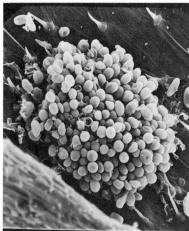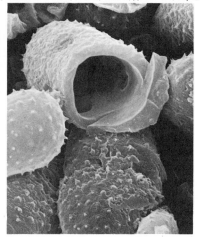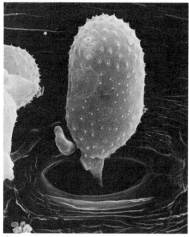

Microscopic pustule of the rust Puccinia graminis *(left) was found on wheat spikelets 3,300 years old. Other views are of a broken spore (center) and of a spore that had germinated on the host plant (right.)*

propagation. Such techniques have been limited by barriers to successful reproduction among different species. These barriers are what makes them different species in the first place. More recent attempts to bring favorable traits together have emphasized genetic engineering techniques, that is, attempts to transfer genetic material for a desired trait from one kind of plant to another. Notable examples of the latter effort are attempts to induce nitrogen fixation in plants heretofore lacking that ability and to increase the quality of protein in corn.

The current excitement over genetic engineering can obscure ongoing research to improve hybridization among species. A good example of this work was reported in the past year by horticulturists S. A. Johnston and R. E. Hanneman, Jr., of the University of Wisconsin. They were attempting to discover what barriers may exist that make hybridization of several species of the genus *Solanum* unsuccessful. Various kinds of potatoes belong to this genus, and because some of the species are best known for disease or weather resistance and others for tuber production, it would be beneficial to bring these traits together into one or more commercially produced kinds.

Johnston and Hanneman noted, as had others before them, that one barrier to successful hybridization has been faulty endosperm in the seed. If the endosperm is aborted, as it is in many hybrid seeds, then the embryo is unsuccessful. One very interesting characteristic of endosperm in angiosperms (flowering plants) is that it is triploid (3x; *i.e.,* has three sets of chromosomes) rather than diploid (2x; two sets), developing from the product of fusion of one paternal nucleus from pollen and two maternal nuclei from the ovule. Because the genetic contribution from parents is normally 2:1, this ratio is considered to be necessary for the production of normal endosperm.

Unfortunately, chromosome number itself is not always the indicator of the normal ratio. Sometimes a species may have a diploid number of chromosomes that is really best understood as four times the chromosome number (4x) of some ancestor of the species. Such complications have led these investigators to propose and test the endosperm balance number (EBN) hypothesis. An EBN (*e.g.,* 2, 1, or ½) is determined for each species by crossing that species to a standard species. Normal endosperm is produced when the maternal–paternal EBN ratio is 2:1, and abnormal endosperm indicates a deviation from that. Manipulation of chromosome numbers in certain species could bring about the appropriate EBN to yield the proper 2:1 ratio and thus eliminate this barrier to hybridization, in *Solanum* at least. So far Johnston and Hanneman have shown that EBN barriers do exist and have been optimistic about being able to overcome them.

Airborne acid effects. Continued concern about the effects of acids in the air is reflected in efforts to understand possible mechanisms of harm to plants as well as animals. Of particular interest is the effect of sulfur dioxide (SO_2) in air, and examples of recent research are numerous. Several British investigators reported that SO_2 decreases resistance to freezing, slows growth, or both. Alan W. Davison and Ian F. Bailey of the University of Newcastle upon Tyne raised *Lolium perenne*, an important forage grass, under a number of varied conditions, including fumigation with SO_2, freezing, and addition of soil nutrients. They found that SO_2 reduces resistance to winter temperatures. Since *Lolium perenne* shows poor resistance to low temperatures anyway, SO_2 may actually be a recent factor in natural selection of resistant strains. Increasing soil nutrients, sulfur, and nitrogen in these experiments decreased the effects of SO_2 on freezing resistance.

Mary E. Whitmore and Peter H. Freer-Smith of the University of Lancaster used greenhouse-grown *Poa pratensis* (bluegrass) to show that SO_2 and nitrogen dioxide (NO_2) in the air at concentrations known to exist in urban Britain reduce growth in the winter and spring. Plants tend to recover growth rates during the summer but suffer inhibited flowering. During winter months the effects of SO_2 and NO_2 together cause greater decrease in growth than they do when their individual effects are simply added.

How these air pollutants actually cause the effects described above is not known, particularly at low levels of pollution. This is due largely to a lack of experimental procedures that can detect changes in physiology in the plant. One example of an attempt to measure such changes was reported by James L. Ellenson and Robert G. Amundson of the Boyce Thompson Institute for Plant Research of Cornell University in New York. They modified the technique of delayed light imaging (DLE) to photograph entire leaves in order to discern just where in the leaves stress is occurring. DLE is particularly useful because it determines effects of stress on photosynthesis and does not necessitate waiting until gross effects such as leaf spotting or necrosis (local tissue death) appear. This technique may even provide a warning for corrective measures to be taken early enough to help the plant.

DLE involves photographing the fluorescence given off by some of the photosynthetic intermediates and thus gives a measure of the amount of photosynthesis occurring. Ellenson and Amundson used an apparatus that allowed each half of a leaf to be treated differently—as when one half is subjected to SO_2 and the other is not, or the two sides are treated with differing concentrations—and thus studied comparatively. This is an improvement over such conventional techniques as measurement of carbon dioxide use.

Hormones. The function of plant hormones has proved to be difficult to understand. Although the overall effects are well known and used commercially, the specific mechanisms producing the effects are elusive. The earliest known plant hormones were called auxins; the most common example is IAA, indoleacetic acid. Auxins stimulate cell growth and so are associated with such phenomena as bending of plant stems toward a light source. Since growth effects may be noted 10–15 minutes following hormone application, some short-term mechanism must be involved.

Two Stanford University scientists, Athanasios Theologis and Peter M. Ray, reported on an IAA-induced genetic effect within 20 minutes of hormone application in peas (*Pisum sativum*). They incubated segments of pea stem in IAA solution for various lengths of time. Then they extracted all nucleic acids and isolated one type of these called poly(A)$^+$mRNA, which is involved in the synthesis of certain proteins expected to be associated with cell growth. Next the isolated poly(A)$^+$mRNA was added to a medium of necessary substances, including wheat germ extract, that made synthesis of cell-free protein possible. Protein synthesis in this case was found to be significantly greater than it was in the same medium without the addition of any isolate or with the addition of poly(A)$^+$mRNA isolated from pea stems that had not been treated with IAA. It was not known what the specific function of these proteins might be; however, information relative to the primary function of auxin is close at hand. These investigators believe that auxin influences the synthesis of the mRNA (transcription), thus making possible a large increase of protein synthesis (translation) related to growth.

Reproduction. The mechanisms of pollination continued to catch the imagination of botanists. Two researchers, Karl Niklas from Cornell and Kyaw Tha Paw U from Purdue University, West Lafayette, Ind., investigated the patterns of pollen impaction (deposition) on the female cones of pines. They reported on experiments of two kinds. In one they collected pollen from several species of pine and then released the pollen upwind of pines that had female cones ready to receive the pollen. Observations were made on the way in which the pollen becomes deposited on the scales of cones. It was found that pollen from the various species became deposited fairly indiscriminately on the cones of each other, but pollen from any given species tended to be found on the inside of cone scales from its own species. This finding is significant because the seed-producing ovules are found near the base of the inside surface of cone scales, and pollen of the same species must reach the ovules for fertilization to occur.

To investigate how the appropriate pollen comes to be deposited, another type of experiment involving a wind tunnel was used. Models of cones were placed at various angles in the tunnel, and air currents were blown over them. Helium-filled bubbles introduced to the air currents made it possible to witness air flow and to make videotapes for study. It was found that individual currents (eddies) swept pollen into the spaces between the scales where the ovules are found. Many factors related to scale shape, scale spaces, and pollen aerodynamic properties appear to provide the combination of conditions that bias deposition of pollen from the appropriate species toward the optimum location. This mechanism seems to work best when cones are oriented at 45° angles to the direction of airflow.

While the foregoing illustrates how structure of reproductive parts facilitates deposition of pollen by wind, there is evidence that structure of the whole floral display (inflorescence) influences pollination and fruit set in insect-pollinated plants. Robert Wyatt of the University of Georgia discussed this phenomenon in the *American Journal of Botany,* noting that some pollinators actually recognize certain forms of inflorescence such as the umbel (umbrella-shaped flower cluster) in wild carrot (*Daucus carota*) and that larger inflorescences increase fruiting success in general.

Once a fruit begins to form, its location within what was the arrangement of flowers in the inflorescence affects its chance of maturing. The probability of a fruit's maturing is affected by the closeness of its connection to the plant's pool of resources and its occurrence in time with respect to other developing fruits. Any arrangement of flowers that distributes reproduction demands more evenly over a plant or that lengthens the time of flowering favors fruit maturity. The former arrangement is accomplished by many few-flowered units rather than a few many-flowered ones and the latter arrangement by indeterminate inflorescences where the number of flowers is not fixed but increases in time. Obviously some factors that favor fruit maturity do not correspond to those that favor other processes such as pollination. For example, a large close grouping of flowers favors pollination but provides competition for resources among the resulting developing fruits. As a rule, fruits that set earlier have a better chance to develop than those appearing later on the same plant.

A fascinating relationship between flower arrangement and pollinator behavior is illustrated in species of *Epilobium* and *Digitalis*. In these plants flowers open in sequence from bottom to top on the stalk (really a raceme). When they first open, the anthers (male parts) are mature and are capable of shedding pollen on passing bees. Later the pistils (female parts) become mature, but newer flowers above them are just producing pollen. It is known that bees, like most insects, work upward. Thus they visit pistils first and deposit pollen brought from other plants. Then they visit stamens higher on the stalk, picking up pollen to take to other plants. Cross-pollination is facilitated and self-pollination reduced.

Seed production is a basic device used by annual plants to ensure survival. Many times it is observed that seeds remain viable for much more than one year, as was illustrated above. Sometimes delayed germination becomes characteristic of a whole community of plants when for some reason the community is destroyed periodically as a whole and is incapable of being restored on an annual basis. Such a case was reported by P. A. Keddy of the University of Guelph in Ontario and A. A. Reznicek of the University of Michigan.

They showed that shoreline vegetation along Matchedash Lake in Simcoe County, Ontario, is affected by water level. During a low-water phase of several years a rich shoreline flora develops, only to be obliterated by a high-water phase. When the next low-water phase occurs, a rich shoreline community should be restored. The reason for expecting this lies in the recoverable seeds present in the shoreline sediments and capable of germination after several years of inundation. Keddy and Reznicek showed that the sediment seed-pool results are similar to the vegetation present on shore when water levels are lower. Of the 15 most abundant species germinated from the seed pool, densities of 4–65 seeds per square meter (about 10.8 sq ft) were estimated.

Springing the trap. Venus's flytrap (*Dionaea muscipula*) is a carnivorous plant that captures insect prey by rapid closure of two parts of its modified leaves when a trigger hair is touched, an action somewhat like closing of the halves of a clamshell or a change purse. Botanists have speculated on the mechanism causing closure of these traps for many years. It has been known that rapid plant movements may be caused by changes in intracellular (turgor) pressure as is the case of leaf movements in the sensitive plant (*Mimosa*).

Two investigators recently provided evidence that Venus's flytrap movements are caused by a rapid growth mechanism triggered by the flow of hydrogen ions (H^+). Stephen E. Williams of Lebanon Valley College in Annville, Pa., and Alan B. Bennett of Cornell measured movements in various parts of the leaves by marking the surfaces to detect actual changes in trap size. They also carried out experiments involving change of pH (degree of alkalinity or acidity). Their observations showed that the outer epidermis of the traps expanded more than 25% during closure while the inner epidermis showed no such increase. Upon reopening of the trap, the inner epidermis increased in size by at least 12% while the outer epidermis did not change significantly. Thus the trap closes by expanding its outer epidermis and reopens by expanding its inner epidermis. Williams and Bennett proposed that the increase of H^+ content of cells produces cell-wall plasticity and allows for the rapid growth necessary to shut a trap fast enough to catch an insect capable of fairly rapid movement.

Urban forestry. The First American Forest Congress was held in 1882 in Cincinnati, Ohio. In commemoration of the centennial year the Second National Urban Forestry Conference returned to Cincinnati. The emphasis on urban forestry indicates a trend promoted in many cities and stated many times over at the conference: the planting of trees in cities is beginning to focus on the needs of people and neighborhoods, not on the needs of trees. An additional feature of this movement is its dependence on volunteer help and private funding. Success stories from Los Angeles, Baltimore, Milwaukee, Seattle, Lake Forest, Ill., Murray City, Utah, New York City, and other cities were reported at the conference.

Plant-animal interactions. Three Australian scientists suggested a way in which choosing appropriate pasture plants may help combat cattle ticks. The latter affect millions of cattle and sheep worldwide. The reason why pasture plants are strategic lies in the habit of tick larvae to crawl up these plants to await the opportunity to brush off on passing animals. Ordinary pasture grasses in tropical and subtropical areas offer little resistance to such use. Robert W. Sutherst, Raymond J. Jones, and Herbert J. Schnitzerling advocated the planting of several species of the legume genus *Stylosanthes* as pasture plants not only because they enhance cattle nutrition but because they combat ticks. These investigators found that tick larvae are caught in a sticky substance when they attempt to climb up the plants and are killed by a still unidentified volatile substance. Plants of the genus *Stylosanthes* will grow in a broad range of soils and climates and thus could be used widely in control efforts.

In a different way defoliated trees are fighting back against the gypsy moth, which has done much damage to forests of the eastern U.S. Jack C. Schultz and Ian T. Baldwin of Dartmouth College, Hanover, N.H., studied what happens to red oaks (*Quercus rubrum*) following defoliation. Their experiments showed that trees defoliated during previous years may produce leaves that are tougher, have less water, and produce more tannins and phenols than other trees. Insect feeding and growth on these new leaves may be affected adversely, particularly by tannins and phenols, an effect that may help explain the population "crashes" that follow gypsy moth outbreaks.

—Albert J. Smith

Microbiology

The past year was an interesting and exciting one in microbiology. Highlights included the emergence of a new disease syndrome, a new symbiotic relationship between bacteria and animals, preparation of a synthetic vaccine, and increasing emphasis in applied microbiology.

Applied and environmental microbiology. The high cost of energy required for conventional metal recovery methods, the environmental problems that result from smelting of ores, and the depletion of high-grade ores contributed to growing interest in the use of microorganisms in mining metals. Microbiological mining, or biomining, is not a new process. There is evidence that the leaching of copper from ore by microorganisms may have been used in the Mediterranean region as early as 1000 BC. It is known that microbial leaching of copper on a large scale was in use in Spain by the 18th century. Microbial leaching was, and generally remains, an uncontrolled process. It was not understood at all until recently and indeed still remains poorly understood.

Microbial leaching of metals from ores depends upon the biological activity of microorganisms that can oxidize ferrous iron to ferric iron and sulfur to sulfuric acid. Formation of acid is important in order to keep ferric iron and other metals in solution. Ferric iron is a strong oxidizing agent that can oxidize other metals such as copper or uranium, changing them into a form that is soluble in an acid environment. In this process ferrous iron is regenerated and can then be reoxidized by the microorganisms in a cyclic manner. The metals thus made soluble then can be recovered from solution by chemical means.

The most common iron-sulfur compound in ores is iron pyrite, or ferrous sulfide. Another common compound is chalcopyrite, which contains copper, iron, and sulfur. These are the major substances useful for the microbial leaching process.

To date microbial leaching has been used to recover only copper and uranium, but it should be possible to recover lead, zinc, tin, nickel, and other metals. Moreover, microbial leaching has been used primarily to recover metals from low-grade ores from which recovery by conventional means would be uneconomical.

Thiobacillus ferrooxidans is a bacterium that can oxidize both iron and sulfur. For many years it was considered to be the only organism important in leaching. Leaching carried out by this organism, however, is a slow process. Recently scientists have been experimenting with other microorganisms, with mixtures of organisms, and with the genetic manipulation of microorganisms to yield more efficient microbial leaching systems. A bacterium that shows much promise is *Sulfolobus*, a member of the archaebacteria. This organism oxidizes sulfur to sulfuric acid, thrives in a highly acidic environment, and grows at high temperatures—in fact at temperatures near the boiling point of water. Recent evidence indicated that *Sulfolobus* is much more efficient than *ferrooxidans* for the leaching of metals.

Other potential microbial processes for the recovery of metals were under investigation in the past year. Many microorganisms have negatively charged surfaces that attract and bind positively charged metal ions. Some of these bacteria, for example, become heavily encrusted with iron. Other bacteria can take up and accumulate inside their cells a wide variety of metals even though many of these metals are toxic and ultimately kill the bacteria. Finally, many organisms secrete chelating, or sequestering, agents that bind specific metals and consequently precipitate or immobilize the metals. Such microorganisms as these were being studied for their potential practical application.

Coal and petroleum desulfurization by microorganisms continued to be an important topic. These processes are similar to microbial leaching of ores in that sulfur-oxidizing organisms form water-soluble sulfuric acid, which then is washed out of the coal or petroleum. Similarly, soluble ferrous iron in water can be oxidized to insoluble ferric iron, thus facilitating iron removal from water. Though experimental, these processes hold great promise, and efforts were under way to increase their efficiency.

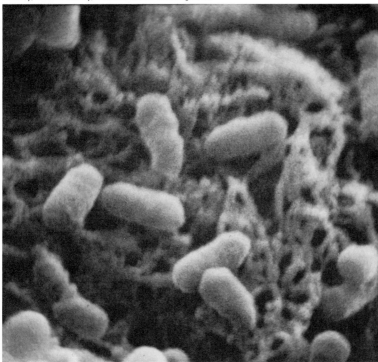

Scanning electron micrograph reveals rod-shaped cells of Thiobacillus thiooxidans, *one of a group of bacteria that are responsible for the biological leaching of metals from ores. T. thiooxidans oxidizes sulfur to sulfuric acid, thus helping to maintain the acid environment needed for rapid leaching to occur.*

Microorganisms can also chemically alter metals by adding methyl groups (CH_3) and by changing metals into volatile forms. So far it has not been practical to trap these volatile compounds, which also happen to be highly toxic. In nature, however, it has been shown that microorganisms have the ability to transform such metals as tin to toxic products and to mobilize the metals in the ecosystem.

Recent evidence indicated that microbial growth in abandoned retorted oil shale or reclamation areas resulted in volatilization of arsenic and, hence, the removal of arsenic from this by-product. Since toxic metals in oil shale have been a matter of concern regarding the disposal of this material after oil extraction by retorting, removal of these metals by microbial action may be a good solution.

New refinements in the use of microorganisms to purify various types of wastewater continued to be studied. Recent experiments by Swedish scientists showed that water contaminated with nitrate could be purified by the action of the bacterium *Pseudomonas denitrificans*, immobilized (entrapped) in a gel. This bacterium can reduce nitrate to harmless nitrogen gas, a process called denitrification.

Another experimental system was being tested to purify wastewater and to produce methane at the same time through the use of immobilized bacteria. In this system microbes capable of degrading organic substances in sewage are densely packed within the pores of ceramics. As the wastewater (sewage) flows around the ceramic material containing the immobilized bac-

teria, the organisms degrade the organic materials and produce methane.

Other workers used immobilized bacterial enzymes to degrade such pesticides as parathion and malathion. It is interesting that immobilized microbial cell and enzyme systems were originally developed within the very recent past for the industrial production of fermentation products.

Man is not the only animal that affects the environment. Production of carbon dioxide through the burning of fossil fuels has been a major concern for many years because its increase in the atmosphere is thought to intensify the greenhouse effect, resulting in unwanted warming of the Earth (*see* Feature Article: THE PROBLEM WITH CARBON DIOXIDE). Methane is another such "greenhouse gas." Recently a team of scientists from the U.S., Kenya, and West Germany reported that termites, through microbial activity in their digestive system, may produce more carbon dioxide than the industrial burning of fossil fuels (although, unlike fossil fuel burning, termites are not a new source of the gas) and that termites are also major producers of methane.

Scientists have estimated that there may be as much as three-quarters of a ton of termites for each person on the Earth. Termites are found in great abundance in wet savannas, temperate grasslands, cultivated land in less developed countries, and areas that have been cleared and burned. Such areas offer abundant food for these insects and are increasing owing to human activities. The biomass ingested by the termites is actu-

Colleen M. Cavanaugh, Marine Biological Laboratory, Woods Hole, Mass.

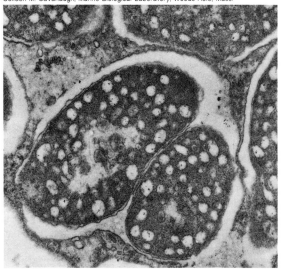

Symbiotic bacteria are visible in this magnified section of trophosome tissue from a tube worm collected from a hydrothermal rift vent. The bacteria produce nutrients for the worm from the oxidation of sulfides.

ally digested by microorganisms in their digestive tracts. In the final analysis it is the microorganisms that produce the gases.

Another rich source of atmospheric methane and carbon dioxide is the flatulence of cattle and other herbivores. As in the case of termites, much of the digestion of the food eaten by these animals is carried out by microorganisms. Finally anaerobic degradation of biomass by methane-producing bacteria in muds and sediments is also a major source of this gas.

Lipids found in the cell membranes of archaebacteria are composed of isoprenoid hydrocarbon chains linked to glycerol by ether bonds. In contrast, in lipids of all other organisms whether microorganisms or higher forms of life, fatty acids rather than isoprenoids are linked to glycerol by ester bonds. By implication the archaebacteria are thought to be modern representatives of forms that existed during the early, Archean period of the Earth. Workers in West Germany and France reported in 1979 that the organic matter called kerogen found in oil shales contained these novel ether-bound isoprenoids (alkanes). Recently the same workers extended their observations to other ancient sediments and to petroleums. Their findings provide further evidence for the participation, at least in part, of the archaebacteria in petroleum formation.

Iguanas are herbivorous lizards that use a microbial fermentation system in their hindgut to break down plant materials. In 1982 researchers reported that in order for hatchling iguanas to develop the complex populations of microorganisms in their hindgut necessary for efficient food digestion and thus for well-being, they must associate with adults during the first few weeks of life. The young iguanas acquire the complex fermentative microbial community from the fecal matter of adults.

Tube worms found in deep-sea, sulfide-rich hydrothermal vents lack mouth, digestive tract, and anus. Thus there has been much speculation about their food sources and feeding mechanisms. New evidence indicates that bacteria with very simple metabolic requirements live in specialized tissues, called the trophosome, in the body cavity of the worms. These bacteria gain energy by oxidizing hydrogen sulfide. The energy is then used to produce organic material from carbon dioxide and other inorganic substances. This process is similar to photosynthesis except that the primary energy comes from sulfide oxidation rather than from light.

The wood and other biomass eaten by termites are actually digested by microorganisms living in their digestive tracts. According to a recent study this microbial activity may be a major source of atmospheric carbon dioxide and methane.

Bottau—Peter Arnold, Inc.

The worm is then able to use the organic substances formed by the bacteria. (See *Zoology*, below.)

A similar process is thought to be used by certain bivalve mollusks (clams) found in sulfide-rich habitats such as hydrothermal vents and intertidal mudflats. These animals have a greatly reduced gut, and some lack a gut entirely. The bacterial activities in the mollusks, however, appear to be restricted to gill tissue.

Health-related microbiology. Joining the ranks of recently recognized diseases such as Legionnaires' disease and toxic shock syndrome is acquired immunodeficiency syndrome (AIDS). The disease was first diagnosed in adults, specifically in male homosexuals, in intravenous drug users, and in Haitian refugees. Most recently it has been found in hemophiliacs and children. On the one hand, the spread of AIDS resembles that of hepatitis B in that one mode of transmission appears to be blood products and contaminated hypodermic needles. It also appears to be sexually transmitted, not only between male homosexuals but between heterosexuals as well. Finally there was evidence that AIDS may be spread by intimate contact between family members. What remained unknown is the length of time between infection and appearance of the symptoms.

Present evidence indicates that AIDS may be caused by a virus. The first stage in the disease syndrome is an impairment of the body's immune defense mechanism. Individuals whose immune systems are rendered defective are then susceptible to a variety of opportunistic, high-mortality infections and to Kaposi's sarcoma, a deadly cancer of the soft tissues. (*See* Year in Review: MEDICAL SCIENCES: *General Medicine*.)

A collaborative effort between U.S. and British scientists resulted in a radically new approach toward the preparation of a vaccine, a totally synthetic vaccine against foot-and-mouth disease (FMD). The virus that causes FMD is composed of one molecule of single-stranded RNA enclosed in a coat containing 60 copies each of four different proteins. The amino-acid sequence was determined for one of the proteins showing promise as a vaccine. By linking amino acids together chemically, the scientists then synthesized seven small chains (peptides) representing different regions of the protein. One of these synthetic peptides was found to effectively stimulate the immune system in guinea pigs against FMD. Moreover, preliminary testing in cattle and pigs appeared promising.

—Robert G. Eagon

Molecular biology

New and exciting discoveries in molecular biology were reported at an astonishing rate during the past year. The number of pages in journals, old and new, devoted to recombinant DNA studies alone increased faster than the U.S. national debt. By early 1983 data

banks set up to store the vast amount of information in published sequences of nucleotides, the building blocks of DNA molecules, were increasing at the rate of 10% per month.

Among the discoveries of this vintage year, to cite some examples, are the role of small RNA-containing particles in guiding ribosomes that synthesize secretory proteins to the membranes that the proteins must cross when they are synthesized and the demonstration that genes can be transferred from bacteria to plants in a manner that permits regeneration of normal plants containing the transferred DNA. But several other sets of experiments—involving cutting and splicing of RNA on one hand and movement of parts of chromosomes in the generation of cancer cells on the other—are so dramatic that they must be described in detail. In 1983 both of these stories continued to unfold, with new results reported almost weekly.

Self-excising RNA. In order to understand the tremendous attention attracted by the work of Thomas Cech and his colleagues at the University of Colorado on the splicing of RNA, it should be recalled that the hereditary units, genes, consist of linear sequences of the nucleotides adenine, cytosine, guanine, and thymine, abbreviated A, C, G, and T. The information in these sequences is expressed in the cell by synthesizing an RNA copy of one of the two helical DNA strands. The resulting RNA molecule will thus contain a linear sequence of A, C, G, and U units (in RNA molecules U, uracil, is equivalent to T) determined by those nucleotides of the DNA that served as template.

There are several classes of genes in all cells and corresponding classes of RNA molecules. One class consists of ribosomal RNA, one of transfer RNA, and one of messenger RNA. Ribosomal RNA is metabolically stable; it plays principally a structural role in forming the scaffold for assembly of RNA and protein particles called ribosomes, which function as workbenches for the synthesis of proteins. Transfer RNA molecules function in protein synthesis by attaching to single amino acids, the building blocks of proteins, and delivering them to the surface of the ribosome, where they are added to a growing protein chain. The third class of RNA, messenger RNA, also associates with the surface of ribosomes. These RNA molecules carry the genetic code which, decoded by transfer RNA molecules reading the nucleotide sequence in groups of three, determines the order of amino acids in the finished protein.

These basic processes are fundamentally similar in all cells, from bacteria to protozoans to plants and animals, including human beings. The advent of recombinant DNA methods, however, made possible sufficiently detailed studies that revealed some crucial differences between bacteria and all other cells. In bacteria, in which no nuclear membrane separates the process of RNA synthesis from that of protein synthe-

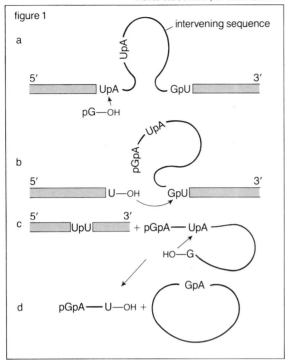

figure 1

a

intervening sequence

UpA

5′ UpA GpU 3′

pG—OH

b

pGpA UpA

GpU

5′ U—OH 3′

c 5′ UpU 3′ + pGpA — UpA

HO—G

d pGpA — U—OH +

GpA

To most molecular biologists the proposition that an RNA molecule could be cut and spliced without an enzyme to do the job sounds preposterous, but Cech and his colleagues presented absolutely convincing evidence that such is the case. Initially they had intended to study the enzymatic removal of the intervening sequence in the *Tetrahymena* ribosomal RNA precursor. It was during attempts to purify such an enzyme that they first noticed that the processing reaction did not seem to need a protein. Eventually they showed that the RNA precursor could be synthesized in the test tube using enzymes from *Escherichia coli*, completely freed of all *E. coli* protein, and still processed.

In addition to the precursor RNA the cleavage and splicing reactions require some salt, some Mg^{2+} (magnesium ion), and guanosine (guanine plus a sugar) or a guanosine nucleotide. The proposed splicing reaction mechanism, shown in figure 1, has several unusual features. The bonds to be broken (*see* 1a) are between U and A on the left of the intervening sequence and between G and U on the right (the p's represent linking phosphate groups). The guanosine monomer (pG—OH) attacks the left side U-A bond, forming a G-A bond instead and leaving a free U end. That U attacks the right side G-U bond (1b), freeing the G end and forming a U-U bond. That completes the splice and frees the 413-nucleotide intervening sequence with the extra G at one end (1c). The intervening sequence is itself processed further: the G end created by cutting at the G-U site attacks a U-A bond near the other end of the fragment (1c), forming a G-A bond that effectively circularizes most of the sequence, splitting off a linear 15-nucleotide piece with G at one end and U at the other (1d).

The intervening sequence is not a mere spectator at these events. It has a distinctive structure that can be deduced by examining the nucleotide sequence and comparing that sequence with those of several genes from the mitochondria of yeast and other funguses. In every case a structure can be drawn that positions the two sites to be joined exactly opposite each other. The way in which the intervening sequence folds in order to do this is shown in figure 2, taken from the work of Wayne Davies, Richard Waring, and their colleagues at the University of Manchester in England. When the nucleotide sequences of four mitochondrial genes from *Aspergillus* and five from yeast were compared, it was noted that, even though the intervening sequences varied considerably in length, they had seven domains in common (*see* 2a). The sequences of the second and sixth, the third and fourth, and the fifth and seventh domains are completely or partially complementary, *i.e.*, capable of forming double-stranded structures in which by means of hydrogen bonds A is paired with U and G is paired with C. Such pairing forces the RNA to fold up to look something like the transfer RNA cloverleaf (2b).

sis, all three classes of RNA are synthesized on their DNA templates in forms that are almost identical to their mature, functional form. This statement is not quite true: the two ribosomal RNA's are synthesized as one extra-long molecule that has to be cut apart and trimmed at the ends, and several transfer RNA molecules are also cut from larger precursors, but there is no splicing together of cut ends of RNA and no processing, in general, of messenger RNA.

The situation in cells with nuclei is quite different. There, many genes have been found to have interruptions, intervening sequences of DNA that disrupt the sequence that codes for protein in messenger RNA. Thus, between the synthesis of the RNA in the nucleus and its use to code for protein synthesis in the cytoplasm outside the nucleus, these intervening sequences must be cut out of the RNA and the cut ends spliced together. Moreover, the cutting and splicing must be perfectly done; if not, nucleotides will either be added to or deleted from the message, converting the amino-acid sequence of the corresponding protein to nonsense.

The precise mechanism for removal of most intervening sequences is still unknown, but this is the question to which, in one special case, Cech and his colleagues found an unexpected answer. Their studies show without doubt that both cutting and splicing of a ribosomal RNA precursor from *Tetrahymena*, a protozoan, to remove a 413-nucleotide intervening sequence, occurs without the participation of protein. This particular RNA molecule can cut and splice itself!

332

The crucial part is the first domain, called the internal guide, which is constrained by the folded structure to pair with the part of the RNA that is to be spliced. The internal guide effectively forms a jig that brings a sequence U-X into juxtaposition with another sequence G-Y in which X and Y may be any of the four nucleotides (2c). Cleavage of the U-X bond and the G-Y bond (2d) is followed by splicing to form a new U-Y bond (2e). The intervening sequence, with X at one end and G at the other, is excised. As far as anyone knows at present, this reaction is catalyzed by enzymes in mitochondria. But the similarity to Cech's ribosomal RNA is striking. Not only is the cleavage chemistry related, but the *Tetrahymena* intervening sequence contains all seven domains, including an internal guide.

A great deal of genetic evidence supports the model described above for mitochondrial RNA splicing. What

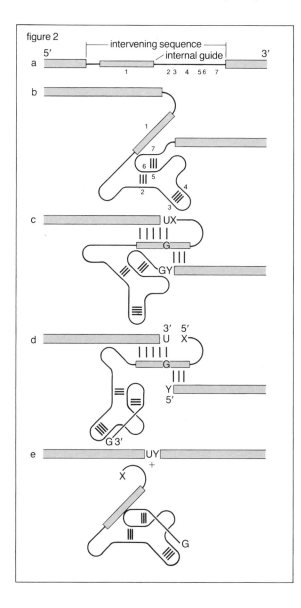

figure 2

remains to be determined is exactly what role proteins play in the reaction and whether other RNA molecules can do things to themselves. The finding of RNA molecules with such unexpected chemical reactivity bears a significant relationship to some questions about primitive living systems. Could the first molecules of nucleic acid condense and replicate without enzymes? Can RNA fragments be transposed from one molecule to another?

Oncogenes. Transposable genetic elements, meaning transposable segments of DNA, have been studied intensively for several years (see *1982 Yearbook of Science and the Future* Year in Review: LIFE SCIENCES: *Molecular biology*). Such elements were first recognized in corn, where they are responsible for, among other things, the striking pattern of colors among the kernels of Indian corn. Until very recently, however, it had not been possible to isolate a DNA fragment containing a transposable genetic element of corn in order to study its molecular properties. Instead, analogous elements were isolated from bacteria, from the fruit fly *Drosophila*, from yeast, and from animals. In the last case the discovery is particularly significant because it bears on the mechanism of transformation of normal cells into tumor cells.

Every transposable element studied thus far has certain features in common with other such elements: the nucleotide sequence at one end of the element is an inverted copy of the sequence at the other end; between these inverted repeated sequences there are stretches of DNA that code for proteins which, in the case of bacteria, are enzymes that catalyze the excision and recombination of the element itself with new sites on the chromosome; and, wherever the element is inserted into the chromosome, a short length of the chromosome (5, 9, or 11 nucleotide pairs) is duplicated on either side of the insertion.

Insertion of a transposable element into a chromosome can have significant consequences. If the insertion occurs in the region of a gene that codes for the amino acid sequence of a protein, that protein will not be made; if the protein was an essential one, the cell will not survive. If the insertion occurs between genes, it may have no measurable effect at all. However, some of the DNA sequence between coding regions of genes is regulatory, determining when and how abundantly the adjacent gene is expressed, *i.e.*, transcribed into RNA. Insertion of a transposable element into such a region may turn on a nearby gene. If that gene codes for a protein that in turn is responsible for regulating cellular processes, the entire network of controls over cell division, for example, may be affected. Such a course of events appears to have occurred in the formation of some tumor cells.

Assume for the moment that in each cell of an animal there exist a small number of genes whose products control a regulatory network and that overproduction of one such protein leads to transformation of the cell into a tumor cell. Now, cells of birds and rodents are known to be transformable by infection with certain viruses. These so-called RNA tumor viruses carry very few genes, of which only one, called the oncogene, is needed for transformation. The product of the oncogene is one of the crucial regulatory proteins mentioned above. Transformation of the infected cell to a tumor cell is due to the abundant production by the virus of the oncogene's protein.

How did the virus acquire an oncogene which, after all, codes for a protein of an animal cell? It turns out that for each different viral oncogene there exists a corresponding cellular gene called a proto-oncogene; these are the cell's crucial regulatory genes referred to above. The tumor viruses probably acquire oncogenes by some form of natural recombination event involving DNA copies of the viral RNA and DNA copies of the proto-oncogene messenger RNA. Details of that event are unknown. However, possession of an oncogene in the viral chromosome is not the only way in which RNA tumor viruses can transform cells. The structure of DNA copies of the viral RNA revealed these molecules to have inverted repeated sequences at each end; in effect, the viral DNA is a transposable genetic element. If this material becomes inserted into a cellular chromosomal site suitably positioned with respect to a proto-oncogene, the latter can be turned on. Thus, the RNA tumor viruses can cause cancer in two ways: rapidly by providing a lot of oncogene product, or slowly by integration into a cellular chromosome and promoting proto-oncogene expression.

Human cancer has not been associated with RNA tumor viruses. But there are proto-oncogenes in human cells, and recently they were implicated in human cancer. In one case the proto-oncogene responsible for a human bladder carcinoma was isolated and shown to differ from the homologous gene in normal cells by only one nucleotide pair. In this case it appears that cell transformation was due to a consequent change in the properties of the oncogene product rather than a change in its abundance. In another striking case a type of human leukemia was shown to be associated with a chromosomal rearrangement that brought a proto-oncogene adjacent to a gene involved in antibody production. As a result a cell that should have been devoted to the synthesis of antibodies became a cancer cell instead.

One should not conclude from these examples that the molecular basis of cancer is now understood. Activation or modification of proto-oncogenes is only one step in what is certainly a multistep process. But molecular biologists, using recombinant DNA technology, have provided the tools to discover the remaining steps. (*See* Year in Review: MEDICAL SCIENCES: *General medicine*.)

—Robert Haselkorn

Zoology

In the past year genetic engineering techniques were used to solve basic problems in development and neurobiology. Investigation of brain transplants in laboratory animals progressed, and recent discoveries indicated that a magnetic sense may be prevalent in animals. Physiologists sought clues about the way in which animals in deep-sea vents survive in a toxic environment. A fossil discovery in Antarctica answered a long-standing question on the route by which marsupials reached Australia.

Developmental zoology. Gene splicing and genetic engineering techniques in the past few years have shown that specific genes can be isolated easily from one organism and transferred to another. Surprisingly these genes are also passed on to offspring, indicating stable integration of the genes into the host's hereditary material. The question currently being asked is whether incorporated genes are expressed in a normal fashion in animals carrying them.

At a recent conference of the New York Academy of Sciences, Richard Axel of Columbia University in New York City described his work with the gene for human growth hormone. The isolated human gene is flanked at each end by regions of DNA that regulate expression of the gene. Only when the gene and surrounding control areas were inserted into cultured mouse cells was the gene expressed. For example, when glucocorticoid

Normal mouse on right is dwarfed by littermate that carries multiple genes coding for rat growth hormone. The genes were injected into mouse eggs, which were implanted in foster mothers and allowed to develop.

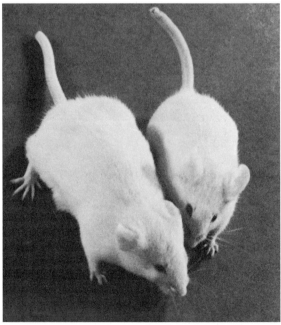

hormones were added to the cultures, the cells responded by producing human growth hormone rather than mouse growth hormone. Axel believed that this response is indicative of two cellular levels of gene regulation. One of them is a long-term regulation related to cellular differentiation, turning the mouse genes off, while the other is a transient control in response to chemical signals, allowing the human genes to be expressed.

Such genetic manipulations have promise for discovering the way in which genes in higher organisms are controlled during normal growth and development. As these mechanisms become better understood, treatments may be developed for genetic deficiencies and new animals may be designed for agricultural purposes. For example, in a cooperative research project involving scientists from the University of Washington at Seattle, the Salk Institute at La Jolla, Calif., and the University of Pennsylvania, the gene for growth hormone was isolated from rats and injected into mouse eggs. The eggs were then implanted into surrogate mothers and were born normally. After birth several mice developed to twice their normal size. Careful analysis of their DNA revealed as many as 20 copies of the rat gene inserted into their genomes. Ralph Brinster, the team member from the University of Pennsylvania, indicated the obvious practical applications of this procedure: if larger mice can be made, then larger farm animals can also be engineered. Though these applications will not develop tomorrow, they are now in the realm of the possible.

Neurobiology. Gene cloning techniques also were applied to research problems in neurobiology. Investigators at Kyoto University in Japan and the Salk Institute announced the succesful cloning and sequencing of the DNA that codes for the acetylcholine receptor in nerve cells. Acetylcholine is one of the transmitter substances allowing signals to pass between adjacent nerve cells or to muscles. These receptors are large cell-membrane proteins that regulate the flow of ions across membranes of excitable cells. In this process when a nerve impulse arrives at the end of a cell, it causes release of acetylcholine, which diffuses to the next cell, binds to receptors there, and causes a change in ion permeability in that cell. This action may trigger formation of a new nerve impulse in the second cell, depending on the amount released and the sensitivity of the cell.

Isolation of the DNA for the receptor now makes possible its insertion into bacteria, which then can be used to make large quantities of receptor for further study. It may be possible to insert the bacterially synthesized receptor into artificial membranes where its effects can be studied. In addition, mutations can be made in the gene, the altered protein manufactured in bacteria, and then the effects of the alteration on function tested in the artificial system.

In another area of neurobiology the advances that most capture the imagination involve brain transplants in mammals. In the early 1970s it was shown that embryonic brain tissue transplanted into brains of adult rodents would develop connections with the host's brain. These experiments have been repeated and furthered in the pursuit of treatments for neurological disorders in humans. For example, Peter J. Whitehouse of Johns Hopkins University in Baltimore showed that Alzheimer's disease, a major brain disfunction of the elderly, involves the degeneration of a specific group of neurons found in the basal forebrain. These cells supply acetylcholine that arouses the cells of the cerebral cortex. Implantations of appropriate neurons might compensate for the degenerated neurons in those afflicted by this condition. Such developments are still remote, however, because transplants involving differentiated brain tissue do not work as well as those from fetal brains; furthermore, studies done of transplants in primates have not yielded the success seen with rodents.

The caterpillar of the gypsy moth defoliates millions of acres of invaluable hardwood forests in the northeastern U.S. every year. In 1982 a team of U.S. scientists visited China, the presumed land of origin for the moth as a species, to hunt for specific parasites that could be used as biological control agents.

Nonetheless, replacement transplants are being performed with interesting results. Ulf Stenevi and Anders Björklund at the University of Lund in Sweden grafted mouse neuronal tissue into the brains of rats and found that the grafts survived for at least six months, developing nerve connections with the host's brain and correcting a surgically induced neurological problem in the rats. These experiments are significant because it is usually impossible to cross species or even family lines in transplant experiments with other types of tissues. When individuals are immunologically different, the grafts are rejected. Apparently the brain is an immunologically privileged site. The blood-brain barrier, a system of cells and capillary walls that retards the passage of substances in the blood to brain tissue, may prevent antibodies from getting to the foreign tissue and destroying it.

Raymond Lund and Stephen McLoon of the University of South Carolina transplanted retinas into blind rats. Because the optic nerves degenerate in blinded rats, the researchers attached the retinas directly to the superior colliculus of adult rats' brains, the area of the brain that normally receives visual information. They found that the retinas grew in this new location, making neural contact with collicular cells. William Freed and Richard Jed Wyatt of the National Institute of Mental Health in the U.S. extended these experiments to determine the extent of communication between the host brain and transplanted retina. They passed a fiber-optic device through the rat's skull so that the transplanted retina could be tested for light reception. Nerve activity was detected, but it is not known whether the rat perceived this as light or simply as a nonspecific stimulus.

While many scientists worked to understand the operation of the nervous system, others delved into its organization at the molecular level. Gerald Edelman and colleagues at Rockefeller University in New York City discovered a large protein containing the sugar sialic acid that they believe serves as a cellular glue to hold nerve cells together in associations necessary for normal functioning. When nerve cells are grown in laboratory cultures, they form an intricate branching pattern reminiscent of their organization in the nervous system. If the large proteins that occur on the outer surfaces of these nerve cells are blocked by specific antibodies, the branching pattern is lost and the culture becomes a tangle of nerve cell processes "resembling a bowl of spaghetti." Knowledge of the surface differences among nerve cells will aid those investigators studying transplant techniques.

Behavior. Marine animals are capable of accurately navigating in the open ocean. Bluefin tuna migrate from the Gulf of Mexico to Norway, a distance of at least 9,000 km (5,600 mi), and green turtles regularly migrate from Brazil to Ascension Island, a trip of more than 2,200 km (1,360 mi) to a target that is only 88 sq km (34 sq mi). To do this requires that the animals have acute navigational abilities.

Until fairly recently scientists had little information about the way in which animals use cues from sunlight, star positions, odors, electric and magnetic fields, and other phenomena to sense direction. In the late 1970s crystals of magnetite, a magnetic oxide of iron, were observed in bees and in pigeons and were implicated in their homing behavior (see *1981* and *1982 Yearbook of Science and the Future* Year in Review: LIFE SCIENCES: *Zoology*). Since then, continually accumulating reports of work with other species suggest that the occurrence of these crystals may be widespread in the animal kingdom. Magnetite has been found by researchers in four common Pacific dolphins in the space between the dura mater and the skull, the same place in which it occurs in pigeons. Similar particles have been found in Cuvier's beaked whale, blue marlins, yellowfin, skipjack, and green turtles. The magnetic particles appear to be closely associated with nervous tissue, suggesting that they may serve as sensors. Robin R. Baker and Jan Mather of the University of Manchester, England, reported that magnetite also occurs in the ethmoid cavities of both human beings and rodents.

Two types of magnetite particles have been found: small granules a few angstroms in diameter (one angstrom is a hundred-millionth of a centimeter) and large spheroids that are 10–50 micrometers (millionths of a meter) in size. Joseph Kirschvink of the California Institute of Technology and Andrew E. Dizon and Michael M. Walker of the National Marine Fisheries Service found that tuna can be taught to discriminate between the Earth's normal geomagnetic field and a slightly stronger artificial field. This may be evidence for two magnetic senses in these fish, one that senses magnetic direction and one that senses small changes in the strength of the geomagnetic field. The latter would provide a map sense for animals as they traveled along a compass bearing. The ocean floor, due to its pattern of rifts and ridges, has a distinct magnetic picture that the animals may very well be able to perceive and to incorporate into their navigational memory.

As in pigeons and bees, homing in marine animals is not entirely attributable to a magnetic sense, and animals use a combination of information in their migrations. It has long been known that salmon rely on a sense of smell to home to specific streams during mating runs. Recent work by Kees Groot and Peter Dill of the Pacific Biological Station in British Columbia showed that salmon also are able to orient to polarized light. In natural environments polarizaton of sunlight is most intense in directions toward and directly away from the Sun and least at angles 90° from the Sun. Though scientists are still not sure exactly how animals navigate during long migrations, the emerging picture is one in which the information available is much greater than had been suspected previously.

Organismal zoology. Significant insect damage occurred in North American forests in 1982, according to Thomas H. Hofacker, an entomologist with the U.S. Forest Service. Thirteen million trees spread over 1.7 million ha (4.2 million ac) were estimated to have been killed by pine bark beetles. Particularly hard hit were forests in Glacier and Yellowstone national parks. Beetle larvae damage trees by consuming the cambium layers beneath the bark, reducing the tree's growth and allowing fungus to invade the wood. The fungus infection eventually kills the tree.

In the northeastern U.S. another insect pest, the gypsy moth, damages 13 million ac of timber annually. The larvae of these insects feed on leaves, especially oaks, reducing the tree's ability to photosynthesize. During the past year a team of U.S. scientists traveled to the People's Republic of China to find new and specific parasites of the gypsy moth that could be used as biological control agents. The gypsy moth is thought to have originated as a species in China, and it was hoped that natural pests would have evolved there. According to William E. Wallner, a U.S. Department of Agriculture entomologist and member of the team, 52 locations were examined, and 13 parasites, 14 predators, and a viral and fungal disease of the gypsy moth

were identified. The Chinese, however, would allow them to take only the viral and fungal diseases out of the country for further testing as control agents.

Though zoologists know a lot about the onshore activities of penguins in Antarctica, they are rather ignorant of the activities of these birds while diving and food gathering. Gerald L. Kooyman of Scripps Institution of Oceanography in La Jolla, Calif., studied the energetics of food gathering in king penguins at South Georgia Island. Foraging at sea does not appear to be expensive for the penguin. The cost in terms of a ratio to resting metabolic expenditure seems to be about the same as for terrestrial mammals and birds. On a foraging trip a penguin must catch 50–90 squid to provide for its own and its chick's needs. Penguins seem to catch squid successfully on only about 10% of their dives, an efficiency ratio similar to that observed in fur seals. One penguin averaged about 304 dives per day for four days. Many dives were more than 100 m (330 ft), and the deepest dive was to 240 m (790 ft).

Environmental biology. Three oceanographic research vessels, the "Melville" and "New Horizon" operated by Scripps and the "Lulu" from Woods Hole Oceanographic Institution in Massachusetts, rendezvoused off the Galápagos Islands to study organisms living in deep-sea vent communities along the East Pacific Rise. The "Alvin," a submersible vessel carried

Three-week-old chick (below) and a pair of yearlings (left) reflect efforts at the Patuxent Wildlife Research Center in Maryland to raise whooping cranes for reintroduction to the wild. Chicks that hatch from extra eggs laid by Patuxent's whoopers are reared by sandhill-crane foster parents.

Photos, Luther Goldman—U.S. Fish & Wildlife Service

Institute of Polar Studies, Ohio State University; illustration, R. W. Tope

Antarctic find of a fossil jaw fragment (above) from a small marsupial animal supports a theory of the way in which marsupials reached Australia from South America. Sketch (left) is an artist's conception of the animal.

by the "Melville," made 18 dives, bringing to the surface clams and vestimentiferan worms for scientists to study in laboratories aboard the other ships. The vent animals depend upon bacteria as their source of nourishment. The bacteria in turn oxidize hydrogen sulfide emanating from the vent to sulfate, releasing energy to drive their own metabolism. John Baross of Oregon State University found that these bacteria are unusual in that they grow rapidly at temperatures as high as 100° C (212° F) and at pressures 200 times greater than those on the surface. Some of these bacteria were even found in water sampled at temperatures above 300° C (570° F), but it is not yet known if they can grow under such conditions.

Animals in vent areas are not exposed to such high temperatures, but they do encounter levels of hydrogen sulfide that usually would be toxic to most animals. Consequently researchers on this voyage were interested in the blood chemistry and aerobic metabolism of the clams and worms and were looking for special adaptations that allow them to live in this potentially toxic environment. Jim Childress of the University of California at Santa Barbara and George Somero of Scripps found that the oxygen-binding capacity of the blood and oxygen metabolism were the same as found in surface animals even though the concentration of hydrogen sulfide in the blood was 25–50 times that found in seawater near the vents. Close examination revealed a blood protein that apparently binds sulfide and holds it so that it does not interfere with metabolism. The protein may unload its sulfide to symbiotic bacteria that are associated with the worms and clams.

In the ever increasing search for oil, companies are drilling wells off the coast of New England on the Georges Banks, a lobster- and fish-breeding area. Jelle Atema and colleagues of Woods Hole looked at what effects drilling mud from these rigs has on immature lobsters. Drilling mud is a complex mixture of clays and organic compounds forced down the drill hole to lubricate the bit and to prevent gas blowouts. Young lobsters may be particularly susceptible because after hatching they drift freely until they reach about 2.5 cm (one inch) in size. They then settle down on the bottom in deep water and build a burrow that they inhabit for the next year. Atema found that if drilling muds were added to aquariums containing young lobsters at this critical stage, behavioral modifications took place. The animals did not feed as vigorously, molts were delayed, and there was excessive loss of limbs. In addition, as the clays settled out forming layers four millimeters (a sixth of an inch) thick, the animals took much longer to construct burrows. The overall results are that the young lobsters grow more slowly and spend more time exposed to predators; the subsequent effect is to reduce lobster populations.

As might be expected, these results were challenged by representatives of the oil industry, who felt that the laboratory tests simply proved the obvious: if you subject confined animals to high concentrations of mud, you get some bad effects. At sea, they claimed, the amount of mud released in proportion to water would lead to much lower concentrations, which would be scattered by ocean currents. In addition, if the few rigs presently in the ocean deposited mud as presumed, only small areas would be affected in proportion to the total area on the banks.

In 1982 a three-year extension of the Endangered Species Act was passed by both houses of the U.S. Congress. No major changes were made in the law, which protects rare plants and animals. The new legislation authorizes the secretary of the interior to establish populations of threatened or endangered species in new locations and thus allows management discretion. This provision may give impetus to federal programs that have existed since the 1960s to breed endangered species and to release offspring to the wild.

One such program for avian species is located at the Patuxent Wildlife Research Center in Maryland.

James Carpenter, head of the propagation section at the center, indicated that in 1982 six species were being bred at Patuxent. Considerable effort is being put into attempts to raise whooping cranes for reintroduction. The whooper flocks were started by removing eggs from nests on natural breeding grounds in Canada. The Patuxent cranes lay up to 11 eggs per breeding season, compared with 2 in the wild. The extra eggs are incubated by sandhill cranes, which are kept at the center as surrogate mothers. The results have been positive so far, but the program is not without critics. Some believe that surrogate-raised birds will not have normal behavior and consequently will not compete or breed effectively with wild stock. Others feel that genetic inbreeding in captive populations will lead to their demise because of a reduction in genetic variability. Biologists at Patuxent consider both criticisms weak. Studies have shown that normal behavior apparently does develop, and records are kept of mating pairs to prevent close relatives from mating.

Evolution. The first discovery of a mammalian fossil in Antarctica was reported in the past year by an expedition sponsored by the National Science Foundation. Michael Woodburne of the University of California at Riverside found the jawbone of a small rodentlike marsupial in a rock he picked up during a rest break from fossil hunting on Seymour Island. The find is significant in that it provides the first evidence sup-

porting the hypothesis that marsupials, which originated in North America, gradually spread to Australia via South America and Antarctica at a time when the three southern continents were joined as the supercontinent Gondwanaland. The movement southward is documented in fossils from the North and South America continents, but Antarctic specimens were lacking. William Zinsmeister of the Ohio State University Institute of Polar Studies, leader of the expedition, reported that other discoveries on this trip added to knowledge of the early Antarctic climate. An abundance of petrified wood suggested that dense forests were present. Skeletal remains from plesiosaurs and mosasaurs, marine reptiles of the Cretaceous Period (which ended about 65 million years ago), indicated the presence of warm tropical seas.

Views on primate and hominid evolution are changing as a result of recent fossil discoveries. After examining new fossils from Pakistan, David Pilbeam of Harvard University's Peabody Museum concluded that *Ramapithecus* was not a hominid ancestor but rather was an ancestor of the orangutan. The view that *Ramapithecus* was a hominid would have required that hominids and apes diverged perhaps 14 million years ago, although the best current evidence indicates that the divergence occurred 7 million to 9 million years ago.

In Kenya Richard E. Leakey of the Kenya National Museum and Hidema Ishida of Osaka University in Japan announced discovery of a jawbone estimated to be eight million years old with apelike and humanlike characteristics. The discoverers believed that it could represent a true intermediate. As this work went on, J. Desmond Clark and Timothy D. White from the University of California at Berkeley found four-million-year-old evidence of walking hominids in the Awash Valley of Ethiopia. This discovery extends the finding of humanlike remains in this valley back 400,000 years from the time of Lucy, the famous hominid fossil described by Donald C. Johanson in 1979. Lucy has been controversial because Johanson had suggested that she walked upright. The new find includes a skull and, importantly, a femur (upper leg bone) fragment that proves bipedalism predated Lucy.

—Warren D. Dolphin

See also Feature Articles: Nature's Remarkable Mosaics; Lights in the Summer Darkness; Plants That Eat Meat; Probing the Origin of Life.

California condor chick Sisquoc, born at the San Diego Wild Animal Park in California in early 1983, is the first of this endangered species ever hatched in captivity.

Materials sciences

Glass fibers that conduct light waves continued to be developed and improved for applications in communications and computers. Ceramics engineers also completed the mirror for the telescope that will be carried into orbit by the space shuttle. Efforts were under way

Bell Laboratories scientist adjusts a laser to obtain the shortest pulse of light ever created, 30 millionths of a billionth of a second long. Approximately 10^{10} such pulses per second in a single glass fiber might someday carry the tens of thousands of conversations now handled by a 144-fiber cable.

by metallurgists to develop cleaner and more energy-efficient methods of extracting copper from its ores.

Ceramics

Some of the most active areas of ceramic research involved contributions to communications and to the rapidly developing computer revolution. As successive developments in the semiconductor industry continue to shrink the size of computers and make them more powerful, their applications may well be limited primarily by the ability of scientists and engineers to communicate and display the vast amounts of information that are processed.

Fiber optics. Glass fibers that transmit light waves have great potential for solving many of these very-high-volume communications needs. More than 50 of these fiber-optic telecommunications links, some of them hundreds of kilometers long, have been installed in the U.S. alone. Their success has been based largely on ceramic research that reduced the optical losses within these fibers so that the distance between optical amplifiers, or repeaters, enabled commercially practical applications to be made. Scientists at Bell Laboratories and Western Electric Co. recently reported device and fiber advances that could further increase the information-handling capacity of future light-wave systems. For example, they demonstrated a laser that generates pulses so short that a single fiber may someday carry the tens of thousands of conversations now carried by a 144-fiber cable. They also demonstrated light-emitting diodes that could be used for wavelength multiplexing. Multiplexing, the combining of optical signals of different wavelengths, could significantly increase the information-carrying capacity of individual glass fibers.

A related field that is just emerging is the use of ceramics in integrated optic circuits. The objective of such circuits is not to transmit large volumes of information over long distances, as in fiber optics, but to condense in size a large number of optical devices and perform a large number of optical functions in a single tiny chip. In such circuits light waves can be made to perform increasingly complex tasks, much the way that electrons do in advanced integrated microelectronic circuits. In current hybrid optical (photonic) devices discrete light sources, modulators, filters, switches, detectors, and waveguides are built into or mounted on a suitable substrate, such as gallium arsenide. Although these hybrid circuits are still comparatively bulky, inefficient, and susceptible to electronic interference, particularly if they involve electronic-to-photonic signal conversions, their construction is relatively straightforward. For example, tiny semiconductor lasers and thin optical waveguides can be fabricated directly within the thin-film gallium arsenide substrate. Small lithium niobate electro-optic crystals can be used to encode or decode the light beams that are formed or to deflect them at any desired point in the circuit. Thin-film iron garnet disks can be used as magneto-optic switches. Birefringent ceramic materials (materials that bend light differently depending on how the light is polarized) can be used to separate light beams. Electro-optic crystal filters can be used to separate different wavelengths of light comprising messages that had previously been multiplexed together.

These hybrid circuits have considerable promise, but work is already under way to produce monolithic, integrated photonic circuits. They would contain large numbers of photonic devices built directly into a single, tiny chip, much as millions of transistors are built into a single silicon chip. They will undoubtedly be very much smaller than hybrid photonic circuits and probably much cheaper and more reliable as well.

As of 1983 photonic circuits were being fabricated to perform complex, demanding military tasks, such as rapid radar frequency identification. Their compatibility with fiber-optic communication links seems certain to spur their use in telecommunication networks. Some researchers, however, were already exploring their use in computer logic and memory circuits, and they may ultimately form the basis of an entirely new family of high-speed computers.

The insensitivity of glass fibers to electromagnetic interference, important for critical military applica-

Ceramist examines samples of silicon carbide, a high-temperature, high-strength ceramic, at the General Electric Research and Development Center.

General Electric Company, Research and Development Center, Schenectady, New York

tions, and their ability to operate in environments where current-carrying wires would represent a safety hazard opened new applications for them as a wide variety of sensors. The U.S. Navy and the Defense Advanced Research Projects Agency, for example, began developing militarily secure fiber-optic acoustic sensors that can detect and precisely locate oceangoing submarines. By 1983 this work had resulted in the development of two promising approaches. One depended on the fact that acoustic (sound) waves in the water change the effective optical path length of the fiber, both by changing its actual physical length and by changing its refractive index as a result of pressure-induced strains in the glass. The other approach depended on the fact that these strains induce birefringence in the glass fiber, causing light polarized in one direction to travel faster than light polarized at right angles to that direction. For both approaches the differences in path length caused by the acoustic signal must be detected by a sensitive interferometer since the differences are typically much less than the wavelength of the light used. The need for interferometric detection will place stringent new demands on optical fibers. Very thin single-mode fibers that measure only a few micrometers in diameter are required. These force all of the light rays to follow the same path in the fiber and make interferometric detection possible.

The electric power industry was developing fiber-optic sensors that can determine currents and voltages in very-high-power lines and transformers. These could replace conventional sensors that are relatively slow, inaccurate, and expensive when used to monitor power levels and to detect transients that could trigger power network failures. Britain's Central Electricity Research Laboratories were ready to begin field tests in British Columbia of single-mode glass fibers that measure current in 500-kv lines. Also, the Electric Power Research Institute, of Palo Alto, Calif., was supporting research on the use of fiber optics to measure temperatures within the windings of high-voltage generators and transformers so that hot spots could be detected before they led to expensive equipment and system failures.

Flat-panel displays. Another area of the information processing and communication problem in which significant advances were made involved the development of improved flat-panel displays. These have been sought for many years as less bulky, lighter, more efficient, distortion-free replacements for conventional cathode-ray tubes. The technology for small, active (light-emitting) panels based on gas plasma effects is quite mature, and some devices using these panels, such as bank teller stations, were already on the commercial market. There has also been considerable work on small passive devices, based on liquid crystal, electrophoretic, and electrochromic effects. These devices do not actually emit light but instead undergo

341

changes in the way incident light is reflected from them when a voltage is applied. Thus, they operate at extremely low power levels. At this time, however, thin-film electroluminescent panels appear to have the most promise for a wide variety of flat-panel display applications. They require much less power than gas plasma devices and should soon be available with full color capability. They will probably be used initially in five- to seven-inch screens for oscilloscope and computer displays.

Almost all of the flat-panel display devices are heavily dependent on ceramic components and processing. Gas plasma displays use glass films with a magnesium oxide dielectric layer on both sides of the gas cavity to form capacitors in series with each pixel (picture element). These capacitors provide a sustaining voltage for image storage, a valuable feature. In the electrochromic display, the normally colorless tungsten oxide is colored a dark blue by the application of a voltage. When the voltage is reversed, the oxide bleaches back to its original colorless state. In the thin-film electroluminescent display, which has the advantage of being an entirely solid-state device with no gas or liquid sealing problems, vapor-deposited zinc sulfide or zinc selenide is the luminescent material itself. One of the major barriers to the development of large electroluminescent displays was expected to be the difficulty of uniformly vapor-depositing the various layers of different materials required for their construction. Almost all of these flat-panel displays use tin oxide and indium oxide deposited on glass substrates as their transparent electrodes.

Space Telescope. Ceramics also played a major role in bringing the Space Telescope a step closer to reality. Scheduled to be placed in orbit by the space shuttle in 1985, this instrument will allow astronomers to conduct their studies free from the distortion and absorption problems caused by the Earth's atmosphere. For example, ground-based optical telescopes operate almost entirely in the visible part of the spectral range since infrared and ultraviolet wavelengths are almost entirely blocked by the atmosphere. The 2.4-m mirror of the Space Telescope will resolve objects seven times farther out in space and will have 40 times the acuity of its most powerful counterpart on Earth, the 5-m mirror of the Hale telescope at the Palomar Mountain Observatory in California.

Since the telescope will undergo large temperature changes as it moves from sunlight to shadow in space, the development and construction of a mirror that will be able to maintain the necessary optical accuracy during long-exposure experiments was a major challenge. To minimize this problem, the large primary mirror of the Space Telescope was constructed of a special ultralow thermal expansion glass consisting of 92.5% silicon dioxide and 7.5% titanium dioxide. The initial glass mirror blank was prepared by the Corning Glass Works. Its final polishing took eight months and was accomplished on a special computer-controlled polishing machine. To be certain that the final shape would be precisely that required for actual operation in space, the final polishing was done under conditions accurately simulating a zero-gravity environment. To do this the mirror was supported at 130 points, with each support exerting a computer-controlled force calculated to exactly counter the forces exerted by the mirror's own weight. The final surface of the mirror was smoothed to about one part in ten million. The mirror was then coated with ultrathin layers of reflective aluminum and magnesium fluoride.

—Norman M. Tallan

Metallurgy

During the past year there were considerable interest and activity in regard to the development and testing of novel copper-making processes. Traditionally, copper is extracted from its ore in a sequence of three separate operations involving roasting, smelting, and converting. The feed material is a concentrated mixture of complex iron-copper sulfides containing, typically, 20–30% copper by weight, and the iron and sulfur are removed by oxidation in the roasting-smelting-converting sequence.

In the roasting operation some oxidation of the sulfides to form iron oxide (FeO) and sulfur dioxide (SO_2) occurs, although the principal purpose is to dry and heat the concentrate in preparation for smelting. Smelting is normally carried out in an oil- or gas-fired reverberatory furnace (a furnace in which heat is radiated from the roof onto the material to be treated). In this process the roasted concentrate and a silica flux are melted to form two immiscible (non-mixable) melts: a matte (a liquid solution of iron and copper sulfides) that contains all of the copper in the charge, and an iron silicate slag that should not contain any copper. The slag is discarded, and the matte is transferred to a Pierce-Smith converter for conversion to copper metal (blister copper). In the conversion process air, introduced to the vessel through submerged nozzles, oxidizes the iron in the matte to form FeO; this oxide is melted with a silica flux to form a separate iron silicate slag phase. The slag is removed intermittently for recycling to the reverberatory furnace, and more matte is added to the converter. When the iron sulfide (FeS) content of the matte has been decreased to about 1%, oxidation of the copper sulfide to liquid copper and SO_2 begins. The process ends when virtually all of the sulfur has been eliminated. The product, blister copper, is then refined and purified.

The primary criteria for any new extraction process are energy efficiency, low labor costs, and the capability of meeting environmental standards for the emission of gaseous and dust pollutants. In the convention-

Rokide C chromium oxide coating is sprayed on a bronze pump impeller that is used to circulate cooling water at a power plant. The coating is expected to double or triple the lifetime of the impeller by protecting it from abrasion by sand, silt, and gravel.

al three-step process the converter and the transfer of molten material in ladles between the smelter and the converter are the main sources of pollution. Furthermore, the reverberatory smelter, which is fired with hydrocarbon fuels, is energy-inefficient, and recovery of SO_2 is made difficult because the large volume of gas produced during the process (the off-gas) contains only 1 to 2% SO_2.

At first the three-step process was changed to one of two steps by combining the roasting and smelting operations in a flash furnace. Flash smelting makes use of the heat released by the combustion of the sulfide concentrate to melt the matte and the slag in a single vessel. In the Outokumpu process finely divided concentrate, sand, oil, and either preheated air or oxygen-enriched air are fed into the furnace in a single stream. Oxidation and melting of the feed occurs in the stream, and the molten droplets fall into the bath, where phase separation of matte and slag occurs. In the Inco process dry concentrate, flux, and pure oxygen are fed into the flash furnace.

The major advantages of flash smelting are that little or no fuel is required, and, by decreasing or eliminating nitrogen, the SO_2 content of the decreased volume of off-gas is increased to more than 10%. This facilitates its removal as either sulfuric acid or liquid SO_2. The only disadvantage of flash smelting is that the copper content of the slag is high, and so additional processing of the slag is required after its removal from the furnace.

The next stage in the development involved attempts to combine all three traditional processes into a single continuous one. In the ideal continuous process air, concentrate, and flux would be continuously fed into the vessel; the copper would be continuously removed as blister copper; the iron would be removed in a copper-free slag; and the sulfur would be removed in an SO_2-rich gas. The process would offer the advantages of a reduction in the amount of materials handling, low or zero energy requirements, production of a high concentration of SO_2 in the gas, and control of emissions.

The continuous process, as perceived, involves a number of interesting metallurgical problems that are caused by the fact that all three liquid phases—blister copper, matte, and slag—occur in the vessel. In the conventional process the oxygen potential is increased gradually, so that, in the converter, the iron content of the matte is decreased to a low value and the slag phase is removed before the blister copper phase appears. (Oxygen potential is a measure of the chemical reactivity of the oxygen at a particular time or place in a process, and increases with increasing oxygen pressure.) This has the advantage that impurities such as bismuth, arsenic, and antimony can be removed in the form of their volatile sulfides before the copper phase appears. Also, removal of the iron before the appearance of the blister copper eliminates the limitation on oxygen potential caused by the formation of magnetite, and the copper, which is oxidized into the slag at the relatively high oxygen potential existing in the convert-

343

er, can be recovered by recycling the slag through the reverberatory furnace. In the continuous process simultaneous transfer of the iron from the matte to the slag and oxidation of the copper in the matte to form blister copper and SO_2 are required.

In the Q-S (Queneau-Schuhmann) process the simultaneous reactions are facilitated by imposing an oxygen potential gradient along the cylindrical reactor vessel and arranging that the slag flows from the high oxygen-potential end to the low oxygen-potential end, where it is discharged, while the underlying matte flows in the opposite direction. Two-thirds of the oxygen requirements for this process are used for flash-smelting of the concentrate introduced at the top of the vessel, and the remainder is injected through submerged nozzles. At the slag-discharge end the oxygen potential is decreased by mixing finely divided coal and SO_2 with the injected oxygen.

The Queneau-Schuhmann process is governed by manipulation of the reaction FeS (in the matte) + 3[O] = FeO (in the slag) + SO_2 (gas). At the low oxygen-potential end this reaction proceeds from right to left. This causes a decrease in the matte grade (percentage of copper in the matte) and therefore causes the desirable transfer of copper from the slag to the matte before the slag is discharged. At the high oxygen-potential end the reaction proceeds from left to right, which decreases the FeS content of the matte to levels at which further oxidation of the matte results in the formation of blister copper. Because the reactions desired at the low oxygen-potential end are favored by low temperature and those at the high potential end are favored by high temperature, a temperature gradient is imposed in the reactor. In 1982 the Q-S process, designated as QSL (Queneau-Schuhmann-Lurgi), was being tested in a pilot plant for continuous lead-making.

The Noranda process for continuous copper-making also employs a cylindrical vessel. Concentrate, coal, and flux are introduced at one end; slag is tapped (withdrawn) at the other end; natural gas or oil burners are located at both ends; air is injected through submerged nozzles; and blister copper is intermittently tapped from the bottom of the vessel. In the pilot-plant stage the Noranda process produced a blister copper containing 1–2% sulfur and high levels of arsenic, antimony, and bismuth, and a slag containing 8–12% copper. Because of the impurity problem with the blister copper and the short lifetimes of the submerged nozzles, the full-size industrial Noranda reactors are being used to produce a very-high-grade matte. In this process the discharged slag is slowly cooled, crushed, and ground, and the copper, which is recovered by froth flotation, is recycled through the reactor. (In froth flotation particles rich in copper are bound by chemical means to air bubbles introduced into a solution and are recovered as froth.)

The other "continuous" process in operation is the Mitsubishi process, which involves a series of three interconnected vessels through which the melts pass by gravity feed. The first vessel is a smelting furnace in which concentrate is oxidized to form a high-grade matte. The matte and slag produced flow continuously to a second vessel, which is an electric settling furnace employed for slag-metal separation. The lean slag (slag with a minimum amount of copper) from this vessel is discarded, and the matte flows to the third vessel; there, continuous oxidation to blister copper occurs. Lime is used as flux, and the small quantity of slag produced is recycled to the smelting furnace.

Further developments in copper making and the design of processes for new plants will be determined primarily by the mineralogy of and impurity levels in the concentrates to be treated and by the cost of energy available at the location of the plant. Continuing attempts were being made to eliminate or minimize the general use of coal and hydrocarbons as fuels; also, because the electric power required for the production of oxygen in tonnage quantities is less than that required to run an electric furnace, the use of oxygen-based smelting seemed certain to increase.

—David R. Gaskell

Mathematics

Research in mathematics thrives in symbiosis with other active research fields. In recent years two of the most active interfaces have been with computer science—leading to progress in algorithms, number theory, and combinatorial mathematics—and with theoretical physics—leading to progress in the geometry of surfaces and their representations in differential equations. The progress in mathematics during the last year reflected these contemporary emphases but was not limited by them.

Prime numbers and secret codes. During the mid-1970s Whitfield Diffie and Martin Hellman of Stanford University and Ralph Merkle of the University of California at Berkeley proposed a system of "public-key" cryptography in which two parties (banks, military agencies, etc.) could communicate with complete secrecy even though the key to their code was published in a public document. Their work depended on certain "trapdoor" functions in mathematics that were easy (for computers) to compute in one direction but essentially impossible to compute in the reverse direction. Transformations depending on these functions were like trapdoors—easy to fall through and hard to climb out of.

Multiplying and factoring are examples of trapdoor calculations. It is rather easy for a computer to multiply two 50-digit prime numbers, but it is essentially impossible for a computer to factor the 100-digit product

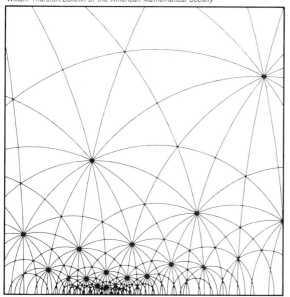
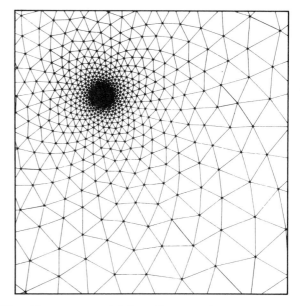

Geometric structures were developed by mathematician William Thurston to model three-dimensional manifolds and thereby aid in the classification of these topological spaces. All manifolds except those of three dimensions have been classified.

into the two 50-digit prime numbers from which it was composed. (A prime number is a number not divisible by any integer greater than one except for its own absolute value.) Therefore, if the sender used a code that depended on a 100-digit number created by the receiver (and published for all the world to see), only the receiver could decode it because decoding would require knowledge of the two prime factors, and only the person who created the number would know what those factors were.

Of course, factoring a 100-digit number that has many small prime factors is rather easy; one just needs to keep dividing by 2 and 3 and 5, etc., until the number is cut down to manageable size. That is why it is important in cryptography systems to form large numbers as products of just two primes—so that the smallest factor of the large number is itself very large and correspondingly hard to determine. This means that in order to ensure the invulnerability of a public-key cryptography system based on prime numbers, there must be easy means of testing large numbers to find out if they are prime. Otherwise, if a bank based its code on the product of two composite (factorable) numbers that it mistakenly thought were prime, a diligent cryptanalyst would be able to break the code by factoring the product of those two fake primes.

On the surface, testing a number to see if it is prime might appear to be just as difficult as factoring it. But that turns out not to be the case. In 1974 a moderate algorithm (polynomial rather than exponential in length) was developed that accomplished this task, but a proof that it always worked depended on the Rie-

mann hypothesis, an as-yet-unproved conjecture in number theory. (An algorithm is a step-by-step procedure for solving a problem.) Thus even though the algorithm seemed to work, it did not provide real security. Subsequently, tests were devised that were even faster and that guaranteed within very small error limits that the numbers that passed the test were indeed prime. But there still was no absolute guarantee.

Recently Carl Pomerance and Robert Rumely of the University of Georgia and Leonard Adleman of the University of Southern California developed a verifiable, rapid means of testing numbers for primality. Their procedure is not as slow as the older, exponential methods but not as fast as a truly polynomial method either; the number of steps it requires to factor a number containing m digits is of the order of $m^{\log \log m}$. So, while the new method cannot test all numbers, it can test in an instant of computer time any that might be involved in public-key cryptography.

Large numbers and undecidable questions. Nearly 50 years ago the Austrian logician Kurt Gödel surprised philosophers and mathematicians alike in his discovery that there were—and, more importantly, always would be—statements in mathematics the truth or falsehood of which could not be determined by logical deduction from the axioms. These so-called undecidable propositions were derived from special statements that, by unnatural quirks of reasoning, could be made to refer to themselves. They were, in effect, more like mathematically coded versions of "This statement cannot be proved" than like the familiar statements of algebra, geometry, or calculus.

In recent years Jeffrey Paris of Manchester University and Leo Harrington of the University of California at Berkeley discovered comparable statements that involved real problems in the arithmetic of very large numbers. They did this by modifying a theorem about infinite sets in Ramsey theory—a branch of combinatorial mathematics devoted to the notion that "complete disorder is impossible" and that in large enough sets there is always some discernible order.

Paris and Harrington proved a theorem about "large sets" of integers, those with at least as many members as the smallest number in them. (Thus a set of integers in which 100 is the smallest number has at least 100 members.) They showed that if one takes a large enough set of this type and assigns the members of the set to two classes, say red and blue, then one can always find a "large" set all of the members of which are either red or blue. In addition, they then showed that it is impossible to decide (prove or refute) this statement by reasoning with the standard axioms of arithmetic because, roughly, the size of the sets involved grows so fast as to stay beyond the range of the axioms.

In 1982 Harvey Friedman of Ohio State University found a second undecidable theorem in arithmetic, again using a function that grows very very fast. He was studying "trees," combinatorial objects that look like genealogical structures. Joseph Kruskal of Bell Laboratories had shown many years ago that in any infinite collection of finite trees, ordered in some way, at least one tree must fit into a later one so that the branches of the first fit exactly inside the branches of the second. Friedman showed that this theorem is still true of large finite sets of trees but that the size of these sets, like the Paris-Harrington result, is beyond the range of the axioms of arithmetic.

Fields Medals. One highlight of the International Congress of Mathematicians, which meets every four years, is the presentation of the Fields Medals, the mathematical equivalent of the Nobel Prizes. In 1982 three awards were announced, for research that bears on fundamental issues in physics and relativity theory.

The 1982 recipients were Alain Connes of the Centre Nationale de la Recherche Scientifique in Paris, Shing Tung Yau of the Institute for Advanced Study at Princeton, N.J., and William Thurston of Princeton University. Their awards were scheduled to be presented at the August 1982 meeting of the Congress in Warsaw, but owing to the political situation in Poland both the Congress and the awards ceremony were postponed.

Connes, a 35-year-old analyst, was cited for two major works. He extended a major theorem linking analysis and topology, the Atiyah-Singer theorem, to certain infinite surfaces. This result, a vast generalization of the fundamental theorem of calculus, helps move mathematics toward a grand unification of its fundamental theories. He also solved many of the major open questions that pertain to the mathematical foundations of quantum theory.

Yau, 33, became famous in the late 1970s when he solved the Calabi conjecture concerning the relationship between the ways volume and distance can be measured in abstract, high-dimensional spaces. Yau proved that the natural measure of volume on certain complex manifolds—curved spaces having coordinates that are complex numbers—determines a unique metric, or measure of length, that is intrinsically related to the geometry of the manifold. Recently he applied these ideas to an important problem in relativity theory, showing that the mass of an isolated system, like its energy, must always be positive.

Thurston, 36, is a topologist who studies three-dimensional surfaces and manifolds. Surprisingly, the mathematical classification of surfaces has been carried out with greater success in high dimensions than in low ones. Thurston's intensive study of three-dimensional surfaces revealed links to eight possible three-dimensional geometries, raising hopes that finally the complete classification of three-dimensional manifolds may be close at hand.

Geometry of manifolds. The work for which Thurston was cited in his Fields Medal was closely related to the work of Michael Freedman of the University of California at San Diego. During the last year Freedman startled the mathematical community with two major results involving four-dimensional manifolds. He completed in four dimensions what Thurston had been working on in three—a complete classification of all surfaces and manifolds. (The classification for higher-dimensional spaces had already been done, more than a decade ago.)

As a result of his classification Freedman verified the four-dimensional case of one of the most famous unsolved problems in mathematics—the Poincaré conjecture. A sphere, the most basic object of elementary geometry, has the property that any circle drawn on its surface can be shrunk continuously to a point. (A doughnut-shaped surface, in contrast, does not have this property, because a circle that wraps around the hole cannot be shrunk to a point.) Henri Poincaré, France's preeminent mathematician of a century ago, conjectured that this fundamental property of a circle must be true of spheres in any dimension. Previously, Poincaré's conjecture had been proved in all dimensions except 3 and 4. Freedman's work completed the verification in dimension 4, leaving only dimension 3 unresolved.

No one was surprised that Poincaré's conjecture in dimension 4 turned out to be correct. However, another consequence of Freedman's work did surprise many people; he discovered that there is more than one manifestation of the standard four-dimensional space-time geometry of Einstein's relativity theory. Freedman's classification of four-dimensional manifolds provided the key link in a chain of results obtained earlier by several mathematicians and theoretical physicists who were trying to understand the theory of "connections," mathematical abstractions of the forces between subatomic particles. It is still too early to determine whether the new models for space-time will yield physically significant results, or whether they might just be a theoretical possibility that is not implemented in nature.

Other prizes. Several mathematicians were awarded distinguished international prizes in 1982 in recognition of fundamental contributions they have made to mathematics research. A new prize, named after the Finnish mathematician Rolf Nevanlinna, was to be awarded at the postponed International Congress of Mathematicians to Robert E. Tarjan of Bell Laboratories for imaginative work in graph-theoretic algorithms. Tarjan helped develop efficient methods for determining when a graph—a network of nodes and connections—can be drawn in the plane (and thereby be incorporated in a printed circuit for computer design). He also developed new combinatorial tree structures that can be used to keep sorted lists in order while elements of the lists are efficiently being inserted and deleted.

The American Mathematical Society awarded four Steele Prizes in 1982. Lars Ahlfors of Harvard University (who received one of the first Fields Medals in 1936) was cited for fundamental contributions to the exposition of complex analysis and conformal mappings. Tsit-Yuen Lam of the University of California at Berkeley was cited for his expositions of the theory of quadratic forms, solutions to Serre's problems, and the theory of formally real fields—all important aspects of contemporary abstract algebra.

John W. Milnor of the Institute for Advanced Study at Princeton, N.J., received a Steele Prize for his 1956 paper in which he described the first known example of surfaces that could be continuously but not smoothly deformed into each other. This work proved to be of fundamental importance in the classification of manifolds, leading indirectly to the work of Thurston and Freedman mentioned above. Finally, Fritz John of the Courant Institute of Mathematical Sciences in New York City was cited for his enormous influence in many fields, notably convexity and inequalities, ill-posed problems, elasticity theory, and nonlinear hyperbolic problems.

—Lynn Arthur Steen

Medical sciences

The most dramatic development during the year in the medical sciences was the first successful implantation into a human being of a permanent artificial heart. At the same time renewed attention was given to the

transplanting of natural hearts and to the testing of devices that can detect and correct abnormal heart rhythms. The often fatal acquired immune deficiency syndrome claimed victims other than homosexuals in 1982, and research continued as to its cause. Fluoride implants showed promise of not only preventing tooth decay but reversing it at its early stages. For the first time a gene carrying the code for growth hormone was transferred from one kind of animal to another, from rats to mouse embryos; the result was mice that were two times normal size. Exposure to low levels of lead was found to cause a variety of health problems.

General medicine

Biomedical engineering left the laboratory for the bedside in 1982, with the year's developments capped by the first successful human implantation of a permanent artificial heart. Genetic engineering provided clues to cancer, while a new way to study body tissues and structures showed promise. Alternatives to coronary artery bypass surgery emerged, and several new vaccines were tested.

Artificial heart. In 1982 the heart joined a growing list of artificial body parts used in humans, a list that also included skin, blood, joints, tendons, and limbs. Barney Clark, a 61-year-old retired dentist from suburban Seattle, Wash., became in December the first human recipient of the Jarvik-7 heart in a 7.5-hour operation at the University of Utah Medical Center in Salt Lake City. A team of surgeons headed by William C. DeVries removed Clark's severely enlarged, scarred ventricles; sewed four Dacron cuffs to his atria, aorta, and pulmonary artery; and snapped on the aluminum and plastic device.

Clark's new heart was powered by a 170-kg (375-lb) air compressor on a cart to which he was tethered by hoses extending from his abdomen. The compressor was linked to a computer that calculated the amount of blood pumped with each beat and displayed the information on a video terminal. The researchers could adjust the pressure and flow of the compressed air and the time the artificial ventricles take to eject blood, although they hoped that recipients could eventually make such adjustments themselves.

The Jarvik-7 heart stemmed from many years of work by Dutch-born Willem J. Kolff, head of the University of Utah's artificial organ program. It is named for his associate, Robert K. Jarvik, a bioengineer and physician, who developed it. A similar device has been implanted in calves, sheep, and brain-dead patients.

The operation that gave Barney Clark a new heart was hailed as a remarkable technical achievement, but it was also criticized on several grounds. Although free to Clark, the procedure was estimated to cost $10,000 for the device, $10,000 for the support equipment, and $20,000 to $25,000 for the surgery. The Congressional

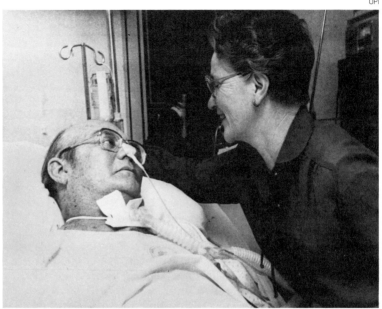

Barney Clark, the first human recipient of the Jarvik-7 artificial heart, is encouraged by his wife after he sat in a chair for the first time after the surgery.

Office of Technology Assessment (OTA) predicted that as many as 66,000 people might eventually be candidates for artificial hearts each year, at a cost of $1 billion to $3 billion, and warned that paying for the surgery would pose a dilemma for the government.

Furthermore, the OTA and other critics concluded that the lack of an implantable power source for the artificial heart was a major limitation of the technology. Efforts to develop such a power source had as of 1983 been unsuccessful, although the Utah team hoped to reduce the size of the compressor and power supply so that it could be carried in a backpack.

Transplants. Among the critics of the artificial heart was Houston heart surgeon Denton Cooley, who believed that the device should only be used as a temporary support measure unless an implantable power source could be devised. Cooley and other heart surgeons recently resumed transplantation of natural hearts after reports from Norman Shumway and his colleagues at Stanford University Medical Center that the immune suppressant cyclosporine produces 80% first-year survival rates in heart transplant recipients. An 18-month study of heart transplantation was begun in 1982 at Stanford and five other medical centers.

Cyclosporine was also being given to patients receiving kidney, liver, bone marrow, and heart-lung transplants. Ten heart-lung transplants had been performed at Stanford by the end of 1982, and the Johns Hopkins University Medical Center announced plans to follow suit. Single-lung transplants were also performed for the first time since 1977, at Toronto (Ont.) General Hospital and Montefiore Medical Center in New York City, on patients who had inhaled large quantities of the herbicide paraquat.

Implantable heart devices. Lithium batteries are crucial to an implanted defibrillator, an instrument that monitors and corrects potentially lethal heart rhythm disturbances. More than 40 patients at Johns Hopkins and Stanford have received the device, which as of 1983 was still being tested. On detecting a potentially lethal abnormal rhythm, it can administer up to four electrical jolts to the heart through an electrode placed near the superior vena cava (a large vein through which blood is returned to the heart) and one located over the apex of the heart. The implant's power supply can produce up to one hundred electrical pulses and is designed to monitor heart rhythm for at least three years.

Long-life batteries are also used in the approximately 125,000 pacemakers implanted each year in people with abnormally slow heart rhythms. Some new pacemakers incorporated microchips that analyzed the heart's response to energy and altered stimulation accordingly. They could be programmed by a patient's physician, and when the computer memory was filled, the information in it could be read out through a communication device called a modem.

The pacemaker industry, however, came under fire in 1982 when the Public Citizen Health Research Group, headed by physician Sidney M. Wolfe, charged that up to 25,000 pacemakers implanted each year at a cost of about $3,500 each may be unnecessary. High-pressure sales tactics and kickbacks in the $650 million industry were also alleged.

Help for the disabled. Computer and electronic technology was being used in aids for the disabled that included electronic communication devices, voice-command control systems, prostheses, insulin pumps, and new types of wheelchairs. Bioengineers at Wright

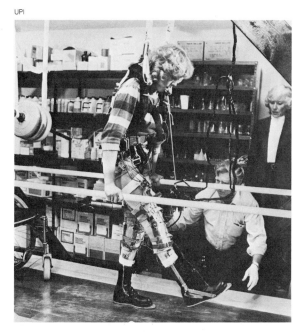

Computerized electrical-stimulation system allows a paralyzed woman to walk using her own muscle power. Electrodes on her legs are connected to a computer.

State University devised a computerized way of helping the paralyzed walk, and in 1982 Nan Davis, 22, took five wavering steps down a ramp in their Dayton, Ohio, laboratory.

Laboratory director Jerrold S. Petrofsky, a neurophysiologist and computer engineer, spent 13 years developing a system that provides and controls electrical stimulation of paralyzed muscles. By 1983 he was working with several quadriplegics and paraplegics. Subjects must spend months building up atrophied muscles and months using a wheelchair and then a stationary bicycle linked to a computer.

The microprocessor and electrodes that helped Davis move are large and clumsy, but Petrofsky and his colleagues maintained that the system could be much smaller. Sensors and electrodes could be implanted in affected limbs and controlled by a microprocessor 2.5 cm (1 in) in diameter. Patients might carry a small gyroscope to help them keep their balance, since they experience no sensation of movement to guide them.

At Chicago's Pritzker Institute of Medical Engineering Robert Jaeger and his colleagues used a pacemaker instead of a computerized feedback system to get quadriplegics on their feet again. Jaeger predicted that his simpler, cheaper method could help about 17,500 people with spinal cord injuries.

Diagnostic imaging. Enthusiasm soared for nuclear magnetic resonance (NMR) as a way of studying body tissues and structures, and some predicted that it might soon supplant computerized axial tomography (CAT scan). Used since 1946 by chemists and physi-cists, NMR was first suggested as having potential applications in medicine in 1971 by Raymond Damadian of the Downstate Medical Center of the State University of New York. Pioneering the currently used imaging technique was Paul Lauterur of the State University of New York at Stony Brook.

The technique used by Lauterur does not employ ionizing radiation or the injection of radioactive substances in the body. Depending on the size of the machine, either a limb or a patient's entire body is placed within a large electromagnet and exposed to a uniform magnetic field. This causes the nuclei of the cells being studied to align in the direction of the field and precess, or wobble much like a spinning top. A radio-frequency electromagnetic current is then applied, causing the cell nuclei to resonate. The radio signal emitted by the cells is recorded and analyzed. In NMR imaging the voltages produced by resonance are relayed to a computer that generates cross-sectional pictures in different planes. In NMR spectroscopy peaks representing absorption are mapped and analyzed.

Images produced by NMR are considered particularly helpful in the diagnosis of multiple sclerosis, showing areas of brain demyelination not detectable by CAT scan or conventional X-ray; brain tumors, especially low-grade infiltration types that are not well shown by a CAT scan; gallbladder disease; chest and vascular lesions; liver disease; and kidney failure. The spine, pelvis, and bone marrow have also been studied by NMR, and some researchers believe that it will be able to predict impending stroke. Although NMR does not show images of bone, some bone diseases causing chemical changes can be detected by employing the technique.

NMR was also being used to study nutritional and metabolic disorders because it allows investigators to study the biochemistry of living organisms. George K. Radda and Brian D. Ross and associates at Oxford University used NMR to diagnose a case of McArdle's syndrome, a rare genetic disorder that causes muscle weakness. Affected people lack an enzyme that converts glycogen to the glucose muscle cells required during exertion. Ross predicted that NMR would eventually be useful in monitoring treatment as well as in diagnosing such metabolic disorders.

Cancer mechanism probed. In 1982 two lines of research converged to provide a clearer understanding of the mechanism underlying the process of cancerous change. Clues came from research groups in the U.S., Great Britain, and France, and several investigators received the 1982 Albert Lasker Basic Medical Research Award for work that "may lead to the development of a human cancer vaccine and other new approaches to the diagnosis, prevention and treatment of human cancers."

Studying human cancer cells were several research groups, including those headed by Robert Gallo of the

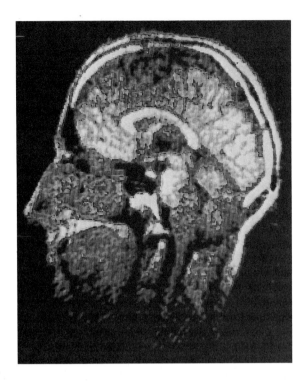

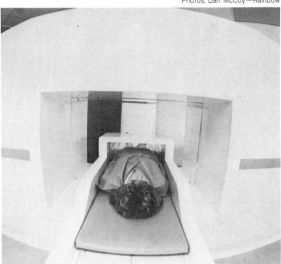

Subjecting body tissues to a magnetic field (above) causes hydrogen atoms to align themselves with the field. After a burst of radio frequency waves is applied, the atomic nuclei release energy which is detected and used to create an image of the tissues (left). This technique is known as nuclear magnetic resonance.

National Cancer Institute (NCI), who received an award, and Massachusetts Institute of Technology's Robert A. Weinberg. Research on viruses that cause cancer in animals, the retroviruses, was undertaken by groups headed by award winners J. Michael Bishop and Harold E. Varmus of the University of California, San Francisco; George Vande Woude of the NCI; and others.

Bishop and Varmus first showed that a gene discovered in an avian sarcoma virus was virtually identical to a gene found in normal human DNA (deoxyribonucleic acid) and closely related to those in the genomes of all vertebrates. Other investigators reported similar findings for other retrovirus genes, leading them to suspect that a group of perhaps 30 to 50 such genes may be present in normal human cells.

Although investigators first thought that the genes studied in retroviruses, called oncogenes, caused cancer in animals when passed to their cells by the virus, Hidesaburo Hanafusa of Rockefeller University showed in the later 1970s that the retroviruses in fact capture those genes from normal cells through genetic recombination. Researchers now believe that the oncogenes in cells must play a vital role in normal cellular function—perhaps related to growth, differentiation, or development. Raymond L. Erikson of Harvard Medical School showed that the viral oncogene produces an enzyme which adds phosphate groups to the amino acid tyrosine. Several other oncogenes have since been found to produce similar products, and the phosphorylation of cell proteins (the combination of these proteins with phosphorus-containing groups) has been

shown to be a central method of governing the growth of normal cells.

At times, however, oncogenes appear to cause normal cells to become malignant, and investigators are attempting to discover how that happens. Still in question is whether they cause cancer by producing too much of a protein or by producing an abnormal form of it. In 1982 research groups at MIT, NCI, and Cold Spring Harbor Laboratory showed that in a bladder cancer cell one alteration in the nucleotide sequence of an oncogene was enough to transform normal cells into malignant ones.

Using genetic engineering techniques, other groups were studying the relationship between oncogenes and chromosome rearrangements that are associated with some forms of cancer. Three groups located the cellular oncogene called MYC because it is analogous to that discovered in the avian myelocytomatosis virus; they found the oncogene on a small portion of chromosome 8 that is often found to be moved, or translocated, to other chromosomes in the cancer called Burkitt's lymphoma and in one form of leukemia. Riccardo Dalla-Favera, Marco Bregni, Jan Erikson, David Patterson, Robert C. Gallo, and Carlo M. Croce, working at the National Cancer Institute, Wistar Institute of Anatomy and Biology, and the University of Colorado, suggested that the relocation of the MYC gene might cause the mechanisms that normally repress its activity to fail or cause it to produce an abnormal product.

Philip Leder, of Harvard Medical School, and his associates also mapped the MYC gene on chromosome 8. In two Burkitt's lymphoma cell lines they found that

350

the MYC gene had been translocated into a piece of DNA that encodes an immunoglobulin-producing gene. In a mouse malignancy it was found to have been moved to a similar area. They suggested that the same processes important in producing immunoglobulin proteins may activate the MYC gene after it has moved from chromosome 8.

Benjamin G. Neel, William S. Hayward, and colleagues also located the MYC oncogene—and another called MOS—on the long arm of chromosome 8 in human cells, near the area where chromosomal breaks occur in Burkitt's lymphoma and in a form of human leukemia. Earlier, Neel, Hayward, and Susan M. Astrin showed that MYC is much more active when viral DNA is placed close to it in chicken lymphoma virus tumors, suggesting one mechanism by which cancer might be produced.

Robert Gallo's work on a virus linked with human cancer also contributed to the identification and analysis of oncogenes in human DNA. The human T-cell leukemia virus (HTLV) can be used in the laboratory to aid researchers studying human blood cell transformation and may eventually be used to produce a vaccine against the disease. Research on HTLV proteins may eventually result in the development of antibodies specific to the cancer cells or methods of blocking protein production.

Gene therapy. In 1982 Timothy Ley and colleagues at the National Heart, Lung, and Blood Institute (NHLBI) and the University of Illinois College of Medicine put an existing drug to a novel use, giving 5-azacytidine to patients suffering from beta thalassemia and sickle-cell anemia. Patients with the diseases suffer anemia, heart problems, and other difficulties because they produce abnormal hemoglobin.

Ley and his colleagues reasoned that activating the gene that produces fetal hemoglobin but is suppressed after birth would improve symptoms in adults. The cytidine analogue that they used reactivated the gene for fetal hemoglobin by removing methyl groups from the bone-marrow DNA near the globin-producing genes. Although the long-term side effects and toxicity of 5-azacytidine are not yet known, researchers believe that this attempt to alter gene activity holds promise.

Growth hormone factors. Several research groups isolated factors that regulate growth. Roger Guillemin and associates at the Salk Institute for Biological Studies found and synthesized a peptide that acts on the pituitary gland to stimulate the release of human growth hormone. The factor could be produced chemically or through recombinant DNA techniques and may be of value in pituitary dwarfism, diabetes, wound and burn healing, and aging.

Other growth factors found in human bone may be necessary to the success of a new treatment in which crushed, demineralized bone powder is used to stimulate new bone growth. In California investigators John

R. Farley and David J. Baylink of Loma Linda University and the Jerry L. Pettis Memorial Veterans' Hospital were attempting to produce antibodies to a skeletal growth factor they discovered and to trace its activity in the body.

Bypass alternatives. Enthusiasm mounted in 1982 for two cheaper, less drastic alternatives to coronary artery bypass surgery in patients who develop arterial clots. Andreas R. Gruentzig of the Emory University School of Medicine reported good results using a procedure called balloon angioplasty in patients with one or two blocked arteries, while the NHLBI started a multi-institution study on the use of an enzyme called streptokinase to dissolve clots.

Gruentzig opened blocked coronary arteries by inflating a small balloon attached to a catheter that can be threaded through a patient's arterial system. He claimed success in about 92% of his recent cases and said that no deaths occurred in the last 900 patients treated at Emory. Although some of the opened arteries close again, the procedure can be repeated.

K. Peter Rentrop of Mount Sinai Medical Center in New York City developed a way of dissolving clots in the coronary arteries with streptokinase, a protein ob-

Lesions are caused by Kaposi's sarcoma, a type of cancer that strikes many of the victims of acquired immune deficiency syndrome (AIDS).

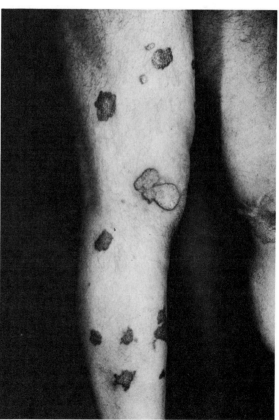

Barromes/Pytkowicz—Gamma/Liaison

Tylenol capsules are tested by technicians at the Chicago Department of Health after cyanide-contaminated Extra-Strength Tylenol killed seven people in the Chicago area in September and October of 1982.

tained from cultures of streptococcus bacteria. This method has been approved for several years for use in patients with pulmonary embolisms and deep-vein blood clots, and investigators believe it has great potential for patients who have suffered or are suffering heart attacks (myocardial infarctions) due to arterial clots. The NHLBI-supported study should offer information on the risks and benefits of the procedure.

Diet and health. Diet guidelines aimed at preventing cancer were issued by the National Academy of Sciences' National Research Council in 1982. Eating less fat and fewer salted and smoked foods; drinking less alcohol; and eating more fruits, vegetables, and whole-grain cereal products were recommended. Yellow and dark-green, leafy vegetables are of particular value because they contain vitamin A and retinoids. Citrus fruits are high in vitamin C, thought to help prevent the conversion of nitrates and nitrites into carcinogenic nitrosamines. The fiber in whole grains is said to dilute the concentration of carcinogens in the bowel and speed their elimination. Fat has been linked to hormone-dependent cancers of the breast, prostate, and reproductive organs, and the panel therefore recommended cutting fat intake from about 40% to about 30% of total diet.

The anti-cancer diet guidelines did not differ much from those recommended for the prevention of heart disease. Some evidence that people in the U.S. have begun to modify their diets, cut down on smoking, and get more exercise emerged in 1982 from a ten-year study of more than 12,000 men throughout the country. The Multiple Risk Factor Intervention Trial was designed by the NHLBI to evaluate the effect on coronary artery disease of reducing smoking, cholesterol levels, and blood pressure. One group of high-risk volunteers received special counseling and treatment, while the others were simply followed by their physicians and examined yearly. Unexpectedly, both groups had lower

blood pressures and fewer smokers at the end of the study, and deaths from coronary artery disease were fewer than predicted in both groups. The investigators concluded that the public's recognition of the importance of a healthy life-style was responsible.

Immune deficiency disease. As feared, the condition now called acquired immune deficiency syndrome (AIDS) spread beyond the homosexual community in 1982. Cases of AIDS in the U.S. doubled every six months to more than 800, causing the U.S. Centers for Disease Control (CDC) in Atlanta, Ga., to warn of an epidemic. By March 1983 more than 1,100 cases had been reported.

Those suffering from AIDS have lower-than-normal numbers of T cells, the white blood cells that fight infection. In contrast to the normal situation they also have more suppressor than helper T cells.

Affected individuals become vulnerable to a wide variety of viral and fungal infections and to a form of soft-tissue cancer called Kaposi's sarcoma. Two cases of lymphoma of the brain were also reported. The average life expectancy for those with opportunistic infections was 7.5 months, and none survived for two years. For those with Kaposi's sarcoma average life expectancy was 16.5 months, and the predicted two-year survival rate was only 27%.

By the end of 1982 about three-fourths of the known cases occurred in homosexual men, and AIDS had also been found in intravenous drug abusers (some of whom were women), Haitian refugees, hemophiliacs, and infants. One of the affected infants had received blood transfusions from a man who later died of AIDS.

As of 1983 no cause for the lethal syndrome had been pinpointed despite a massive research effort involving the CDC and scientists at medical centers throughout the U.S., but investigators suspected a virus that can be transmitted through blood and sexual contact. The CDC believed that the affected hemophiliacs acquired the syndrome from the transfusions they must regularly receive to aid blood clotting.

Some researchers believe that the first sign of AIDS may be generalized swelling of the lymph glands that persists over several months. In one study of 41 homosexual men with such lymph gland swelling who had T-cell abnormalities but were otherwise apparently healthy, five have so far developed Kaposi's sarcoma. In 1982 and early 1983 investigators also found immunological abnormalities in apparently healthy homosexual men. Michael Lange and colleagues found reversed T-cell ratios in more than 80% of 81 apparently healthy homosexual men.

The CDC warned those working with AIDS patients and materials taken from them to take precautions against possible infection. Although no general threat to the country's blood transfusion supply was perceived, the virulence of AIDS and the lack of information about its cause and spread were causes of concern for the future.

Drugs and vaccines. Humulin, a form of insulin produced by recombinant DNA techniques by Eli Lilly and Co., was approved for marketing in 1982 in the U.S. and Great Britain. Though it did not demonstrate any therapeutic advantage over other purified insulin, its

The sale of "starch blockers" was prohibited by the FDA, which ruled that the diet tablets were drugs that required testing before they could be marketed.

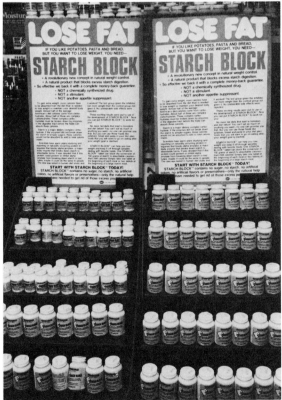

Jacques M. Chenet—*Newsweek*

production did not depend on the availability of animal organs.

Diltiazem became the third calcium-blocker to win approval by the U.S. Food and Drug Administration (FDA) for treatment of angina in 1982. These agents are thought to dilate arteries and lower myocardial oxygen demand by blocking calcium ion movement. Physicians were also testing calcium blockers for hypertension and such conditions as asthma, achalasia, and migraine.

A drug for genital herpes simplex was reported safe and effective in an oral form. Although acyclovir does not eradicate the virus, it does speed up healing, shorten viral shedding, and reduce pain and itching. If approved, the oral form was expected to become more widely used than the topical or intravenous varieties already approved. Some physicians feared, however, that misuse or excessive use of acyclovir might produce a resistant herpes strain.

Much work on vaccines was under way in 1982. Merck Sharp & Dohme began distributing the hepatitis B vaccine that had been approved in 1981 and was working on a vaccine for hepatitis A. Several groups reported progress on a vaccine for cytomegalovirus, which can damage the central nervous system in babies and is associated with Kaposi's sarcoma in people with AIDS. One form developed by Stanley Plotkin and associates at the Children's Hospital of Philadelphia was being tested.

Tests were also being done on four possible live vaccines for cholera. Also, promising results were reported by Rene Germanier and associates at the Swiss Serum Vaccine Institute on an oral typhoid vaccine given to more than 32,000 schoolchildren in Alexandria, Egypt. Several countries began using the vaccine.

A 1982 television documentary charged that the standard diphtheria-pertussis-tetanus vaccine given to children could cause neurological damage. This aroused fears in the U.S. medical community that parents would refuse to have their children vaccinated, leading to an outbreak of whooping cough like those that followed similar bad publicity in Japan and Great Britain. Although physicians believed the vaccine to be reasonably safe, the FDA said that new and possibly safer versions were being tested in Japan and the U.S.

Several nonprescription drugs attracted attention in 1982. Tainted Extra-Strength Tylenol capsules caused seven deaths from cyanide poisoning in Chicago and led to a massive recall and changes in the packaging of Tylenol—a brand of the aspirin substitute acetaminophen—and of other over-the-counter drugs.

Parents were warned not to give aspirin to children with fever and chicken pox or influenza because the drug has been associated with Reye's syndrome, but the U.S. Department of Health and Human Services backed away from requiring warning labels on aspirin bottles. First reported in 1963, the syndrome can follow viral infections in children and cause vomiting, confusion, delirium, and even coma and death.

Extracts of kidney beans were sold widely as "starch blockers" for dieters, although researcher George W. Bo-Linn and colleagues at Baylor University Medical Center found that they did not inhibit the digestion or absorption of food starches. Sold as food supplements, the starch blockers were declared drugs and banned by the FDA.

—Susan V. Lawrence

Lead intoxication

Although the dangers of high-dose lead exposure have been known since the time of the ancient Greeks, it was not until the latter part of the 20th century that medical science focused on the question of low-level lead exposure and was able to demonstrate that extremely small doses of lead were hazardous to human health. In 1982 substantial progress was made in a number of areas related to this issue. Among the most important areas were the following: a major epidemiologic investigation showed that exposure to lead was more widespread than had been generally acknowledged; a number of biochemical investigations demonstrated previously unrecognized toxic effects of lead; three studies of psychological performance in children added weight to the thesis that significant deficits are produced by lead at low doses; some progress was made in controlling lead in one important source, the air.

While lead is relatively easy to measure, both in the environment and in human blood, efforts to control the disease of lead intoxication have lagged. This has been true because of a number of stubborn misconceptions about the disease. In the past lead intoxication had been believed to be exclusively a disease of the urban poor and to be due solely to the ingestion of lead-based paint. Important progress was made in 1982 in understanding the true extent and nature of lead toxicity and in demonstrating that other sources besides paint contribute to intake by humans.

Landmark regulation of lead in the atmosphere took place in 1977 when the U.S. Environmental Protection Agency (EPA), after extensive study and considerable controversy, set a standard for lead in the air. The allowable amount under the standard was 1.5 millionths of a gram of lead per cubic meter of air. This standard enabled the agency to reduce, in stepwise fashion, the concentration of lead in gasoline. Such gasoline, when burned, is a major source of lead in the atmosphere. Manufacturing processes that use or produce lead-containing materials also release lead into the air, water, and soil.

The regulatory activities in the United States were closely watched throughout the world, and the ambient lead standards in many countries became the subject of study and debate. In Great Britain the Department of Health and Social Security set a standard for the stepwise reduction of lead additives, and similar steps were taken in Australia. In the U.S. the EPA standard was undergoing careful review under the statutes of the Clean Air Act. Given the wealth of new data testifying to lead's toxic potential at low doses, it seemed likely that the allowable level of lead in the atmosphere would be further reduced.

Prevalence of lead exposure. A carefully executed nationwide survey of about 16,500 people in the U.S., chosen to give a representative profile of citizens of all races, ages, incomes, and areas of residence, demonstrated clearly that lead exposure was more widespread than had been previously thought. This study, under the direction of Joseph L. Annest of the National Center for Health Statistics and Kathryn Mahaffey of the U.S. Food and Drug Administration (FDA) showed that 3.9% of children six months to five years of age had blood lead levels greater than 30 micrograms per deciliter (μg/dl).

Inner-city minority children from poor families were not the only children to be exposed, but low income, urban residence, and minority racial status were clearly found to be associated with higher risk for elevated blood lead levels. For white children whose family incomes were over $15,000 per year, the incidence of elevated blood leads was 0.9%; for those with family income below $6,000, the incidence was 5.9%. For black children whose families earned more than than $15,000, the incidence was 3%, while for those of lowest income it was 18.6%. These figures indicate that more than 600,000 U.S. children have blood lead levels in the hazardous range and that the hazard is not limited to the inner-city poor.

Psychological effects. Over the past ten years considerable progress has been made in demonstrating adverse health effects in children at low levels of lead exposure. Much of this was accomplished in 1982. For children the most significant health effect is altered brain function, usually recognized by decreased intellectual function or disordered behavior. As recently as 1960 the "safe" level of lead in the blood of children was thought to be 60 μg/dl. However, a number of investigations showed that children with blood lead levels in the range of 40–60 μg/dl had lower IQ scores or more behavior disorders and learning problems than classmates with lower blood lead levels. Because of this the U.S. Centers for Disease Control established that the defined threshold for "undue lead exposure" was 30 μg/dl.

Human studies can never hope to obtain the same degree of control of lead exposure or the other variables that affect behavior that animal investigations achieve. For this and other reasons the question of low-level lead toxicity has become one of considerable controversy. Three separate investigations, one conducted

Until recently lead intoxication was believed to be a disease that afflicted only the urban poor and was caused solely by the ingestion of peeling lead-based paint.

in the United States, one in Great Britain, and one in West Germany, presented evidence that strongly supports the thesis that lead at doses considerably below those formerly assumed to be safe has harmful effects on children's brains.

Herbert Needleman, David Bellinger, and Alan Leviton extended their previous investigations of children without other symptoms but who had elevated lead levels in their shed teeth, and showed that having high tooth lead levels increases by fourfold the risk of having an IQ score below 80. William Yule and colleagues classified London schoolchildren by blood lead levels and found that having a level above 13 μg/dl was associated with decreased IQ and reading scores. Gerhard Winneke and his colleagues in Düsseldorf, West Germany, also studied school-age children classified by tooth lead levels and reported lead-related decreases in IQ scores and in parents' ratings.

The consistency of these three studies, in three different cultures, adds considerable conviction to the case for lowering the defined threshold for the effect of lead on a child's brain. In a series of investigations in North Carolina, David Otto and associates found a relationship between the amount of lead in the blood and the voltage waveform recorded at the scalp, with no evidence of a threshold.

Biochemical effects. The pathway for the synthesis of hemoglobin is the best studied biochemical target for lead. Sergio Piomelli first demonstrated that lead interferes with the normal incorporation of iron into the heme molecule, resulting in the production of an abnormal zinc-containing pigment, zinc protoporphyrin. In a large study of New York City children not considered poisoned, Piomelli showed that an increase in this abnormal pigment began to occur in children when their blood lead level reached 15 μg/dl. The correspondence of this figure with that of Yule's mentioned above is intriguing.

The discovery of the relationship between lead and zinc protoporphyrin has made a rapid, inexpensive, and relatively easy screening test available for public health departments and pediatricians. In areas where routine screening programs were undertaken, the incidence of severe lead poisoning declined rapidly because of early detection and the educational value of having such a program in place.

Two other important biochemical systems were shown to be lead-sensitive. Kathryn Mahaffey, John Rosen, and colleagues examined the activity of 1,25-dihydroxyvitamin D, the active form of the vitamin, across the range of blood levels from 12 to 120 μg/dl. Their results suggested that there was no threshold for lead's effect on this target.

Tetrahydrobiopterin (BH4) is an essential co-factor in the synthesis of two important neurotransmitters, dopamine and noradrenaline. Studies have shown that its activity in rodents is inhibited by very small amounts of lead. In Birmingham, England, J. A. Blair and colleagues showed that in 137 healthy humans the activity of this co-factor declined as lead concentration increased.

A number of investigators have in the past attempted without success to show that lead is an essential trace element. The nature of these experiments usually involves attempting to produce a deficiency state by raising experimental animals in a lead-free environment, measuring their growth, and comparing them with animals given trace amounts of lead. Decreases in weight and iron deficiency were reported by two German scientists in lead-deprived rats. In order to achieve

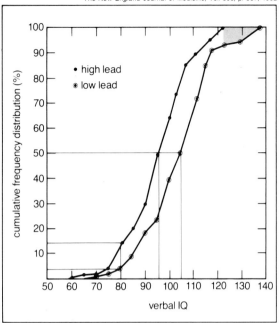

Reprinted by permission of
The New England Journal of Medicine, vol. 306, p. 367, 1982

Cumulative frequency distributions of verbal IQ scores of children with high and low levels of lead in their baby teeth reveal a fourfold increase in the risk of having an IQ below 80 in the high-lead group.

the lead-free diet, however, the animals' food was treated with edetic acid, and it is likely that this drug was responsible for the changes.

Lead exposure and pregnancy. Considerable concern has been expressed over the effects of lead on the fetus. Animal studies demonstrated that lead can produce birth anomalies and that the fetal rodent is much more sensitive to lead than the juvenile. Older reports of women exposed to lead in the workplace clearly indicated that lead was associated with both barrenness and excess morbidity in those infants who were brought to term.

In 1982 Michael Rabinowitz and Needleman reported on umbilical cord blood lead levels of 12,000 consecutive live births at an urban Boston hospital. The mean blood level was 6.6 μg/dl. As cord lead levels increased, the incidence of minor congenital anomalies increased in dose-related fashion. At one year of age those children who had higher blood lead levels at birth had lower scores on an infant intelligence test. Most interestingly, the average blood lead level dropped about 10% per year. This corresponded closely with data from New York City reported earlier. Although many factors may have contributed to this decline, one likely candidate is the reduction in gasoline lead additive consumption. This possiblity was further supported by the finding that the input of lead to a New Hampshire forest ecosystem has decreased over recent years.

—Herbert L. Needleman

Dentistry

Among health practitioners in the United States dentists were probably one of the first group to feel the pinch of the recession. Since 1979 the volume of dental practice throughout the nation has been declining. One of the reasons for this was the fact that about 27% of the younger-than-18 population is totally cavity free, thanks to fluoridation and other preventive measures such as anti-decay sealants.

Dental education has not escaped the effect of slipping business, as attested by the 40% drop in applications for dental schools between 1975 and 1980. As a result some experts are now seeing a drastic change in the way dental schools will operate in the future. They predict the emergence of generalists who will be trained to perform a variety of tasks now performed by specialists.

According to U.S. government statistics there is still much work needed in the mouths of Americans. In the younger-than-17 population alone there are a projected 32 million cavities that need permanent fillings, one million teeth that need extracting, and 1.3 million crowns to be installed. Elderly people have a high percentage of unmet dental care needs, and as a result the American Dental Association (ADA) launched access programs for senior citizens. In 1980 the ADA decided that access programs were needed to make dental care available to those unable to afford it. By 1983 the ADA had made remarkable strides, initiating such programs in 31 states and Puerto Rico.

Dental fear. If the thought of a visit to the dentist gives you sweaty palms, it may be comforting to know that you are not alone. An estimated 9% of the U.S. population, nearly 19 million people, shun dental treatment because of fear. They often learn to live with the most troublesome dental disease, fearing that the cure would be more painful. Modern dentistry's response came in 1982, when the ADA convened a special conference of experts to discuss new and innovative ways to alleviate patient fear and improve anxiety management. Calling it the third phase of the organization's access program—reaching out to the psychologically impeded—Robert H. Griffiths, president of the ADA in 1982, urged dentists to spend more time listening to patients.

Some of the proposed techniques to make anxiety-prone patients more comfortable included using videotaped programs featuring children, designed for children's viewing in the reception area; distraction and relaxation techniques such as video games and tape recordings designed to help patients relax muscles; and biofeedback devices to assist in regulating patient breathing patterns, in order to achieve greater relaxation.

Successful anxiety management also hinges on greater patient compliance, said a behavioral scientist

Dale B. Mirth, National Institutes of Health

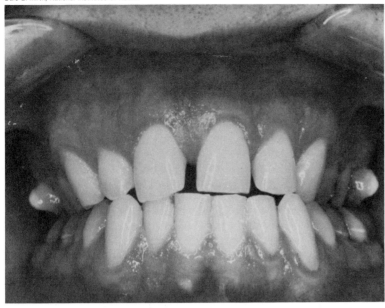

Sodium fluoride implants (protrusions on the right and left of the upper teeth) are attached to the first molar on each side of the upper jaw. Designed to "time release" fluoride 24 hours a day, they may not only prevent tooth decay but also reverse the decay process at its earliest stages.

from the University of Kentucky. Citing research not limited to dental patients, Thomas Garrity noted that "anywhere from 20 to 80% of patients don't fully comply with a doctor's orders, and about 50% don't comply in the long term." However, if the clinician is a teacher and employs a liberal use of repetition, giving more specifics than ambiguities, and is open to patient questions, the doctor can expect better patient compliance, Garrity suggested.

Fluoride implants. Researchers at the National Institute of Dental Research (NIDR) in Bethesda, Md., completed the first successful test on humans of an oral implant designed to "time release" sodium fluoride 24 hours a day. Results showed a "significant increase" in saliva fluoride levels among the 11 volunteers in the month-long study. Dale Mirth, an NIDR research chemist, said that the study indicated that such fluoride implants may not only prevent decay but may actually reverse the decay process at its earliest stages. The implants, which are the same width as a tooth and about half as thick as an aspirin tablet, were attached to the first molar on each side of the upper jaw and were bonded in a reversible, 30-minute procedure. Each contained 42 mg of sodium fluoride wrapped in a membrane that allowed the release of 0.5 mg of fluoride per day.

Outside sources of fluorides were kept to a minimum. The subjects did not use sodium fluoride toothpastes or rinses. However, the local water supply was fluoridated, and some fluoride was also present in foods consumed by the subjects. But the effect of these exposures on the study results were slight, Mirth noted. The subjects were monitored for 30 days prior to receiving the implants in order to establish a "baseline" for purposes of comparison. The implants were then attached and a further 30 days of study undertaken. After the devices were removed, the subjects were monitored for an additional two weeks. "This study indicates that from the point of view of safety, durability, performance, and patient acceptance, implants could be the key to eliminating tooth decay in the future," concluded Mirth.

Another effective anti-cavity measure was a weekly fluoride mouth rinse program in schools; this can reduce decay by up to 55%, according to NIDR scientists.

Scanning electron micrograph shows the bond between a plastic filling material (top) and the dentin of a tooth (bottom). Such bonds can withstand great stress without breaking.

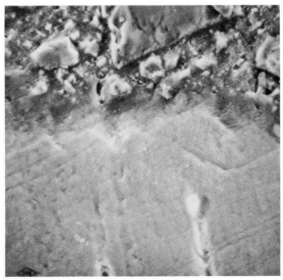

R. L. Bowen, American Dental Association Research Unit, National Bureau of Standards

The results of a 30-month study in Des Moines, Iowa, junior high schools showed a striking reduction in cavities between children who rinsed daily or weekly with sodium fluoride rinses and a control group that rinsed with a placebo. "While both daily and weekly rinsing impart significant anti-caries benefits, there was very little difference between the group that rinsed daily and the group that rinsed weekly," said William S. Driscoll. "As a result, we feel a program of weekly fluoride rinsing in schools would be more cost-effective, easier to implement, and just as effective as a daily classroom regimen." In the Des Moines program students in nine junior high schools rinsed for one minute, daily or weekly, under the supervision of the classroom teacher. Comparisons to baseline studies were made at 18 and 30 months and showed reductions of 28–55% in standard decay rates.

Gum disease. Juvenile periodontitis, a rapidly advancing form of gum disease that can cause loss of permanent teeth in otherwise healthy teenagers, may be inherited from a person's mother through an X-linked dominant genetic pattern. Thomas Leinbach of Charlottesville, Va., traced the dental history of a Virginia family through four generations and found evidence that susceptibility to juvenile periodontitis (also known as periodontosis) is probably inherited through the maternal side. "Women who have a history of periodontosis in their family should be counseled about the probability of passing the trait to their children. Sons can be expected to have particularly virulent periodontosis. It rarely appears in males, but when it does, it's generally quite severe," he said.

The eight-year study began when researchers noted that the children of one family seemed to be developing the disease despite excellent oral hygiene. Of the four girls and one boy in the family three girls experienced onset of the disease near puberty, with progressive soft tissue involvement and loosening of permanent teeth. The tissue breakdown continued despite treatment with antibiotics and rigorous oral hygiene. The son began developing the disease much earlier, at age six, and many of his deciduous (baby) teeth were lost because of damaged bone structure. The fifth child, a daughter, never developed the disease. The researchers traced the family's history back to a great-grandmother on the mother's side and found a history of the disease among several female family members. Existing dental records for male family members showed no sign of the ailment. "Periodontosis, or juvenile gum disease, has been affecting an estimated 10% of the children in the U.S.," Leinbach noted. While the disease can be slowed, it is virtually impossible to stop. "Therefore, the sooner we can detect it, the better the chances of treating it successfully."

New filling material. A National Bureau of Standards researcher developed a new process to bond plastic filling materials to cavities. The new method can be applied in restoring teeth when decay has penetrated the surface enamel of the tooth and attacked the dentin, the underlying bonelike tissue forming the body of the tooth. It is expected to be of particular benefit to adults who are subject to deeper, more penetrating forms of decay.

Adults also are particularly susceptible to root-surface caries—cavities along the gum line. These are linked to periodontal (gum) disease, which causes the gums to recede slowly, exposing some of the tooth's root surface. "Because the process requires less drilling than traditional cavity repair, the technique also increases patient comfort," said R. L. Bowen, associate director of the ADA Research Unit at the National Bureau of Standards. For decades dentists have relied on metal alloys known as dental amalgam, silicates, and, most recently, composites to restore teeth when decay involved the dentin. Bowen's procedure employed a ferric oxalate solution capable of actually changing the composition of the atoms in the hard surfaces of teeth, both enamel and dentin. He also applied two surface-active monomers, chemical agents that greatly improve the adhesion required between a tooth and the plastic restorative material.

Vitamin C and oral health. Too much of a good thing can be harmful, and that includes the otherwise healthy intake of vitamins and minerals, a Temple University nutrition expert suggested. "Many consumers will take a megadose of vitamin C as insurance against colds, but that can be dangerous," said Robert L. Pollock of Philadelphia. "If they suddenly stop taking the vitamin, it could lead to bleeding gums and a general decline in oral health." He explained that large doses of vitamin C force the body to speed up the metabolic process. "This accelerated metabolic rate persists even after the patient stops taking the vitamin. As a result, essential vitamin C may be washed out of the system and can cause damage to the oral tissue."

In addition to vitamin C many people also take supplemental zinc, believing that it will improve their capacity to heal properly and for other reasons. This, too, can be harmful. "Too much zinc causes the body to ignore copper, which is required for healthy gums," said Pollock, chairman of the department of biochemistry and nutrition at Temple. "A patient getting a normal level of copper but too much zinc will suffer from a copper deficiency."

—Lou Joseph

Veterinary medicine

The steady expansion of the veterinary educational system since World War II ended by 1983 as a result of the downturn in the economy. Beginning in 1945 the number of veterinary schools in the United States and Canada increased from 11 to 29, and one in Wisconsin was scheduled to open in the fall of 1983. During that time undergraduate enrollment increased from a total of about 2,100 to 9,500, and postgraduate enrollment from 80 to 1,900. Average class size at the existing schools doubled from about 45 to 90 students, thus requiring greatly expanded facilities.

Veterinary medicine was the fastest growing health profession from 1950 to 1980, during which time the number of veterinarians per 100,000 population increased from 8.8 to 16.1 (83%); during the same period the numbers of physicians and dentists increased 40% and 9%, respectively. By 1983, however, for the first time since the depression years of the 1930s, most of the veterinary colleges were facing substantial retrenchment, in large part because of federal budget cutting. Increases in undergraduate enrollment had been stimulated by federal grants (recently abolished), and the great expansion of postgraduate programs had been financed mostly (more than 90% at most schools) by federal money. At some schools increases in the 1982–83 budget were enough to allow for inflation, but at others there were actual decreases of up to nearly 10%. As a result faculty positions were left unfilled or eliminated at some institutions, and first-year enrollment was cut by 10–20% at others. Tuition had been essentially free at most of the state schools for many years and was as low as $150 per year (at Texas A & M) in 1971, but there had been sharp increases during the past decade to as high as $6,950 per year (University of Pennsylvania). Totally dependent on private funding since it opened in 1979, the veterinary school at Tufts University set tuition at $18,600 per year for students not subsidized by one of the New England states.

A further complication for many students was the lessened availability of scholarship and loan funds. During recent years it was not unusual for students to graduate with a loan debt of $20,000 or more, which would require an annual income of $30,000 or more to service on schedule. However, the average starting salary for new graduates (as employees) has been only about $15,000, and for the first time a few were having difficulty in finding employment. Formerly, many new graduates had started their own practices, but the cost of adequate facilities today has greatly restricted this option. The problem was more acute for women graduates, whose income after several years of experience averaged about $5,000 per year less than for men of comparable age.

Rabies. In 1982 the U.S. Public Health Service Centers for Disease Control in Atlanta announced that from 1978 to 1981 the reported cases of animal rabies increased from 3,298 to 7,211. In 1981 for the first time cat rabies cases (285) exceeded those in dogs (216). Skunks accounted for 4,480 cases in 1981, probably because of an increase in the skunk population in many states. Traditionally cats have been allowed to roam freely, and few are vaccinated against rabies, thus making them more likely than dogs to contract rabies via skunk bites. In Iowa cats were responsible for 42 of the 57 cases involving persons bitten by known rabid animals. Iowa also led the nation in total animal (889) and feline (83) rabies cases. As in some other states veterinarians and animal control officials in Iowa were considering a statewide requirement for rabies vaccination of cats.

The nature of the rabies problem in many communities was exemplified by that in Broward County, Florida, where, despite a statute requiring vaccination of all warm-blooded pets, only 25% of the estimated dogs and cats had been vaccinated in 1981. The World Health Organization stated that a 70% vaccination rate is necessary for an animal population to be protected. In Broward County cases of animal rabies increased

Baby alligators were hatched from a nest of 11 eggs that resulted from artificial insemination of the mother. This was the first application of this technique to alligators.

Gatorland Zoo

39% during 1981, and 34 of the 3,078 persons bitten by animals had to undergo rabies treatment. In an unusual move county officials gave the local veterinary association $15,000 for an advertising campaign aimed at encouraging rabies vaccination of pets.

There were only two cases of human rabies in the U.S. during 1981, but aside from the fact that few persons who develop symptoms of infection survive, the cost of controlling the disease has placed an increasing burden on local health departments. Thus after a dog that had bitten three persons in Yuba County, California, proved to be rabid, a health department investigation identified 70 persons with known or probable exposure to the dog. All were given antirabies treatment, at a cost of $92,650, and this along with other expenses including emergency animal vaccination clinics brought the total cost of the episode to $105,790. Only 20% of the dogs and cats in the area had up-to-date rabies vaccinations.

Animal reproduction. During 1982 several new developments were reported in the field of animal reproduction. A set of "cloned" identical twins produced by splitting an embryo recovered from a donor cow was born at Colorado State University in May, at which time another ten or more such sets were on the way. According to university veterinarian R. Peter Elsden these twins would be used to compare the responses of animals having identical genetic backgrounds to various drug and other treatments. By eliminating the effects of heredity many fewer animals would be required to establish reliable results in a great variety of experimental studies.

About eight progeny are needed to prove whether a cow carries a particular recessive trait, which at the rate of one calf every 12–13 months would ordinarily require most of her reproductive lifetime. With nonsurgical embryo recovery and transfer by pipette, however, a valuable cow can produce that many calves in less than a year, and embryo splitting would double the number. Such twins had been produced earlier at Cambridge University, England, but by surgical techniques that prevented the use of an individual cow as a donor or recipient more than once or twice.

In a related development scientists at Genetic Engineering, Inc., of Denver, Colo., reported the birth of a female calf whose sex had been determined as a six-day-old embryo, after which it was transferred to another cow. Although the cost of embryo transfer limits its application to relatively valuable animals, veterinarians have increasingly found it economically feasible to offer this service. The demand would be even greater if the sex of the calf could be guaranteed, and embryo splitting would substantially reduce the cost per calf. Both of these techniques have great potential for increasing the productivity of cattle in less developed countries, where scrub cows could be used as foster mothers for genetically superior embryos.

Although frozen semen had been used for artificial insemination of cattle for many years, the first litter of puppies (poodles) registered by the American Kennel Club (AKC) after being so produced was born in May 1982. The semen used had been collected seven years earlier and kept frozen at −168° C (−360° F) in liquid nitrogen. The research on which this technique is based was begun in 1968 by Stephen W. J. Seager, now at the Texas A & M College of Veterinary Medicine. He and two colleagues operated the first AKC-certified canine semen collection center, the vaults of which held semen from some 100 dogs of 50 breeds.

A nest of 11 eggs was hatched at Gatorland Zoo near Orlando, Fla., following artificial insemination of a female alligator in the first such application to this species. The technique was developed by Paul Cardeilhac and Rolf Larsen at the University of Florida College of Veterinary Medicine as a means of preserving crocodilian species facing extinction.

Genetic engineering. In a first-of-its-kind feat of genetic engineering researchers at the University of Pennsylvania School of Veterinary Medicine in cooperation with others transferred a gene carrying the DNA (deoxyribonucleic acid) code for growth hormone from rats to mouse embryos. This resulted in mice that had up to 20 times the normal level of growth hormone in their blood and which grew to twice normal size. An application of this work having great potential for agriculture would be the creation of giant animals capable of producing large amounts of meat and milk. As indicated by veterinary microbiologist Ralph Brinster, "If we can make bigger mice, we can make bigger cows." The high level of growth hormone produced by these animals, some of which passed this trait on to their offspring, suggested the possibility of producing other medically useful substances.

Researchers at Ohio University (Athens) reported the transfer of genes from rabbits to mice, which in turn passed the rabbit genes to two generations of mice. According to geneticist Thomas Wagner, "Application of this technique to animal breeding could dramatically shorten the time necessary to selectively breed species of animals with improved food-producing characteristics." His team was working on "three-parent" cattle, which would carry genes from an otherwise unrelated animal having an especially desirable trait such as faster growth or increased milk production.

—J. F. Smithcors

Optical engineering

The use of optical devices and techniques, especially those associated with lasers, continued to expand in 1982 despite the world business recession. The laser market in the United States alone was estimated as be-

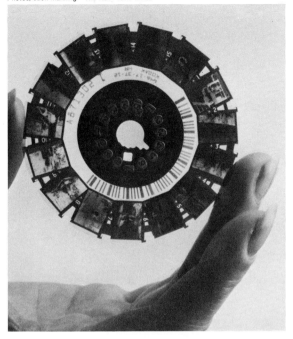

Pocket-sized Disc camera (above), developed by
Eastman Kodak Co., features a wide-angle lens system
and a wafer-thin disk (left) containing 15 tiny film
frames. The camera's miniaturized lens has a slightly
aspherical refracting surface.

ing in excess of $500 million, and continued growth
was predicted. During the past year commercialization
of most types of lasers was attained, with these sources
of coherent light becoming as standardized as ordinary
light bulbs. (Coherent light as produced by lasers is
light of a single frequency in which all the components
are in step with each other.) The reliability and lifetime
of the common helium-neon laser in recent months
improved to the extent that commercial products using
those devices could exceed the expectations usually
reserved for instruments containing tungsten light
sources. Other varieties of lasers, including ion and
solid-state diode devices, were expected to attain this
status in the near future. As a result competition in the
optical instrument field became more price conscious,
with many instrument designs striving for simplicity
rather than elegance. It is unlikely that the economies
demonstrated in the microelectronics field will ever
fully apply to optical instruments because of the requirement of these devices for precise mechanical and
optical components, but the market was moving in that
direction.

Videodiscs and audiodiscs. The growth in optical
instruments in the U.S. as of 1983 was still largely
oriented toward military applications, with most of the
commercial and civilian consumer products coming
from other nations. The consumer product situation
remained mixed in regard to sales. The apparently
ultimate recording device, the optical videodisc, still
suffered from a lack of a large market. Its most promising application appeared to be in the area of digital
data storage, where extremely large amounts of storage could be made rapidly accessible to a computer

with only minor extensions of current technology. The
data-storage applications were limited by the inability
of engineers and technicians to write data to be stored
on videodiscs directly by any computer rather than on a
special recorder. During 1982 several techniques for
accomplishing local computer-controlled writing of
data on an optical disc were demonstrated, but no mar-
ketable products had been developed by the end of the
year. The major requirements that still needed to be
met appeared to be in the area of materials and included metals that melted at low temperatures when
struck by light focused from a low-power laser.

The digital audiodisc, in which the sound is converted to a stream of digital bits during recording, finally
reached the market in 1982. However, it was offered
only in an expensive top-of-the-line form of optical
playback system. It seemed doubtful that this development would achieve success until pocket-sized repro-
ducers were offered on the market. The audiodisc does
have the potential of placing on line to a microcomputer a program library equivalent to about a hundred of
the currently popular 5.25-in magnetic floppy disk-
ettes. If the economics of widespread computer program sales and updating can be solved, this may prove
to be the principal application for optical storage devices in the near future.

Fiber optics. Communication systems using glass fibers to conduct light waves reached a new stage of development in 1983 with the demonstration of 100 km
(60 mi) of an eventual Atlantic undersea cable. The cable was designed to contain seven optical fiber links
and will permit the simultaneous transmission of several video signals as well as numerous voice and data

Optical engineering

signals. (For additional information on fiber optics, *see* Year in Review: MATERIALS SCIENCES: *Ceramics.*)

Cameras. In the more traditional optical areas some notable successes were attained. The Eastman Kodak Disc camera, which records images on a rotating film chip in a thin pocket-sized case, introduced an entirely new concept in convenient amateur photography. The image quality was superb due to a combined development of optics, electronics, and mechanics and demonstrated that film-based systems would continue to be the major part of the photographic market. The miniaturized lens for this camera contains a glass aspheric refracting surface (one departing slightly from the spherical form), which represents the widest successful use of precision aspherics in history. Although published details are somewhat sketchy, this is a major innovation, the success of which seems certain to have an impact in many areas of optics. The new class of sensitized material demonstrated quality superior to that of electronic sensors. A demonstration of electronic enhancement of enlarged pictures from this small-image format produced quality equal to that expected from cameras having much larger formats. For this imaging system Kodak demonstrated in 1982 some potential new components that use a photoelectric array sensor and a television set for viewing and editing frames to be printed.

Developments in the photographic camera area by other manufacturers centered on increased automation of the camera functions. Automatic focusing and automatic exposure determination both became common features of new cameras. Lens designs for compact and wide-range zoom lenses for 35-mm format cameras were introduced.

Telescopes. The principal optical engineering achievements in astronomy were associated with the large Space Telescope, a 2.4-m aperture instrument to be launched on the space shuttle in about 1985, and the Infrared Astronomy Satellite (IRAS), launched in early 1983. The Space Telescope primary and backup primary mirrors are the most precise large telescope mirrors ever manufactured, and either one should permit the theoretical physical limits of resolution and light-gathering power of the telescope to be attained. (*See* Year in Review: MATERIALS SCIENCES: *Ceramics.*) The IRAS system is of modest aperture, only about 0.6 m in diameter, but the entire optical system is cooled cryogenically to almost absolute zero; this removes the thermal background interference that limits the capability of most infrared telescopes.

In ground-based astronomy the predicted beginning of the very large next-generation telescopes was delayed. Although the technology for fabricating telescopes having diameters as large as 15 m, using segmented mirrors, appeared to be available, no single project was identified as the best general telescope design. Since the current world economic situation

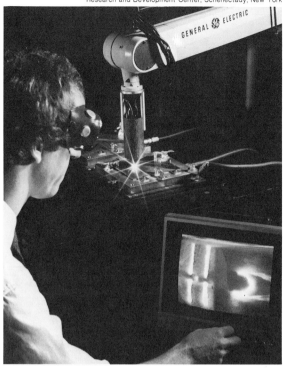

Welding robot steers itself along irregularly shaped joints by continuously observing the joint and weld "puddle" and making the necessary adjustments. In the foreground the television screen shows the scene observed by the system's "eyes," which are located in the welding "torch" assembly. The device is expected to be more productive than previous models.

does not permit the funding of multiple projects, the actual construction of these telescopes remained in the design stage.

Materials and manufacturing processes. Optical materials introduced in 1982 included the use of chemically etched antireflecting coatings on glass. The principal use for these coatings initially was for the protection of glass surfaces to be used in high-energy laser systems for laser-initiated nuclear fusion. It seemed likely, however, that this technology would become available in the consumer area and would, for example, provide economies in the fabrication of some camera lenses.

Manufacturing processes using optical techniques continued to increase. The use of lasers to machine metals and ceramics became commonplace and was competitive in cost with ordinary tooling. The flexibility of laser cutting and trimming of parts and dies led to economies in the making of very complex or delicate components. But some cost advantage can be found in even mundane applications when it is noted that the cutting tool itself does not wear out because there is no mechanical contact between the laser probe and the work being produced.

362

Another application that achieved commercial success in 1982 was a laser gyroscope as the inertial sensor for an aircraft navigation system. Some Boeing 767 jetliners were equipped with the device. Late in the year there was a demonstration of a laser gyroscope that used fiber optics, a potentially more economical approach that might lead to widespread application of this instrument.

Holography became a widely used engineering laboratory tool through the introduction of instant holographic cameras with reusable interference pattern storage medium. The stored hologram can contain either the representation of a three-dimensional object or an encoded form of digitized numerical data. The projected data storage applications for this holographic medium did not take place during the last year, but the use of multiple-exposure holography as a diagnostic tool in analyzing mechanical structures became commonplace.

The use of industrial robots increased during the year. Most of these devices were blind, in the sense that computers directed them to specific locations to carry out such operations as welding or joining parts. A new field of optical engineering is robot vision, in which the robot arm is equipped with an optical sensor that can use a pattern-matching approach to locate the surface or part to be worked on. This was expected to ease significantly the difficulty of programming the action of such devices. Some sensor devices of this type were announced in 1982.

A short prediction of possibilities for future months includes the following: Optical data-storage discs will reach the market in limited applications. The extensive use of a variety of electro-optical devices in manufacturing and quality control can be expected. The first representatives of a new generation of large telescopes will become a reality. Continued automation of photographic cameras, with more compact lenses, can be expected.

—Robert R. Shannon

Physics

The past year was a fruitful one for physicists seeking experimental verification of some key predictions of a number of models and theories. Good preliminary evidence emerged for the existence of an intermediate vector boson called the W particle; the first detailed observations of the B meson firmly established the reality of a fifth member of the quark family, known as the b quark; and a special detector recorded a single event that had all the required characteristics of a magnetic monopole. Nuclear physicists confidently reported the creation of element 109 even though only one atom of the substance was detected. The fields of solid-state physics and solid-state electronics contin-

ued to experience a high degree of "cross-fertilization" as basic research both benefited and benefited from computers and other technological products.

General developments

By 1982, after years of collecting radio pulses from a binary pulsar, astrophysicists had convincing evidence that gravitational radiation exists. A low-temperature physicist set a trap for the mythical magnetic monopole and possibly caught one, and an international conference announced that it would soon post a fixed speed limit for light.

Gravitational radiation. According to Einstein rapidly moving masses should emit waves made of gravitational fields. Although many physicists had constructed antennas to detect such radiation coming from exploding or co-orbiting stars, they had never found convincing evidence for its existence (see *1981 Yearbook of Science and the Future* Feature Article: THE SEARCH FOR GRAVITATIONAL WAVES). Recently, however, after timing the radio pulses arriving from a binary pulsar, astrophysicists Joseph Taylor and Joel Weisberg of Princeton University felt that they had sufficient proof that gravitational radiation is real, even though they did not detect it directly.

For more than six years they used the giant Arecibo radio telescope in Puerto Rico to monitor the short bursts of radio noise emitted by the pulsar PSR 1913 + 16. (The pulsar is at right ascension 19 hours 13 minutes and declination + 16 degrees in the constellation Aquila. It is estimated to be about 15,000 light-years away.) Pulsars are very small, very dense, rapidly rotating stars composed mostly of neutrons. They are thought to be the remnants of supernova explosions. These spinning neutron stars have hot spots that emit radio beams. As the star rotates, the beam sweeps across the sky like the beam from a lighthouse. Because the star is small and massive the spin speed remains extremely constant. The rotating pulsar thus can be used as an extremely accurate clock. The radio pulses from this pulsar clock come 16.94054014 times a second. When found by Taylor and Russell Hulse in 1974, the pulsar was first thought to be just like any other, but Hulse found that its pulse rate increased and decreased with a period of 7.75 hours. The pulsar turned out to be one component of a binary star system, with the two stars rotating about each other in highly elliptical orbits with a period of 7.75 hours.

When the pulsar is moving toward the Earth in its orbit, the pulses become crowded together, and the pulse-repetition frequency is slightly higher than the average 16.94 pulses per second. When the pulsar is moving away from the Earth, there are slightly fewer pulses per second. The increase in pulse rate occurs faster than the decrease, indicating that the pulsar is in an elliptical orbit, where it travels faster when it is

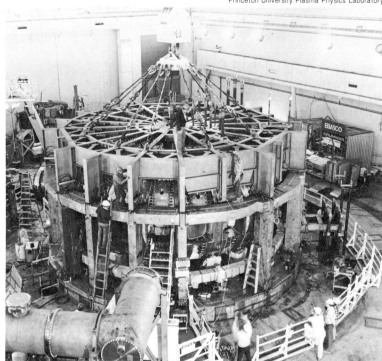

In December 1982 the experimental Tokamak Fusion Test Reactor (right) at Princeton University achieved a milestone when it successfully produced its first magnetically confined plasma. The gas used for the test was ordinary hydrogen, which was heated to 100,000° C for a fraction of a second. The eventual goal would be to bring fuel made of the hydrogen isotopes deuterium and tritium to the 100,000,000° C temperature and one-second containment time believed necessary for fusion reactions in the machine to produce more energy than is needed to keep them going.

close to its companion. When the pulsar is on the near side of its orbit, the pulses arrive more than three seconds earlier than they do when it is on the far side, showing that the orbit is about three light-seconds (about a million kilometers) across. Since the orbits are only about twice the diameter of the Sun while the orbital dynamics indicate that both stars have a mass of 1.4 solar masses, it is probable that the companion star is also an ultradense pulsar. If it emits radio pulses, they are not beamed in the direction of Earth.

The two stars are moving so rapidly in their orbits that they should emit significant amounts of gravitational radiation. Because of the loss of energy through gravitational radiation, the orbital period should decrease by 67 billionths of a second each orbit. Normally it would be impossible to detect such a small change in the orbital period of a star system 15,000 light-years away, but because the pulsar is a very accurate clock, the change in period can be measured quite accurately. The decrease in orbital period that Taylor and Weisberg found agrees to within 10% of that predicted by Einstein's equations for gravitational radiation, while all other competing theories of gravity predict a value inconsistent with the observed value. Thus, tiny pulses of radio energy from a pair of invisible stars 15,000 light-years away have given hope to all those researchers building instruments to detect gravitational radiation directly.

Trapping a monopole. In a simple but elegant experiment Blas Cabrera excited the world of physics when he obtained evidence that a magnetic monopole

may have passed through a special detector in his laboratory at Stanford University. A magnetic monopole is an elementary particle postulated to exist by a number of theories. All other elementary particles with magnetic properties are magnetic dipoles, with both a north and a south pole like a household magnet. The magnetic monopole has only one pole, either north or south. The mass of a monopole is unknown, but current theories predict an extremely large mass (for a particle) of 20 billionths of a gram, about the mass of an amoeba! A particle this massive usually would be traveling slowly and could not be detected by the standard particle detectors that look for ionization tracks or radiation resulting from the passage of the particle through matter.

The detector at Stanford is a coil five centimeters (about two inches) in diameter containing four turns of niobium wire made superconductive (made to lose all electrical resistance) by cooling it in liquid helium to a few degrees above absolute zero. A current set up in such a coil will flow indefinitely without any external power source. Quantum theory indicates that the amount of magnetic flux that passes through the loop must be quantized into discrete amounts, which are called magnetic flux quanta. Each increase in the number of flux quanta passing through the coil causes a corresponding jump in a persistent current circulating in the loop. Any such increase in the persistent current is measured by an ultrasensitive current detector called a SQUID (superconducting quantum interference device). Passage of a magnetic monopole through

364

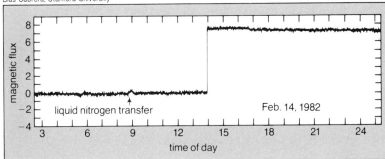

Chart recording of "Valentine's Day event" at Stanford University shows the sudden jump of eight flux quanta consistent with the detection of a magnetic monopole. Slight disturbance due to a scheduled transfer of liquid nitrogen coolant was also recorded.

one turn of superconducting wire causes the magnetic flux to jump two flux quanta. Thus, the four turns in Cabrera's detector produce an eight-quanta jump in the trapped flux. The beauty of the detector is that it only gives a response to the magnetic charge of the monopole. The detector output is independent of the mass, velocity, electric charge, or magnetic dipole characteristics of any other particle.

On Valentine's Day in 1982, after more than 200 days of observation, Cabrera found a single eight-magnetic-flux quantum event consistent with the passage of one unit of magnetic charge through his coil. The cleanness of the data and the low noise level attained by his apparatus is apparent in the chart recording of the event. As one noted theorist remarked, "One shouldn't be convinced by one event. But it's about as impressive as one event can be."

Since the magnetic fields that Cabrera is trying to measure in the coil are billions of times smaller than even the Earth's rather small field of half a gauss, it is essential that the detector be well shielded. To achieve the ultralow levels needed for his work, he uses a novel superconducting magnetic shield—a lead balloon.

To make the shield Cabrera begins with a long cylindrical bag made of lead foil 60 micrometers (a little more than two-thousandths of an inch) thick, then pleats and folds it into a compact strip. The strip is inserted into the low-temperature chamber. Although the chamber has ordinary magnetic shielding around it, there is still some residual magnetic field inside the chamber and this field penetrates the pleated strip of foil. As the foil cools and turns superconducting, the magnetic field lines passing through the thin strip are trapped in the foil. Then using a piston, Cabrera inflates the lead balloon. As it expands, two things happen. The superconducting lead foil pushes the magnetic field outside its surface away from the center of the chamber, while the small amount of magnetic field trapped on the inside expands and decreases in strength. Cabrera then inserts additional pleated lead-foil strips into this attenuated field region and goes through the process again and again until the field inside the last balloon shield is low enough to allow his detector to work.

With only one event recorded, there is no doubt that much more needs to be done to prove the existence of magnetic monopoles. There could be other causes for the jump of eight flux quanta. (Cabrera was able to cause a six-quanta jump by striking the outside of the low-temperature chamber with a screwdriver handle, but mechanically induced jumps show spikes and drifts that are not seen on the Valentine's Day event.) In 1983 Cabrera was continuing to monitor the detector (after adding an accelerometer to monitor for mechanical disturbances) and was using another detector made of three coils ten centimeters in diameter wound around a glass bulb at right angles to each other. If a monopole passes through this detector it will very like

Improved three-coil monopole detector built by Blas Cabrera is 50 times more sensitive than the previous version and covers a larger field of entry.

ly trigger two or three coils in coincidence. Only time will tell if Cabrera's valentine from nature was an isolated, never-to-be-explained "glitch" in the apparatus or the first evidence that the mythical magnetic monopole exists. (See *High-energy physics,* below.)

Fixing the speed of light. Scientists wanting to measure the speed of light for themselves appeared to have only until the fall of 1983, when the General Conference on Weights and Measures was expected to set the speed of light at exactly 299,792,458 meters per second while letting the length of the meter vary. Presently the second is defined as the duration of 9,192,631,770 cycles of a certain frequency of radio waves from a cesium atom, while the meter is defined as 1,650,763.73 wavelengths of a certain frequency of light from a krypton atom. The krypton atom was a fine standard for many years, but its accuracy of about four parts per billion does not compare well with the new frequency-stabilized lasers that are accurate to parts in a trillion. The length of the meter could be redefined in terms of some laser wavelength, but newer lasers are coming along all the time.

Rather than redefining the meter each time there is a better laser, the conference would define the meter as "the length equal to the distance travelled in a time interval of 1/299,792,458 of a second by plane electromagnetic waves in a vacuum." Now as each improved laser comes along, its frequency can be measured using the cesium clock. Then, because the speed of light is fixed, the laser wavelength is immediately known and the laser can be used as a length standard. Thus, the accuracy of the meter will improve along with each improvement in the frequency stability of lasers.

—Robert L. Forward

High-energy physics

During 1982, elementary particle physicists gathered further experimental support for the "standard model" of strong, weak, and electromagnetic interactions, and this theoretical framework became increasingly understood and accepted. One specific dramatic prediction of the standard model, the existence of intermediate vector bosons, received initial experimental confirmation in January 1983. Effects leading to possible extensions of this model, such as neutrino oscillations, had been reported but are regarded with some skepticism. Grand unified theories (GUT's) have been proposed that would wrap the weak, electromagnetic, and strong interactions into one glorious theoretical scheme. Some experimental consequences of this, the existence of magnetic monopoles and the decay of the proton, were in the news in recent months.

The standard model. All hadrons—strongly interacting particles such as protons, neutrons, and pi mesons—are now understood to be composed of quarks; each "flavor" of quark has three "color" states, and for

Table I. The Elementary Particles of Physics

	Electric charge[2]	Generation[1] I	II	III
quarks[3]	$+\frac{2}{3}$	u (~10)[4]	c (1,500)	$[t$ (?)][5]
	$-\frac{1}{3}$	d (~20)	s (170)	b (5,000)
leptons	-1	e (0.511)	μ (106)	τ (1,784)
	0	ν_e (0?)	ν_μ (0?)	$[\nu_\tau$ (0?)][5]

[1] It is not known whether or not there are more generations of particles beyond the three listed.
[2] Electric charge is in units of the magnitude of the charge of an electron.
[3] Each quark is found in three color states.
[4] The numbers in parentheses are approximate masses in units of MeV/c^2 (energy in millions of electron volts divided by the square of the speed of light). In these units the proton mass is 940, for example. The e, μ, and τ masses are well established.
[5] The t quark and the ν_τ (tau neutrino) have not been experimentally observed.

each of these in turn there is a corresponding antiquark. The known quarks are listed in Table I. The quarks interact strongly through the exchange of massless, "colored" field particles, called gluons, very much as electromagnetic interactions between electrically charged particles are understood in quantum electrodynamics (QED) in terms of the exchange of photons of electromagnetic radiation. Both the gluons and photons are vector particles; *i.e.,* they contain one unit of intrinsic spin. The strong-interaction theory analogous to QED has been extensively developed and is called quantum chromodynamics (QCD). The weak and gravitational interactions are also expected to have their own field particles. A summary of the four fundamental interactions of nature is given in Table II on the opposite page.

Jets. During 1982 a new accelerator system had its first serious data run. This machine is the colliding-beam system at CERN (European Organization for Nuclear Research) in Geneva, Switz., wherein protons and antiprotons, each of an energy of 270 GeV (billion electron volts), circulate in opposite directions in the magnetic field of the super proton synchrotron and collide head-on to provide an energy of 540 GeV in the center of mass, equivalent to a proton of about 200 TeV (trillion electron volts) of energy striking a stationary proton target. One particular result reported from such collisions is the clear observation of preferentially directed "jets" of particles, which are interpreted as the result of the scattering of the pointlike fundamental constituents of the colliding proton and antiproton.

Most of the time at lower energies and at high energies the interaction of two protons, or of a proton and an antiproton, results in a large number of mesons; at energies of the CERN collider the average number of charged particles is about 30. It had been predicted that on occasion two quark constituents of the protons or perhaps two gluons (also found in the protons) would pass close enough to each other to recoil strongly, much like two billiard balls. Free quarks or gluons, however, cannot emerge from the collision; rather they "materialize" as a group of mesons moving in the general direction of the scattered quark or gluon and with a total energy and momentum equal to that of the constituent. These bundles of mesons, which are the visible manifestation of the scattered quark or gluon, are called jets. At lower energies the mesons of the jets are too similar in their energy and direction to the large numbers of mesons that generally result from inelastic collisions between protons or between a proton and an antiproton to be readily resolved. At the very high energies now accessible with the CERN collider, however, these jets occasionally stand out as exceedingly clear pairs of bundles of particles, each moving at large angles to the paths of the incident particles and at almost 180° with respect to each other.

B mesons. In 1977 a new, fifth quark was discovered in experiments at the Fermi National Accelerator Laboratory near Chicago. There, using a 400-GeV proton beam against a stationary metal target, physicists observed a "resonance" marked by an increase in the production of pairs of muons of a certain combined mass. This resonance, the Υ (upsilon), was interpreted as the production of a new, nearly stable particle that decayed almost immediately into the observed muons. The particle in turn was interpreted as being composed of a quark and an antiquark of a new flavor, b (for "bottom" or "beauty"). Subsequent experiments in the U.S. and in West Germany confirmed these observations and showed that the upsilon consists of a series of four separate states closely spaced in mass. The highest energy upsilon, however, was a broad resonance, and

this was interpreted as evidence that the state decayed not into known mesons but into a new pair of shortlived mesonic particles, each containing a b quark. During 1982 definitive experiments at the Cornell Electron Storage Ring (CESR) of Cornell University, Ithaca, N.Y., revealed detailed characteristics of these B mesons. The fifth, or b, quark thus is quite firmly established.

Searches for the t quark and intermediate vector bosons. One outstanding gap in particle physics generated by the discovery of the b quark relates to its logical companion, the t (for "top" or "truth") quark. The lighter quarks come in pairs of $+\frac{2}{3}$ and $-\frac{1}{3}$ units of electric charge, as noted in Table I, and it would be surprising if the b quark had no massive partner with a $+\frac{2}{3}$ charge. At the positron-electron colliding-beam facility at DESY in Hamburg, West Germany, energies as high as 38 GeV have been made available in collisions of electrons with positrons, and the predicted particle composed of a t quark and a t antiquark (analogous to the Υ) would have been observed if the t-quark mass were less than 19 GeV. Hence it is believed to be greater than 19 GeV, although how much greater is not predicted by the standard model, which does not allow one to calculate any quark masses. It is very uncomfortable to consider that the t quark might not exist, because according to the standard model the properties of the b quark imply t-quark existence. Only higher energies in electron-positron colliding beam systems will settle this question, and new facilities are being built in both the U.S. and in Europe.

A very sharp prediction of the standard model is the existence of the intermediate vector bosons: the $W^\pm$ (carrying one unit of positive or negative electric charge) of about 83 GeV rest mass and the Z^0 (an electrically neutral particle) of about 94 GeV mass. A primary reason for building the CERN antiproton-proton collider facility had been the observation of these field particles, which serve to mediate the weak interaction (see Table II).

In January 1983 a group of physicists working at CERN reported several events from a two-month run of proton-antiproton collisions that fit all the requirements for the W^+ and the W^-. Once produced, these particles are predicted to decay almost immediately by any of several routes; a distinctive one is their decay into an electron (in the case of the W^-) or a positron (in the case of the W^+) plus a neutrino, which are ejected from the site of interaction in nearly opposite directions at high energy and at a large angle from the line of the colliding beams. In about six cases out of roughly a billion proton-antiproton collisions produced during the run were electrons or positrons observed with these characteristics. Moreover, in each case a certain amount of missing energy—energy released from the collision but not accounted for by all of the particles recorded emerging from the event—indicated the pro-

Table II. The Force Fields of Elementary Particle Physics

Interaction	Field particle	Mass of field particle	Particles with which field particle interacts
electro-magnetic	γ (photon)	0	all electrically charged particles; all quarks and all charged leptons
weak	$W^\pm$ Z^0 (intermediate bosons)[1]	83 GeV/c^2 94 GeV/c^2	all particles
strong	g (gluon)[2]	0	all hadrons (all particles composed of quarks)
gravitational	G (graviton)[1]	0	all objects with mass

[1] Evidence for the W is preliminary; the Z^0 and the graviton have not yet been experimentally observed.

[2] There are eight color combinations of gluons.

367

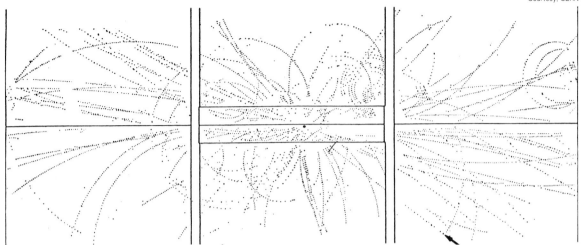

Trace of a high-energy electron (arrow) captured in the record of a 65-particle spray from a proton-antiproton collision at CERN *offers evidence for the production and decay of the long-sought W particle. Center horizontal lines mark the paths of the incoming beams.*

duction of a neutrino, which particle detectors do not record. As a further check, when the rest masses of the decay products were used to estimate the mass of the original particle, the result agreed well with the predicted value for the W. In 1983 the results of further beam runs would receive scrutiny for other characteristic decay-product combinations of the W particle including muons and neutrinos, tau leptons and neutrinos, and pairs of oppositely directed jets of pi mesons. Experimental observation of the Z^0 will be the highest priority; the decay of a Z^0 into an electron and a positron should be a particularly distinctive signature.

Neutrino oscillations. Negative evidence may be as significant as a new discovery, although more often it creates an ambiguous situation in which physicists do not know exactly what to believe, and further experiments are necessary. In 1980 Soviet scientists presented evidence from the spectrum of electrons from the radioactive decay of tritium (hydrogen-3) that the electron neutrino had a finite rest mass of about 30 eV/c^2 (about a twenty-thousandth of the rest mass of an electron). Meanwhile, physicists at the University of California at Irvine reported evidence of neutrino oscillations. In this experiment, performed with antineutrinos from a nuclear reactor, there appeared to be evidence that electron antineutrinos spontaneously transform with a certain time constant into some other type of neutrino.

The standard model comfortably allows neutrinos to have a finite rest mass but predicts no particular value for this mass. And if the mass of the neutrinos is not zero, the separate neutrino generations, ν_e, ν_μ, and ν_τ, would most probably result in three neutrino mass states, m_1, m_2, and m_3. A consequence of such a mass spectrum would be transformations, or oscillations of state, such as the Irvine group reported.

Since the experiment that showed evidence of oscillations was published, other experiments have been carried out at reactors and with particle accelerators seeking confirming evidence of oscillations or other manifestations of neutrino mass. Physicists at the California Institute of Technology, in particular, studied antineutrinos from a reactor in a way that would have been sensitive to oscillation. They reported that their result explicitly contradicts the earlier Irvine data.

As of early 1983 the Soviet experiment on tritium had not been repeated with sufficient precision to confirm or refute the initial results, although several groups were pursuing experiments designed to be sufficiently sensitive to see the effect. (See *1983 Yearbook of Science and the Future* Feature Article: THE PHANTOM NEUTRINO.)

Magnetic monopoles. Grand unified theories predict that there should be free magnetic monopoles—isolated north and south "magnetic charges" quite analogous to free positive and negative electric charges. If they exist, they would be very, very massive, about 10^{25} eV/c^2, or 10^{16} times the mass of a proton. With such masses it would be impossible to produce them at the large particle accelerators in the way that antiprotons, B mesons, and other particles are made. They might possibly be drifting about through the universe, however, just as starlight and cosmic rays do. They could have been produced in the first moments of the life of the universe, in an early stage of expansion of the big bang. There is no crisp prediction concerning their number or density, but some upper limits may be set. For example, it is known that there is a magnetic field (about a millionth of the intensity of the Earth's magnetic field) in our Galaxy. If the monopole flux exceeded some value, it would neutralize this field, just as an electrically ionized plasma neutralizes an electric field.

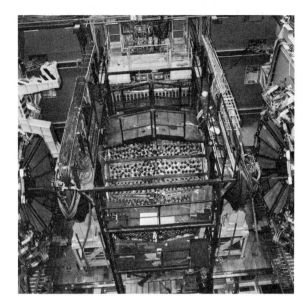

Giant UA1 and UA2 detectors (left to right) recorded collision events at CERN that gave scientists their first look at evidence for the W particle. Observation of the Z⁰, perhaps by virtue of its decay into an electron and a positron, would be the next goal.

There have been searches for magnetic monopoles in the past, all with negative results.

In early 1982, using a small superconducting coil in a magnetically shielded cryostat, Blas Cabrera of Stanford University reported a signal that was exactly the value and character predicted for the passage of a monopole through his coil (see *General developments*, above). Based on the running time of his experiment this signal would correspond to a monopole flux many orders of magnitude greater than that which would discharge the galactic magnetic field. Other experiments using superconducting coils have since been used to seek monopole signals. As of early 1983 no confirmation of Cabrera's original observation had been reported.

Proton decay. One of the most dramatic consequences of GUT's is that all hadronic matter is ultimately unstable. The proton, for example, is predicted to decay spontaneously into mesons and either an electron or a neutrino. The time constant for this decay must be very, very long indeed. Theory predicts it to be at least 10^{30} years, or about 10^{20} times the age of the universe. Nevertheless, in a ton of matter there are about 6×10^{29} protons and neutrons, so that there might be a spontaneous nucleon decay on the average once every 1½ years per ton. In the past, several groups have looked for spontaneous signals from large tanks of scintillator liquid located underground in mines. These experiments, originally designed to study cosmic-ray neutrino interactions, incidentally set lower limits to the proton-decay lifetime of about 10^{31} years.

The development of GUT's has stimulated several new large experiments deep underground designed to make a dedicated search for proton decays. In 1981 an experiment operated by an Indian-Japanese collaboration in a mine in the Indian Kolar Gold Fields reported possible evidence for a proton-decay event. This experiment, employing 150 tons of steel, has since reported two more proton-decay candidates, although it has been argued that the experimenters cannot rule out other interpretations. Several other experiments were under way at the beginning of 1983, the largest being an 8,000-ton water detector in an Ohio salt mine operated by a collaboration from the University of Michigan, University of California at Irvine, and Brookhaven National Laboratory in New York. After three months of operation this experiment had found no evidence for proton decay into a neutral pi meson and a positron (a predicted dominant decay mode). The finding set a lower limit of 6.5×10^{31} years for the lifetime of the proton into this decay channel, in contradiction with the possible evidence reported by the Indian-Japanese collaboration.

—Lawrence W. Jones

Nuclear physics

The past year in nuclear physics was characterized by the development of elegant and powerful new instruments and techniques. At the same time there was a growing feeling throughout the science that quantum chromodynamics may play the same role in describing the strong nuclear interaction that quantum electrodynamics enjoys in the field of electromagnetic interactions, where it remains the most precise theory known to man.

Element 109. Indicative of this new experimental elegance was the discovery by Peter Armbruster and his collaborators at GSI in Darmstadt, West Germany, of element 109. After ten days of heavy-ion bombardment of heavy-element targets Armbruster and his collaborators found only a single atom of the element, yet it is a measure of the elegance of the experimental techniques used that essentially no one doubts the correctness of this identification. It may well be that element 109 will be the heaviest of the transuranic species produced directly in this fashion, since no one is enthusiastic about the presumably much longer and more difficult measurements that would be required for the production of an atom of element 110.

The year 1982 marked the 50th anniversary of the discovery of the neutron and the 40th anniversary of the first sustained, controlled nuclear chain reaction that first made neutrons available in quantity. In this context it is appropriate to note that the elements from uranium up through fermium (element 100) were all produced by exposing heavy elements to intense neutron fluxes, wherein neutron capture followed by beta decay led to ever heavier elements. Beyond element 100, however, lifetimes become so short that production by way of stepwise neutron pickup is no longer feasible. Element 101 was produced by bombarding heavy targets with helium nuclei, and all elements from element 102 through element 109 were produced by bombardment with ions heavier than helium. It remains a tantalizing possibility—based on extrapolation of present knowledge of the structure of heavy nuclei—that there exist islands of stability far beyond any that could have been reached by nature itself, where nuclei, once produced, might be either totally stable or at least somewhat stable. The search for these super-transuranic or superheavy species continues in the Soviet Union, at Darmstadt, and at the Lawrence Berkeley Laboratory in California, although the initial optimism associated with these searches has been somewhat dampened over the past few years by the total lack of evidence for the existence of such superheavies.

Dipole collectivity in nuclei. After the discovery of the nuclear shell model by Maria Mayer and Hans Jensen in the early 1950s, it rapidly became clear that the basic concept—namely, that neutrons and protons (nucleons) behave quite independently and as individual entities within the nucleus—would not suffice to describe many phenomena, in which nucleons appeared to be behaving in a collective or cooperative fashion. Aage Bohr, Ben Mottelson, and James Rainwater received the 1975 Nobel Prize for Physics for the development of the collective model of nuclear phenomena, which explicitly takes into account this cooperative behavior. Fundamental to this approach was the recognition that nuclei generally are not spherical but have a so-called quadrupole deformation, which

Wide World

Upper yoke of new 500-MeV cyclotron is lowered into place at Michigan State University in East Lansing. Together with a larger machine being built nearby, it will be used for studies of the atomic nucleus.

can be either prolate or oblate—either football- or doorknob-shaped. The shell model and the collective model together were remarkably successful in correlating, organizing, and making possible the understanding of a vast body of information about all nuclei. As the quality of measurements has continued to improve, however, and as nuclear structure has become better understood, gaps and tears in the fabric of these two models have become increasingly evident and embarrassing.

Following on the success of group theoretical methods in providing an alternate understanding of many aspects of nuclear behavior, Franco Iachello of Yale University and Andrew Jackson of the State University of New York at Stony Brook suggested that in addition to the quadrupole type of collectivity, there might exist in nuclei a dipole kind of collectivity, which had not yet been identified but which would have very characteristic signatures in special families of nuclear quantum states, with equally special electromagnetic transitions linking these states to one another and to the more familiar quadrupole states. Very recently Moshe Gai and his collaborators at Yale obtained measurements both in light nuclei, such as oxygen-18, and in very heavy nuclei, such as radium-218, that have almost all the characteristics of the proposed dipole collectivity. Instead of a football or doorknob shape, the dipole configurations studied thus far have a dinuclear molecular configuration in which one of the participants is an alpha particle, the nucleus of helium. Even at this early stage the discovery of dipole collectivity shows promise of resolving many of the outstanding remaining puzzles concerning nuclear structure.

Delta isobars. One of the continually fascinating questions in any quantum science is what happens as more energy is pumped into a given system. In the nuclear case the question has as one of its aspects whether the neutrons and protons simply behave in ever more complex fashion as they have more energy available to them or whether some of the available energy can be used to change the neutrons and protons themselves into their so-called isobars or excited states. The first of these is the delta isobar, which requires about 300 MeV (million electron volts) of energy to produce it from an ordinary neutron or proton inside a nucleus. During the past two years an extensive series of measurements was carried out by Charles Goodman and his collaborators at Indiana University on reactions involving incident protons and outgoing neutrons, and complementary studies were done by Achim Richter and his collaborators at the University of Darmstadt on inelastic electron scattering involving magnetic transitions. The two groups demonstrated conclusively that it is not possible to understand the experimental data without invoking the presence of the delta isobars. This provides an entirely new nuclear degree of freedom, and although it complicates the thermodynamics of the hot nuclei produced in nuclear interactions, it provides an even richer spectrum of phenomena for study. It also forms a natural bridge between nuclear physics of the more classical sort and what until very recently was solidly in the domain of high-energy physics.

Uranium acceleration in the Bevalac. This move to higher energies is evident throughout nuclear science and nowhere more so than at the Bevalac at the University of California at Berkeley. Until recently the Bevalac and the synchrophasotron at Dubna in the Soviet Union shared the honor of being the only two facilities that could accelerate nuclei at the lower end of the periodic table to energies in excess of 1 GeV (a billion electron volts) per nucleon; the Bevalac reached energies slightly over 2 GeV per nucleon, while the synchrophasotron reached energies in excess of 4 GeV per nucleon but at substantially lower intensities. Because it was recognized from the outset that some of the most interesting phenomena should occur only when the most massive possible amounts of nuclear material smashed into one another, there was great pressure to extend the capability of one at least of these machines to accelerate the heaviest possible projectiles. On Sept. 25, 1982, as a result of an intensive development program, Hermann Grunder and his associates at the Bevalac for the first time successfully accelerated uranium ions to an energy of about 1 GeV per nucleon—that is, to an energy of 238 GeV per uranium nucleus.

Four high-energy uranium ions (left) at the Bevalac are recorded in photographic emulsion as they enter the material and slow down, fissioning in the process. "Plastic ball" lined with triangular detectors (below) will be used to study uranium-target collisions.

Photos, Lawrence Berkeley Laboratory/University of California

This advance opens up an enormous new field of study with qualitatively different characteristics from any previously available. In particle physics the goal over the years has been the delivery of ever increasing amounts of energy to ever smaller volumes in the hope of breaking loose and studying ever more fundamental constituents of matter. On the other hand, with extremely high-energy heavy ions of the sort available from the Bevalac the goal is that of providing ever increasing amounts of energy to a volume which remains sufficiently large to contain a large number of neutrons and protons and which therefore allows for the possibility of cooperative interactions involving those neutrons and protons.

One of the major open questions in this regard has been whether, as the energy is increased, the neutrons and protons present will show cooperative behavior or whether they will simply behave more and more as independent entities that happen to be in the same general region during the interaction. Preliminary studies on helium-helium collisions at 500-GeV energies using the facilities at the European Organization for Nuclear Research (CERN) were carried out by Sherman Frankel and his collaborators at the University of Pennsylvania and a number of European centers. Furthermore, new data were collected by Walter Benenson of Michigan State University and his collaborators on the production of pi mesons when neon beams with energies of 80 MeV per nucleon interacted with a variety of targets and by Yves LeBornec and his collaborators at Saclay Nuclear Research Centre in France, who examined pi meson production from the bombardment of helium-3 with 282-MeV helium-3 ions. All three studies provided evidence supporting the presence of quite strong collective phenomena in these collisions. To what extent the collective phenomena persist or change character as the available energy is increased remains an open question. It has been possible, however, for physicists to obtain a broad overview of some of the characteristic features of these very high-energy interactions from the fragmentary data thus far available.

Hot regions in nuclear collisions. Since only very few of the collisions between two heavy nuclei are head-on, in most cases of peripheral collision it might be expected that only the region in each nucleus that overlaps the other would be violently heated, while the rest of the two nuclei would remain essentially undisturbed as spectators. Using techniques based on thermodynamic analyses of the fragments boiled off from these collisions and on a technique that was developed for stellar interferometery to measure the diameter of the evening star Sirius, groups at the Berkeley Bevalac led by Reinhard Stöck and Shoji Nagamia succeeded in demonstrating that the characteristic size of the hot region in these collisions indeed is substantially smaller than either of the participant nuclei.

It also was possible to measure the temperature and show that it increases with the available energy until it reaches a value of about two trillion degrees (about 165 MeV equivalent), where it levels off. This leveling off is in itself a very important observation because it provides vital input into understanding the equation of state of nuclear matter itself as well as an indirect measure of whether the quantum spectrum of excited nucleons continues without limit or whether it is terminated at some appropriate high value. The fact that the temperature appears to saturate at about two trillion degrees is consistent with a limiting finite spectrum—a matter of crucial importance not only to elementary particle physics but also to a better understanding of the earliest moments of the big bang, during which the universe was created, and of the very last instants of gravitational collapse of a giant star, during which gravitational energies become sufficiently large to create these exotic species.

Anomalons. In the area of exotic species perhaps nothing stands out more than the so-called anomalons that have been discovered in recent years both in cosmic ray interactions and in accelerator-based experiments carried out at Berkeley and Dubna. In 1980 Erwin Friedlander and Harry Heckman of Berkeley published the results of experiments with photographic emulsions exposed to cosmic rays and to beams from the Bevalac. They found that occasionally an incoming ultrahigh-speed nucleus began to behave in anomalous fashion after colliding with nuclei in the emulsion. The unusual behavior suggested that the incoming nucleus had for some reason become very much larger as a result of its first collision or that for some other reason it was interacting much more strongly with the emulsion nuclei than would an ordinary nucleus. Recent measurements by the same group confirmed this behavior repeatedly. To give a specific example, a normal iron nucleus at Bevalac energies tends to travel about 7.3 cm (almost three inches) in a photographic emulsion between collisions. Six percent of the time, however, after a particular collision the iron nucleus travels only 2.5 cm (one inch) on the average between subsequent collisions, indicating that some extraordinary change has taken place.

This change has posed a very real challenge to theorists, and a large number of explanations have been advanced. One of the most far-reaching is that the first collision has converted the iron nucleus into an entirely new kind of matter, in which the constituent quarks and gluons play a much more direct and obvious role. Indeed it may be a form of quark-gluon plasma. Should subsequent measurements and studies confirm this explanation it would again act to lower the barrier between nuclear and particle physics, which like all too many other interfield boundaries is not only artificial but frequently counterproductive.

—D. Allan Bromley

Solid-state physics

Research in solid-state physics progressed rapidly during the past year. One highlight was the awarding of the 1982 Nobel Prize for Physics to Kenneth G. Wilson of Cornell University, Ithaca, N.Y., for theoretical work in condensed-matter physics and in particular "for his theory for critical phenomena in connection with phase transitions." The phenomena of phase transitions, like the melting of ice and the boiling of water, are well known and common occurrences for which a theoretical understanding has been lacking. They belong in the realms of statistical physics and thermodynamics and involve the treatment of fluctuations. Wilson realized that in order to treat critical phenomena one must be able to treat fluctuations extending from atomic lengths to those covering the entire macroscopic system. By combining mathematical analytical techniques with computer calculations and modeling, Wilson provided theoretical tools for understanding very complex physical systems.

The awarding of the Nobel Prize to Wilson is also a recognition of a new approach to physics, one which makes use of the recent dramatic progress in computing power. The use of the computer for numerical calculations as well as for data collection, storage, and processing of experimental data is commonplace today. With the emergence of such powerful computers as array processors and special-purpose hardware, computer simulation of the chaotic behavior of systems, of turbulence in fluids, of crack propagation in solids, and of other complex phenomena has become feasible. In fact the computer can be used to study and understand itself; namely, the dynamic behavior of very complex circuits such as a transistor array on a so-called VLSI (very-large-scale-integration) chip with 100,000 or more transistors or the elements constituting a large computer network.

This emerging field, sometimes called digital physics, is a good example of the "bootstrapping" and cross-fertilization that occur in science and technology. The year 1982 marked the 35th anniversary of the invention of the transistor, which grew out of fundamental studies of the properties of solid-state semiconductor materials. The modern computer, which was enabled by the invention of the transistor, is now one of the most important tools for further research in solid-state physics. This in turn is expected to lead to new device applications in solid-state electronics.

New semiconductor materials. Many of the technologies on which modern society is based are founded on specific materials and their specific properties. The Industrial Revolution was essentially a "steel revolution." The ability to make steel with specific properties was essential for the development of machinery. In a corresponding way the information revolution of the 1980s is based on semiconductor materials and in particular on single-crystal silicon. In fact the early progress of transistor technology was made possible by progress in refining semiconductor single crystals to an unprecedented purity. The ability to manufacture dislocation-free single-crystal silicon in large boules is a triumph of modern materials science and is the basis for VLSI technology. On the other hand, crystalline silicon has some severe limitations such as size, cost, and mobility (speed) of the carriers of the electrical signals within it. Moreover, it cannot be made to emit visible light efficiently. There are, however, other semiconductor materials being developed that compete with and complement single-crystal silicon.

The need to use single-crystal silicon imposes a particularly severe constraint in applications involving large-area devices. A typical example is the electronics for controlling large-area, flat-panel displays that require an active element at each pixel (picture element). Another constraint is the cost of the device. For solar cells the cost of manufacturing devices with necessarily large area is crucial for this technology to work. A new class of semiconductors, called amorphous semiconductors, appears promising for such applications

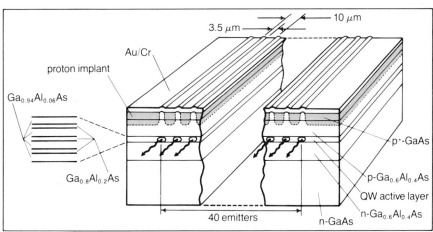

Figure 1 illustrates a heterostructure made of many different materials in the form of a high-power, solid-state laser. Applying a small voltage between the top and bottom of the device causes the laser to emit high-intensity, coherent infrared light. Some of the layers, such as those shown in the left of the figure, are only a few atomic layers thick.

Courtesy, D. Scifres, Xerox Palo Alto Research Center

Courtesy, IBM

Figure 2 diagrams the basic operation and depicts some results of the recently invented scanning tunneling microscope, which allows scientists to map surface topographies with a resolution of a single atomic step. A metal tip is scanned in a vacuum a few atomic distances above the surface of the sample with piezoelectric drivers. Application of a voltage between the tip and the sample results in the tunneling of electrons across the vacuum. Measurement of tunneling voltage and current allows mapping of a surface; e.g., one of silicon at the right. Three-dimensional model of a silicon surface on the opposite page, assembled from individual scans, shows vertical as well as horizontal separations. The individual bumps are as little as six angstroms apart.

(see *1982 Yearbook of Science and the Future* Feature Article: A NEW WORLD OF GLASSY SEMICONDUCTORS). As a result of intense research efforts during the past decade, amorphous silicon alloyed with hydrogen, usually abbreviated a-Si:H, has become the prime material candidate in this new class. In an amorphous system the ordered network of silicon atoms in crystalline silicon is replaced by a more irregular network. Such a disordered network contains many broken bonds, *i.e.*, many silicon atoms that do not connect to neighboring atoms. These so-called unsaturated bonds give the material undesirable electrical characteristics and make it unsuitable for transistor applications. By connecting hydrogen atoms to these broken bonds, they can be passivated, *i.e.*, made not to interfere with the electrical transport of carriers. In order to create a transistor of a semiconductor material one must also be able to dope it, that is, to add foreign atoms in minute quantities. In 1975 Walter E. Spear and collaborators at the University of Dundee in Scotland demonstrated the doping of amorphous silicon and thereby opened up the possibility of making controlled variations for studying these materials in detail and using them for device applications.

Another class of semiconductor materials of growing usefulness consists of the III-V (or 3-5) compound semiconductors, in which one element is derived from column III and the other from column V of the periodic table. The prime example is gallium arsenide (GaAs). Many of these semiconductors, like GaAs, have properties that are very similar to silicon and in some cases better suited. In addition they are efficient light emitters. Devices made from III-V compounds therefore can use the flow of photons as well as electrons as carriers of information. In analogy with the word electronics, in which the primary carrier of information is the electron, the new field is called photonics. Much of the research progress in this area also can be attributed to new synthesis methods.

New synthesis methods. Many scientists and research groups have been working on methods to synthesize new materials for specific applications. A group at the Xerox Palo Alto (Calif.) Research Center refined the plasma deposition technique to produce high-quality a-Si:H. In this process a plasma (hot ionized state) is set up in silane gas (SiH_4), causing the molecules to break down and form a deposit of amorphous silicon. The hydrogen liberated in the process is partially incorporated in the deposit. By varying the process parameters such as gas pressure and power input, the properties of the resulting silicon films can be modified to obtain desired electrical characteristics. By adding other gases in small amounts to the silane, one can also dope the resulting silicon material.

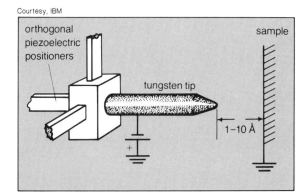

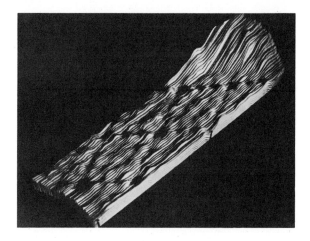

A similar process has been applied to the synthesis of GaAs and its alloys. In this case the gas consists of organometallic molecules containing the desired elements, such as Ga, As, and Al (aluminum). In this case the decomposition of the molecules does not occur in a discharge but rather on a heated substrate. The process is called organometallic vapor-phase epitaxy (OM-VPE). Varying the composition of the reacting gases during growth allows layered structures consisting of different materials to be formed. An example of such a heterostructure is a recently developed high-power solid-state laser consisting of 40 optically coupled laser elements (*see* figure 1 on p. 373).

Such heterostructures can also be produced by co-evaporation of the constituent elements in an ultra-high vacuum. This growth process, called molecular beam epitaxy (MBE), allows control of the thickness and composition of the layers on an atomic scale.

New characterization methods. The solid-state physicist investigates materials with a wide variety of tools. Their measured properties form the basis for theoretical models of solids. They also provide a very important feedback mechanism for materials synthesis, since many of the properties can be precisely modified by varying the process parameters to tailor-make materials with desired characteristics.

The tremendous sensitivity of modern measurement techniques can be illustrated with two characterization tools developed in the past few years. The first one directly maps the geometrical topography of a surface with a sensitivity of single atomic steps. Developed by Gerd Binnig and collaborators at the IBM Research Laboratory in Switzerland, the device is a surface microscope using vacuum tunneling and is called the scanning tunneling microscope (STM). In operation a very narrow metal tip just above the surface is scanned parallel to the surface of the sample with piezoelectric drivers. Surface electrons cross the gap between the probe and the sample by means of a quantum physics process called tunneling and set up a current that varies with the gap's thickness. The tunneling current between the probe and the sample is monitored by readjusting the tip height to maintain constant current, allowing a topographic map of the surface to be obtained. Figure 2 illustrates the principle of STM and its capability of detecting individual atoms. The technique should find a wide range of applications in surface studies and appears a promising instrument for measuring the topography of semiconductor surfaces having very complex structures.

Measurements of optical absorption in a sample yields a wealth of information about its electronic structure and the atomic bonds. The measurement of absorption in very thin samples is a problem because the amount of energy absorbed is very small and difficult to detect. With photothermal deflection spectroscopy it has been possible to increase measurement sensitivity by two orders of magnitude. In this case a thin-film sample is illuminated with a laser beam. The absorbed light causes a temperature rise in the sample as well as in an adjacent layer of liquid. By probing the gradient of the varying index of refraction of the liquid with a second laser beam and measuring the deflection of this beam, one can determine the optical absorption of the sample. In this way temperature fluctuations as small as a ten-millionth of a degree can be detected. During the past year this technique provided important information on the unsaturated bonds in a-Si:H and thus on the suitability of this material for electronic applications.

New devices. Progress in the areas mentioned above culminated in the creation of new devices. A driving force for the development of a-Si:H is its application in solar cells. In 1982 scientists at RCA Laboratories in the U.S. reported an energy-conversion efficiency of 10% for such devices. This figure is considered to be the break-even point for the economical application of a-Si:H solar cells. The new material also has been explored as a photoreceptor in television cameras and copying machines.

The heterostructure shown in figure 1 is an array of solid-state lasers. Progress in this field was spectacular during the past year. The highest power obtained from a solid-state laser source, 2.5 watts, was recorded from

Photos, courtesy, L. Fennell, Xerox Palo Alto Research Center

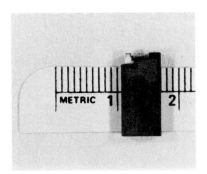

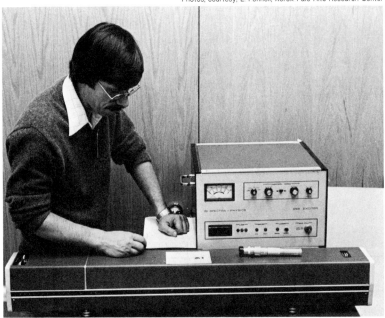

Figure 3 compares the size of a gas laser (right) with that of the solid-state laser (above) diagramed in figure 1. Both lasers emit 2.5 watts of light power. The former requires glass tubes, mirrors, and a water cooling system, whereas the latter, actually smaller than a pinhead, is mounted on a small copper block that suffices to carry away the generated heat.

the laser configuration in figure 1. Figure 3 compares that laser with an argon gas laser that produces the same amount of power. The solid-state laser is mounted on a copper block, which acts as a heat sink. The size of the laser itself is less than that of a pinhead.

—Stig B. Hagstrom

See also Feature Article: PHYSICS UNDER PRESSURE.

Psychology

Despite the continued severe slashing of social science research and training budgets by the Reagan administration, the social and behavioral sciences in the U.S. experienced a reasonably good year. Social and behavioral research was given strong support by two high-level national scientific committees.

A special committee of the National Research Council was formed in 1979, at the request of the National Science Foundation, to evaluate the merit and utility of social and behavioral research. Its report offered a vigorous endorsement. While acknowledging that the fruits of social research are not likely to be immediately obvious, the 104-page report concluded that they are both "significant and lasting" and that such research "has yielded an impressive array of accomplishments." Responding to the criticism that social science is not really science, Frank Press, president of the National Academy of Science, commented that "social sciences follow the scientific method and even understand it better perhaps than the physical sciences do."

In the second report, which was prepared by the Institute of Medicine of the National Academy of Sci-

ence, the role of behavioral factors in preventive medicine was stressed. At a panel meeting assembled to explain the report, chairman David A. Hamburg summed up the committee's intention: "As we knit the fields of psychology and medicine together, it should be possible to construct a unified biomedical science which will require a deeper understanding of human adaptation." The rationale underlying the presumption that psychology can make a substantial contribution to the prevention of disease is the growing consensus that mental and emotional states affect the chemical balance of the body, which in turn is a crucial factor in many common diseases such as cardiovascular disorders and diabetes.

Also related to the way psychology is perceived—though on a much more localized level—was a traveling "psychology fair," which was entertaining and, it was to be hoped, enlightening young people in northeastern Kansas. The concept of the fair was originated by Fred L. Yaffe, chairman of the psychology department at Washburn University in Topeka, Kan., and it was developed with support from the National Science Foundation. The fair consisted of 24 exhibits concerned with such topics as perception, intelligence, and learning and memory. It traveled to a different junior high school each week. Its major objective was to show students that psychology is a science—a proposition that is not usually encountered until the introductory psychology course is taken at the college level.

Applications. One of the most rapidly developing trends in the health field was the movement away from orthodox hospitals and toward a variety of noninstitutionalized forms of treatment. A recent review of ten studies comparing hospitalization with alternative

376

forms of mental health care found that in no case did hospitalization result in more favorable outcomes. Outpatient care in the U.S. had increased about 20-fold from 1955 to 1975. Unfortunately, despite this growth and despite a national policy calling for deinstitutionalization, the rate at which mental patients were being admitted to hospitals had not shown the anticipated decline.

A related development was the dramatic increase in hospices, again as opposed to hospitals, as care centers for the terminally ill. The hospice offers an informal, homelike atmosphere free of the regimentation of the typical hospital. Although the first hospice in the U.S. was not established until 1974, by 1981 there were more than 800 such programs. The hospice concept was thoroughly examined in a set of seven articles in the November 1982 issue of *American Psychologist*.

Another innovation that showed considerable promise was the use of master's-level psychologists to provide certain psychological services in rural communities. Doctoral-level psychologists seemed no more willing to practice in rural areas than were their medical counterparts; a recent survey found that more than half of 952 rural counties in 19 eastern states were not served by a single psychologist. Consequently, Mansfield State College in rural Pennsylvania developed a program to meet these needs. Since 1975 more than 30 master's-level psychology students have been trained

specifically for this role and have gone to work in rural communities after graduation. When they perform psychological services, they are expected to do so under the supervision of regularly licensed (doctoral-level) psychologists. Thus services are expanded as the comparatively few licensed psychologists in those areas assume a largely supervisory function. Individuals so trained may be counted on to provide services generally superior to those offered by bartenders, industrial supervisors, divorce lawyers, and hairdressers, whose informal psychological services were reviewed in an article entitled "Help Is Where You Find It" in *American Psychologist* (April 1982).

Also promising was "paraverbal therapy," introduced by Evelyn Phillips Heimlich, a child psychotherapist on the staff of St. Luke's Hospital in New York City. This treatment was designed to offset the difficult-to-reach child's negative reaction to objective language. Nonverbal forms of communication, encouraged by the therapist's participation with the child in various play activities, are believed to be effective in establishing rapport because they are less threatening to the child. Heimlich states that "I deliberately sit knee to knee with the child. I take their hands, creep on the floor." Improvised songs play a major role in this kind of therapy. The therapist is encouraged to copy the child's made-up songs and chants on the grounds that this tends to validate the child's own behavior and

"Psychology fair," consisting of exhibits on such topics as perception and learning, traveled to junior high schools in Kansas in an effort to demonstrate to students that psychology is a science.

Fred L. Yaffe, Washburn University of Topeka, Kansas

Terminally ill patient paints in a hospice. Such facilities offer surroundings that are informal and homelike, contrasting with the regimentation at most hospitals.

consequently improve his or her self-regard.

Personality and social psychology. One of the most fascinating topics in psychology is the phenomenon of multiple personality—the apparent alternation of two or more distinctly different and independent personalities in a single individual. The subject was popularized in the book and motion picture *The Three Faces of Eve.* New evidence for the validity of this phenomenon was reported by Frank W. Putnam, staff psychiatrist at the National Institute of Mental Health. Using a combination of electroencephalogram and computer, NIMH researchers found that the dramatic differences in behavior characteristic of the different personalities were correlated with correspondingly different brainwave patterns. These results were not obtained in matched control subjects instructed to show alternating personality patterns.

The expression of anger generally has been regarded as a helpful coping mechanism, but a new perspective on this problem was presented by psychologist Carol Tavris. Interpreting anger and aggression as primarily social phenomena, Tavris, in her book *Anger: The Misunderstood Emotion,* raises questions about many widely accepted beliefs. For example, she found that overmotivated individuals typically overexpress anger, thereby presumably tending to increase their risk of cardiovascular disorder. Students who express anger are less healthy than those who suppress it, and the alleged cathartic role of aggression is evidenced only when the aggression is directed against peers or subordinates, not against one's boss. This new perspective, pointing up the essentially social role of anger, could produce considerable modification of the "conventional wisdom" on emotional control.

The field of social psychology has been subjected to many critical attacks in recent years, from within as well as from outside the field. Prominent among these

criticisms has been the contention that experimental approaches are so seriously lacking in ecological validity (that is, are so "artificial") that they should be minimized if not ignored. Social psychologists Leonard Berkowitz and Edward Donnerstein strongly rebutted this criticism in an article with the engaging title "External Validity Is More Than Skin Deep: Some Answers to Criticisms of Laboratory Experiments" (*American Psychologist,* March 1982). This detailed rebuttal should be consulted by anyone interested in information on this timely issue.

Experimental psychology. Research on memory continued to be a prominent feature of experimental psychology. One recent report was especially noteworthy. Peter Polson of the University of Colorado noticed that the waiter at a fashionable Boulder restaurant was not writing down any of his orders. The waiter, John Conrad, was quite willing to talk about his memory capacity. He recalled that on one occasion he had handled a table of 19 complete dinner orders without an error and without making any written notes, thereby earning a tip of $85 rather than the customary $35.

Although exceptional memories have been studied occasionally in isolated individuals (perhaps the best-known having been described in *The Mind of a Mnemonist* by the Russian psychologist Aleksandr R. Luria), systematic analysis of this kind of performance is relatively recent. Waiter Conrad was studied by both Polson and K. A. Ericsson, who earlier had spent three years, in collaboration with William Chase, investigating the memory capacities of an "average student" (an undergraduate at Carnegie-Mellon University). Ericsson and Chase were able to develop some very exceptional abilities in this typical student; for example, a memory span of 80 digits (compared with the 5 to 9 digits that can be immediately repeated correctly by most people after they have been randomly presented).

The important conclusion to be drawn from these studies is that exceptional memory abilities are learned skills rather than inherited or otherwise special ones, as is still commonly believed. This conclusion was reinforced by Polson and Ericsson's testing of Conrad, whose motivation to improve his memory by hard work was found to be the key to his success.

Perceptual learning in animals was another topic attracting considerable research attention. For instance, Donald Blough of Brown University, Providence, R.I., demonstrated that pigeons could be trained to discriminate every letter of the alphabet. Moreover, the errors they made tended to resemble those made by human subjects performing the same task. A similar relationship between animal and human pictorial memory was also reported. A rhesus monkey was found to show performance almost identical to that of a human subject when presented with previously used pictures in a scanning test.

The molecular basis of learning was being actively investigated, for the first time, by means of an analysis of the role of the chemical transmitter at the synapse, where an impulse passes from one neuron to another. It was shown to be possible to produce prolonged changes in synaptic strength and corresponding memory persistence. Details appeared in a review article by Eric R. Kandel and James H. Schwartz in *Science* (Oct. 29, 1982).

Physiological psychology. The exciting vistas offered by neurotransmitter research represent only one of many developments in physiological approaches to behavioral problems. During the past year, for example, new research findings were reported on brain receptors for appetite, brain controls of birds' songs, and brain cells for color vision.

A novel approach to the link between mental (or behavioral) phenomena and disease was offered by "psychoneuroimmunology." This rapidly expanding research area had been anticipated by some post-Pavlovian Russian research in which guinea pigs were conditioned to secrete antibodies in response to a skin-scratch stimulus. Early in the century there was also a Japanese report that tubercular patients showed reduced immune reactions during periods of intense emotional excitement, and a U.S. worker observed a reduction in lymphocytes (important components of the immune reaction) during similar excited states.

The primary catalyst for the recent surge of concentrated research in the role of psychological factors in immunology was provided by Robert Ader, a psychologist, and Nicholas Cohen, an immunologist, at the University of Rochester, N.Y. In all of their ingeniously designed and carefully executed experiments, Ader stated that "we have observed a conditioned suppression of the immune reaction." Confirming results were reported from a number of other laboratories. At the Ontario Cancer Research Institute, for instance, it was shown that conditioning can facilitate as well as suppress immune reactions. Details of this research, with its promise of opening new therapeutic avenues, were given in Ader's book *Psychoneuroimmunology* (1981) and, more briefly and on a popular level, in Alan Anderson's review article in the December 1982 issue of *Psychology Today*.

—Melvin H. Marx

Space exploration
Manned flight

Two communications satellites became the first commercial payloads to be placed into Earth orbit by the U.S. space shuttle orbiter "Columbia." The Soviet Union continued its development of a continuously manned space station, as two cosmonauts spent 211 days living and working aboard the Salyut 7.

Space shuttle. The March 22, 1982, launch of the third flight of "Columbia," STS-3, went flawlessly after an hour's delay caused by a faulty nitrogen gas purge line heater. "Columbia" carried a Canadian-designed 15-m (50-ft) robot arm for its first test in space. Despite the failure of a television camera on the arm's "wrist" that gives astronaut operators "eyes" to maneuver the arm for grasping cargo, crewmen Jack Lousma and Gordon Fullerton were able to lift an experiment package from the payload bay to "sniff" ionized gases, or plasma, and magnetic fields generated by "Columbia's" movement through space. Other experiments in the payload bay measured "Columbia's" interaction with the space environment. Among experiments in the crew cabin was the first of a series of student projects submitted in a competition sponsored by the National Aeronautics and Space Administration (NASA) and the National Science Teachers Association. Minnesota high-school student Todd Nelson's experiment investigated insect adaptation to zero-gravity space flight. Also flown on STS-3 was a prototype electrophoresis experiment for organic cell separation, which may lead to commercial pharmaceutical processing in space. Heavy winter rains at Edwards Air Force Base in California caused the landing site for STS-3 to be shifted to White Sands Missile Range in New Mexico. Then a dense sandstorm there forced the landing to be delayed one day, to March 30.

"Columbia" completed its four-flight engineering shakedown in June and July with the seven-day STS-4 flight. This mission included the first commercial shuttle experiment, the continuous-flow electrophoresis system (CFES). Built as a joint venture between McDonnell Douglas Astronautics Co. and Ortho Pharmaceutical Division of Johnson & Johnson Co., CFES was the first attempt to separate biological materials and achieve the purity needed for pharmaceutical manufacturing in space.

U.S. space shuttle orbiter "Challenger" is launched on its first mission from Kennedy Space Center at Cape Canaveral, Florida, on April 4, 1983.

STS-4 crewmen Ken Mattingly and Henry Hartsfield again operated the robot arm to maneuver a large contamination sensor package. Another experiment called for the crew to photograph lightning and thunderstorms from orbit to gain information that will help in the development of techniques for weather forecasting from a satellite.

Heavy rain and hail prior to launch on June 27 caused concern among test engineers that "Columbia's" spun-glass heat shield tiles had absorbed so much water that they would be damaged when the water froze in space. A planned program of prolonged periods when the spacecraft would point various sides to the Sun was changed to allow the water to be baked out of the tiles.

STS-4 was the first flight to carry a small self-contained payload—the Getaway Special—in the cargo bay. Packed with nine biological and materials experiments, it was designed and built by students at Utah State University. When a faulty circuit prevented the crew from turning on the experiment, Mission Control Center-Houston radioed instructions for building a connector cable that "jump started" it.

Mattingly and Hartsfield brought "Columbia" to a smooth landing on July 4 on the main concrete runway at Edwards Air Force Base before some half million people, including Pres. Ronald Reagan. With the successful completion of that flight the shuttle system was ready to begin routine commercial space operations.

Launched November 11, STS-5 was the first flight to carry a crew of four. Commander Vance Brand and pilot Robert Overmyer were joined by mission specialists Joseph Allen and William Lenoir. As the first commercial mission of "Columbia," STS-5 carried two communications satellites, Satellite Business Systems SBS-3 and Telesat Canada Anik C-3. Each was equipped with an upper stage to propel it into geosynchronous orbit. SBS-3 was spring-ejected from "Columbia" during the first day of the flight. Allen and Lenoir deployed the Canadian satellite on the second day and had been scheduled to make the shuttle program's first walk in space later in the flight. The walk was canceled, however, when a pressure regulator and a fan motor in spacesuit backpacks failed. The on-time, accurate deployment of the commercial satellites prompted Allen and Lenoir to coin the first space advertising slogan: "We deliver!"

Experiments on STS-5 included three student projects, on surface tension, sponge growth, and crystal growth in zero-gravity. From the West German Ministry of Research there was also an experiment to investigate the mixing of metals during weightlessness.

The STS-5 mission ended on November 16, when the crew brought "Columbia" down to the Edwards Air Force Base main runway shortly after sunrise. "Co-

380

Story Musgrave (left) and Donald Peterson float in space in the open cargo bay of the shuttle orbiter "Challenger." Their space walks were the first for U.S. astronauts since 1974.

lumbia" was ferried back to Kennedy Space Center for modifications needed to carry the European Space Agency's Spacelab on STS-9, scheduled for September 1983. Meanwhile, the shuttle orbiter "Challenger" had been transported to Kennedy to be readied for STS-6.

A 20-second firing of "Challenger's" liquid-oxygen–liquid-hydrogen main engines on the launch pad revealed a potentially dangerous level of hydrogen in the orbiter's aft compartment after shutdown. "Challenger's" main engines were test-fired again on Jan. 25, 1983, and the STS-6 was launched on April 4.

STS-6 crewmen Paul Weitz and Karol Bobko and mission specialists Donald Peterson and Story Musgrave deployed the first in a network of data and tracking satellites. The geosynchronous satellites were designed to provide almost total voice and data coverage of shuttle flights starting with STS-9/Spacelab. Later in the five-day mission Musgrave and Peterson performed space walks outside the shuttle, the first for U.S. astronauts since 1974.

Flight crews for STS-7 through 10 were named during 1982. They were: STS-7, Robert Crippen, Frederick Hauck, and mission specialists John Fabian, Sally Ride, and Norman Thagard; STS-8, Richard Truly, Daniel Brandenstein, and mission specialists Dale Gardner, Guion Bluford, and William Thornton; STS-9/Spacelab, John Young, Brewster Shaw, mission specialists Owen Garriott and Robert Parker, and payload specialists

Byron Lichtenberg (U.S.) and Ulf Merbold (European Space Agency); STS-10, Ken Mattingly, Loren Shriver, and mission specialists Ellison Onizuka, James Buchli, and a U.S. Air Force engineer still to be selected. Physician-astronauts Thagard and Thornton were added to STS-7 and STS-8 late in 1982 to observe and gather information on space sickness, which was affecting almost half the U.S. astronauts.

Soviet missions. The Salyut 7 space station was inhabited by a two-man crew for a record 211 days during 1982. Cosmonauts Anatoliy Berezovoy and Valentin Lebedev returned to the Earth December 10 in a snowstorm, landing at night in Central Asia after seven months of Earth resources survey and photography, scientific experiments, and growing of vegetables in the space station's hothouse.

Two crews of three cosmonauts and two unmanned Progress supply vessels docked with Salyut 7 while Berezovoy and Lebedev were aboard. The flight duration exceeded the previous record of 185 days when cosmonauts worked aboard Salyut 6 in 1980.

Salyut 7 was launched April 19, 1982, from the Tyuratam Cosmodrome. Berezovoy and Lebedev were launched aboard Soyuz T-5 on May 13 and docked with the space station the following day.

Crews that visited Salyut 7 were Vladimir Djanibekov, Aleksandr Ivanchenkov, and Frenchman Jean-Loup Chretien aboard Soyuz T-6, launched on June 24

381

Svetlana Savitskaya (foreground, with camera), Valentin Lebedev (left), and Anatoliy Berezovoy were among the eight cosmonauts who visited the Soviet space station Salyut 7 in 1982. Lebedev and Berezovoy remained aboard for a record 211 days.

for a nine-day stay in which life sciences and materials processing experiments were performed; and Leonid Popov, Aleksandr Serebrov, and Svetlana Savitskaya, launched aboard Soyuz T-7 on August 19 and returned to Earth August 27 aboard Soyuz T-5. The newer Soyuz was left for Berezovoy and Lebedev to use for their return.

—Terry White

Space probes

For unmanned probes 1982 was clearly the year of Venera. William H. Gregory, writing in *Aviation Week & Space Technology*, stated of the Soviet Union's Venus probes: "Not only were these landings a hard-earned success after a series of discouraging early failures, but they also have the potential for a significant contribution to planetary science."

Probing the Sun. On January 22 the French and Swiss ambassadors and representatives from the Italian embassy delivered a memorandum to the U.S. State Department expressing European concern about U.S. commitments for the Solar-Polar mission. They were told that the Reagan administration would guarantee its commitment to launch and track the European satellite and provide a radioisotope thermoelectric power generator for the probe. U.S. policies on future international cooperation in space were not given. However, supplemental funding by the U.S. Congress provided $80 million for the conversion of the Centaur rocket stage so that it could be used with the space shuttle. This indicated that Centaur would be used to boost

the Solar-Polar satellite from Earth orbit.

On March 2, 1982, Pioneer 10 completed ten years in space and was still transmitting data as it moved along a path that would take it out of the solar system. At the time it was about halfway between the orbits of Uranus and Neptune, some 4.6 billion km (2.8 billion mi) from the Sun. Scientists predicted that the probe would leave the heliosphere and enter the interplanetary medium by 1990. In commenting on that event, James Van Allen of the University of Iowa said, "This crossing, if observed, will be the crowning achievement of its extended mission and a milestone in human achievement. It is difficult to imagine any deep-space missions that have as favorable a ratio to prospective scientific yield to cost as the extended missions of Pioneer 10 and 11 do.... There is no prospect for getting any other spacecraft to such enormous distances from the Sun before the year 2010 or thereabouts."

On October 7 Pioneers 8 and 9, two sister probes orbiting the Sun, passed within 2,413,950 km (1.5 million mi) of each other, a close distance by solar system standards. Pioneer 8 was launched in 1967 and orbits the Sun every 388 days, and Pioneer 9, launched in 1968, has a solar period of 298 days. The two probes, with Pioneers 6 and 7, make up a solar "weather forecasting network" and transmit data to the National Oceanographic and Atmospheric Administration's Solar Disturbance Center at Boulder, Colo., via NASA's Deep Space Tracking Network.

Future repair of the Solar Maximum satellite in Earth orbit by astronauts from a space shuttle received a boost when President Reagan signed a supplemental funding measure for the NASA budget for fiscal year 1982. The measure also mandated that the U.S. Air Force support the effort with $6.6 million because of the future possibility of in-orbit repair or retrieval of its military satellites.

Venus missions. Venera 13, launched on Oct. 30, 1981, sent its lander on a 62-minute plunge through the Venusian atmosphere to a touchdown in the Phoebe plain. It transmitted data for 127 minutes, four times longer than expected. During the descent by parachute, instruments made chemical and isotopic studies of the atmosphere and clouds and registered lightning discharges. At 50 km (31 mi) the temperature was 270° C (518° F), and there was a pressure of 4.7 atmospheres. More precise determinations of the atmospheric content of argon, neon, and krypton were made than were achieved by previous probes.

Once on the surface the lander began taking panoramic pictures in color by means of special photometers. A soil-gathering device drilled to a depth of 30 mm (1.2 in), and placed samples into a compartment for X-ray fluorescent analysis to determine elemental components of the soil. The material so analyzed indicated that the soil was similar to the basalts found on Earth in lava flows and in the rocks associated with the volcanically active mid-ocean ranges. Other instruments sought to measure seismic activity and the mechanical properties of the soil. The lander reported a surface temperature of 457° C (855° F) and an atmospheric pressure of 89 atmospheres. (One atmosphere equals 14.7 lb per square inch.)

The lander of Venera 14 touched down on March 5 after taking 63 minutes to descend. It landed to the east of the Phoebe region, some 1,000 km (620 mi) from the Venera 13 lander. It reported a surface temperature of 465° C (869° F) and a pressure of 94 atmospheres. However, the lander transmitted data for only 57 minutes. Soviet scientists reported that pictures of the site "reveal large thick boulders of dark gray rock with surfaces of a cellular texture formed as a result of chemical erosion. The surface between rock outcrops is covered with brownish-black fine-grained material." Chemical analysis of the rocks according to the Soviets "shows that 60–70 percent of the planet's surface is covered with ancient basalt melt." While such highly alkaline potassium basalts are rare on Earth, they do occur in parts of Wyoming and Montana.

Other data indicated that solar ultraviolet radiation is largely absorbed by the Venusian atmosphere at an altitude of about 60 km (37 mi) and that the planet's clouds are composed mostly of sulfur. The sky, seen from the surface, is a reddish brown, probably caused by reflections from the surface.

In both Venera probes the spacecraft that relayed transmissions from the surface of the planet to the Earth was placed on a trajectory that went past Venus rather than into orbit about it because of the anticipated short lifetimes of the lander instrumentation. Both Soviet and U.S. scientists had hoped that Venera 14 would land in an area with granite-like material as did the earlier Venera 8. In commenting upon the Venera missions and results Harold Masursky, chairman of the U.S. Pioneer Venus mission operations group, said, "If these are broadly representative of Venus then that is really a profound cosmochemical statement, and the processes that lead to this involve very peculiar chemistry."

Further speculation on Venus during the year came from Thomas M. Donahue, an atmospheric scientist of the University of Michigan, who concluded that the planet once had enough water to provide for oceans 30% or more the size of those on Earth. He based his theory largely on data from Pioneer Venus, the orbiter of which continued to circle Venus and return data. After reexamining data studied earlier, Donahue and his colleagues postulated that the present ratio of deuterium to hydrogen on Venus is of the order of approximately 1 to 160. This ratio, compared to estimates of

Panoramic view of the surface of Venus was photographed from the lander of the Soviet probe Venera 13. The craft transmitted data for 127 minutes, about four times longer than had been expected. It reported a surface temperature on the planet of 457° C (855° F).

Jet Propulsion Laboratory/NASA

Artist's drawing shows the U.S. probe Galileo, scheduled to be launched in May 1986 toward a rendezvous with Jupiter. The long wand-like boom extending from the spacecraft carries magnetometers to measure Jupiter's magnetic field. To the right of the boom base is the scan platform, carrying cameras and other instruments. The probe's power sources are located on the outriggers to the upper left and lower right.

the original ratio of deuterium to hydrogen on the planet, considered to be approximately 1 to 15,000, led the scientists to suggest that originally Venus had an ocean that was lost because of a hydrodynamic outflow of hydrogen to space. After an initial outgassing of water the familiar "greenhouse" effect drove the light hydrogen atoms from water into the atmosphere from where it escaped to space, leaving behind the heavier deuterium. Thus, Donahue theorized, the deuterium detected today in the Venusian atmosphere probably is a remnant of an early ocean. Current NASA planning for a radar mapping probe to Venus could help reinforce the theory by providing topographical evidence of former watercourses and oceans.

Looking toward Jupiter. In July President Reagan signed a supplemental funding measure to the fiscal 1982 NASA appropriations that included funds for the modification of the Centaur stage as the high-energy booster for the space shuttle payloads. Previous planning had included an inertial upper stage (IUS) for such a boost from Earth orbit for the Galileo probe to Jupiter, initially planned for a May 1985 launch. Selection of the Centaur for the mission was expected to delay the launch of the probe by one year, but it also will allow Galileo to arrive at Jupiter 12 to 18 months earlier than if it had been launched by the IUS in 1985. The reduced time of the voyage was expected to save approximately $100 million in operational costs, but probe development costs were increased by about $50 million.

The possibility that low forms of Earth life could exist on Europa, a satellite of Jupiter, was raised by Steven Squyres and Ray Reynolds, of NASA's Ames Research Center. The two scientists suggested that if some such life forms could have been transplanted they might well thrive in oceans on Europa, which is slightly smaller than the Moon. They based their supposition on photographs from probes and other observational measurements.

Analysis indicates that Europa is covered by a layer of ice 5 km (3 mi) thick, which in turn covers a liquid ocean as deep as 50 km (30 mi). Squyres and Reynolds point to the analogy of organisms that exist under the permanent ice over Earth's Antarctic water bodies. These organisms get the light that they need for survival and multiplication through the ice. Since some form of heat energy would also be required, it could be provided by radioactive decay in the satellite's rocky interior and, perhaps, by heat generated from the tidal forces created by Jupiter's gravitational field. The heat would keep the ocean liquid, and the sunlight would provide the energy needed for photosynthesis.

Pictures of Europa made by the Voyager 2 probe show the satellite to resemble a smooth white billiard ball with a fractured surface. Scientists believe that these fractures vary in width from 1 km (0.6 mi) to 70 km (43 mi) and are caused by the tidal forces of Jupiter. As these cracks form and freeze over, they may provide windows that allow sunlight to penetrate to the oceans during Europa's 60-hour-long days. Other possible energy sources for organisms could be from electrical currents induced by Jupiter's enormous magnetic field or heat from volcanic vents in the ocean floor. Thus, Squyres and Reynolds suggest that Europa could have relatively small areas of life-supporting "oases" in its oceans.

Probes to other planets. By the end of the year Voyager 2 had traveled about one-tenth of the total distance to its planned arrival at Uranus on Jan. 24, 1986. The probe was approximately 1.7 billion km (1 billion mi) from Earth. Of the original 104 kg (230 lb) of propellants used for attitude control and trajectory correction, a sufficient 67 kg (147.7 lb) remained. The two radioisotope thermoelectric generators were producing 422 W, 92 W more than required. However, several mechanical and electronic troubles plagued the probe. Bradford Smith of the University of Arizona described its condition as: "It is the human equivalent of arthritic, and [it is] senile and slightly deaf. . . . We don't have to talk louder to it, but we have to talk at just the right key. It can hear only a certain tone now." Overall, though, there was a great deal of optimism that the probe would be able to perform its mission at Uranus and possibly be operational later at Neptune.

Continuing study of pictures of Saturn returned by Voyager 2 provided evidence for the existence of four new satellites of that planet and the possibility of as many as six. In another area of study G. Leonard Tyler of Stanford University, who analyzed radio signals that were transmitted by the Voyager 1 probe in 1980, said that their pattern suggested that particles in two of Saturn's rings were chunks of ice that ranged in size from 1.3 cm (0.5 in) to 9.1 m (30 ft). He concluded that the ice particles were left over from the formation of the solar system.

During the year the Viking Mars mission was declared a complete success six years after the arrival of the two probes at Mars. The Viking 1 lander was still transmitting pictures and meteorological, radio science, and engineering data. This one remaining probe entered a new phase of operation, a continuous but low-activity program of providing data on eight-day cycles through 1994.

A step toward the future exploration of Mars by space probes was taken during the year. NASA and the European Space Agency (ESA) began consideration of a joint program to place a U.S. and a European probe into orbit about that planet. One scheme proposed a geochemical mapper provided by NASA and an atmospheric explorer provided by ESA. It was envisioned that both probes would be placed into orbit by a Centaur upper stage after launch from the space shuttle. By using the highly successful imaging radar demonstrated on the second space shuttle mission, scientists could gather data that would be useful in future missions that would sample the Martian soil.

During 1982 scientists in the U.S.S.R. also began looking forward to future exploration of the surface of Mars by an unmanned probe. Tests were made of a potential automatic Mars station which would have a design similar to the Soviet Luna 2 probe that landed on the Moon in 1959.

Planning for Halley's Comet. During the year planning continued worldwide for the preparation of probes to study Halley's Comet when it comes closest to the Earth in 1986. Probes were to be launched by the U.S.S.R., Japan, and ESA, two each for the Soviet Union and Japan and one for ESA. Representatives of the countries met in Budapest, Hungary, to endorse an international cooperative program. All probes were scheduled to pass by the comet in March 1986, when it is some 145 million km (90 million mi) from the Earth. The U.S., which was not launching a probe, will coordinate the International Halley's Watch program. U.S. participation also includes the possible use of the Space Telescope, IMP 8, and Pioneer 7.

The Soviet probes were scheduled to pass Venus in 1985 and drop off two subprobes to study the Venusian atmosphere and then continue on to the vicinity of the comet. Each probe was to be launched by a separate space vehicle. The Soviets revealed that experiment payloads for their two craft were being developed in France, West Germany, Austria, Czechoslovakia, Hungary, Bulgaria, and Poland, as well as in the U.S.S.R. Instruments to be included were a two-camera television system, three-channel spectrometer, three-channel infrared spectrometer, dust-mass spectrometer, dust-particle counters, neutral-gas mass spectrometer, ion-mass spectrometer, high-energy particle counter, plasma-wave analyzers, and magnetometers. The Soviets stated that while the probes could be targeted for a flyby with a precision of 100 km (62 mi), the planned distance for the first craft was 10,000 km (6,200 mi) and for the second was 3,000 km (1,860 mi).

The ESA cometary probe was named Giotto after the Italian painter Giotto di Bondone, who saw the comet in 1301 and depicted it in his fresco "Adoration of the Magi." The 950-kg (2,095-lb) probe was to be launched by an Ariane vehicle from the ESA launch center at Kourou, French Guiana, in July 1985. It would be equipped with ten instruments, including a multicolor camera, neutral-mass spectrometer, ion-mass spectrometer, dust-mass spectrometer, dust-impact detector, two plasma analyzers, energetic-particle analyzer, magnetometer, and optical probe. This instrumentation was provided by scientists in West Germany, Switzerland, Great Britain, France, and Ireland. Giotto was expected to bypass the coma of the comet at distance of a few hundred kilometers in early March 1986. The Japanese A probe was designed to pass by the comet at a distance of approximately 100,000 km (62,100 mi) on March 8, 1986.

While the U.S. will not send a probe to Halley's Comet, it planned to divert the ISEE 3 spacecraft now in orbit to fly by Comet Giacobini-Zinner in September 1985. The gravitational field of the Moon would be used to shape the trajectory to the comet. Although ISEE 3 has no camera or photometer, its six instruments can furnish significant data on plasma densities, flow speeds, temperatures, and the types of heavy ions in the comet's tail. Targeting had not been selected, but scientists believed that the probe can be positioned to within an accuracy of about 990 km (614 mi).

—Mitchell R. Sharpe

Transportation

While fuel conservation continued to be a major objective in transport technology programs during 1982, the sharp decline in petroleum demand worldwide and the resulting lower costs allowed the addition of another objective. This was the increased automation and computerization of controls and other equipment, and it was most evident during the year in the aviation industry.

The Interstate Commerce Commission (ICC) on two occasions took steps to encourage the use of advanced communications technology in transportation. One was its ruling to permit the electronic transmission and disposition of carriers' freight billings, as well as claims

for loss and damage, overcharges, duplicate billings, and over-collection. This will replace the cumbersome, slow, and costly use of paper billings and claims. To protect shippers unable to employ such technology, the Commission ruled that the use of electronic transmissions would be on a voluntary basis between carrier and shipper, with shippers continuing to receive paper billings and claims if they so wished.

The ICC also agreed to give serious consideration to an industry proposal—developed as part of a program to utilize computer technology in carrier tariffs—that the Commission adopt an electronic tariff filing 'system. This would replace the system of paper filings and tariff publications. In explaining the proposal in a formal ICC hearing, an industry spokesman claimed that carriers, shippers, and the Commission itself could collectively save millions of dollars by the switch from paper to electronics. An officer of Sea-Land Industries Inc. reported that its Sea-Land ocean carrier subsidiary (not under ICC jurisdiction) currently handles interchange shipping data, container status reports, and billing information electronically.

One of the last joint Soviet-U.S. cooperative space programs promises benefits for small aircraft and vessels that have crashed or are lost in remote land or water areas. Such benefits will be provided by search-and-rescue satellites called SARSATS, which are able to

Flight deck of the Boeing 757 and 767 jetliners contains automated controls for almost all major functions, replacing electromechanical instruments with digital electronic equipment.

Widebody A310 jetliner, which can accommodate 195–225 passengers, was developed by the European consortium Airbus Industrie. Like the Boeing 767 it has a fully automated flight deck.

pick up standard international distress frequencies from almost any point on Earth.

The first real-life test of such a satellite, a Soviet craft, indicated what is ahead. A small airplane forced to make an emergency landing in a vast and rugged area in western Canada fortunately was equipped with an automatic emergency beacon. The signals of the beacon were picked up by the satellite, which relayed the distress information to a ground antenna near Ottawa. A computer quickly established the location of the landing, enabling a rescue helicopter to pick up the three men downed in the aircraft.

Air transport. The Boeing Company's new, advanced-technology 767 was certified by the Federal Aviation Administration (FAA) and placed in scheduled commercial service by United Airlines. The twin-engine, widebody aircraft can carry, in various configurations, from 211 to 255 passengers. Its two-man cockpit crew (pilot and copilot, but no longer a flight engineer) will be surrounded by automated controls for virtually all major functions. As a result, despite one less crew member, the cockpit workload should be reduced thanks to the advances in reliable digital avionics, highlighted by the use of the cathode-ray-tube displays.

The use of automation includes an engine indication and crew alerting system to show engine performance and to provide warning and advisory information. There is also an electronic horizontal situation indicator to help plan and confirm routes prior to takeoff and to furnish navigation data such as the aircraft's present position, distance to route points, and estimated time of arrivals. An electronic attitude director indicator provides the flight crew with visual data regarding the aircraft's flight, attitude, and ground speed.

Airbus Industrie, a European consortium, continued flight tests of its twin-engine, widebody A310, with expectation of certification in 1983. This aircraft, like the Boeing 767, features extensive use of full-color cathode-ray-tube displays to ease the burden on its two-man cockpit crews. Also like the 767 the A310 will use the so-called dark philosophy for its automated panels, with an all-lights-out situation indicating normal operations.

Boeing's other advanced-technology transport, the smaller, narrow-bodied, twin-engine 757, was rolled out for flight tests. The 176-passenger (in standard configuration) aircraft was designed to replace older fleets of transports that were servicing short-to-medium routes. Boeing predicted a demand for about 1,350 such aircraft in the next decade. In addition to the automated cockpit for its two-man flight crew the 757 will offer dramatic fuel economies compared to aircraft it is replacing; operating cost reductions per seat-mile are expected to be about 40%. This saving will be made possible by the use of more efficient engines, of lightweight composite materials, and improved aircraft design.

As part of a two-year study under contract with the U.S. National Aeronautics and Space Administration, Lockheed Corp. designers proposed as a "freighter for the 1990s" a dual-fuselage transport. They claimed that it would be more feasible than the so-called flying wing concept in which the payload is carried in huge wings. The dual-fuselage proponents pointed out that their plane would be able to carry 700,000 to 1,000,000 lb of freight, more than that carried by two B-747s. While operating costs would be about the same as those for the flying wing, the dual-body craft's 35-m- (115-ft-) wide landing gear would be able to use existing 45-m- (150-ft-) wide runways, while the former could not. The flying wing thus would require widening of runways, at considerable cost, or would need a

Prototype of the airship Cyclo-Crane, 55 meters (184 feet) in length and capable of carrying two tons, is docked at a mooring mast at the Tillamook County Airport in Oregon. Designed and built by Aerolift Inc., it gets most of its lift from helium and is powered by four 90-horsepower engines. Four T-shaped wings extend from its midsection.

much stronger wing structure in order to permit use of a narrower landing gear.

The Boeing Co. developed a new automated, belt-loader system to handle both baggage and freight in the 727 and 757 narrow-bodied aircraft. It was designed to permit loading of eight large shipper-packed cardboard boxes, each carrying 1,500 lb of freight, in eight minutes with a single handler. This compared with the current practice of using two ground handlers able to handle parcels up to 250 lb plus a third handler inside the aircraft to position the packages. The system includes a conveyor belt for loading and unloading, plus tracks in the airplane to roll the standardized boxes into place automatically. Despite the obvious advantages Boeing reported that it had not yet been able to persuade airlines to formally test the system—the cost of which was estimated at about $500,000 per plane.

The DeVore Aviation Corp. of Albuquerque, N.M., announced that the FAA had given approval for use of its Pulse Light Approach Slope Indicator (PLASI) in both fixed-wing aircraft and helicopters. Extensively developed and tested over a five-year period, PLASI is a new visual approach system for aircraft landings in a variety of environments; these might include small airports in mountainous terrain, landing platforms on offshore oil rigs, center-city heliports, and rooftop helipads.

DeVore claimed that PLASI as a single-unit system is economical to install and operate, making it ideal for small airports where no visual landing systems are available. PLASI is simple to interpret, with a steady white light indicating that a plane is on course, a pulsing red light for below course, and a pulsing white light

for above course. The farther an aircraft goes off course, the more rapid are the pulses. Another feature is an automatic lamp-changing system to prevent equipment failure from a burnout; additional spare lamps take over automatically, and a red warning light signal flashes when the last lamp is in place.

Another technological innovation being developed largely for general aviation was demonstrated by the Mitre Corp. under a program sponsored by the FAA. Unofficially called AWARE (Aviation Weather Alert Reception Equipment), the innovation was designed as a low-cost ($2,000) system to visually provide detailed information about weather along the aircraft's route. Also provided was a small printout of weather conditions.

Highway transport. Despite the reluctance of the automobile manufacturing industry to undertake research and development on a new engine valve that initial tests indicate will boost both fuel economy and power as well as reduce emissions, its developers were able to generate strong investor and political support. As a result the U.S. Department of Transportation agreed to sponsor further tests, which were to be conducted with the cooperation of the Chrysler Corp.

The developers claimed that their intake manifold valve allows use of 75 octane gas (compared to today's low of 87 octane), thereby eliminating the need for lead and other additives. In turn, this eliminates the need for pollution-control devices. The valve, it was claimed, can boost fuel economy by 6–20% and power by 13–40%, as well as reduce emissions of nitrogen oxide and carbon monoxide by up to 50% and of hydrocarbons by up to 13%. At present prices the 75 octane gasoline

388

would be about 20 cents per gallon cheaper than the 87 octane variety.

The developers described the valve as using bonded wire mesh screens to vaporize gasoline entering the cylinder. This eliminates gasoline droplets that produce the hot and cold spots in the cylinder which now must be dealt with by using lead and other additives.

Claims of another additive to boost motor fuel economy sharply were announced by the Rolfite Corp. of Stamford, Conn., which cited actual operating tests as evidence. Called "Propel," the additive reportedly will boost motor fuel economy by about 11%. The developers said that two operators of motor carrier fleets, Coca-Cola Bottling Co. of New York and Connecticut Limousine, reported savings of from 12 to 20%. The additive is a manganese-based chemical that acts as an oxygen scavenger and is contained in a light-lube oil carrier. It permits greater utilization of oxygen in the cylinder, thus allowing more complete combustion than is possible at present and emitting less carbon monoxide and unburned hydrocarbons.

A potential threat to the use of diesel engines in heavy-duty trucks has not been overcome, according to General Motors Corp., which formally told the U.S. Environmental Protection Agency that it could not meet EPA's proposed 1986 particulate emissions standard for such engines. GM, which for several years had been conducting extensive research on methods to control diesel exhaust particulates, claimed that its ef-

forts revealed no acceptable solution to either the 1986 requirement or the 1985 passenger car and light-duty truck diesel particulate standards.

GM extensively tested the use of an exhaust trap oxidizer, which would trap the microscopic particles resulting from incomplete combustion and burn them off internally at very high temperatures. GM reported that tests of the traps on both passenger cars and trucks resulted in success only with small engines. The company said that application of the traps to heavy-duty trucks was more difficult because exhaust flow rates are higher (requiring larger traps), exhaust temperatures are generally cooler (requiring auxiliary heat for burn-off), and the vehicles operate under more hostile conditions for longer distances than do automobiles and light trucks.

The auto manufacturing industry encountered another setback when a U.S. appellate court ruled that builders must install either air bags or automatic safety belts in 1984-model automobiles. This action overturned an administrative ruling by the National Highway Safety Traffic Administration, which rescinded an earlier NHSTA order that required such so-called passive (automatic) restraints on 1983-model large and medium-size cars and 1984-model small cars. The court ruling made the requirement effective on Sept. 1, 1983, for all cars.

On a more positive note, from a truck manufacturer's standpoint, was a ruling by the EPA that delayed

Riding on a specially designed flatcar, the Santa Fe Railway's new containers are designed to be stacked two-high and to handle dry and liquid bulk commodities and/or packaged freight.

Santa Fe Railway

High-speed train in West Germany links Dusseldorf, Cologne, and Bonn with the Frankfurt airport. It was hoped that this service would reduce the number of uneconomic short flights between those cities and thus save the national airline, Lufthansa, a substantial amount of money.

the implementation of its 1983 truck noise emission standard until 1986. The EPA said that a reason for the delay was to provide economic relief to the currently hard-pressed trucking industry. Spokesmen for the industry contended that the technology that would permit compliance with even the 1986 deadline would not be available unless excessive operational and economic burdens were placed on the manufacturers.

Pipelines. An innovative project calling for construction of the first capsule pipeline in the U.S. was being promoted by W. R. Grace & Co. Called "Aquatrain," it would utilize water as the carrier of pulverized coal through the pipeline; however, the coal would be moving in plastic bags, or capsules, rather than suspended in a coal-water mixture. Of major significance, instead of fresh water—which is scarce in the western portion of the U.S. where several large slurry lines are to be built—the capsule line would use unwanted saline water.

If the project is approved, its first application could be a 1,600-km (1,000-mi), 90-cm- (36-in-) diameter pipeline from mines in Colorado to a west-coast terminal. Such a line could move from 15 to 20 million tons of coal a year, which would be transported at 8 km/h (5 mph) in 4.5-m- (14.8-ft-) long plastic capsules, each containing two to three tons of coal. The capsule would have a specific gravity equal to the saline water used to transport, or float, it. Total construction costs would exceed $2 billion, and Grace determined that the first line could be under way in early 1984 if remaining technical problems could be worked out.

The company said that the water to be used for moving the capsule could be drawn from saline springs in the Colorado River basin. After use it would be cleaned, to the extent necessary, for dumping into the ocean.

U.S. Department of Interior officials expressed enthusiasm about the project, particularly its potential for helping to control Colorado River basin salinity.

Such a capsule line presumably would face the same eminent domain problems that were delaying construction of several long-distance coal-slurry pipelines. Congressional clearance of legislation that would permit such lines to obtain federal eminent domain rights to cross private property—including that of railroads that strongly oppose them—thus appeared to be a necessity.

Congressional passage of such legislation would open the door to rapid development of coal-slurry pipelines in the U.S. The largest of the seven lines being planned is one from the Powder River basin in Wyoming to Oklahoma and Arkansas, with possible extensions to Louisiana and Texas. Another large-diameter line, the Coalstream project, would deliver coal from West Virginia and southern Illinois to utilities in Georgia and Florida.

The coal-slurry pipeline promoters foresee a potential export market for U.S. coal of one billion tons per year. They also predict sizable savings in transportation costs in comparison with moving coal by rail. As to the claims of the huge drain on scarce water supplies in U.S. western states, the promoters maintained that more water was available than environmentalists believed, that considerable water unsuited for agriculture or human consumption could be used, and that the dewatering and cleaning of slurry pipeline water at terminals should ease the demand for water and prevent waste.

Rail transport. Spurred by deregulation of rail movements of TOFC/COFC (trailer and container on-flatcar traffic), the railroad and rail equipment manufactur-

390

ing industries were working to produce new and innovative cars and containers to handle such traffic. The Atchison, Topeka & Santa Fe Railway developed a 14-m (45-ft) intermodal container able to handle a variety of products ranging from palletized goods to bulk commodities. To reduce weight the prototype is fabricated from fiberglass and is shaped at the top like an "A" to permit stacking two-high. The trailer's reverse "U"-shaped bottom straddles either the "A" on a bottom trailer or the center sill of the special Fuel Foiler flatcar used to carry the trailers. This provides a low center of gravity. Each trailer can carry up to 55 tons of bulk commodities or palletized packaged goods.

Trailer Train Co., the railroad industry's subsidiary responsible for development and supply of rail TOFC/COFC equipment, began testing two intermodal car prototypes. One, built by the Rail Division of Itel Corp., can be used in various ways, one version being a ten-platform and another a five-platform car. The cars are articulated, with each platform able to handle a trailer up to 15 m (50 ft) in length. Each prototype makes extensive use of aluminum to keep the weight under 11,365 kg (25,000 lb), thus lowering fuel costs.

A similar car was being built by Thrall Car Manufacturing Co. Similar in design to that of Itel, it uses skeleton-framing to hold down weight. The cars are equipped with high-capacity hydraulic draft gears, cushioned trailer hitches, and a specially designed air brake system to reduce brake-shoe wear and prolong wheel life.

The Santa Fe Railway tested an aluminum gondola car able to handle 10% more coal than present hopper cars, and it turned the prototype over to the Burlington Northern Railroad for further tests. Called the "Algola" car, it is 33% lighter than a standard steel gondola car—18,600 vs 28,200 kg (41,000 vs 62,000 lb)—and it can carry an extra ten tons of coal. As it also saves fuel on empty back hauls, its benefits are said to far outweigh the 35% additional cost. Because most of the cars used in U.S. railroad coal operations are owned by the utilities being served, the tests were designed mainly for influencing shippers.

The International Association of Refrigerated Warehouses (IARW) announced progress on its efforts to develop an innovative refrigerated rail car able to preserve frozen food in transit by using dry ice produced from liquid carbon dioxide, which would be supplied by a thermostatically controlled system on the car. According to IARW about $250,000 was pledged to build the car, the second phase of a research program studying the use of such a refrigeration system. The program was begun in 1980 to meet concern about the deterioration of the rapidly aging refrigerated rail car fleet, since such cars are expensive to build, maintain, and operate. Tests to date were described as encouraging.

Encouraged by rulings by the ICC, the Bi-Modal Corp., builders of the RoadRailer—a trailer with interchangeable steel and rubber-tired wheels to permit rail and highway use—sharply stepped up its operational tests and research programs. The ICC not only gave its clearance for use of RoadRailers in rail freight service but also ruled that the rail portions of such service were exempted from the economic regulation of rail TOFC/COFC service.

Results of the first operational tests of RoadRailer by the Illinois Central Gulf Railroad between Louisville, Ky., and Memphis, Tenn., were described as mixed. The railroad said that some problems arose because the single rear axle of the unit carries all the wheel weight in highway use, causing difficulties in some instances in meeting state highway truck weight limits. Bi-Modal said that this could be overcome by better loading techniques.

Following a successful test run of RoadRailers through New York City's Hudson River tunnels, which have been restricted to rail passenger cars because conventional rail freight and TOFC/COFC cars are too large, Bi-Modal worked out a cooperative pact with Conrail and the state of New York for service from New York City to Buffalo, N.Y. Bi-Modal was to furnish the RoadRailers; Conrail would operate the specialized trains; and New York state would help to finance terminal improvements.

In the area of research and development Bi-Modal introduced two new models of RoadRailers to broaden their market potential. One was made to handle 12- or 13-m (40- or 45-ft) seagoing containers for fast, direct roll-on/roll-off service to customers. The other was a special automobile carrier that uses a unique cable-and-rack loading/unloading technique to accommodate loads of up to five autos per unit. Such a carrier could quickly be converted to a regular dry van model for back-haul cargo movements. Enclosing the autos helps overcome the serious problem of loss and damage, especially from vandalism, that is characteristic of open-transit movements of new cars.

Water transport. British use of hovercraft for passenger travel continued to advance, as sea trials of the diesel-powered API-88 of British Hovercraft Corp. got under way. The craft, which rides on a cushion of air compressed in a flexible skirt around its bottom, was scheduled to provide service between the Isle of Wight and the British mainland. The hull was constructed of welded aluminum for lighter weight and lower operating cost. The craft has four Deutz air-cooled diesel engines. The two engines that are used for propulsion drive twin propellers which are ducted to reduce noise levels; the other two engines drive eight centrifugal fans to achieve lift. Hovertravel, the buyer and operator, ordered two 80-seat models of the craft.

Atlantic Container Line began building five new third-generation roll-on/roll-off containerships for North Atlantic service. Designed specifically for flexibility in loading and cargo carrying, the ships featured large quarter ramps and deck space able to accommodate a variety of cargo, such as cars, containers, and tractor-trailers of different sizes. A unique feature was to be a three-deck garage-type stern section with hoistable decks. To conserve fuel the ships were to use new, slow-speed diesel engines that would require only about one-third the amount of fuel of the firm's second-generation containerships.

Substitution of coal-fired ships for diesel-propelled ones is unlikely in regard to general cargo liners in the near future, according to the Australian National Line. ANL concluded that coal-fired ships would be economical for bulk cargo only if they were very large, 50,000 deadweight tons or more. The savings of the low-cost coal are offset—proportionally more as the ship size decreases—by the 15–20% higher ship construction cost and the reduced cargo capacity because of the extra fuel bulk of coal. ANL also pointed out some loss of cargo capacity because coal contains less energy per ton than fuel oil.

To correct the problem of moisture causing deterioration of the BTU content of coal being shipped in open river barges, Proform Inc. of Minneapolis, Minn., developed a special cover made of structural fiberglass-reinforced plastic. The firm claimed that tests revealed that coal shipped in such covered barges maintained temperatures and BTU values that were stable over a 40-day period.

The first of an order of 116 super jumbo open hopper barges for river travel was christened by Bergeron Barges, Inc., for use by Central Gulf Lines Inc. of New Orleans, La. The huge barges, called "the world's largest" open hoppers, are 79 m (260 ft) long, 16 m (52.5 ft) wide, and 3.6 m (12 ft) high. The capacity of one barge is said to equal that of 31 rail hopper cars, and Central Gulf Lines claimed that their use in hauling coal for Seminole Electric Cooperative of Tampa, Fla., would save the utility more than $3 billion over a 28-year period. The $60 million contract, largest ever made for barges, led to the development of a special $10 million facility to build them; it can produce ten such barges each month.

Another huge barge, this one for ocean transport, was launched at Bath Iron Works at Bath, Maine, for the California and Hawaiian Sugar Co. in order to transport raw sugar, grain, or nonhazardous granular fertilizers between Hawaii and the west coast of the U.S. Called "the largest vessel of its kind constructed in the U.S.," it is 196 m (643 ft) in length and has a beam of 26 m (84 ft) and a draft of 11 m (36 ft). It was designed to be propelled by a specially designed catamaran tugboat, which, when linked to the barge, will create an integrated unit 209 m (687 ft) in length. The barge will have a capacity of 40,200 cu m (1,420,000 cu ft) of cargo in six holds.

—Frank A. Smith

U.S. science policy

During the year under review an extraordinary variety of signals were sent back and forth between the federal government and the U.S. scientific community. The year opened with statements of grave concern from laboratories expressing fears that threatened cutbacks in federal funding would irreparably damage the fabric of the U.S. scientific enterprise. As months passed and earlier budgetary allocations were modified by a combination of White House and congressional action, the scientific leadership acknowledged that the funding situation was not quite as bleak as had been feared. But the year brought other causes for concern, including what might be the beginning of a showdown between the demands of military security and the need for freedom of scientific communication.

Funding problems. The scientists' early concern about the availability of research support was based on statements from the Reagan administration that nondefense expenditures were to be drastically reduced and an observation by the president's science adviser that the government was going to be far more selective than previously in the kinds of research it would choose to fund. When the budget finally settled down, a report from the National Science Foundation told the good news and the bad news. The good news was that the White House was planning for a 11% increase in R and D (research and development) support, compared with a 5% increase in the overall budget. The bad news was that most of the increase was going into military research. Basic researchers, who depend almost entirely on federal funding, would find that their portion of the R and D sector would rise by 9%, but once again the military would receive the lion's share. R and D related to energy and the environment was cut heavily, and basic research in medicine would not keep up with inflation.

In its annual review of the science budget the American Association for the Advancement of Science displayed equanimity:

R & D budgets received a sharp jolt in the first Reagan budget, but on the whole survived fairly well. The 12 percent cuts of the September budget would have spelled disaster for much of federal R & D; the lesser reductions actually approved forced significant but generally not fatal cutbacks in nondefense R & D. The President's [fiscal year] 1983 Budget ... treated R & D fairly well, given the difficult circumstances.

The president of the National Academy of Sciences, formerly science adviser to Pres. Jimmy Carter, was similarly relieved. In an interview with the editors of *Chemical and Engineering News* Frank Press said:

The 1983 budget proposed by the Administration is not so bad as many thought it would be [in late '81] ... if you look at the proposed 1983 federal budget for research and compare it with the rest of the civil sector, you can see that the Administration took special pains to treat science sensitively, although

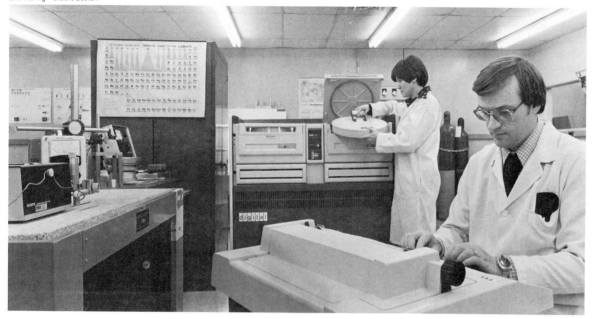

Research laboratories in the United States feared that cutbacks in federal funding would severely curtail their efforts. In the final budget, however, research and development funds were increased 11%.

some think it could have done a little more. If you look at the rhetoric and the budget papers you can see that the Administration believes in the philosophy that it is the government's role to keep science healthy in this country.

... I believe the Administration is right if it means that ... if scientists don't [select the most promising opportunities for research] it will be done by lawyers and accountants. It will be very hard to walk away from that kind of challenge.

... as an individual ... I think that we should have real growth in defense R & D. I think real growth on the order of 5% may be overdue because of neglect over the years. But I also think that the amount of real growth that is proposed is so large that I am not sure it can be well spent and that it will drain resources from other important national needs [such as] education, precollege math and science, the support of basic science, the infrastructure of aging physical plants in this country.

On the other hand the members of the National Academy of Sciences, at their annual meeting, expressed their "deep concern with the current erosion in the support of basic scientific research by the federal government. Budgetary reductions, combined with uncertainty and instability as to the level of funding, are having profound detrimental effects on our efforts to maintain the present level of world leadership in many fields of scientific endeavor."

Both points of view found supporting evidence by the end of the year. At a time when severe budgetary cuts were being made in almost all nondefense spending, the R and D sector of the budget was hurt less than most. On the other hand the announcement that a large team of nuclear physicists based in Switzerland had discovered the long-sought W particle evoked, on the other side of the Atlantic, murmurs of profound re-

gret that the U.S. no longer was able to keep pace in that fundamental area of research.

One other effect of the reductions in federal support received far less publicity. Reports from a number of funding agencies made it clear that, despite the restoration of much of the severe fiscal 1982 cutback in the support of social and behavioral research, the number of grant proposals had dropped off precipitously. The director of the National Science Foundation's division of social and economic sciences predicted that, instead of the 1,200 proposals his office usually received during a year, he would get only 800. By contrast, however, the Office of Naval Research, the Air Force Office of Scientific Research, and the Army Research Institute reported that they had received about one-third more applications than in the preceding year.

Still another effect of the cutbacks in federal support surfaced in April. A group of manufacturers of memory chips announced plans to expand university research spending to more than $20 million over the next two years. According to an industry association, the program was intended to encourage long-term semiconductor research and to increase the supply of professional staff. In effect, the beleaguered U.S. industry, faced with increasingly aggressive and effective competition from Japan, was seeking to accomplish privately what the Japanese were doing with government support. U.S. companies were prevented by antitrust legislation from pooling research results in product development but not from joint funding of fundamental research in universities. (*See* Feature Article: SCIENCE AND THE PRIVATE SECTOR.)

University-industry partnerships. U.S. industry spends somewhere between $250 million and $300 million each year on R and D in universities. This is only a tiny fraction of industry's total R and D investment, but it is concentrated. Only about 100 universities can be classified as "major" research universities. Together they receive some 85% of all federal funds for research. Ten companies fund one-third of all industry-supported R and D in universities, and two companies alone fund 20% of all university basic research. A New York University study identified a total of 465 industry-supported research programs, 67% of which were in engineering and computer sciences and only 14% in biotechnology.

Although biotechnology accounted for only a small proportion of the partnerships between campus and corporation, the rapid advances in recombinant DNA research stirred up high interest among a variety of industrial organizations. The nature of the field and its applications to human health created problems quite different from those of the more established fields. For one thing almost all the work that led to the new biotechnology came from university research; there were, with few exceptions, no parallel efforts in industry. Although a number of new companies were carrying out such research on their own premises, most of the larger firms preferred to depend on an association with university research teams. They were willing to pay a high price for the association if it included first-refusal rights to the product.

It quickly became evident that there were side effects to these relationships that threatened the traditional independence of university research and—to a worrisome extent—the easy relationship between scientists traveling parallel paths of investigation. Much of the work in biotechnology was being done at Stanford University, and early in 1982 Stanford invited the senior officials of 11 biotechnology firms and the presidents of several other major universities in the field to a meeting at Pajaro Dunes, Calif., March 25–27. So sensitive was the agenda that the meeting was closed to the news media. A Stanford press release promised that any agreed-upon principles would be revealed to the public, but—in any case—such principles would be intended only to serve as guidelines rather than as a basis for self-regulation.

The press announcement also listed a brave agenda of questions:

Should universities seek to return value from research developments to nurture the research enterprise and if so under what constraints?
Should all research agreements between universities and companies be made public?
Should universities aggressively patent and license faculty inventions?
What should be the guidelines for universities holding stock in companies owned by faculty members?
What are the consequences of industry-supported pro-

grams to the free exchange of knowledge and to the training of graduate students?
How can the traditions of open research be preserved without forfeiting property rights necessary for companies to make commercial use of the research results?
Are new conflict-of-interest rules needed?

At the conclusion of the meeting, a statement was issued that served more to demonstrate the concerns of the participants about the nature of the problem than to assure others that the problem was under control. The statement opened with this profession of faith:

It is important that universities and industries maintain basic academic values in their research agreements. Agreements should be constructed, for example, in ways that do not promote a secrecy that will harm the progress of science, impair the education of students, interfere with the choice by faculty members of the scientific questions or lines of inquiry they pursue, or divert the energies of faculty members from their primary obligations to teaching and research.

The statement then went on to list a number of cautionary observations, but those who had hoped for a solid demonstration of self-regulation were disappointed.

The British journal *Nature* made its disappointment plain. It listed a number of problems sure to occur on campuses where the product of laboratory research was good enough to have immediate value to industry, perhaps to competing firms. Would professional colleagues, each with a consultancy, begin to avoid consulting each other? Would their graduate students think twice about exchanging information? Said *Nature*:

The Pajaro Dunes communiqué would have been more helpful if it had openly acknowledged that problems such as these exist. It should also have recognized that the difficulties occasioned by biotechnology differ only in degree from those with which universities have learned, however uneasily, to live.
Some thought should . . . be given to the question of why the commercialization of basic research has recently thrown up so many problems. Government support for basic research is shrinking everywhere, while universities are being urged to look to industry for sponsorship. Universities and individual academics are being driven into the arms of those companies farsighted enough to recognize that they have much to gain from partnerships like these. There is much to be said for finding ways of turning academic discoveries into prosperity for the wider community. But while some academics appear genuinely to be excited by the challenge of turning their bright ideas into business enterprises, others appear to be at least as much intrigued by the prospect of monetary rewards. . . . Compared with their students who make a success in industry, academics are scandalously paid. . . . But has the traditional loyalty of academics to the institutions which employ them been eroded? And if so, what will be the consequences of that? . . .

A. Bartlett Giamatti, president of Yale University, agreed: "I doubt that a faculty member can ordinarily devote the time and energy the university requires and also pursue a substantial involvement in any such outside company." He promised that Yale would require

professors to disclose their relationships with corporate sponsors.

Jonathan King, professor of molecular genetics at the Massachusetts Institute of Technology, told the annual meeting of the American Association for the Advancement of Science that university scientists who have a financial stake in companies benefiting from their research should be disqualified from receiving public support for such research. "The dominant ethos of the scientific community up to the present day has been absolutely free exchange of information and materials [but] individuals planning to profit by, for example, assigning patents to their own firms, tend to cut down communication with their colleagues."

King went on to argue that the availability of large amounts of support from industry would inevitably skew the course of research. "The commercialization of research focuses on the production of products for sale. It distorts priorities, biases research, and biases individuals in the field into shaping research to go in that direction. . . ." He observed that as an inevitable consequence there would be less interest in finding a cure for diabetes, for example, than in finding better ways to make insulin.

In December more than 400 executives from industry and universities gathered in Philadelphia at the invitation of eight university presidents. Like Pajaro Dunes, the meeting produced more of a credo than an analysis of the problems caused by the troubled relationship. Herbert I. Fusfeld, director of the center for science and technology policy at New York University, saw the relationship as something of a Faustian bargain, in which the university relinquishes some of its freedoms in exchange for an offer of financial support

in an era of reduced federal funding. Then he stated what appeared to be the central tenet of the universities—certainly those research universities that had accepted the trade-off: "There are no absolutes, and the issue becomes one of degree and common sense." Others were not so sure that academic traditions were powerful enough to prevent the new relationships from permanently eroding the historic roles of the research university: to pursue knowledge for its own sake and to promote the free exchange of information.

National security and scientific communication. The pressure on some research universities to accept a certain level of restriction on open communication as a condition of industry sponsorship seemed less troublesome than another restriction that resulted from a growing concern on the part of the military.

The National Science Foundation reported in 1982 that, by 1979, 20% of all full-time graduate science and engineering students in U.S. universities were foreign nationals. In engineering they made up 40% of the total and comprised 50% of all those being graduated with doctoral degrees. In the computer sciences, one of the areas notably of interest to the military, they comprised 30% of the enrollment. In general, the 1979 figures, the latest available, represented a 41% increase over 1974, compared with a 9% increase in graduate students with U.S. citizenship.

Bobby Inman, then deputy director of the Central Intelligence Agency, spelled it out to the House Committee on Science and Technology in March: "Since the late 1970s, there has been an increased emphasis by . . . hostile intelligence services on the acquisition of new Western technology emerging from universities and research centers. . . . It's time for the scientific community to accept that there is an outflow, that the outflow is potentially damaging, certainly to the national interest and, in specific cases, to the national security. . . ." Inman went on to suggest that if the scientific community could not develop procedures to "limit the outflow," government agencies would do it for them.

> . . . I have begun to worry what other branches of the government might ultimately propose in the way of regulation. . . . I think six months, a year, 18 months down the road, as the full magnitude of the Soviets' success in acquiring technology in the West comes to the front of the agenda to be considered by the government, and the government decides how to react, at this point I believe there will be proposals. It may come from a combination of Commerce, Defense, State, and the national security apparatus. . . .

The warning from Inman was clearly aimed at eliciting some reaction from the scientific community, and in this he succeeded. The National Research Council hastily brought together a committee of scientists and policymakers and asked them to report at an early date. Granted access to classified material supplied by the military, the committee found that, although there was evidence of a flow of militarily valuable information to the Soviet Union, virtually none of it came from academic research facilities.

The committee observed that the U.S. would be better off counting on an unfettered research community to maintain a vital lead in research of military value than trying to protect that lead by cutting off open communication. It also recommended that the government notify its contractors of its intentions to restrict publication during the negotiation of the research contract rather than when the contractor announced his intention to publish.

It appeared that the Pentagon was waiting for such a set of proposals. The *Science and Government Report* of Dec. 1, 1982, cited a memorandum from Richard D. DeLauer, undersecretary of defense for research and engineering, to his chief subordinates. With one eye on the research community, whose effective goodwill was absolutely necessary to an increasingly technological military force, he declared, "It is extremely important that you realize that review of research papers is for comment and not for approval" and urged them not to "unduly restrain the open exchange of unclassified information among members of the scientific community."

With respect to the irritations that arose over the inclusion of scientific information among those items that could be barred from international commerce, the memo went on: "It is recognized that the current export regulations are not well-defined and it is impor-

tant that the Program Managers do not apply unnecessary restrictions on the dissemination of research results which would be harmful to the strength and standing of the national research effort."

The science of arms control. During the year there was also a quickening of interest within the scientific community—as well as among the public at large—on the dangers of nuclear arms. Ever since the atomic bomb explosion over Hiroshima in World War II, a large sector of the scientific community had felt a special responsibility to raise the level of public awareness and concern over the nuclear arms race, but there had been no large-scale effort in this direction for several decades. In 1981, however, and increasingly in 1982 the tempo of activity began to quicken.

A group of medical scientists played a notable role, holding briefings in many cities, in the White House, in the Vatican, and from a television studio in the Soviet Union. Their plea was simple in the extreme: reassuring predictions on the survivability of a nuclear exchange between the major powers simply did not take into account one essential fact; *i.e.,* all predictions involving survivability of populations were based on the assumption of an effective system of health care. Impossible, they said. In the event of a nuclear war, there would be no doctors, no hospitals, no burn and trauma centers. It could very well be that far more people would die from neglect of the long-term effects of nuclear explosions than would die as an immediate result of the detonations.

A number of scientific organizations departed from their traditional reluctance to take a stand on current political issues. With only one dissenting vote the U.S. National Academy of Sciences issued a strong statement at its annual meeting in April. The distinguished members of the Academy declared that a general nuclear war would not only kill hundreds of millions of people but would also "destroy civilization as we know it." They called upon the president and Congress to "intensify substantially, without preconditions and with a sense of urgency, efforts to achieve an equitable and verifiable agreement between the United States and the Soviet Union to limit strategic nuclear arms and to reduce significantly the numbers of nuclear weapons and delivery systems."

Some months later Pope John Paul II invited the heads of the world's leading scientific societies to the Vatican to discuss the threat of an uncontrolled arms race. Within days that group, too, had issued a statement aimed at awakening the public to the dangers of a heedless pursuit of nuclear superiority by the two major powers.

—Howard J. Lewis

Scientists of the Year

Honors and awards

The following article discusses recent awards and prizes in science and technology. In the first section the Nobel Prizes for 1982 are described in detail, while the second is a selective list of other honors.

Nobel Prize for Chemistry

The Nobel Prize for Chemistry was conferred upon Aaron Klug, a South African expatriate who is joint head of the division of structural studies of the Medical Research Council at Cambridge, England. Klug was cited for his investigations of the three-dimensional structure of the combinations of nucleic acids and proteins, the forms in which the genetic material is present in living cells and viruses; his work on the tobacco mosaic virus, in particular, extended over 20 years and resulted in a highly detailed understanding of the arrangement of its components and of the selective process by which the single-stranded molecule of ribonucleic acid and more than 2,000 identical molecules of its protective protein assemble themselves to form the rodlike virus particle. Klug made his discoveries in biology in conjunction with an outstanding achievement in physics, namely, the development of a versatile technique for studying crystalline materials by taking advantage of the way they diffract electron beams. In this program, which established the new science of crystallographic electron microscopy, Klug unified the concepts of image formation and the diffraction of beams of X-rays, light, or electrons. He concentrated on electron beams because their wavelengths are best suited for producing images of the biological particles in which he was interested; these particles are inconveniently large for examination by X-ray methods but too small to be seen by optical microscopy.

By perfecting new methods of refining electron micrographs, Klug showed how a series of them, representing views of a particle from different angles, can be combined to produce a three-dimensional image of the particle. His method has been widely used to study proteins and viruses; he himself has applied it, in combination with other methods, to investigations of the structure of the filaments of chromatin, which is the combination of deoxyribonucleic acid with five different kinds of proteins called histones in the genetic material within cells.

When a virus invades a cell and takes over its protein-making activity, the viral nucleic acid directs the synthesis of the protein which will form the protective coat of new virus particles that will contain new copies of the nucleic acid. In 1957 Francis Crick and James Watson (who later shared a Nobel Prize for the double-helix theory of nucleic acid structure) pointed out that the nucleic acid content of a virus is so small that it could not govern the formation of a single protein molecule large enough to form its own coat. It seemed plausible that the coat was built up from many identical molecules of a smaller protein that could all hang together as a stable shell, either a cylinder, like that of tobacco mosaic virus, or a sphere, like the coats of the viruses that cause polio or warts. Klug and D. L. D. Caspar investigated the possibilities of spherelike shells, taking clues from the geodesic domes designed by Buckminster Fuller, and showed that the largest number of protein units that can be arranged symmetrically on the surface of a sphere is 60. In such an aggregation five of the units would interact at each of the 12 vertices of a regular icosahedron (a solid figure with 20 plane faces, each of which is an equilateral triangle). If both five- and sixfold interactions could occur, a definite series of larger numbers (180, 240, 420, and so on) of protein units could participate. Because of the two different modes of protein association (involving either five or six molecules) all of the cohesive forces between protein units could not be exactly the same. They would be quite similar, however, as would the dispositions of the molecules themselves in space. This scheme, now called the Caspar-Klug quasi-equivalence theory, accurately accounts for the composition of the spheroidal shells that have been experimentally demonstrated in the cases of many small virus particles.

In the presence of certain compounds the tobacco mosaic virus particle breaks apart into its nucleic acid and the numerous protein molecules that make up its jacket; if, however, the disruptive ingredient is removed, the virus slowly puts itself back together. Klug found that the slow step in the regenerative process is the assembly of 34 protein molecules into a disk with a central hole and a narrow gap, like a doughnut with a thin slice cut from it. Klug directed a 12-year program of X-ray diffraction analyses that revealed the details of the arrangement of the proteins in the disks. He also showed that when the nucleic acid attaches itself to one of the disks, the edges of the gap move past each other, twisting the disk into the shape of a lock washer. Further growth of the particle proceeds by accumulation of additional disks, and the final cylindrical form of the protein coat is not that of a simple stack of individual flat disks but is a continuous helical sequence of the protein molecules.

Klug, who was born in Lithuania on Aug. 11, 1926, was taken by his parents to South Africa when he was three years old. He entered the University of the Witwatersrand at Johannesburg intending to study medicine but graduated with a science degree. He then began a doctoral program in crystallography at the University of Cape Town under the supervision of

Aaron Klug

R. W. James, a former collaborator of Lawrence and William Bragg, who shared the Nobel Prize for Physics in 1915 for the application of X-ray diffraction to the determination of crystal structures. Klug left Cape Town with a master's degree upon receiving a fellowship at Trinity College of the University of Cambridge. In 1954 he completed his doctorate there and accepted a research fellowship at Birkbeck College of the University of London, joining the department headed by John D. Bernal, a noted X-ray crystallographer. In Bernal's laboratory Klug undertook the study of the structure of tobacco mosaic virus and other viruses; one of his colleagues was Rosalind Franklin, a biophysicist whose X-ray diffraction patterns had provided Watson and Crick with vital clues in their development of the double-helix model of nucleic acids. In 1958 Klug became director of the virus structure research group at Birkbeck. In 1962 (at the invitation of Crick) Klug returned to Cambridge as a staff member of the Medical Research Council; in 1978 he was named joint head of the division of structural studies.

Nobel Prize for Physics

The Nobel Prize for Physics was awarded to Kenneth G. Wilson of Cornell University, Ithaca, N.Y., who developed a general procedure for constructing improved theories concerning physical transformations of matter called continuous or second-order phase transitions. Exact understanding of these changes formerly had been unattainable, partly because of the mathematical difficulties of dealing with problems in which it is necessary to account for effects that involve neighboring atoms or molecules as well as those that influence the whole of a specimen of material large enough to be observed experimentally. Wilson's prize recognizes his success not only in explaining the details of a specific kind of phase transition but also in establishing a strategy that is already being applied to the solution of problems in many fields of physics that had seemed quite unrelated. These problems, all of which deal with long-range effects that are traceable to very complex, short-range cooperative behavior of matter,

include the percolation of liquids through porous solids, the growth of microscopic flaws in materials into cracks that cause structural failure, the properties of rubbers and plastics that depend on the shapes adopted by long-chain molecules that can coil up or stretch out, the onset of turbulence in moving fluids, and the nature of the puzzling forces that exist among quarks within subatomic particles.

Well-defined substances—pure elements, compounds, homogeneous mixtures of known composition—undergo several kinds of changes of form in response to externally controllable conditions such as temperature, pressure, magnetic field strength, or—in the case of mixtures—composition. The changes among liquid, solid, and gaseous forms of common substances are familiar to everyone, as is the process of dissolving salt or sugar in water. These are all recognized as simple physical events that take place without alteration of the identity of the materials: ice, liquid water, and steam are all composed of the same kind of molecules.

In addition to these common phase transitions, as they are technically known, many others have been recognized and studied. These include the interconversions of the different crystalline forms of many solids; the change of certain solids upon heating to so-called liquid crystals, which on further heating change to typical liquids; the loss of electrical resistivity of some metals when they are cooled to very low temperatures; the loss of viscosity of liquid helium when it is cooled below 2.2 K; and the disappearance of the magnetic susceptibility of certain metals (notably iron) when they are heated above their Curie temperatures (for iron, about 750° C).

Systematic knowledge of what happens during phase transitions has been accumulated in slow and sometimes difficult stages by different investigators over a period of more than two hundred years. By the end of the 18th century it was well established that the conversion of a solid to a liquid or a liquid to a gas took place at a constant temperature and required the absorption of a definite amount of energy. The existence of a critical temperature, above which a gas cannot be liquefied by compression alone, was clarified in the 1860s by Thomas Andrews of Ireland, who made a careful study of the liquid-vapor transition of carbon dioxide. During the 1870s the U.S. physicist J. Willard Gibbs made a fundamental contribution to the emerging discipline of thermodynamics by formulating precise mathematical expressions of the principles that govern the conditions under which phases exist in equilibrium.

At the University of Leiden in The Netherlands W. H. Keesom discovered in the late 1920s that liquid helium becomes superfluid (loses all resistance to flow) at temperatures below 2.2 K, and during the next decade Paul Ehrenfest established the classification of phase transitions now in general use. He pointed out the distinctions between transitions of the first order, such as boiling, melting, and sublimation, and those of the second order, such as the onset of superfluidity in liquid helium and of superconductivity in metals at low temperatures. A first-order transition always involves an abrupt change, or mathematical discontinuity, in fundamental thermodynamic functions such as entropy and volume; the difference between the entropies of a liquid and its vapor is an expression of the fact that the process of vaporization requires the input of energy, and the difference between the volumes (of a given mass) of the two phases is an alternative way of stating that their densities are not the same. Second-order transitions, on the other hand, take place without sharp changes in the entropy or density, but other thermodynamic quantities (heat capacity, compressibility, and—in the case of ferromagnetic materials—magnetic susceptibility) are discontinuous at the transition point.

Under a given set of conditions the properties of any substance are determined by the combined interactions among its smallest constituent particles. Ordinarily the influence of any one particle is exerted most stongly upon its nearest neighbors, and its effect on other particles rapidly diminishes as their distance increases. For most purposes the bulk behavior of a material can be understood without taking account of these microscopic interactions. Even though the density, viscosity, and surface tension of liquid water are the resultants of the tiny individual forces, which are ineffective at distances larger than a few billionths of a meter, waves on the surface of a body of water, a teaspoonful or an ocean, can be analyzed quite accurately in the absence of information concerning the intermolecular behavior.

If a magnetic field is applied to a ferromagnetic material, that material becomes stongly magnetized to a degree that depends upon the strength of the applied field. The ratio of the magnetization to the strength of the field is called the magnetic susceptibility of the material. This susceptibility is also influenced by the temperature, particularly at temperatures close to the second-order transition point, which differs from one ferromagnetic substance to another. Measurements reveal that, for every material studied, the susceptibility is proportional to a characteristic power of a quantity called the reduced temperature, which is designated t and defined as $(T - T_c)/T_c$, in which T is the temperature at which the measurement is made and T_c is the temperature at which the transition occurs. The magnetization itself, as distinguished from the susceptibility, is proportional to a different power of the reduced temperature.

Furthermore, the compressibilities of fluids (the changes in their densities in response to changes in the applied pressure) turn out to be related to just the same power of the reduced temperature as that observed for the magnetic susceptibility of ferromagnets, and the difference between the densities of a liquid and its vapor obeys the same equation that expresses the effect of temperature on magnetization. The properties of certain pairs of liquids that are completely miscible above a critical temperature, but not below, and those of alloys that undergo a transition from an orderly to a disorderly crystalline structure also have been found to share these exponents.

The fact that groups of apparently disparate physical systems share sets of critical exponents led to what is called the universality hypothesis, the proposal that the behavior of systems near their critical points is determined by the values of two underlying parameters. One of these is the dimensionality of the space in which the system exists; in most cases three dimensions are necessary and sufficient, but transitions that take place in very thin films of material require only two, and those involving the appearance and disappearance of particles and antiparticles within some time span require four. The other parameter is the number of dimensions needed to specify the property that vanishes at the transition point. For ferromagnets in which the magnetic field can be oriented only along a single axis the value of this parameter is 1, as it is for fluids near their critical points, at which the density difference between liquid and gas becomes zero (the density difference is a one-dimensional number). For ferromagnets in which the field can be oriented in any direction this second parameter has the value 3.

Many physical systems can be represented by extensions of a type of model introduced in the 1920s by the German physicists Wilhelm Lenz and Ernst Ising, who were seeking an explanation of the existence of the Curie point of ferromagnets in terms of the microscopic interactions of the atoms. In these models, now called Ising lattices, each point on a grid is the site of some entity that can have one of two possible values. On an Ising lattice populated by atoms of iron the two-valued entity is the orientation (up or down) of the atomic magnetic field; if the lattice represents a thin film of brass, the two-valued entity is the identity (copper or zinc) of the atoms themselves. The energy asso-

Kenneth G. Wilson

ciated with the value at any point is assumed to be influenced in some way by the values or states at other points, and this dependence, in turn, can vary in response to an external condition such as the temperature.

Lev Landau of the Soviet Union showed in 1937 that the state of the whole Ising lattice could be calculated and that the effect of varying the temperature was in qualitative agreement with the temperature dependence of thermodynamic properties in the neighborhood of second-order phase transitions. Landau's calculations of the values of critical exponents did not agree closely with experimental data, but they did confirm the usefulness of the Ising lattice as a model.

In 1944 Lars Onsager of the United States obtained an exact mathematical solution of a two-dimensional Ising problem, from which the correct values of critical exponents can be calculated. Onsager's and Landau's results differed because they did not make the same assumptions regarding the nature of the interaction between the occupants of the lattice.

In Landau's model the state at any given lattice site is assumed to be determined by the net state of the entire system, a situation equivalent to viewing each particle as interacting equally strongly with every other particle. A more realistic assumption is that any two particles affect each other most strongly when they are closest together and that their mutual influence decreases as the distance between them increases. This state of affairs is the source of the difficulty in analyzing the phase transitions, but it also explains the significance of one of the striking visual phenomena of the critical behavior of liquid-vapor systems.

Below 374° C (the critical temperature of water) the liquid is denser than the vapor, and in a vessel containing both phases the liquid lies in a layer at the bottom. Within the liquid or the vapor the density in any small region may be slightly higher or lower than the average, but the existence of two separate phases is not affected by these fluctuations, which are only the minor variations resulting from the random motion of the individual molecules, crowding together briefly in some places and thinning out in others. Nowhere does the density of the vapor rise to that of the liquid, nor does the density of the liquid fall to that of the vapor. As the temperature is raised toward the critical point, however, the bulk density of the liquid decreases and that of the vapor increases, and as the densities converge upon the same value the size of the fluctuating regions increases. Just at the critical point the density difference vanishes and, with it, the boundary between liquid and vapor; the largest fluctuations extend throughout the vessel, but smaller ones persist and interconvert droplets of liquid and bubbles of vapor. Because the sizes of many of these droplets and bubbles are within the range of lengths of waves of visible light, the whole sample becomes opalescent.

In 1966 Leo Kadanoff, then at Brown University in Providence, R.I., proposed a technique for dealing with the great range of the fluctuations; he used an intuitive procedure to show how the interactions of individual molecules form the basis of the properties of successively larger groups. In this way the effects of the microscopic fluctuations are smoothed out so that, though the molecular interactions remain responsible for the bulk properties of a substance, it is not necessary to evaluate every single one of them to arrive at the final result. Kadanoff's work validated the hypothesis of universality—that the various kinds of second-order transitions fall into classes, each of which should have the same values of the critical exponents—but it did not provide a method of evaluating any of these exponents.

In 1971 Wilson published his crucial demonstration that Kadanoff's concepts could be quantitatively substantiated by applying the mathematical strategy of the renormalization group. This approach had been developed during the 1950s to unite quantum mechanics and relativity theory in a successful attempt to explain the interactions of elementary particles with electromagnetic fields, and Wilson had mastered it in the course of his doctoral research at the California Institute of Technology. The universality classes appear as a natural consequence of Wilson's theoretical formulation, and the critical exponents obtainable from Onsager's work are accurately duplicated by Wilson's procedures. Although Wilson's methods do not generate mathematically exact formulas like Onsager's, they can be applied to a much wider range of problems, including formerly intractable situations in branches of physics that had not been associated with phase transitions before Wilson established his unifying approach.

Wilson, who was born on June 8, 1936, in Waltham, Mass., was the only U.S. citizen to win a Nobel Prize in the physical sciences in 1982 and is the first person to win the whole prize for physics since 1971. His maternal grandfather was a teacher at the Massachusetts Institute of Technology, and his father, E. Bright Wilson, Jr., was professor of physical chemistry at Harvard University. Wilson graduated from Harvard in 1956, and he received his Ph.D. in 1961 from the California Institute of Technology, where he completed a dissertation in quantum field theory under the direction of Murray Gell-Mann (the winner of the Nobel Prize for Physics in 1969) and Francis Low. After spending a year at the European Council for Nuclear Research, near Geneva, Wilson joined the faculty at Cornell as an assistant professor in 1963; he was named professor of physics in 1971.

Nobel Prize for Physiology or Medicine

The Nobel Prize for Physiology or Medicine awarded in 1982 evoked a classic motif of scientific endeavor, one that has recurred in the citations of the persons who have won the prizes and in the accounts of their achievements in that field and in chemistry from their earliest years: the perseverance—at times approaching passion—of the pioneer dedicated to the quest for some substance that makes up only a tiny fraction of its most promising source material. Sir William Ramsay won a Nobel Prize (chemistry, 1904) for the discovery of several of the noble-gas elements, including xenon, which is present in the Earth's atmosphere to the extent of about one part in 10,000,000. Marie Curie (chemistry, 1911) is revered for her efforts in isolating radium for the first time, in an amount so small that it could not be weighed, and then—to get enough to purify and study—starting all over again with several tons of the mineral pitchblende. Edward Kendall and Tadeus Reichstein (physiology or medicine, 1950) discovered cortisone and several other steroidal hormones that are essential in the metabolism of glucose and minerals: as much as 500 milligrams of cortisone, but only 35 milligrams of hydrocortisone, could be isolated from 1,000 pounds of adrenal glands, which in turn had been obtained from about 20,000 cattle. Roger Guillemin and Andrew Schally (physiology or medicine, 1977) obtained their specimens of neurohormones only after refining brain fragments from several million sheep and pigs. The compounds that were the focus of the achievements honored by the Prize for Physiology or Medicine in 1982 are not only very scarce but are highly labile as well, and it was necessary to invent specialized techniques to make it possible to isolate them without destroying them.

The Nobel Prize for Physiology or Medicine for 1982 was divided equally among three scientists who have carried forward the investigation of the prostaglandins, a family of natural and synthetic compounds that play important parts in a wide variety of physiological processes and are being introduced into medical and veterinary practice. One of the prize winners is an Englishman, John R. Vane, a pharmacologist and director of research at Wellcome Research Laboratories, a pharmaceutical manufacturing firm in Beckenham, Kent. The other two laureates are Swedes: both of them have backgrounds in medicine and biochemistry and are members of the faculty of the Karolinska Institute at Stockholm. Sune K. Bergström retired as rector of the institute in 1977 but has remained active in research and consultation; Bengt I. Samuelsson succeeded Bergström as dean of the Karolinska medical faculty in 1967. In 1977 the same three men were presented the Albert Lasker Basic Medical Research Award in recognition of their successful efforts in isolating, identifying, and systematically clarifying the biological functions of the prostaglandins.

Prostaglandins are now known to be present in minute quantities in many of the tissues of mammals. Two of them also have been found in much larger amounts in the sea whip, a coral that grows in the Caribbean Sea; this coral served as an important source of prostaglandins until methods could be developed for synthesizing them in the laboratory. During the 1960s and 1970s the prostaglandins became one of the most intensively studied classes of physiologically active substances because of the diversity of their effects and the connections between those effects and many disorders of the circulatory, reproductive, respiratory, and nervous systems. More than 100 natural compounds that belong to the family have been discovered, and several thousand man-made analogues have been prepared in the search for correlations between their molecular structure and their physiological activity.

Prostaglandins have been shown to influence blood pressure, inflammation, body temperature, muscle contraction, blood coagulation, pain, and allergic reactions. Several members of the group make up pairs that have opposing effects: one causes muscles to contract, while another makes them relax; one promotes the formation of blood clots, while another inhibits that process; one dilates blood vessels, while another constricts them. The unusually broad range of consequences of administering these compounds quickly attracted the attention of pharmacologists, who are continually seeking connections between the chemical structure of substances and their physiological actions as guides to the design of new and more efficacious drugs. An ideal drug brings about a single, predictable result and has no other consequence; it relieves the headache without upsetting the stomach, for example (and it is free from a long list of other undesirable properties, such as toxicity, interaction with other drugs, and the induction of dependence, resistance, or hypersensitivity). Investigators throughout the world are trying to disentangle the different expressions of the prostaglandins in the hope of devising new drugs specifically useful in the treatment of peripheral vascular disease, angina, respiratory failure resulting from trauma or shock, coagulation of the blood during extracorporeal circulation (diversion of the bloodstream through equipment such as hemodialyzers or heart-lung machines), peptic ulcer, inflammations of the stomach, liver, and kidney, and the rejection of transplanted organs.

Since 1973 several prostaglandins have been approved for use in the United States for inducing abortion or expulsion of a dead fetus and for treating certain congenital malformations of the heart and the great blood vessels. Others have been introduced into veterinary practice: they synchronize estrus in herds of animals and raise the efficiency of breeding and artificial insemination.

The prostaglandins do not fit neatly into the standard classifications of biologically active substances, but they behave more like hormones than anything else. The resemblance includes their production by cells other than those on which they act, although the targets of the prostaglandins are very close to their sources (the phrase "local hormones" has been employed to emphasize this fact), and their effects are very brief. The transience of their action has been found to result from their chemical instability: almost as soon as they are released and perform their function, they are broken down into inactive compounds under the influence of enzymes that are always present in the tissues. Their short lives, coupled with the smallness of the quantities present in the body at any one time, have made the prostaglandins difficult to study, particularly during the early stages of the research, when practically nothing was known of their properties.

The first clue to the existence of the prostaglandins was detected in 1930 by a group of U.S. scientists who were seeking methods of treating infertility; they found that fresh semen caused the muscles of the uterus to contract, but they did not attempt to isolate the component responsible. In 1933 Ulf von Euler of the Karolinska Institute (a Nobel Prize winner in 1970 for research on the transmission of nerve impulses) discovered that the blood pressure of experimental animals was reduced by injecting preparations of seminal fluid. He surmised that the effect was due to an acidic, fat-soluble substance originating in the prostate gland and named it prostaglandin. Late in 1945 Euler called Bergström's attention to some similarities between his own earlier work and a piece of research that Bergström had just carried out on the reaction of oxygen with an unsaturated fatty acid in the presence of an enzyme obtained from soybeans. Bergström thereupon undertook the isolation and identification of prostaglandin, undeterred by the prospect of obtaining and then refining about 100 kilograms of seminal vesicles from slaughtered rams.

By 1949 Bergström had demonstrated that Euler's term prostaglandin would have to be broadened to include more than a single compound. He also mastered an analytical technique that had been recently developed by a Nobel laureate in chemistry, A. J. P. Martin. The procedure proved to be ideally suited to the separation of mixtures containing small amounts of lipids, including prostaglandins.

Samuelsson attended Lund during Bergström's tenure there, and when Bergström joined the faculty at the Karolinska in 1958, Samuelsson—as a doctoral candidate—became a member of the prostaglandin research group. By 1960 this team was able to announce the elemental composition of the first two members of the series of compounds, and two years later they published the molecular structures of these substances. These structures were the first to be determined by the application of still another analytical innovation, the direct coupling of a mass spectrometer to a gas chromatograph.

The structures of the prostaglandins strongly indicated that they are formed in the tissues by a process in which oxygen combines with arachidonic acid, as Euler had divined at least 15 years earlier. This hypothesis was confirmed by Bergström and Samuelsson in collaboration with David van Dorp of the Unilever Laboratories in The Netherlands; both groups demonstrated that radioactive arachidonic acid and similar compounds are transformed to radioactive prostaglandins in living tissues.

After completing the requirements for his doctoral degrees, Samuelsson spent a year at Harvard University, then returned to Stockholm to join the faculty of the Karolinska Institute. Organizing his own research group, he initiated two further programs; the first of these was an investigation of the metabolic fate of prostaglandins, and the second was a study of the details of their formation from arachidonic acid. The identification of the metabolites of the various prostaglandins formed the basis of procedures by which their production in the body can be measured by analyzing samples of blood and urine. Tracing the pathways by

Bengt I. Samuelsson

John R. Vane

Sune K. Bergström

Svenskt/Pictorial Parade

Svenskt/Pictorial Parade

Wide World

which arachidonic acid is converted to prostaglandins involved the isolation and identification of several dozen subtly different compounds and the recognition of numerous enzymes that catalyze the reactions in which the various substances are created and destroyed. The first step in the sequence, the reaction of arachidonic acid with molecular oxygen, is controlled by an enzyme named cyclo-oxygenase.

Vane's first major contribution to the understanding of the prostaglandins resulted from his application of a very sensitive technique that he had devised for detecting the presence of substances that cause tissues to contract. The slightest movement is instantly transmitted to a recording instrument, and even if the stimulating material appears and disappears within a few minutes, its effect is reliably documented. The equipment can be set up to measure several kinds of tissue simultaneously, so that the successive transformations of a substance into a series of others can be monitored. Vane had used this apparatus to measure the formation and destruction of angiotensin II, a short-lived compound that plays an important role in the minute-to-minute regulation of blood pressure.

During his affiliation with the Institute of Basic Medical Studies in London, Vane used this technique (called cascade superfusion bioassay) in differentiating among various members of the prostaglandin family and to study the release of these substances from animal tissues under experimental conditions. He found that, during anaphylactic shock, lung tissue liberated a substance that caused rabbit aorta to contract; however, this activity was lost within a few minutes. Further experiments proved that the release of this new compound is prevented by aspirin and several other drugs. By 1971 Vane had demonstrated that aspirin, acetaminophen, and indomethacin (all of which are nonsteroid drugs used to relieve pain and to reduce fever and inflammation) stop the formation of the prostaglandins from arachidonic acid by interfering with the action of the enzyme cyclo-oxygenase. This finding indicated that prostaglandins are involved in producing pain, fever, and inflammation and probably are connected with the development of rheumatoid arthritis. It also provided a physiological rationale for the effectiveness of aspirin, which was introduced in 1899 and has become the world's most widely used drug although no one had been able to show why it works. (Richard Gryglewski, one of Vane's colleagues, later found that steroidal antiinflammatory drugs—such as hydrocortisone—also block prostaglandin formation; they do so by interfering with the liberation of arachidonic acid from cell membranes.)

Vane continued to explore the properties of the substance that caused rabbit aorta to contract, and he discovered that it also promoted the clumping of blood platelets. This unexpected combination of activities caught Samuelsson's attention, and he joined the chase. He showed that Vane's aorta-contracting substance indeed contained one of the known prostaglandins but, in addition, a component of novel structure. This newcomer proved to be the first example of a new class of the eicosanoids (a general term derived from the systematic name of arachidonic acid and based on the Greek word for 20 (the number of carbon atoms in the molecule). This compound, a thromboxane, was extremely potent in aggregating blood platelets and constricting blood vessels.

In 1976 Vane, in turn, observed that the prostaglandin identified by Samuelsson in the aorta-contracting substance is convertible to a compound belonging to still another class of eicosanoids; it was a prostacyclin, and it proved to be the most powerful agent yet found in dilating blood vessels and preventing the clumping of platelets. The confusion was finally resolved when it was found that the prostaglandin released by lung tissue is transformed to a thromboxane by an enzyme in blood platelets but to a prostacyclin by a different enzyme in the walls of the blood vessels. Vane has written that "the generation of prostacyclin by the vessel wall is surely the mechanism by which healthy blood vessels prevent the deposition of platelets on their inner surfaces."

Bergström was born in Stockholm on Jan. 19, 1916, and was educated at the Karolinska Institute, which granted him doctorates in medicine and biochemistry in 1944. He held research fellowships at Columbia University and the University of Basel in Switzerland, and then returned to Sweden to accept a professorship of chemistry at the University of Lund. In 1958 he joined the faculty of the Karolinska Institute, where he was appointed dean of the medical faculty in 1963 and rector in 1969. In 1975 he became chairman of the Nobel Foundation, an administrative post that has no influence over the committees that recommend candidates for the Nobel Prizes.

Samuelsson was born in Halmstad, Sweden, on May 21, 1934. He graduated from the University of Lund, where Bergström was one of his professors. He continued his studies with Bergström at the Karolinska Institute, earning doctorates in biochemistry in 1960 and medicine in 1961. He became a member of the faculty of the institute, eventually succeeding Bergström as dean of the medical faculty. He has also been a visiting professor at Harvard University since 1976.

Vane, who was born on March 29, 1927, in Tardebigg, Worcestershire, England, graduated from the University of Birmingham and then earned a doctorate at the University of Oxford in 1953, concentrating in chemistry and pharmacology. He spent two years on the faculty of Yale University before returning to England to join the Institute of Basic Medical Sciences of the University of London. He moved to the Wellcome Research Laboratories in 1973.

—John V. Killheffer

AWARD	WINNER	AFFILIATION
ANTHROPOLOGY		
MacArthur Prize Fellow Award	William Durham	Palo Alto, Calif.
ARCHITECTURE		
Architectural Firm Award of the American Institute of Architects	Gwathmey Siegel & Associates	New York, N.Y.
Frank P. Brown Medal	Lynn S. Beedle	Fritz Research Laboratory, Lehigh University, Bethlehem, Pa.
Frank P. Brown Medal	Vincent G. Kling	Kling Partnership, Philadelphia, Pa.
Gold Medal of the Royal Institute of British Architects	Berthold Lubetkin (Retired)	Gloucestershire, England
Honor Award of the American Institute of Architects	Joseph W. Casserly; and Stanley Tigerman and Associates	Chicago, Ill.
Honor Award of the American Institute of Architects	Eisenman/Robertson Architects	New York, N.Y.
Honor Award of the American Institute of Architects	Michael Graves	Princeton, N.J.
Medal of the American Institute of Architects	Sir John Newenham Summerson	Sir John Soane's Museum, London
Royal Institute of British Architects Award	Gerard Connolly and Douglas Niven	United Kingdom
Royal Institute of British Architects Award	Percy Thomas Partnership	London
ASTRONOMY		
Albert A. Michelson Medal	R. Hanbury Brown	University of Sydney, Australia
Albert A. Michelson Medal	Richard Q. Twiss	Royal Greenwich Observatory, England
Annie Jump Cannon Award	Judith Young	University of Massachusetts, Amherst
Catherine Wolfe Bruce Medal	E. Margaret Burbidge	Center for Astrophysics and Space Science, University of California, San Diego
Charles Doolittle Walcott Medal	Martin F. Glaessner (Emeritus)	University of Adelaide, South Australia
Dannie Heineman Prize	American Institute of Physics	New York, N.Y.
Dannie Heineman Prize	P. J. E. Peebles	Princeton University, N.J.
Dirk Brouwer Award	George Contopoulos	University of Athens, Greece
Dorothea Klumpke-Roberts Award	Bart J. Bok (Emeritus)	University of Arizona, Tucson
George Ellery Hale Prize	John W. Evans, Jr.	Sacramento Peak Observatory, Sunspot, N.M.
Helen B. Warner Prize	Roger D. Blandford	California Institute of Technology, Pasadena
Henry Norris Russell Lectureship	Bart J. Bok (Emeritus)	University of Arizona, Tucson
John Adams Fleming Medal	Thomas M. Donahue	University of Michigan, Ann Arbor
Newton Lacy Pierce Prize	Marc Davis	University of California, Berkeley
William Hopkins Prize	M. J. Rees	King's College, University of London

AWARD	WINNER	AFFILIATION
CHEMISTRY		
American Chemical Society Award for Creative Invention	O. A. Battista	O. A. Battista Research Institute, Research Services Corp.
American Chemical Society Award for Nuclear Chemistry	Darleane C. Hoffman	Los Alamos National Scientific Laboratory, N.M.
American Chemical Society Award in Inorganic Chemistry	George W. Parshall	E. I. Du Pont de Nemours & Co.
American Chemical Society Award in Inorganic Chemistry	Norman Sutin	Brookhaven National Laboratory, Upton, N.Y.
American Chemical Society Award in Pure Chemistry	Michael J. Berry	Rice University, Houston, Texas
Chemical Instrumentation Award	Velmer Fassel	Iowa State University, Ames
Chemical Pioneer Award	R. L. Pruett	Exxon Research and Engineering Co.
Claude S. Hudson Award	Bengt Lindberg	University of Stockholm, Sweden
Davy Medal	Michael J. S. Dewar	University of Texas, Austin
Ernest H. Volwiler Award	Gerhard Levy	State University of New York, Buffalo
Harry and Carol Mosher Award	Ernest L. Eliel	University of North Carolina, Chapel Hill
Horace N. Potts Medal	Charles G. Overberger	University of Michigan, Ann Arbor
Ipatieff Prize	D. Wayne Goodman	Sandia National Laboratories, Albuquerque, N.M.
James Flack Norris Award in Physical Organic Chemistry	Glen A. Russell	Iowa State University, Ames
Joel Henry Hildebrand Award	Jiri Jonas	University of Illinois, Urbana
John Labatt Award	Bryan Jones	University of Toronto, Canada
MacArthur Prize Fellow Award	Mark Wrighton	Cambridge, Mass.
Perkin Medal	N. Bruce Hannay (Retired)	Bell Laboratories
Peter Debye Award in Physical Chemistry	George C. Pimentel	Laboratory for Chemical Biodynamics, University of California, Berkeley
Priestley Medal	Robert S. Mulliken	University of Chicago, Ill.
Roger Adams Award in Organic Chemistry	Alan R. Battersby	University of Cambridge, England
Welch Award in Chemistry	Frank H. Westheimer	Harvard University, Cambridge, Mass.
Willard Gibbs Medal	Gilbert Stork	Columbia University, New York, N.Y.
Wolf Prize	George C. Pimentel	University of California, Berkeley
Wolf Prize	John Polanyi	University of Toronto, Ontario
DEFENSE RESEARCH		
DeFlorez Training Award	Richard J. Heintzman	U.S. Air Force Systems Command
Delmer S. Fahrney Medal	Bernard A. Schriever (Retired)	Schriever and McKee, Inc.

AWARD	WINNER	AFFILIATION
EARTH SCIENCES		
Arthur L. Day Medal	Eugene M. Shoemaker	U.S. Geological Survey, Flagstaff, Ariz.
Award for Outstanding Contribution to the Advance of Applied Meteorology	Charles J. Neumann	National Hurricane Center, Coral Gables, Fla.
Carl-Gustaf Rossby Research Medal	Joanne Simpson	Goddard Space Flight Center, Greenbelt, Md.
Clarence Leroy Meisinger Award	Chih-pei Chang	Naval Postgraduate School, Monterey, Calif.
Clarence Leroy Meisinger Award	Joseph B. Klemp	National Center for Atmospheric Research, Boulder, Colo.
Clarence Leroy Meisinger Award	Robert B. Wilhelmson	University of Illinois, Urbana
Cleveland Abbe Award for Distinguished Service to Atmospheric Sciences	David Atlas	Goddard Space Flight Center, Greenbelt, Md.
Cleveland Abbe Award for Distinguished Service to Atmospheric Sciences	Helmut E. Landsberg (Emeritus)	University of Maryland, College Park
James B. Macelwane Award	Rafael Luis Bras	Massachusetts Institute of Technology, Cambridge
James B. Macelwane Award	Donald W. Forsyth	Brown University, Providence, R.I.
James B. Macelwane Award	Steven C. Wofsy	Harvard University, Cambridge, Mass.
Jule G. Charney Award	Francis P. Bretherton	National Center for Atmospheric Research, Boulder, Colo.
Maurice Ewing Medal	John I. Ewing	Woods Hole Oceanographic Institution, Mass.
Penrose Medal	Aaron C. Waters	Los Alamos National Laboratory, N.M.
Robert E. Horton Medal	John R. Philip	Commonwealth Scientific and Industrial Research Organization, Australia
Sverdrup Gold Medal	Michael S. Longuet-Higgins	Institute of Oceanographic Services, Wormley, England
William Bowie Medal	Henry M. Stommel	Woods Hole Oceanographic Institution, Mass.
ELECTRONICS AND INFORMATION SCIENCES		
A. M. Turing Award	Stephen A. Cook	University of Toronto, Ontario
Computer Pioneer Medal	Jeffrey Chuan Chu	Sanders Technology, Inc.
Distinguished Information Sciences Award	Jerome W. Geckle	PHH Group, Inc.
Eckert-Mauchly Award	C. Gordon Bell	Digital Equipment Corp.
Grace Murray Hopper Award	Brian K. Reid	Stanford University, Calif.
Harry Goode Memorial Award	King-sun Fu	Purdue University, West Lafayette, Ind.
L. M. Ericsson Prize	Leonard Kleinrock	University of California, Los Angeles

AWARD	WINNER	AFFILIATION
L. M. Ericsson Prize	Lawrence Roberts	Telenet Telecommunications Co.
Medal of Achievement Award	Frank T. Cary	IBM
Stewart R. Dewar Award	F. Thomas Hogan	Monsanto Co.

ENERGY

Award of Excellence	L. Y. Stroumtsos	Exxon Research and Engineering Co.
Enrico Fermi Award	Wilfrid B. Lewis (Retired)	Atomic Energy of Canada Ltd.
Levey Medal	G. Swan	Exxon Research and Engineering Co.
MacArthur Prize Fellow Award	R. Stephen Berry	Chicago, Ill.
Tyler World Prize in Ecology and Energy	Southern California Edison Co.	Los Angeles, Calif.

ENVIRONMENT

American Chemical Society Award for Creative Advances in Environmental Science and Technology	F. Sherwood Rowland	University of California, Irvine
Award of the Decade of the Council on Environmental Quality	Engelhard Industries	
Priestley Award	Peter H. Raven	Missouri Botanical Garden, St. Louis
Tyler World Prize in Ecology and Energy	Carroll L. Wilson (Emeritus)	Massachusetts Institute of Technology, Cambridge
Wolf Prize	Wendell L. Roelofs	Cornell University Experiment Station, Geneva, N.Y.

FOOD AND AGRICULTURE

Babcock-Hart Award	John C. Ayres	University of Georgia, Athens
Bio-Serv Award in Experimental Animal Nutrition	Ann C. Sullivan	Hoffmann-LaRoche, Inc.; College of Physicians and Surgeons, Columbia University, New York, N.Y.
Borden Award in Nutrition	Conrad Wagner	Veterans Administration Medical Center, Nashville, Tenn.; Vanderbilt University School of Medicine, Nashville, Tenn.
Bristol-Myers Award for Distinguished Achievement in Nutritional Research	Elsie May Widdowson	Addenbrooke's Hospital, Cambridge, England
Conrad A. Elvehjem Award for Public Service in Nutrition	Guillermo Arroyave	Institute of Nutrition of Central America and Panama
Distinguished Service Award of the American Institute of Biological Sciences	Karl Maramorosch	State University of Rutgers, New Brunswick, N.J.
Lederle Award in Human Nutrition	Charles E. Butterworth, Jr.	University of Alabama, Birmingham
Mead Johnson Award for Research in Nutrition	Michael F. Holick	Harvard University Medical School, Cambridge, Mass.
Nelson J. Shaulis Advancement of Viticulture Award	Peter Hemstad	Cornell University, Ithaca, N.Y.

AWARD	WINNER	AFFILIATION
Nicholas Appert Award	Clinton O. Chichester	University of Rhode Island, Kingston
Osborne and Mendel Award of the Nutrition Foundation	Frank Chytil	Vanderbilt University School of Medicine, Nashville, Tenn.
Osborne and Mendel Award of the Nutrition Foundation	David Ong	Vanderbilt University School of Medicine, Nashville, Tenn.
Ratnabhorn Medal	Quentin Jones	Agricultural Research Service, U.S. Department of Agriculture
Scholar of the Year Award	Huai C. Chiang	University of Minnesota, St. Paul
LIFE SCIENCES		
Alan T. Waterman Award	Richard Axel	Institute of Cancer Research, Columbia University, New York, N.Y.
Antonio Feltrinelli International Prize in Biological Sciences	Sol Spiegelman	Institute of Cancer Research, Columbia University, New York, N.Y.
Bernard B. Brodie Award in Drug Metabolism and Disposition	Donald Jerina	National Institutes of Health, Bethesda, Md.
Biological Physics Prize	Roderick K. Clayton	Cornell University, Ithaca, N.Y.
Biological Physics Prize	George Feher	University of California, San Diego
Distinguished Service Award of the American Institute of Biological Sciences	George M. Woodwell	Marine Biological Laboratory, Woods Hole, Mass.
Eugene Eisenmann Medal for Excellence in Ornithology	Ernst Mayr (Emeritus)	Harvard University, Cambridge, Mass.
F. H. A. Marshall Award	Andrew V. Nalbandov (Emeritus)	University of Illinois, Urbana
Fisher Scientific Lecture Award	William C. Purdy	McGill University, Montreal, Quebec, Canada
Freeman Award for Innovative Research in the Chemoreception Sciences	Pasquale P. C. Graziadei	Florida State University, Tallahassee
Garvan Medal	Ines Mandl	College of Physicians and Surgeons, Columbia University, New York, N.Y.
Linnean Medal	Peter Davis	Royal Botanic Garden, Edinburgh, Scotland
Linnean Medal	Humphry Greenwood	Natural History Museum, London
Louisa Gross Horwitz Prize	Barbara McClintock	Cold Spring Harbor Laboratory, N.Y.
Louisa Gross Horwitz Prize	Susumu Tonegawa	Massachusetts Institute of Technology, Cambridge
MacArthur Prize Fellow Award	David Felton	Indianapolis, Ind.
Neill Prize	A. Rodger Waterston	Edinburgh, Scotland
Waterford Biomedical Science Award	Karl F. Austen	Harvard University Medical School, Cambridge, Mass.
Waterford Biomedical Science Award	Bengt I. Samuelsson	Karolinska Institute, Stockholm, Sweden
W. S. Bruce Memorial Prize	Andrew Clarke	British Antarctic Survey, Cambridge, England

AWARD	WINNER	AFFILIATION
MATERIALS SCIENCES		
F. H. Norton Distinguished Ceramist Award	James Pappis	Raytheon Co.
James Douglas Gold Medal Award	Morris E. Fine	Northwestern University, Evanston, Ill.
Karl Schwartzwalder-Professional Achievement in Ceramic Engineering Award	Richard E. Tressler	Pennsylvania State University, University Park
Richard M. Fulrath Memorial Award	H. Kent Bowen	Massachusetts Institute of Technology, Cambridge
Richard M. Fulrath Memorial Award	Michio Matsuoka	Matsushita Electric Industrial Co., Japan
Richard M. Fulrath Memorial Award	Tadashi Shiosaki	Kyoto University, Japan
Richard M. Fulrath Memorial Award	Kohji Tada	Sumitomo Electric Industries, Ltd., Japan
Warren Award	Benjamin Post	Polytechnic Institute of New York, N.Y.
MATHEMATICS		
Crafoord Prize	V. I. Arnold	Moscow University
Crafoord Prize	Louis Nirenberg	Courant Institute of Mathematical Sciences, New York University, N.Y.
Fields Medal	Alain Connes	Centre Nationale de la Recherche Scientifique, Paris
Fields Medal	William Thurston	Princeton University, N.J.
Fields Medal	Shing Tung Yau	Institute for Advanced Study, Princeton, N.J.
MacArthur Prize Fellow Award	Bradley Efron	Palo Alto, Calif.
MacArthur Prize Fellow Award	Charles Peskin	Hartsdale, N.Y.
MacArthur Prize Fellow Award	Julia Robinson	Berkeley, Calif.
Wolf Prize	Mark G. Krein	Institute of Physical Chemistry, Odessa, U.S.S.R.
Wolf Prize	Hassler Whitney	Institute for Advanced Study, Princeton, N.J.
MEDICAL SCIENCES		
Albert Lasker Basic Medical Research Award	J. Michael Bishop	University of California, San Francisco
Albert Lasker Basic Medical Research Award	Raymond Erikson	Harvard University, Cambridge, Mass.
Albert Lasker Basic Medical Research Award	Robert Gallo	National Institutes of Health, Bethesda, Md.
Albert Lasker Basic Medical Research Award	Hidesaburo Hanafusa	Rockefeller University, New York, N.Y.
Albert Lasker Basic Medical Research Award	Harold Varmus	University of California, San Francisco

AWARD	WINNER	AFFILIATION
Albert Lasker Clinical Medical Research Award	Roscoe Brady	National Institutes of Health, Bethesda, Md.
Albert Lasker Clinical Medical Research Award	Elizabeth Neufeld	National Institutes of Health, Bethesda, Md.
Alfred P. Sloan Jr. Medal	Stanley Cohen	Vanderbilt University School of Medicine, Nashville, Tenn.
American Association for the Advancement of Science-Newcomb Cleveland Prize	Howard L. Bachrach	Plum Island Animal Disease Center, Greenport, N.Y.
American Association for the Advancement of Science-Newcomb Cleveland Prize	Donald Dowbenko	Genentech Inc.
American Association for the Advancement of Science-Newcomb Cleveland Prize	Marvin J. Grubman	Plum Island Animal Disease Center, Greenport, N.Y.
American Association for the Advancement of Science-Newcomb Cleveland Prize	Dennis G. Kleid	Genentech Inc.
American Association for the Advancement of Science-Newcomb Cleveland Prize	Peter D. McKercher	Plum Island Animal Disease Center, Greenport, N.Y.
American Association for the Advancement of Science-Newcomb Cleveland Prize	Douglas M. Moore	Plum Island Animal Disease Center, Greenport, N.Y.
American Association for the Advancement of Science-Newcomb Cleveland Prize	Donald O. Morgan	Plum Island Animal Disease Center, Greenport, N.Y.
American Association for the Advancement of Science-Newcomb Cleveland Prize	Betty H. Robertson	Plum Island Animal Disease Center, Greenport, N.Y.
American Association for the Advancement of Science-Newcomb Cleveland Prize	Barbara Small	Genentech Inc.
American Association for the Advancement of Science-Newcomb Cleveland Prize	Daniel Yansura	Genentech Inc.
Bristol-Myers Award for Distinguished Achievement in Cancer Research	Denis P. Burkitt	St. Thomas's Hospital, London
Bristol-Myers Award for Distinguished Achievement in Cancer Research	Michael A. Epstein	University of Bristol, England
Charles F. Kettering Medal	Howard E. Skipper (Emeritus)	Southern Research Institute, Birmingham, Ala.
Charles S. Mott Medal	Denis P. Burkitt	St. Thomas's Hospital, London
Epilepsy Foundation of America Award	T. H. Brown	City of Hope National Medical Center, Duarte, Calif.
Ernst Jung Prize for Medicine	Hartmut Wekerle	Pathology Institute, University of Zürich, Switz.
Ernst Jung Prize for Medicine	Rolf M. Zinkernagel	Pathology Institute, University of Zürich, Switz.

AWARD	WINNER	AFFILIATION
Franklin Medal	Cesar Milstein	Medical Research Council Laboratory of Molecular Biology, Cambridge, England
Gairdner Foundation International Award	Gilbert Ashwell	National Institutes of Health, Bethesda, Md.
Gairdner Foundation International Award	Günter Blobel	Rockefeller University, New York, N.Y.
Gairdner Foundation International Award	Arvid Carlsson	University of Göteborg, Sweden
Gairdner Foundation International Award	Paul Janssen	Janssen Pharmaceutica, Beerse, Belgium
Gairdner Foundation International Award	Manfred Mayer	Johns Hopkins University School of Medicine, Baltimore, Md.
G. H. A. Clowes Award	George Weber	Indiana University School of Medicine, Bloomington, Ind.
Hammer Prize	Ronald Levy	Stanford University Medical Center, Calif.
Hammer Prize	George Stevenson	Tenovus Research Laboratory, Southampton, England
Human Genetics Award	Akira Yoshida	City of Hope National Medical Center, Duarte, Calif.
International Cancer Prize	Charles Heidelberger	University of Southern California, Los Angeles
International Recognition Award of the Heart Research Foundation	Norman E. Shumway	Stanford University Medical Center, Calif.
Lita Annenberg Hazen Award	Michael S. Brown	University of Texas, Austin
Lita Annenberg Hazen Award	Joseph L. Goldstein	University of Texas, Austin
National Academy of Sciences Public Welfare Medal	Paul G. Rogers	Former congressman from Florida
Novo Prize	Christian Crone	Panum Institute, University of Copenhagen, Denmark
Rameshwardas Birla International Award	William Trager	Rockefeller University, New York, N.Y.
Wakeman Award	Albert J. Aguayo	McGill University, Montreal; Montreal General Hospital
Wolf Prize	Sir James W. Black	Wellcome Research Laboratories, Beckenham, London
Wolf Prize	Jean-Pierre Changeux	Pasteur Institute, Paris
Wolf Prize	Solomon H. Snyder	Johns Hopkins University School of Medicine, Baltimore, Md.

OPTICAL ENGINEERING

C. E. K. Mees Medal	Robert W. Ditchburn (Emeritus)	University of Reading, England
Charles Hard Townes Award	Robert W. Hellwarth	University of Southern California, Los Angeles
David Richardson Medal	Harold Osterberg (Retired)	American Optical Co.
Frederic Ives Medal	Boris P. Stoicheff	University of Toronto, Ontario
Joseph Fraunhofer Award	Robert M. Burley	Baird Corp.
Joseph Fraunhofer Award	Robert E. Hopkins (Emeritus)	University of Rochester, N.Y.

AWARD	WINNER	AFFILIATION
PHYSICS		
Beams Medal	Arthur T. Fromhold, Jr.	Auburn University, Ala.
Bertram E. Warren Award	Benjamin Post	Polytechnic Institute of New York, N.Y.
Biennial Service Award of the Acoustical Society of America	Ralph N. Baer	Naval Research Laboratory, Washington, D.C.
Charles Hard Townes Award	Chandra Kumar Naranbhai Patel	Bell Laboratories
Dannie Heineman Prize in Mathematical Physics	Martin D. Kruskal	Princeton University, N.J.
Edward Longstreth Medal	Erich P. Ippen	Massachusetts Institute of Technology, Cambridge
Edward Longstreth Medal	Peter V. Shank	Bell Laboratories
Elliott Cresson Medal	Harold P. Eubank	Plasma Physics Laboratory, Princeton University, N.J.
Elliott Cresson Medal	E. Bright Wilson (Emeritus)	Harvard University, Cambridge, Mass.
Franklin Medal	Kenneth G. Wilson	Cornell University, Ithaca, N.Y.
Gold Medal of the Acoustical Society of America	Isadore Rudnick	University of California, Los Angeles
John Price Wetherill Medal	Lawrence A. Harris (Posthumous)	General Electric Corporate Research and Development Center, Schenectady, N.Y.
Makdougall Brisbane Prize	Walter Spear	University of Dundee, Scotland
Otto Hahn Prize	Walter Greiner	University of Frankfurt, West Germany
Pioneers of Underwater Acoustics Medal	Arthur O. Williams, Jr. (Emeritus)	Brown University, Providence, R.I.
Silver Medal in Engineering Acoustics	Per V. Brüel	Brüel & Kjaer A/S, Sweden
Soviet Academy of Sciences Commemorative Medal	Robert W. Freyman	Los Alamos National Laboratory, N.M.
Wallace Clement Sabine Medal	Thomas D. Northwood (Retired)	National Research Council, Washington, D.C.
Wigner Medal	Yuval Ne'eman	Tel Aviv University, Israel; University of Texas, Austin
William F. Meggers Award	William C. Martin	National Bureau of Standards, Washington, D.C.
Wolf Prize	Leon M. Lederman	Fermi National Accelerator Laboratory, Batavia, Ill.
Wolf Prize	Martin L. Perl	Stanford University Linear Accelerator Center, Calif.
PSYCHOLOGY		
Distinguished Contribution to Psychology in the Public Interest	Edward F. Zigler	Yale University, New Haven, Conn.
Distinguished Professional Contribution Award	Asher R. Pacht	University of Wisconsin, Madison

AWARD	WINNER	AFFILIATION
Distinguished Professional Contribution Award	Carolyn R. Payton	Howard University, Washington, D.C.
Distinguished Professional Contribution Award	Roy Schafer	New York, N.Y.
Distinguished Professional Contribution Award	Milton Theaman	New York, N.Y.
Distinguished Scientific Award for the Applications of Psychology	Robert M. Gagné	Florida State University, Tallahassee
Distinguished Scientific Contribution Award	Daniel Kahneman	University of British Columbia, Vancouver
Distinguished Scientific Contribution Award	Mark R. Rosenzweig	University of California, Berkeley
Distinguished Scientific Contribution Award	Amos Tversky	Stanford University, Calif.
Gold Medal of the American Psychological Foundation	Nancy Bayley (Retired)	Carmel, Calif.
Hermann von Helmholtz Award	Vernon Mountcastle	Johns Hopkins University School of Medicine, Baltimore, Md.
MacArthur Prize Fellow Award	Bela Julesz	Murray Hill, N.J.

SPACE EXPLORATION

Distinguished Service Medal	R. E. Smylie	NASA
Exceptional Scientific Achievement Medal	Mark Settle	NASA
Exceptional Scientific Achievement Medal	James V. Taranik	NASA
Exceptional Service Medal	Irving Davids	NASA
Exceptional Service Medal	William D. Goldsby	NASA
Exceptional Service Medal	James L. Graham, Jr.	NASA
Exceptional Service Medal	Bobby G. Noblitt	NASA
Exceptional Service Medal	Bruton B. Schardt	NASA
NASA Distinguished Public Service Medal	George W. Jeffs	Rockwell International
NASA Distinguished Public Service Medal	Lloyd F. Kohrs	McDonnell Douglas Astronautics Co.
NASA Distinguished Public Service Medal	Edward P. Smith	Rockwell International
NASA Distinguished Service Medal	Clifford E. Charlesworth	Johnson Space Center, Houston, Texas
Outstanding Leadership Medal	Ivan Bekey	NASA
Outstanding Leadership Medal	C. Robert Nysmith	NASA

TRANSPORTATION

Aircraft Design Award	Paul B. MacCready, Jr.	Aero Vironment, Inc.
Collier Trophy	T. A. Wilson and Boeing Co.	Seattle, Wash.
Guggenheim Medal	David S. Lewis	General Dynamics Corp.
Wright Brothers Trophy	Willis M. Hawkins, Jr.	Lockheed Corp.

AWARD	WINNER	AFFILIATION
SCIENCE JOURNALISM		
American Medical Writers Association Award	Gregory Freiher	Research Resources Information Center, Md.
American Medical Writers Association Award	Robin M. Henig	Silver Spring, Md.
Bradford Washburn Award	Thor Heyerdahl	
Chemical Reporter of the Year	John Whitehead	*Plastics and Rubber Weekly*
Chemical Writer of the Year	David Fishlock	*Financial Times*
James T. Grady Award for Interpreting Chemistry for the Public	Matt Clark	*Newsweek*
Walter C. Alvarez Memorial Award	Louis J. West	University of California, Los Angeles
William Harvey Award	Jane Clute	*Evening Herald,* Rock Hill, S.C.
MISCELLANEOUS		
Charles Lathrop Parsons Award	James G. Martin	U.S. congressman from North Carolina
Distinguished Public Service Award of the National Science Foundation	William T. Golden	New York, N.Y.
Vannevar Bush Award	Lee A. DuBridge (President emeritus)	California Institute of Technology, Pasadena
Westinghouse Science Talent Search	1. Paul Chih Ning	Bronx High School of Science, New York, N.Y.
	2. Michael I. Hyman	Centennial High School, Ellicott City, Md.
	3. Eric A. Koide	Dobbs Ferry High School, Dobbs Ferry, N.Y.
	4. L. Gene Spears, Jr.	Cypress Creek High School, Houston, Texas
	5. Caroline M. Gomez	Shaker High School, Latham, N.Y.
	6. Elihu H. McMahon	Bronx High School of Science, New York, N.Y.
	7. Alexandra Kroeger	Shoreham-Wadding River High School, Shoreham, N.Y.
	8. Gina R. Levy	New Rochelle High School, New Rochelle, N.Y.
	9. Jeannie P. C. Lo	Stuyvesant High School, New York, N.Y.
	10. Janet L. Pan	Bronx High School of Science, New York, N.Y.

Obituaries

Amoroso, Emmanuel Ciprian (Sept. 16, 1901—Oct. 30, 1982), British veterinary physiologist, was professor of veterinary physiology at the Royal Veterinary College of the University of London from 1947 to 1968. He studied in Dublin, Berlin, and London before joining the Royal Veterinary College in 1934. Amoroso made outstanding contributions to research in animal physiology, especially to the understanding of the role of the placenta in reproduction. Besides publishing numerous papers on this and a variety of other topics, he was a fellow of the Royal Society and after his retirement was visiting lecturer and special professor at the University of Nottingham. Amoroso was made Commander of the Order of the British Empire in 1969 and was awarded the Trinity Cross by the government of Trinidad and Tobago in 1977.

Barsky, Arthur Joseph (Dec. 7, 1899—Feb. 9, 1982), U.S. plastic surgeon, as the pioneering chief of plastic surgery at Mount Sinai Hospital in New York City led a team of surgeons that in 1958 performed more than 150 operations on deformed orphans of the 1945 Hiroshima bombing. Besides participating in the "Hiroshima Maidens Project," Barsky and lawyer Thomas R. Miller established (1966) Children's Medical Relief International and, with U.S. federal assistance, a 50-bed hospital in Saigon, which opened in 1969 to treat children in war-torn South Vietnam. From 1969 to 1975 he saw some 7,000 children, whom he treated for severely burned faces and hands as well as other ailments. Barsky, who was educated at the University of Pennsylvania and New York Medical College, founded plastic surgery services in several New York hospitals and wrote *Principles and Practice of Plastic Surgery* (1950), one of the first textbooks in the field.

Bellamy, Lionel John (Sept. 23, 1916—May 9, 1982), British chemical spectroscopist, made a major contribution to the advance of chemical spectroscopy as the author of *The Infra-red Spectra of Complex Molecules* (1954), a masterly work of reference that compiled the results of earlier dispersed and isolated research. Bellamy studied at the University of London and gained his Ph.D. in 1939 before joining the Chemical Inspectorate of the Ministry of Supply. There he conducted important work on spectroscopic techniques, notably in relation to penicillin. In 1954 he went to the Explosives Research and Development Establishment of the Ministry of Defence and served as its director ten years later. When his department merged with the Rocket Propulsion Establishment to form the Propellants, Explosives, and Rocket Motor Establishment, he became director (1975–76) of the latter. Bellamy continued to pursue a career in research and teaching, as a visiting lecturer at the Massachusetts Institute of Technology and, from 1968 to 1982, as a professor at the University of East Anglia. He was a member of the editorial board of *Spectrochemica Acta* and of the council of the Chemical Society. He was made Commander of the Order of the British Empire in 1970 and gained awards from the Coblenz Society, the Optical Society of America, and the Society of Applied Spectroscopy.

Bird, Junius Bouton (Sept. 21, 1907—April 2, 1982), U.S. archaeologist, was curator of South American archaeology at the American Museum of Natural History from 1957 to 1973 and became a recognized authority on pre-Columbian textiles while leading expeditions in South America. Bird interrupted his studies at Columbia University to join an expedition to Baffin Island in Canada in 1927. In 1931 he became a field assistant of the Museum of Natural History. From 1934 to 1937, while excavating at Fell's Cave and Palli Aike Cave in southern Chile, he unearthed what were then the earliest human remains in South America. These remains helped him to reconstruct the lives of the Alacaluf Indians of Chile. The site also contained knives, basalt scrapers, and fossilized bones of horses and guanacos. In 1946 and 1947 he headed an expedition to Huaca Prieta, Peru, the first Preceramic site to be excavated. He and his team found twined textiles of highly stylized crabs, double-headed snakes, birds, and human beings. These findings were a valuable addition to the museum's textile collection. Besides his 54-year association with the American Museum of Natural History, Bird wrote scholarly articles about his research and taught at several universities.

Charnley, Sir John (Aug. 29, 1911—Aug. 5, 1982), British orthopedic surgeon, as professor of orthopedic surgery, University of Manchester (1972–76), was responsible for making the replacement of the hip joint a matter of routine surgery by enabling the new joint to be fixed in place. He studied at the University of Manchester, became a fellow of the Royal College of Surgeons in 1936, and worked at Manchester Royal Infirmary. In 1966 he was appointed honorary lecturer in bioengineering at the University of Manchester Institute of Science and Technology. Charnley received many awards for his work on joint replacement, which covered all aspects of the mechanical, surgical, and engineering problems raised by this branch of orthopedics. He was the first orthopedic surgeon to be elected a fellow of the Royal Society (1975), and he was knighted in 1977. Charnley's publications include *Compression Arthrodesis* (1953) and *Acrylic Cement in Orthopaedic Surgery* (1970).

Dick, Philip K(indred) (Dec. 16, 1928—March 2, 1982), U.S. science fiction writer, was the prolific author of more than 35 novels, many of which probed the inability of ordinary people to distinguish between illusion and reality. Dick, who made his first professional sale in 1952 with "Beyond Lies the Wub" for *Planet Stories*, later became one of the most important writers in the genre with such novels as *Flow My Tears, the Policeman Said* and *The Man in the High Castle*, which won the 1963 Hugo Award. Other works that gained critical acclaim include *Time Out of Joint, Solar Lottery, The Three Stigmata of Palmer Eldritch,* and *Do Androids Dream of Electric Sheep?*

Dubos, René (Jules) (Feb. 20, 1901–Feb. 20, 1982), French-born microbiologist, conducted pioneering work in bacteriology and discovered that by isolating antibacterial substances from certain microbes, he could obtain germ-fighting drugs. This 1939 research led to the production of the first commercial antibiot-

René Burri—Magnum

René Dubos

ics. After Dubos earned a Ph.D. (1927) from Rutgers University, he spent the bulk of his scientific career at Rockefeller Institute and Rockefeller University, where he also did research on acquired immunity, soil bacteria, human fungal infections, and the microbes that cause dysentery, pneumonia, and tuberculosis. In the 1960s Dubos became a concerned environmentalist who warned of man's harm to himself through environmental pollution. He was also the author of 20 books, including *Bacterial and Mycotic Infections of Man* (1948), *Pasteur and Modern Science* (1960), *Only One Earth* (written with Barbara Ward for the 1972 UN Conference on the Human Environment), and *So Human an Animal*, which won the Pulitzer Prize for nonfiction in 1969. Dubos's last book, *Celebrations of Life*, was published in 1981.

Fehr, Howard F. (Dec. 4, 1901–May 6, 1982), U.S. educator and author, was instrumental in introducing new math (a unified system of teaching arithmetic and mathematics in accord with set theory) into U.S. classrooms. He was the principal author of an exhaustive

246-page report, *New Thinking in School Mathematics,* which was published by UNESCO in 1961. He then traveled and promoted UNESCO's program for advancing education in other countries. Fehr, who earned a Ph.D. from Columbia University in 1940, joined the staff of his alma mater's Teachers College. He served as head of the mathematics department there from 1949 until his retirement in 1967, after which he remained active in educational work. He was co-author or co-editor of 23 books.

Feingold, Benjamin Franklin (June 15, 1900–March 23, 1982), U.S. pediatric allergist, created a stir when he proposed that artificial color and flavor in food caused hyperactivity in children. To suppress this condition Feingold suggested an additive-free diet. He believed that at least half of the children afflicted with hyperactivity could be helped if soft drinks, cake, candy, pudding, ice cream, luncheon meat, and many processed cheeses were eliminated from their diet and if the intake of chemicals called salicylates, which are found in some fruits, was strictly monitored. His theory, which was based on clinical observations rather than controlled experiments, outraged both physicians and food processors. Though further studies indicated that artificial food dyes might adversely affect the behavior of children, other researchers could not find conclusive evidence to support Feingold's theory. Feingold, who received his M.D. from the University of Pittsburgh in 1924, was associated with various hospitals before joining the Kaiser Foundation Hospital and Permanente Medical Group in 1951. In early 1982 he retired as head of the hospital's department of allergy. Feingold was the author of *Why Your Child Is Hyperactive* (1975), and *The Feingold Cookbook for Hyperactive Children* (1979).

Fenton, Clyde Cornwall (May 16, 1901–Feb. 27, 1982), Australian "flying doctor," was a pioneer of Australia's flying doctor service and a folk hero whose exploits were appreciated more by his patients and the general public than by the civil aviation authorities. He graduated as a physician in 1925 and learned to fly four years later. After conducting research in England, Fenton was appointed medical officer at Katherine, Northern Territory, in 1934 and started to use his own Gipsy Moth biplane to attend patients in the outback, thus initiating the Northern Territory Medical Service. A fearless and even a reckless pilot, he flew in all weather and was forced down several times, surviving sometimes for days in a desert or jungle. Fenton also indulged in feats such as landing in the main street of Katherine to buy a drink, which added to his legend but did not endear him to the authorities. In 1940 he was appointed Officer of the Order of the British Empire for his work in the flying doctor service, and he served with the Royal Australian Air Force during World War II as an instructor. His other pioneering exploits included the first solo flight across the Gulf of Siam.

Anna Freud

Fenton's autobiography, *Flying Doctor*, describes his adventurous career.

Freud, Anna (Dec. 3, 1895—Oct. 9, 1982), Austrian-born psychoanalyst, was a pioneer in the field of child psychoanalysis. The youngest child of Sigmund Freud, and the only one to follow her father in the profession of psychoanalysis, she was his close collaborator during his last years. She studied at the Cottage Lyceum in Vienna and later taught there. Freud became a member of the Vienna Psycho-Analytic Society in 1922 and acted as its chairman from 1925. Her specialized interest in child psychology was evident in her first major work, *The Ego and Mechanisms of Defence* (1936). After the family was obliged by the Nazi occupation to move to London in 1938, she set up a nursery in Hampstead and published *Young Children in Wartime* (1942) with her close friend Dorothy Burlingham. The Child Therapy Course, which Freud set up after World War II, became a leading center for the study of child development, engaging in research, training, and therapy and attracting students from all parts of the world. Her publications at this time confirmed her as an outstanding authority and her inspiration was felt by her many colleagues and students. Freud's later publications, including *Beyond the Best Interests of the Child* (1973), reflected her growing concern with social problems in relation to child psychology and the legal rights of young people.

Frisch, Karl von (Nov. 20, 1886—June 12, 1982), Austrian zoologist, was joint winner (with Nikolaas Tinbergen and Konrad Lorenz) of the 1973 Nobel Prize for Physiology or Medicine and was widely known for his remarkable research into insect behavior. Dedicated from childhood to the study of biology, he attended the Universities of Munich and Vienna and later served briefly as professor at the Universities of Rostock, Breslau, and Graz. Most of Frisch's career was spent at Munich's Zoological Institute, where he served as director for nearly 30 years. Before World War I he undertook research into the sensory perception of fish and found them to have exceptionally acute hearing. Frisch made similar studies of sensory perception in insects. In 1919 he began his most astounding work, which was to prove that bees communicate

Karl von Frisch

by means of ritual "dancing" movements to show the location of food. His studies in the late 1940s proved bees can navigate by the sun and duplicate an excursion by remembering patterns of polarized light. The results of Frisch's early research, described in his book *Aus dem Leben der Bienen* (1927; *The Dancing Bees*, 1954), were so unexpected that the scientific community at first doubted their validity.

Giauque, William Francis (May 12, 1895—March 28, 1982), U.S. chemist, won the 1949 Nobel Prize for Chemistry for his studies concerning the behavior of substances at extremely low temperatures. Giauque invented a magnetic cooling device that allowed him to attain temperatures one degree above absolute zero (−273.15° C). His research confirmed the third law of thermodynamics, which states that the entropy of ordered solids reaches zero at the absolute zero of temperature, and also established a firm experimental basis for quantum statistics. His work led to improved gasoline, stronger steel, longer-wearing rubber, and better glass. In the course of his low-temperature studies of oxygen Giauque discovered with Herrick L. Johnston the oxygen isotopes of mass 17 and 18. This revelation upset the periodic table of elements and warranted the creation of a second table with altered weights. After earning his Ph.D. from the University of California in 1922, Giauque served as professor of chemistry there until he retired in 1962. He rejoined the university in the same year, however, to direct research in the chemistry department and held that post until 1981.

Grosvenor, Melville Bell (Nov. 26, 1901—April 22, 1982), U.S. magazine editor, as the enterprising editor and president (1957–67) of the National Geographic Society increased membership from 2.1 million to 5.5

Melville Bell Grosvenor

million, increased funds for research, exploration, and public service, and launched numerous important expeditions. Grosvenor's great-grandfather, Gardiner Greene Hubbard, founded the society in 1888 and served as its first president. Grosvenor's grandfather, the inventor Alexander Graham Bell, was its second president, and his father, Gilbert Hovey Grosvenor, served as the editor of the magazine from 1899 to 1954. When Grosvenor became editor in 1957, he abandoned the traditional gold-bordered cover in favor of color photographs and turned out the massive *Atlas of the World*. Under his leadership members of expeditions scaled the highest peak in Antarctica, planted the

first U.S. flag on Mt. Everest, reconstructed ancient ruins of Mayan cities in Yucatán, and conducted underwater exploration of the Red and Mediterranean seas. In 1967 Grosvenor became editor in chief and chairman of the board.

Heidelberger, Charles (Dec. 23, 1920—Jan. 18, 1983), U.S. biochemist, was an internationally renowned cancer researcher who was best known for the development of 5-fluorouracil, a powerful drug that is widely used primarily to treat cancers of the stomach, colon, and breast. Heidelberger, the recipient of numerous awards, was credited with introducing chemotherapy as an alternative to radiation or surgery in the treatment of cancer. Shortly after Heidelberger earned (1946) a Ph.D. in organic chemistry at Harvard University, he joined the University of Wisconsin's McArdle Laboratory for Cancer Research, where he spent 27 years of his career. In 1976 he became director of basic research at the University of Southern California's Comprehensive Cancer Center. Heidelberger's research also shed light on the chemical processes of malignancy. His work led to a greater understanding of the way in which some chemicals distort the cellular machinery to convert normal cells into wildly growing cancer cells.

Hill, Sir (John) Denis Nelson (Oct. 5, 1913—May 5, 1982), British psychiatrist, was professor of psychiatry at the University of London from 1966 and a pioneer in the use of electroencephalography as a clinical tool. Probably the most eminent and respected figure in British psychiatric medicine of his generation, he also made a notable contribution to forensic psychiatry and to medical education. Hill trained as a doctor at St. Thomas' Hospital, London, and worked under Russell Brain at Maida Vale Hospital, where he first became interested in electroencephalography. During World War II, at the Maudsley Hospital, he led research into its use in psychiatry and during the postwar period helped to establish psychiatry as a respected branch of medical science. In 1961 Hill became professor at the Middlesex Hospital and five years later was knighted in recognition of his services to psychiatric medicine and education. He was a member of the General Medical Council from 1961 and was a member of the Butler Committee on Mentally Abnormal Offenders. Until his retirement in 1979 Hill also played a central role in the administration and organization of psychiatric medicine in the London teaching hospitals.

Kamanin, Nikolay Petrovich (Oct. 18 [Oct. 5, old style], 1908—March 14, 1982), Soviet aeronautical and space pioneer, was associated with his nation's military and space programs from 1928. In 1934 he piloted an aircraft that rescued marooned members of an expedition from ice floes. The party had been aboard the ship "Chelyuskin," which sank in the Arctic Ocean. For his heroism Kamanin received the title Hero of the Soviet Union. During World War II he commanded the 5th

Assault Aviation Corps, which helped liberate the Ukraine, Poland, Romania, Hungary, and Czechoslovakia from the Germans. Following the war he held posts in civil aviation, commanded an air army, and was deputy chief of staff of the Soviet Air Force. In 1960 Kamanin became an air force representative on the State Selection Commission that in 1961 designated Yury Gagarin as the first man to be launched in orbital flight. Kamanin was named colonel general of aviation in 1967 and became increasingly involved in the operations and planning of astronaut training at the space center in Zvezdny Gorodok, an installation built especially for that purpose some 30 km (19 mi) northeast of Moscow. Kamanin commanded the center from 1966 until his retirement in 1971.

Khan, Fazlur R(ahman) (April 3, 1929—March 27, 1982), Bangladesh-born structural engineer, was an innovative skyscraper designer who invented the "bundled tube" system, a structural network consisting of a group of narrow cylinders that are clustered together to form a thicker tower. The system was innovative be-

Courtesy, Skidmore, Owings & Merrill

Fazlur Khan

cause it minimized the amount of structural steel needed for high towers and eliminated the need for internal wind bracing since the perimeter columns carried wind loadings. His most spectacular projects included such Chicago landmarks as the 110-story Sears Tower and the 100-story John Hancock Center; he also designed the One Shell Plaza building in Houston, Texas. Khan, who did his undergraduate studies at the University of Dacca, India (now Bangladesh), qualified for a scholarship and entered the University of Illinois, Urbana, where he earned two master's degrees and a Ph.D. in structural engineering. For a short peri-

od he served as executive engineer for the Karachi Development Authority in Pakistan, but he returned to the U.S. in 1955 to join the Chicago architectural firm of Skidmore, Owings & Merrill. During his long association with the firm he also devised engineering designs for the solar telescope at Kitt Peak, Ariz., the U.S. Air Force Academy in Colorado Springs, Colo., and the Hubert H. Humphrey Metrodome in Minneapolis, Minn. His long-span structural designs led to the construction of the Haj Terminal of the King Abdul Aziz International Airport in Jidda, Saudi Arabia.

Koenigswald, G. H. Ralph von (Nov. 13, 1902—July 10, 1982), Dutch paleoanthropologist, was a pioneer in the discovery of hominid fossils. Koenigswald, who made his most important finds in the Far East, believed that it was there, rather than in Africa, that mankind first emerged. From 1928 to 1930 he was assistant at the Munich Geological Museum; then he joined the Geological Survey for the Dutch East Indies, where, between 1936 and 1941, he made his major discoveries of *Pithecanthropus* and *Meganthropus*. When the Japanese occupied Java during World War II, Koenigswald was imprisoned but managed to conceal his most important materials, which escaped loss or destruction. He specialized in the study of fossil teeth, recovering many from Chinese apothecaries' shops, where they were sold as medicines. After World War II he continued his work for the Geological Survey until his appointment in 1948 as professor at the State University at Utrecht in The Netherlands. He also served as curator of paleoanthropology at the Senckenberg Museum, Frankfurt am Main, West Germany. Koenigswald published two books on early man, *Begegnungen mit dem Vormenschen* (1956) and *Geschichte des Menschen* (1968), and many scientific papers. He was awarded the Royal Anthropological Institute's Huxley Medal in 1964.

Kollsman, Paul (Feb. 22, 1900—Sept. 26, 1982), U.S. aeronautical engineer, during the 1920s invented the altimeter, an instrument that measures and registers the altitude of an airplane. The Kollsman altimeter revolutionized aviation because it converted barometric pressure into feet and enabled the pilot to "fly blind." Kollsman's altimeter was first tested on Sept. 24, 1929, by Lieut. Gen. James H. Doolittle, who made a historic 15-mi flight guided exclusively by instruments. Kollsman's invention was considered an aviation milestone in the advance of piloted aircraft. After immigrating to the U.S. from Germany, Kollsman was unable to sell an automobile engine that he had invented. He then joined the Pioneer Instrument Co. in New York. When the latter refused to consider his recommendation for an altimeter, he founded Kollsman Instrument Co. and marketed his invention. In 1940 he sold his company to the Square D Company of Detroit and served as a consultant and vice-president of the parent company.

Lawson, James Llewellyn (Dec. 17, 1915—May 25, 1982), U.S. physicist, joined the General Electric Co. in 1945 and became instrumental in the development of radar and nuclear-particle accelerators and electronics as one of the company's chief scientists. After earning his Ph.D. at the University of Michigan, Lawson worked for G.E., where his accomplishments included the design and construction of a sophisticated atom smasher and the planning and supervision of a gamma-ray spectroscope for analyzing X-ray particles. He also headed research in advanced military communications systems, solid-state physics, integrated circuitry, and computer science.

Margulies, Lazar (1895—March 7, 1982), U.S. obstetrician-gynecologist, invented a flexible plastic intrauterine coil that was used to prevent conception. The device, which was the first made from molded polyethylene, was widely used because it was well tolerated by the body and it did not have to be surgically inserted. Margulies, who earned his M.D. at the University of Vienna, practiced medicine there from 1929 to 1938. In 1940 he immigrated to the U.S. and established a practice in New York City. He joined the staff of Mount Sinai Hospital in 1953 and at the time of his death was lecturer in the department of obstetrics and gynecology at the Mount Sinai School of Medicine of the City University of New York and senior clinical assistant in the department of obstetrics and gynecology at Mount Sinai Hospital.

Moore, Stanford (Sept. 4, 1913—Aug. 23, 1982), U.S. biochemist, shared the 1972 Nobel Prize for Chemistry for his fundamental contributions to enzyme chemistry. Specifically, Moore and William H. Stein, his co-researcher for 40 years, were the first to apply chromatographic procedures for the separation of amino acids, which are the basic components of proteins. By separating biological substances in amino acids, the two were able to establish the molecular structure of proteins. In 1959, using these analyses, Moore and Stein were able to determine the structure of the enzyme ribonuclease. The discovery paved the way to a clearer understanding of how a biological malfunction might be repaired in the human body. Moore, who earned a Ph.D. from the University of Wisconsin in 1938, joined the staff of the Rockefeller Institute for Medical Research (now Rockefeller University) the following year and remained there throughout his career. At the time of his death he was John D. Rockefeller professor at the university.

O'Gorman, Juan (July 6, 1905—Jan. 18, 1982), Mexican architect and painter, created imaginative mosaic designs that adorned the facades of buildings, the most elaborate example being the exterior walls of the library at the National Autonomous University of Mexico, which he helped plan and build in 1950. The windowless library featured a tower containing book stacks covered with mosaics constructed of natural minerals. After graduating in 1927 from the school of architecture of the National University of Mexico, Mexico City, O'Gorman began designing houses and buildings in Mexico in the International Style, including the house-studio of muralist Diego Rivera. Some of O'Gorman's major works in Mexico City include murals and frescoes at the National Museum of Anthropology, the airport, and the Museum of National History in Chapultepec Castle. His important mosaics appear on the Ministry of Communications and Public Works (1952), and on the facade of the Hotel de la Misión in Taxco. His most extraordinary work was considered his own house outside Mexico City (1953–56, demolished 1969), which was in part a natural cave in rocks and was designed to accentuate the lava formations of the landscape. It was also decorated with mosaic symbols and images from Aztec mythology. O'Gorman, despondent over a heart ailment that prevented him from working, apparently took his own life.

Peters, Sir Rudolph Albert (April 13, 1889—Jan. 29, 1982), British biochemist, was Whitley professor of biochemistry at the University of Oxford from 1923 to 1954 and thereafter conducted experiments at Cambridge until his retirement in 1976. Peters made many original contributions to his field and was outstanding as a coordinator of research and as an interpreter of the implications of advances in biochemistry. He had studied at the University of Cambridge and had undertaken research into hemoglobin before entering military service during World War I. After obtaining his medical degree at St. Bartholomew's Hospital, London, 1919, Peters returned to Cambridge for four years before his appointment in Oxford. There he set up a school of research which made a notable contribution to the understanding of vitamin B1. He returned to Cambridge in 1954 and established a biochemical laboratory at the Institute of Animal Physiology at Babraham. His later research concerned particularly the properties of compounds containing carbon-fluorine linkages. A fellow of the Royal Society, Peters was also a member of its council (1944–46). He was awarded the medal of the Royal Society in 1949 and was knighted in 1952.

Pilyugin, Nikolay Alekseyevich (May 18, 1908—Aug. 2, 1982), Soviet scientist, was a key figure in the early stages of the Soviet space program. His major contribution was to the development of control systems, first for satellite-launching rockets and later for the first Soviet spaceships and space stations, of which he was chief designer. Educated at the Bauman Higher Technical College in Moscow, from which he was graduated in 1935, he later taught at the Moscow Institute of Radiotechnology, Electronics, and Automation, where he was appointed professor in 1969. He became a member of the Communist Party of the Soviet Union in 1940 and among other decorations was awarded the Lenin Prize (1957) and the U.S.S.R. State Prize (1967).

Ritchie-Calder, Peter Ritchie Ritchie-Calder, Baron (July 1, 1906—Jan. 31, 1982), British science writer, trained as a journalist and used his skill as a publicist to interpret developments in science in light of his concern for social justice. He began writing in Dundee, Scotland, in 1922 and later worked for the *Daily News* (1926–30) and the *Daily Herald* (1930–41). As a reporter he experienced the social deprivation of the 1930s firsthand and became an active member of the Labour Party. During World War II he was director of plans at the Foreign Office Political Warfare Executive. Afterward he returned to journalism as science editor of the *News Chronicle* (1945–56) and served on the British delegations to the first UNESCO General Conference and to those in 1947, 1966, and 1968. He also attended the 1955 and 1958 UN conferences on the Peaceful Uses of Atomic Energy. Ritchie-Calder was a prominent member of the Campaign for Nuclear Disarmament and president of the National Peace Council. In 1961 he was appointed professor of international relations at the University of Edinburgh, where he remained until 1967. Ritchie-Calder was made a life peer in 1966, and from 1972 to 1975 he was senior fellow at the Center for the Study of Democratic Institutions, Santa Barbara, Calif.

Selye, Hans (Hugo Bruno) (Jan. 26, 1907—Oct. 16, 1982), Austrian-born endocrinologist, discovered in 1936 that the human body's physical response to stress could cause disease and even death. Selye first detected the effects of stress when he injected ovarian hormones into the glandular system of laboratory rats. He found that the hormone stimulated the outer tissue of the adrenal glands of the rats, caused deterioration of the thymus gland, and produced ulcers and eventually death. Selye correlated his findings to man and demonstrated that a breakdown of the body's hormonal mechanism could initiate disease and lead to death. He published his discovery in *Nature* magazine in 1936 and later gained world renown for his expertise on stress.

Hans Selye

© Karsh, Ottawa—Woodfin Camp & Associates

He wrote 33 books, most notably *Stress Without Distress*, which was translated into more than 12 languages. Selye, who by 1931 had earned both his M.D. and Ph.D. in chemistry at the German University in Prague, then came to the U.S. to serve as a research fellow at Johns Hopkins University. In 1932 he continued his fellowship at McGill University in Montreal, where he conducted his pioneering studies. Selye was later director of the International Institute of Stress at the University of Montreal.

Slone, Dennis (1930—May 10, 1982), South African-born epidemiologist, together with his research team examined the link between birth defects and drugs used by pregnant women and concluded that common painkillers, sleeping pills, and tranquilizers posed little risk to fetuses. After Slone published his findings in *Birth Defects and Drugs in Pregnancy* (1977), he conducted other research on the incidence of heart attacks in women who use or had used birth control pills. Slone found that women who were long-time users of oral contraceptives faced a double or triple risk of heart attack up to nine years after they had discontinued the pill. He also reported that women who both smoked and used birth control pills were at much higher risk than those who did not smoke. Slone, who earned an M.D. from the University of the Witwatersrand Medical School in Johannesburg, South Africa, was trained as a pediatrician there before he continued his studies in pediatrics and endocrinology at Harvard University. He later served (1969–75) as co-director of the Boston Collaborative Drug Surveillance Program and then as research professor of epidemiology and co-director of the drug epidemiology unit at Boston University Medical Center.

Szmuness, Wolf (March 12, 1919—June 6, 1982), Polish-born epidemiologist, as head of the laboratory of epidemiology (1973–82) at the New York Blood Center designed studies that determined the effectiveness of the first vaccine against hepatitis B. A group of 1,083 male homosexuals were selected to participate in the trials because homosexuals have a tenfold greater risk of contracting hepatitis B than the general population. After spending ten years in a Siberian labor camp, Szmuness received an M.D. in 1950 from the University of Tomsk, U.S.S.R., and earned advanced scientific degrees from the universities of Kharkov and Lublin, the latter in Poland. In 1968 he emigrated to New York, where he became a medical technician at the New York Blood Center, but it soon became evident that Szmuness was a brilliant researcher, and by 1970 he was head of his own laboratory there. In 1978 he began classic field studies that led to the production of the new hepatitis vaccine in 1980.

Theorell, (Axel) Hugo Teodor (July 6, 1903—Aug. 15, 1982), Swedish biochemist, won the Nobel Prize for Physiology or Medicine in 1955. His work on enzymes was a major contribution to the understanding of cell metabolism, one of the basic processes in all living organisms. Theorell's studies also had an immediate social effect: the development of a valid blood test for suspected drunken drivers. He studied at the Royal Caroline Medico-Surgical Institute in Stockholm, becoming a member of the staff there and gaining his M.D. in 1930 for his work on red blood cells. Theorell went on to work at the Uppsala University, Sweden (1932), and at the Kaiser Wilhelm Institute, Berlin (1933–35), where, with Otto Warburg, he began the enzyme research that led to his Nobel award. He also discovered an antibiotic for the treatment of tuberculosis. In 1937 he joined the Nobel Medical Institute in Stockholm; there he served as professor and head of the department of biochemistry.

Tuve, Merle Antony (June 27, 1901 — May 20, 1982), U.S. physicist, made observations of short-pulse radio waves reflected off the ionosphere that became the theoretical foundation for the development of radar. After Tuve received a Ph.D. from Johns Hopkins University in 1926, he joined the staff of the Carnegie Institution, where he used high-voltage accelerators to define the structure of the atom. In 1933 he confirmed the existence of the neutron and measured the bonding forces in atomic nuclei. During World War II Tuve conducted research that led to the development of the proximity fuse, which was highly effective against German V-1 buzz bombs launched at Britain and Japanese kamikaze air strikes. Tuve then returned to Carnegie, where, as director of the department of terrestrial magnetism, he made seismic measurements of the Earth's crust. In recognition of his achievements Tuve was knighted in 1948 and received numerous awards in the U.S.

Vernov, Sergey Nikolayevich (July 11, 1910—Sept. 26, 1982), Soviet physicist, director of the Nuclear Physics Research Institute at Moscow University, was much honored for his work, which included research into the action of cosmic rays in the stratosphere. During the 1930s he worked at the Radium Institute of the Academy of Sciences and became professor at Moscow University in 1944. Vernov was twice awarded the Order of Lenin and in 1960 gained the Lenin Prize.

Weiner, Joseph Sidney (June 29, 1915—June 13, 1982), South African-born environmental physiologist and anthropologist, helped to uncover the Piltdown forgery. The Piltdown skull "discovered" by Charles Dawson had long been accepted as that of an early hominid of previously unknown type. Weiner became convinced that it was not genuine and called on Sir Wilfred Le Gros Clark and Kenneth Oakley to help him show that it was a hoax. They did so, implying (though they never openly said so) that Dawson was responsible. Weiner studied at the University of the Witwatersrand, then qualified as a physician at St. George's Hospital Medical School in London. A reader in physical anthropology at the University of Oxford in 1945, he became director (1962–80) of the Medical Research Council's Environmental Physiology Unit and professor (1965–80) of environmental physiology at the University of London. He helped found the Society for the Study of Human Biology and was its chairman (1968–71). From 1964 to 1974 he was world convener of the Human Adaptability Section of the Human Biological Programme. Weiner's numerous books and papers included *The Piltdown Forgery* (1955).

Zworykin, Vladimir Kosma (July 30, 1889—July 29, 1982), Russian-born electronics engineer, was dubbed "the father of modern television" after inventing the iconoscope (1923; the first practical television camera tube) and the kinescope (1924; a television picture tube). The two inventions comprised the first all-electronic television system and paved the way for future technological advancements. After Zworykin emigrated to the U.S. in 1919, he joined the Westinghouse Electric Corp. The company showed little interest in Zworykin's 1923 demonstration of his television or in his subsequent improvements. In 1926 he earned a Ph.D. from the University of Pittsburgh, and three years later he was recruited by RCA, where he obtained his first patent for color television. Zworykin, who held more than 120 patents, also developed an early form of the electric eye, initiated development of the electron microscope, and constructed an image tube that was sensitive to infrared light. The latter was the basis for the snooperscope and sniperscope used during World War II. He also perfected a secondary-emission multiplier often used for sensitive radiation detection. Zworykin, who retired from RCA in 1954, was honored for his technical achievements in 1966 when he was awarded the National Medal of Science, one of the highest scientific awards in the U.S.

Vladimir Kosma Zworykin

Courtesy, Westinghouse Electric Corporation

Contributors to the Science Year in Review

C. Melvin Aikens *Archaeology.* Chairman, Department of Anthropology, University of Oregon, Eugene.

D. James Baker *Earth sciences: Oceanography.* Dean, College of Ocean and Fishery Sciences, University of Washington, Seattle.

Frank Barbetta *Electronics and information sciences: Communications systems.* Senior Editor, Communications, *Electronic News,* New York City.

Fred Basolo *Chemistry: Inorganic chemistry.* Morrison Professor of Chemistry, Northwestern University, Evanston, Ill.

Louis J. Battan *Earth sciences: Atmospheric sciences.* Director, Institute of Atmospheric Physics, University of Arizona, Tucson.

Keith Beven *Earth sciences: Hydrology.* Hydrologist, Institute of Hydrology, Wallingford, Oxon, United Kingdom.

Eric Block *Chemistry: Organic chemistry.* Professor of Chemistry, State University of New York, Albany.

David Boore *Earth sciences: Geophysics.* Consulting Professor, Department of Geophysics, Stanford University, Stanford, Calif.

Harold Borko *Electronics and information sciences: Information systems and services.* Professor, Graduate School of Library and Information Science, University of California, Los Angeles.

D. Allan Bromley *Physics: Nuclear physics.* Henry Ford II Professor and Director, Wright Nuclear Structure Laboratory, Yale University, New Haven, Conn.

James W. Canan *Defense research.* Defense Correspondent, McGraw-Hill World News, Washington, D.C.

John Davis *Architecture and civil engineering.* Engineering Consultant and Technical Writer, Alexandria, Va.

Warren D. Dolphin *Life sciences: Zoology.* Professor of Zoology, Iowa State University, Ames.

F. C. Durant III *Electronics and information sciences: Satellite systems.* Aerospace Historian and Consultant, Washington, D.C.

Robert G. Eagon *Life sciences: Microbiology.* Professor of Microbiology, University of Georgia, Athens.

Lawrence E. Fisher *Anthropology.* Director of Graduate Studies, Department of Anthropology, University of Illinois, Chicago.

Robert L. Forward *Physics: General developments.* Senior Scientist, Hughes Research Laboratories, Malibu, Calif.

David R. Gaskell *Materials sciences: Metallurgy.* Professor of Metallurgical Engineering, Purdue University, West Lafayette, Ind.

Richard L. Gordon *Energy.* Professor of Mineral Economics, Pennsylvania State University, University Park.

Stig B. Hagstrom *Physics: Solid-state physics.* Manager of the General Sciences Laboratory, Xerox Palo Alto Research Center, Palo Alto, Calif., and Consulting Professor of Physics, Stanford University, Stanford, Calif.

Index

This is a three-year cumulative index. Index entries to feature and review articles in this and previous editions of the *Yearbook of Science and the Future* are set in boldface type, *e.g.,* **Astronomy.** Entries to other subjects are set in lightface type, *e.g.,* Radiation. Additional information on any of these subjects is identified with a subheading and indented under the entry heading. The numbers following headings and subheadings indicate the year (boldface) of the edition and the page number (lightface) on which the information appears.

> **Astronomy 84**–256; **83**–256; **82**–254
> archaelogical findings **82**–250
> asteroid extinction theory **82**–124
> honors **84**–404; **83**–402; **82**–404
> optical engineering **84**–362
> physics research **83**–363
> quasars **84**–160

All entry headings, whether consisting of a single word or more, are treated for the purpose of alphabetization as single complete headings and are alphabetized letter by letter up to the punctuation. The abbreviation ''il.'' indicates an illustration.

U

Acknowledgments

18   From *Life Beyond Earth* by Gerald Feinberg and Robert Shapiro. Copyright © 1980 by Gerald Feinberg and Robert Shapiro. By permission of William Morrow and Company, Inc.

20   (Top) J. William Schopf, University of California, Los Angeles; (bottom) from "Archean Microfossils Showing Cell Division from the Swaziland System of South Africa," Andrew H. Knoll and Elso S. Barghoorn, *Science*, vol. 198, pp. 396–398, October 28, 1977. © 1977 AAAS

46   (Top) J. A. L. Cooke—Oxford Scientific Films, (center and bottom) Peter Parks—Oxford Scientific Films

46–47   W. H. Hodge—Peter Arnold, Inc.

62–63   Photograph, Peter Ward—Bruce Coleman Inc.; details, Kjell B. Sandved

162   (Top) Maarten Schmidt; (bottom) Kitt Peak National Observatory

163   Maarten Schmidt